THE
MEDAL
YEARBOOK
2002

Edited by
James Mackay, MA, DLitt
John W. Mussell
and
the Editorial Team of MEDAL NEWS

ISBN 1 870 192 443
(Hardback edition 1 870 192 435)

Published by

TOKEN PUBLISHING LIMITED

Orchard House, Duchy Road, Heathpark, Honiton, Devon EX14 1YD, UK
Telephone: 01404 46972   Fax: 01404 44788
e-mail: info@tokenpublishing.com   Website: www.tokenpublishing.com

USA distributor: Steve Johnson, Worldwide Militaria Exchange Inc., PO Box 745, Batavia, IL 60510
Canadian distributor: Eugene G. Ursual, PO Box 788, Kemptville, Ontario, K0G 1J0

© Token Publishing Ltd.

All rights reserved. No part of this publication may be reproduced, stored in a retrieval system, or
transmitted, in any form or by any means, electronic, mechanical, photocopying, recording or otherwise,
without the prior permission of Token Publishing Ltd.

Printed in Great Britain by Polestar Wheatons Ltd, Exeter, Devon

Gordons Medals Ltd.

Specialising in:
ORDERS, DECORATIONS & MEDALS, MINIATURE MEDALS, GERMAN MILITARY COLLECTABLES, THIRD REICH DOCUMENTS AND AWARDS, EXTENSIVE AND VARIED STOCK AVAILABLE

Comprehensive Catalogue issued regularly
Annual subscription rates: £6.00 UK & BFPO, £12.00 Overseas Airmail
Send 50p stamp for Free sample catalogue

TOP PRICES PAID FOR EVERYTHING FROM VICTORIA CROSSES TO VICTORY MEDALS

Visit our West End Showrooms
STAND G14-16,
Grays In the Mews Antique Market
1-7 Davies Mews, Davies Street, London W1K 1AB
Tel: 0207 495 0900 • Fax: 0207 495 0115

Mobile Numbers: Malcolm Gordon 07976 266293
Hilary Powell 07971 840642
EMail sales@gordonsmedals.co.uk
Websites: www.gordonsmedals.co.uk
www.cocollector.co.uk

BY APPOINTMENT
TO HER MAJESTY THE QUEEN
SUPPLIERS OF GOLD AND SILVER LACES
INSIGNIA AND EMBROIDERY
TOYE KENNING & SPENCER LTD LONDON

Toye, Kenning & Spencer Ltd

FOUNDED 1685

THE UK'S LEADING MANUFACTURER OF MEDAL RIBBONS
ISO 9001 QUALITY ASSURED

The TKS Medal Chart (34" x 24")
The most comprehensive illustration of UK, Commonwealth & United Nations from
1914–1995
Available at £15.00

A quarterly publication of stocked full-size and miniature medal ribbons available at £12.00 each or if combined with a medal chart £22.00. All prices include packing and postage (also VAT if applicable). We accept cheques or credit card payments through American Express, Mastercard or Visa.

We are the leading manufacturer of an extensive range of medal ribbons, clasps, emblems, brooch bars and ribbon bars (all spaces) in both full-size and miniature. Full medal-mounting, presentation casing and framing services are available.

Trade special commissions undertaken to design and manufacturer medals and ribbons to customers own requirements

We are proud to have such a wide international customer base for our unique service of being able to strike the medal, weave the ribbon and assemble to specific requirements.

REGALIA HOUSE, NEWTOWN ROAD, BEDWORTH, WARWICKSHIRE CV12 8QR GREAT BRITAIN

TEL: 0044 (0) 2476 315634   FAX: 0044 (0) 2476 643018   WEB: WWW.TOYE.COM

The leading suppliers of Uniforms, Accoutrements, Equipment, Headdress & Flags

C. J. & A. J. DIXON LTD.
Publishers of *Dixon's Gazette*

Published four times a year, the Gazette lists over 1,000 medals each issue. Many interesting articles which enable the collector to broaden their knowledge and develop their collecting skills. Updates on fakes and probably the largest listings of British Orders, Medals and Decorations in the world.

The Rare Triple D.S.O. group to Lt. Col. J.G. Rees, Welsh Horse, Royal Welsh Fusiliers, 13th Hussars Sold in Dixon's Gazette No. 26 for £13,000

Highest prices paid for your collection or surplus pieces
Immediate payment. No waiting months for your money!

We particularly wish to purchase Victoria Cross and Gallantry Groups, Peninsular Gold Medal - Military General Service - Waterloo - Naval General Service Crimea - Light or Heavy Brigade - Rorke's Drift - Isandhlwana - Maiwand - Indian Mutiny - Boer War - 1st World War. We also purchase all single Campaign Medals, Orders and Decorations, Long Service & Good Conduct

Auction Commission Agents. We act for clients throughout the UK and the world at auctions in the UK. All the major auctions are covered by our buyers and our integrity is second to none. We also take payment for auction lots in part exchanges, by arrangement.

Dixon's Gazette
Published every 3 months
Subscription: for 4 issues UK and EEC £12 incl p&p
USA and Rest of World £16 incl airmail p&p
Callers welcome by appointment
1ST FLOOR, 23 PROSPECT STREET, BRIDLINGTON
EAST YORKSHIRE, YO15 2AE, ENGLAND
Tel: (01262) 676877 / 603348   Fax: (01262) 606600
Email: chris@dixonsmedals.co.uk   Website: www.dixonsmedals.co.uk

Contents

Index to advertisers

JEFFREY HOARE
AUCTIONS INC.

Canada's Foremost Military Auctioneer

A. SJT Thomas G. Prince, MM
Double Gallantry Group to a Canadian Native Who Served With the Devil's Brigade.
Realised Can$82,500

We Are Proud To Have Sold The Medals Of **Lt. Col. John McCrae** Who Penned *"In Flanders Fields".* A World Record Price For A Military Medal Group, **$440,000** CDN.

Minimum Three Sales Annually - Canadian, British, World Medals, Cap Badges & Military Items.

May We Be Of Service To You In The Sale Of Your Militaria? Please Contact Mrs. Wendy Hoare For Details.

319 Springbank Drive
London, Ontario Canada
N6J 1G6

www.jeffreyhoare.on.ca

Ph: 519•473•7491
Fax: 519•473•1541

Preface

THIS IS THE eighth annual edition of the MEDAL YEARBOOK and we hope readers will like the new look cover. One of our readers produced a very interesting analysis of last year's edition which concluded that there was such a high proportion of new material in it that no serious collector of medals could afford not to buy the latest edition. Catalogues and yearbooks are not generally purchased every year, although publishers are obliged to bring them out annually; but we have found the very high take-up rate each year extremely heartening. This, in turn, encourages us to be constantly looking for ways and means of providing fresh material each year, as well as vigorously updating the core text.

We have taken out the Indian section this year but in its place comes the long-awaited and much-demanded section covering Canadian awards, compiled for us by Roger Campion (who also produced the popular Police Medal section). Eugene Ursual kindly provided many of the illustrations for this new section. It is our intention to continue producing sections devoted to the medals and decorations of Commonwealth countries, but clearly we have reached the stage where the Yearbook cannot practically be expanded much further. The long-term solution may be to split the Yearbook into two sections, keeping the more traditionally British material in one volume and the Commonwealth medals in another. We would welcome the views of readers on this matter.

An indication that the last word on the subject is far from written yet, is the astonishing number of additions to the main listing of medals in this edition. No fewer than 18 medals have been added, mainly in the category of life-saving and industrial bravery awards, clearly a field where much work remains to be done as more and more medals of this type, instituted by railway companies and civic corporations, come to light. Several medals have been added to the Australian and the New Zealand sections, the latter including the recently instituted East Timor Medal. The South Africa section has been radically revised with the valuable advice and assistance rendered by Peter Digby and other members of the Military Medal Society of South Africa. In the section on Unofficial Medals we have added both the earliest and latest, the former being the rare Cherry Medal of 1904, which very occasionally turns up in Royal Naval groups.

As always, we are immensely indebted to readers for helpful and constructive criticism as well as specific details of errors of commission or omission. We do take note of all readers' comments and do our best to act on them where possible. One recommendation which recurs from time to time is the inclusion of regimental names and their forebears, so with the assistance of Lieut. Colonel Ashley Tinson, we have supplied a list of the current British Army regiments and their predecessors. We also include a fascinating article on collecting Royal Naval medals and decorations by John Cooper.

Several hundred amendments have been incorporated in this edition, ranging from correction of minor printer's errors to substantial revisions of text. Among the shoals of letters from readers unanimously congratulating us on yet another fine piece of work we do get quite a few from readers prefacing their remarks on some error on our part with an abject apology for being so nitpicking. Frankly, the more nitpicking our readers are the better we like it, for it is only by attention to the smallest detail that we can ever hope to achieve that standard of accuracy which ensures that the MEDAL YEARBOOK remains the standard reference work. The entries on the badges of Baronets, Knights Bachelor and King's and Queen's Messengers have been virtually rewritten in light of fresh material submitted from several authoritative sources. Less spectacular but no less vital have been the various corrections in regard to the numbers of certain gallantry decorations and campaign medals awarded.

Further improvements have been wrought in the medal ribbon charts, as a result of suggestions by various readers as well as the on-going work of the Ribbon Branch of the Orders and Medals Research Society. The result is, we hope, evidence of a continual improvement in the text, but we are not sitting back on our laurels by any means. No sooner will this volume have gone to press than we will be opening the file on amendments and additions for the 2003 edition.

As in previous years, we are deeply indebted to those many readers who have taken the trouble to give us corrections, amendments or additional material and in some cases supplied illustrations. In particular we wish to thank Chris Allen, Commander R. G. Avis, Sir Robert Balchin Bart, Iain Bamber, Andrew Barrowcliff, Howard Chamberlain, John Chidzey, Roger Colbourne, Lieut. Colonel J. P. B. Condon, K. D. Cooper, Lieut. Colonel P. A. Crocker, David Deptford, Craig Fourie, A. R. Freeman, Clive French, Melvyn A. Gallagher, Bob Garner, Jean-Claude Gelhaar, G. E. Harris, Ian Hartley, Harry Hendry, Colin Hole, Bryce Horrell, B. Maddocks, Tony Mann, Glenn and Wendy Mason, Raymond Mills, Michael O'Brien, Jonathan Pittaway, Denis J. Poole, Lieut. Colonel N. W. Poulson, Malcolm Rouse, R. Rowell, Mike Smith, Allan Stanistreet, Nick Tucker, Kevin Tuhey and Ron Wallace. The universality of medal-collecting is reflected in the fact that our post-bag has included letters from Canada, the United States, South Africa, Australia, New Zealand and even Kosovo and Macedonia.

Our special thanks are also due to a number of dealers and professional numismatists, but particularly Philip Burman, Mark Cline, Chris Dixon, Daniel Fearon, John Millensted, Malcolm Rouse and John Wilson for checking the prices of medals and miniatures in light of auction results and dealers' lists in the course of the past twelve months.

YOU WILL BE AMAZED
AT WHAT YOU CAN FIND
AT
7 WHITCOMB STREET
LONDON WC2H 7HA
(Next to the National Gallery at Trafalgar Square)

Raymond D. Holdich
International
Medals & Militaria • Medals mounted for wear
Full size and miniature medals supplied
10 am to 5 pm Monday to Friday

Telephone: 020 7930 1979 • 07774 133493
Fax: 020 7930 1152 • E-mail: rdhmedals@aol.com

Visit our Website: www.rdhmedals.com

• MEDALS, ORDERS AND MILITARIA PURCHASED •

R & M INTERNATIONAL INC

Richard McDonald, OMSA, OMRS, MCC
Dealer since 1967

PO Box 6278, Bellevue, Washington, USA 98008–0278
Telephone: (425) 865–8104
Fax: (425) 643–3006
www.randminternational.com

OFFICE HOURS: 8.30am – 11.30pm (PST) 11.30am – 2.30 am (EST)
5.00pm – 8.00am (GMT). Answering Machine: 24 hours/holidays

BUY – SELL – TRADE

WE HANDLE ORDERS, MEDALS & DECORATIONS OF THE WORLD, SPECIALISING IN BRITISH EMPIRE & UNITED STATES MEDALS

WE ARE INTERESTED IN RECORDING YOUR WANTS. IF YOU COLLECT A PARTICULAR UNIT, CAMPAIGN ETC., PLEASE LET US KNOW, SO WE CAN CONTACT YOU AS NEW MATERIAL COMES AVAILABLE.
PAYMENTS ACCEPTED IN STERLING US & CANADIAN DOLLARS, AS WELL AS VISA, MASTERCARD AND BARCLAYCARD. LAY-AWAY PLAN AVAILABLE. DEALER ENQUIRIES INVITED.
EXPERIENCED, KNOWLEDGEABLE, CONVENIENT, GUARANTEED SERVICE TO CUSTOMERS WORLDWIDE.

Buying on the Internet can be disappointing!

Why don't you check the reputation of the homepage owner first?

www.Detlev-Niemann.com

One of the leading German specialist on Orders and Medals
Detlev Niemann, Ballindamm 9, 20095 Hamburg, Germany
Tel: +49+40+32525354   Fax: +49+40+32525454
e-mail Detlev-Niemann@t-online.de

Advantage:

1. Speak to the Medal Departments of: Sotheby's, Dix Noonan Webb, Glendining's, Chris Dixon, Liverpool Medals and check my reputation.

2. Full English website, every item pictured in colour, obverse and reverse, details, prices in English pounds

3. 100% lifelong guarantee and every item priced £170 or more comes automatically with a photographic authentication.

4. We never ever handle reproductions on our site!

5. Updated every Friday.

www.Detlev-Niemann.com

That was THE YEAR that was!

An at-a-glance résumé of the main events and occurrences that affected the medal hobby during the past months, as reported in MEDAL NEWS . . .

May 2000

HRH Prince Philip, Duke of Edinburgh, unveils a memorial dedicated to Edward Robinson who won his VC (now preserved at the Royal Naval College, Greenwich) at Lucknow during the Indian Mutiny. Prior to his death in 1896, Robinson was a gardener at Windsor Castle. The refurbishment of his memorial was a Millennium project of the Dedworth, Old Legion.

June 2000

A permanent exhibition of the Victoria Crosses awarded to members of the Medical Services opens at Keogh Barracks, Mytchett, Surrey on June 26. Over 20 Crosses are on display, including the VC and bar awarded to Lt-Col Arthur Martin-Leake and the VC awarded to Surgeon Reynolds for his gallantry at Rorke's Drift.

Captain Ganju Lama, VC, MM dies on June 30 aged 77. Unusually, he was born of a Tibetan father and a Nepalese mother in Sikkim and was only admitted into the Gurkhas as a result of the relaxation of the rules of recruitment in wartime. He won his Cross in Burma in June 1944. Previously, another Gurkha VC, Agansing Rai, had died on April 24. Of the 30 VCs awarded to the Indian Army in World War II, ten were won by members of the Gurkha Rifles. Their deaths reduce the number of living VCs to 25.

July 2000

The campaign in and out of Parliament to secure special recognition of the men and women who served in the Suez Canal Zone 1951–54 gathers momentum, with extensive coverage on BBC's Newsnight programme. In particular, attention was drawn to the fact that there had been 333 fatalities—279 Army and 54 RAF—recorded in that turbulent period. The precedent of Australia and Canada in issuing retrospective campaign awards for the period between 1945 and 1975 was cited.

Service in multinational operations resulting in the issue of multinational medals may now count towards the Accumulated Campaign Service Medal. This ruling will only apply to new awards and is not retrospective.

One of the last surviving veterans of the Battle of Jutland, Captain de Courcy-Ireland, celebrates his 100th birthday. He joined the Navy at the age of 12 and was serving on board the battleship *Bellerophon* when the Grand Fleet had its historic encounter with the German High Seas Fleet in May 1916. During World War II he commanded HMS *Nelson* and served on the staff of Combined Operations, planning the D-Day landings.

August 2000

The Inland Revenue announces that medals and awards will in future be exempt from inheritance tax.

The *Daily Telegraph* publishes a list of over 700 members of the armed forces killed in Northern Ireland since the beginning of "The Troubles" in 1971. The list is subsequetly reprinted by Spink as a 52-page booklet.

September 2000

Thames Television releases its acclaimed documentary series, "The World at War" on video and DVD.

Margaret Purves, GC proposed a permanent memorial to all 1,350 winners of the Victoria Cross, suggesting a site in Trafalgar Square.

John Kenneally, the last surviving VC from the Irish Guards, dies on September 27 at the age of 79. He earned the last VC to be granted during the North African campaign in April 1943 when serving with the 1st Battalion in the assault on Tunis.

October 2000

Family Learning Weekend is organised by the National Army Museum on October 7–9 and helps to focus public attention on the army of today.

On the 195th anniversary of the Battle of Trafalgar an oak tree was planted in St Mary's churchyard, Market Drayton, to the memory of William Wilkinson, Master of HMS *Sirius* which sighted the enemy that led to the historic naval engagement. A brass plaque mounted alongside records the details. The memorial was the

To keep up to date . . . **Read MEDAL NEWS every month**

One year's subscription is £29 (UK), £35 (World surface mail), £45 (Airmail). Call 01404 44166 to subscribe.

culmination of a Millennium project and the ceremony was attended by civil and military dignitaries and representatives of the services.

The Dickin Medal of the People's Dispensary for Sick Animals is awarded posthumously to Gander, a Newfoundland dog which was the mascot of the Royal Rifles of Canada at Hong Kong in the early years of World War II, killed at the battle of Lye Mun in December 1941 when he picked up a grenade and carried it towards the Japanese lines. This is the first award of the "animal VC" since 1949.

Gander the dog with members of the Royal Rifles of Canada in 1941.

The National Army Museum in Chelsea receives a most unusual and bizarre gift of 15 fingers and toes, which had been amputated as a result of frostbite during a descent from Everest in May 1976. The gift was presented by Bronco Lane, who lost five fingers and all his toes but continued to serve in the army till 1992. The digits go on display alongside Bronco's ice-axe in the new Modern Army Gallery.

A memorial to the crews of two motor torpedo boats who lost their lives in World War II is unveiled at North Ness, near Lerwick, Shetland.

Diana Brooks, former chief executive and president of Sotheby's USA, pleads guilty in a US Federal court to a charge of price-fixing in collusion with Christie's during the period 1993 to 1999. Sotheby's also pleaded guilty to criminal charges of price-fixing and other anti-trust violations under American law and agreed to pay a $45 million fine over a five year period. Ms Brooks was due to face trial the following January.

The Royal Australian Mint issues a dollar coin commemorating the heroic action of the country's first VC holder, Captain (later Sir) Neville Howse who won his Cross in July 1900 for saving the life of a comrade under fire during the Boer War. Howse's name and the date of his award flank an image of the Cross on the reverse of the coin, while the details of Australia's other 95 VC winners are given in the presentation folder.

Royal Marines from 45 Commando are sent to Kosovo on a six-month tour of duty.

After a gap of half a century, a memorial is dedicated to the assault on Fortresse Le Havre, the remains of two Churchill tanks forming the centrepiece.

Sotheby's simplify and merge their two on-line sales sites under the web-site address of sothebys.com.

More than 70 war grave gardeners threaten industrial action in response to proposed pay cuts of 30 per cent. Negotiations between the TGWU and the Commonwealth War Graves Commission hope to resolve the situation.

Her Majesty the Queen approves the institution of a new Canadian award, the Order of Merit of the Police, in three classes, Commander, Officer and Member, with respective post-nominal letters COM, OOM and MOM. It is expected that there will be about 50 recipients each year.

November 2000

The sixth Weekend of Medals takes place November 4–5, organised by Peter and Dee Helmore.

An exhibition of portraits of 46 early VC winners goes on show at the Masonic Hall, Alfred Street, Wantage. Donated in 1900 by Baron Wantage, himself a winner of the VC, this unique collection was originally displayed at the Corn Exchange, renamed the Victoria Cross Gallery, which continued till the 1940s. During World War II the paintings were placed in storage but by 1947 had deteriorated and thereafter they were dispersed to the appropriate regimental museums of the various VCs. The recovery and restoration of the paintings was undertaken as a Millennium project.

Defence Minister Geoff Hoon announces the erection of a memorial in Whitehall, near the Cenotaph, to all those service personnel killed in 16 minor wars and conflicts from Korea to Northern Ireland.

Andrew Bennett MP convenes a meeting at Westminster of the campaign to secure a medal for veterans of the Suez Canal conflict of 1951–4.

December 2000

The last survivor of five miners awarded the Edward Medal (substituted for the George Cross in 1971) for their part in a rescue operation at the South Garesfield Colliery, County Durham, dies on December 7, aged 88. At the time of the incident John Baker was a "pit lad" aged 17.

The death of Colonel Pat Porteous at the age of 82 reduces the number of surviving VCs to 23. Porteous, latterly Vice-Chairman of the VC and GC Association, earned his Cross on August 19, 1942 as a captain with 4 Commando during the Dieppe Raid. A street in Dieppe was named in his honour. The death is also announced of Lieutenant Colonel Paddy Doyle, aged 86, the last British CO of the 4/5th Mahratta Light Infantry. He earned the Military Cross as a lieutenant during the Keren campaign in Ethiopia in 1944.

The oldest surviving Empire veteran of the Gallipoli campaign, Percy Goring, celebrates his 106th birthday on December 16. Born in Shoreditch, he emigrated to Australia in 1948 and now lives in Bunbury, Western Australia.

Percy Goring pictured in Syria in 1916.

January 2001

The Royal Navy announces the award of the clasp "Air Operations Iraq" to all personnel who served aboard HMS *Invincible* between January 17 and March 19, 1998. Previously this clasp was confined to air crew of the aircraft carrier.

The Special Forces Association launches an appeal for funds to establish a courtyard memorial garden in Hereford, dedicated to the 500 men and women who lost their lives during and after World War II. The garden will be an integral part of a new Resource Centre, Museum and Library to Special Forces.

The Tradings Standards Office exposes a plan to market a quantity of fake or bogus Nelson relics in Wareham, Dorset. The racket comes to light when the purchaser of a piece of a flag, allegedly draped over Nelson's coffin, has it tested and discovers that the weave is different from the genuine article.

The first award of the Military Cross to a Royal Marine since the Falklands War, and only the second of the "other ranks" to receive the award since the regulations were altered in 1993, is Sergeant Mark Cox, who served with a patrol of 20 Marines attached to the mainly Australian UN force in East Timor, in defence of the airport at Dili. The first "other rank" MC was awarded to Corporal (now Sergeant) Andy Dynes for his service in Northern Ireland in 1996.

The organisation entitled Friends of War Memorials is founded with the avowed aim of raising money for the care and maintenance of the war memorials (estimated between 50,000 and 60,000) throughout the British Isles, and still rising. The most recent memorials recall Admiral Sir Bertram Ramsey, architect of the Dunkirk evacuation and D-Day landings, and the allied navies which took part in the Normandy invasion.

A memorial plaque to the Special Boat Squadron is unveiled at the Ingledene Hotel, Glen Sannox, Isle of Arran, where the original SBS was trained during World War II.

The Enigma machine, stolen from Bletchley Park, is sent to television presenter Jeremy Paxman by special delivery. Unfortunately, it lacks the vital three rotors for which a ransom of £25,000 is demanded.

Peter Helmore is elected General Secretary of the Orders and Medals Research Society.

The Australian government retrospectively awards the Australian Victoria Cross to John Simpson, the hero of Gallipoli who, with his donkey Duffy, rescued more than 300 wounded soldiers from the battlefield. He had been recommended for the VC at the time but this was rejected by the British authorities when it was discovered that Simpson had deserted from the Merchant Navy to enlist in the Australian Army under a new name. Since the inception of the Australian VC, however, awards no longer have to be referred to Westminster. Simpson was killed in action later in 1915. Simpson and his donkey are depicted on the reverse of the ANZAC medal awarded to surviving veterans in 1975. Despite this, the Returned Servicemen's League publicises their disapproval of further retrospective VCs being awarded.

February 2001

Admiral Sir Michael Boyce, First Sea Lord and Chief of the Naval Staff, succeeds General Sir Charles Guthrie as Chief of Defence Staff, the first admiral to hold this position since 1988. Sir Michael entered the Royal Navy in 1961 and commanded three submarines, *Oberon*, *Opossum* and the nuclear powered *Superb*.

A monument commemorating the 306 British and Commonwealth soldiers shot for desertion in 1914–18 is planned for the National Memorial Arboretum in Staffordshire. Centre-piece is a blindfolded statue of a boy who lied about his age to enlist and was shot only a few months later, the most monstrous injustice of that cruel conflict. Each man shot is to be commemorated by a pine cross bearing a metal plaque giving name, rank and date of birth.

The famed Enigma machine.

March 2001

The Government announces the institution of a medal to mark the Queen's Golden Jubilee in 2002, and that it will be awarded to all service personnel who have completed five years' service as of February 2002. About 156,000 personnel will qualify for the medal, issued in gilt metal and unnamed.

Lieutenant-Commander Lindy Mackenzie-Philips, serving in the Pacific aboard HMS *Newcastle*, is the first recipient of the new Volunteer reserve Service Medal, presented by her commanding officer, Commodore Steve Pearson.

The Government announces its intention of introducing a humanitarian and peacekeeping medal for service personnel and civilians in conditions for which the Operational Service Medal is not warranted.

At the Oscars ceremony in Los Angeles on March 26, Russell Crowe, winner of the Motion Picture Academy award for best actor in respect of his role in *Gladiator*, is observed proudly wearing the MBE which had been awarded to his late grandfather in recognition of his services as a cameraman in World War II. The resultant publicity around the world generates incredible interest in medals.

May 2001

Sotheby's hold their final sale of coins, medals and decorations on May 2–3, going out on a high note with 59 lots of superlative medal material. Anchor members of the Coins and Medals Department, James Morton and Tom Eden, subsequently join forces with Paul Wood to form an independent auction house specialising in numismatic sales.

The set of medical instruments used by Surgeon James Henry Reynolds VC at Rorke's Drift is sold at Spink on May 11. Together with his service revolver, set of

Sotheby's, New Bond Street, London.

The Queen Mother attends muster of VC &GC Association.

medal miniatures and other memorabilia, this lot sells for £41,400 against a pre-sale estimate of £20,000.

The Military Medallists League hold their annual church parade on Sunday, May 13, at the Royal Hospital, Chelsea.

The annual reunion of holders of the Victoria Cross and George Cross takes place in London, May 29–31.

The new Royal Artillery Museum at Woolwich is opened by Her Majesty the Queen. Exhibits range from cannon from Henry VIII's ill-fated flagship *Mary Rose* to a portion of the supergun commissioned by Saddam Hussein.

The Australian Prime Minister, John Howard, announces the award of a medal to all Australians who completed National Service between 1951 and 1972.

June 2001

The revised criteria for the award of the Meritorious Service Medal to Royal Naval ratings comes into force. Henceforward, instead of the long service requirement previously taken into account, "the most compelling candidates" are now to be selected, reflecting the diversity of roles in the modern Navy.

The Henderson Collection of military cap badges, probably the largest and most comprehensive of its kind ever formed, is dispersed by auction at Wallis & Wallis of Lewes, Sussex on June 12.

August 2001

A three-day study tour organised by the University of Birmingham over the weekend of August 3–5 deals with War in the Desert on Horseback and focuses on the role of cavalry in World War I, with specific reference to Allenby's campaign in Palestine, 1917–18.

September 2001

The Millennium Muster of the Gallantry Medallists League takes place at the Royal Hospital, Chelsea and the Victory Services Club over the weekend of September 14–16. Membership is open to all who have been granted a second-level gallantry award.

The annual convention of the Orders and Medals Research Society takes place over the weekend of September 21–22 at the New Connaught Rooms, London.

CHELSEA MILITARY ANT QUES

Buying & Selling
Campaign and Gallantry Medals
British and Foreign Militaria

N13/14 ANTIQUARIUS
131-141 KINGS ROAD
CHELSEA, LONDON
SW3 4PW

Tel/Fax: 020 7352 0308
e-mail: richard@chelseamilitaria.co.uk
website: www.chelseamilitaria.co.uk

Quarterly lists available. Send 40p stamp for
complimentary copy

FLOYD, JOHNSON & PAINE, Inc.
PO Box 34679, Chicago, IL, 60634, USA

THE ONLY AUCTION FIRM IN THE UNITED STATES SPECIALISING IN
ORDERS, MEDALS AND DECORATIONS OF THE WORLD

FOUR SALES PER YEAR, INCLUDING:

- UNITED STATES GALLANTRY
- UNITED STATES CAMPAIGN MEDALS
- BRITISH ORDERS, DECORATIONS AND MEDALS
- IMPERIAL GERMAN MOUNTED GROUPS AND SINGLE AWARDS
- ORDERS, DECORATIONS AND MEDALS FROM AROUND THE WORLD
- BOOKS FOR MEDAL COLLECTORS WORLDWIDE

For further information or consigning or bidding,
visit our website, www.FJPAuction.com
or contact:

Jeffrey B. Floyd
PO Box 9791, Alexandria, VA 22304
USA
Telephone: (703) 461 9582
Fax: (703) 461 3059

Worldwide Militaria Exchange Inc.
PO Box 745, Batavia, IL 60510, USA
Telephone: (630) 761 4004
Fax: (630) 761 4006
E-mail: sales@wwmeinc.com

Sheperd Paine
PO Box 34679,
Chicago, IL 60634 USA
Telephone: (773) 777 0499
Fax: (773) 777 0417

Antiquitäten & Historica
Auktionen Carsten Zeige

3 AUCTIONS PER YEAR

**German and Foreign Orders and Decorations
plus a wide selection of Military Items and Books.
Over 2000 items per catalogue
Five Large Colour Illustrated Catalogues Per annum
Subscriptions 35 $.**

**Carsten Zeige, Dammtorstr. 29, D-20354 Hamburg
Germany**
Tel: +49 40 35713636
www.zeige.com, e-mail : info@zeige.com

WALLIS & WALLIS EST. 1928

WEST STREET AUCTION GALLERIES, LEWES, SUSSEX, ENGLAND BN7 2NJ
TEL: +44 (0)1273 480208 FAX: +44 (0)1273 476562

Britain's Specialist Auctioneers of Militaria, Arms, Armour & Medals

A selection of military headdress badges from The Henderson Collection, which realised an all time record auction price for a military badge collection—£61,200.

A catalogue of the sale, with prices realised, is available price £4.50 post free.

2001/2002 AUCTION SALES

SALE	DAYS	FINAL ENTRIES (am)
450	October 9th & 10t	—
	Connoisseur Collectors' Auction	
	October 9th & 10th	—
451	November 20th	October 13th
452	January 8th	November 24th
453	February 12th	January 12th
454	March 19th	February 16th
455	April 30th & May 1st	March 23rd
	Connoisseur Collectors' Auction	
	April 30th & May 1st	**March 19th**
456	June 11th	May 4th
457	July 16th	June 15th
458	August 27th	July 20th
459	October 8th & 9th	August 31st
	Connoisseur Collectors' Auction	
	October 8th & 9th	**August 27th**
460	November 19th	October 12th

• All sales comprise Military Medals, Militaria, Arms, Armour and Collectors Items
• Fine illustrated catalogues £8.50, Overseas Airmail £9.50
• Connoisseur Sale Catalogues £12.50 (post free worldwide)
• All Catalogues contain a "prices realised list" of the previous Sale

email: auctions@wallisandwallis.co.uk   **web site: http://www.wallisandwallis.co.uk**

Market trends

In the period under review (mid-2000 to early 2001), the pound continued very strong for the first six months but then dropped from an average of $1.60 to $1.40, although it remained relatively constant in regard to the Euro. Despite early indications of a rise in unemployment at the beginning of the period, this situation had begun to improve before the end of 2000 and by the middle of the following year was at a 25-year low again. Despite the general election in June, delayed on account of the foot and mouth epidemic, the economy remained remarkably stable. On the other hand the stock market remained slack throughout the entire period and the FTSE index had actually dropped by about 10 per cent. The sluggishness of traditional stocks and shares seems to have led to a renewed interest in collectables as alternative investments and, in turn, this has undoubtedly had an impact on the medal market. The overall trend in prices has been upward over the past twelve months, although there are many factors which have to qualify this. As we detected last year, however, buyers have shown a keener sense of quality which explains some results which, on the face of it, appear to have been disappointing. At the same time, the personal element, always a major factor in assessing the desirability (and therefore the market value) of British medals, has played an increasingly important role.

If last year seemed to lack the truly spectacular pieces, though redeemed by the appearance of no fewer than eleven Victoria Crosses in the saleroom, this year was even quieter, with only four VCs under the hammer, although the inclusion of a George Cross (and a female award at that) went some way to maintain headline interest in the lay press. The plain fact is that, just as the surviving holders of these coveted awards dwindle every year, the number of crosses available to the market decreases even more sharply. More and more of these awards are gravitating towards the appropriate service or regimental museums, while the unlimited funds at the disposal of one or two really determined individual collectors inevitably forces up the price for the remaining pieces.

This comment also applies to very large groups of decorations and medals which were conspicuous by their absence during the period under review. Groups with more than ten medals were a rare occurrence, and those which did make their fleeting appearance were not unduly spectacular or valuable. The group of eleven to Colonel Sir Eric Gore-Browne was a case in point. Consisting of a World War I trio, DSO, OBE and Croix de Guerre with the Territorial Decoration, Coronation and 1935 Jubilee medals and a Knight's Bachelor badge for good measure, it sold for exactly £1,000. A group of twelve, including the Royal Victorian Order, to a Guards sergeant-major who became a wing-commander in the RAF sold for £900 which, considering James Edward Parkin's varied and distinguished career, seems like a terrific bargain which will undoubtedly repay research. The best of the larger groups was that awarded to Brigadier General Sir Denis Delmé-Radcliffe, comprising 21 items, including KCMG, CB and CVO, a clutch of foreign decorations, and campaign medals covering

Some of the medals awarded to Brigadier-General Sir Charles Delmé-Radcliffe (pictured right).

service in various parts of the world from 1884 till the end of World War I. This impressive group fetched £15,000 at Spink (July 2000) against an estimate of £5,000–£7,000). The estimate for the group to Field Marshal Sir Arthur Barrett, including the Second Afghan, three India GSMs and World War I trio, in the same sale was comparable, yet it fetched a more modest price of £6,000. Similarly the medals and decorations of Air Chief Marshal Sir Charles Medhurst, KCV, IBE, MC fetched £7,500 at the DNW sale in December. On the other hand Sotheby's in November sold a World War I group of flying ace Squadron Leader T. F. Hazell, comprising DSO, MC and DFC and bar, with Indian campaign medals as well as the war medals; together with miniatures and assorted artefacts, this group fetched £33,000 (estimate £8,000–£12,000).

The auction scene was not enlivened, as in previous years, by any really large "named" collections other than that of the late John Cooper which was broken up by Dix Noonan Webb in April 2001, although there was a good range of smaller and less spectacular collections, often specialising in the medals of a particular regiment, which ensured a healthy injection of material that was either new to the market or had not passed through the saleroom for many years. On the other hand, interest in medals, not only as collectables as such but also as the tangible documents of our military past, is definitely on the increase, fuelled no doubt by the never ending stream of documentaries, films and dramas about the world wars and lesser conflict or individual campaigns and actions. As the last National Serviceman reaches the age at which he draws his Old Age Pension, two generations have grown up in which military involvement has become more and more remote in one

Doreen Ashburnham-Ruffner with Anthony Farrer whom she saved.

sense—the involvement of kith or kin—yet more and more immediate in another—the ability of television to bring the action straight into the living-room night after night. The Gulf War was the first of the really "immediate" conflicts, and if British involvement in Sierra Leone has not had the coverage it deserves, British participation in the UN and NATO peace-keeping roles in the Balkans has maintained a very high profile, reflected in the inordinate interest shown in the very few medals from these trouble spots which have so far come on to the market.

Although the general trend of prices is upwards there have been some fluctuations, although there is generally some good reason behind what might otherwise seem to be the caprice and quirks of the market. Last year, for example, we highlighted the very

The Great War DSO, MC, DFC and bar group to the thirteenth highest scoring British Ace, Squadron Leader T. F. Hazell. Sold at Sotheby's in November 2000.

1914 VC, MM and Russian Cross of St George group of 10 awarded to Drummer S. J. Bent, sold for £92,000.

high prices paid at auction for World War I memorial plaques to women. At least two plaques sold around £1,000 apiece while one, awarded to Hilda May Bowman, realised £1,600. By contrast a similar plaque at a Spink sale in April 2000 made only £780, even though the circumstances of the award were very similar in all of these cases. Could this merely represent an adjustment to a more sensible price level, or an indication that the demand had now been satisfied by the supply? On the other hand, a good example of the Women's Social and Political Union's Medal for Valour, awarded to Lavender Guthrie who was force-fed during her imprisonment, went for £8,200 at Spink in November, more than double the upper pre-sale estimate.

Apart from that, it has not been a year in which female awards were particularly noteworthy, with one other outstanding exception. This was the George Cross awarded to Doreen Ashburnham-Ruffner, who, at the age of eleven, with her brother fought off a large cougar on Vancouver Island in September 1916. For this she was awarded the Albert Medal, subsequently exchanged for the George Cross. Doreen was the youngest ever female recipient of the highest civilian award and this doubtless explained the extraordinary interest which pushed up the price of this medal to £9,000—50 per cent above the lower pre-sale estimate—at Spink's sale on July 27, 2000. It is interesting to note that the suffragette medal and the youngest girl GC are virtually on par. Nevertheless, the disparity between the value of the most mundane VC (if there is such a thing!) and the most spectacular or outstanding GC is enormous, and the gap seems to get wider with the passage of time.

Nevertheless we detect an upsurge of interest in civilian medals and this is reflected not only on the firmer prices obtained at auction for life-saving awards and even meritorious service awards, but also in the recording of such by-ways of the hobby, as the increasing number of such medals chronicled in this Yearbook testifies. This even extends to the Dickin Medal, often described in the lay press as the animals' VC. Two of these rare gallantry awards came up at Spink's sale in July 2000. The medals named to Peter, a Scotch collie, and Tyke, a homing pigeon, fetched

£4,000 (estimate £4,000–5,000) and £4,200 (£3,000–£3,500) respectively.

A Mesopotamian VC group of six medals to Sergeant Readitt made £40,000 (the lower end of the estimate) at Spink's sale in April 2000, whereas the 1914 VC group of ten to Drummer (later CSM) S. J. Bent went for £92,000 at Dix, Noonan and Webb's sale two months later—almost double the estimate. The apparent discrepancy between these prices is due almost entirely to the personal circumstances of the awards, together with the other medals reflecting the careers of the recipients. Once more, this demonstrates the paramount importance of the personal factors. Dix Noonan Webb's sale in September also boasted a fine posthumous VC group, with the two-clasp India Medal and QSA with three clasps to John Barry of the Royal Irish regiment which sold for £85,000—well above the estimate of £50,000—£60,000. The season was rounded off triumphantly, however, in May 2001 when Sotheby's disposed of the World War I VC group of Sergeant Meekosha for a staggering £101,200, twice the pre-sale estimate.

If there were no really spectacular groups during the past year, there was a formidable array of lesser

"Peter", the RAF patrol dog at work in the rubble of the Blitz. His Dicken medal was sold by Spink in July 2000 for £4,000.

The NGS medal sold well above estimate by Dix Noonan Webb in April 2001 for £20,000.

groups. Those incorporating the DSO or MC performed very much in line with expectation—the DSO group of eight in Bosley's March 2001 sale being a prime example, selling for £3,000 in line with the top estimate, while a World War I group of eight to an officer of the Indian Army, with the MC, made a more modest £850. On the other hand, this past year has witnessed quite a number of groups with RAF gallantry awards which rose well above estimate. Spink's November sale included the CGM and four World War II medals awarded to Flying Officer W. G. Buckley who flew with Leonard Cheshire as his rear gunner. This unusual group made £8,000, exactly on the upper pre-sale estimate. A seven medal group including MC and DFC for World War I, awarded to Captain P. F. Clayson, realised £8,800, almost twice the top estimate of £4,500 in Glendining's sale on March 28, 2001.

A fine DCM Boer War group, including QSA with six clasps, to one of the defenders of Ladysmith, realised £3,600 at DNW's sale on December 15. Top price in the Cooper Collection at DNW in April 2001 was £6,800 paid for the Distinguished Service Medal awarded to B. A. Smith, owner of the motor boat *Constant Nymph*, one of only two civilians to win this naval decoration for gallantry in the evacuation of Dunkirk. The same sale included a fine Empire Gallantry Medal of 1920 which went for £6,000, twice estimate.

Campaign medals of all periods performed above expectation. Predictably the biggest increases in market value were to be found in the earlier items, with the few gold medals and crosses of the Napoleonic period breaking records. Pride of place must go to the rare regimental commander's gold cross with four clasps awarded to Colonel the Honourable Sir Robert le Poer Trench which fetched £52,000 at the

DNW sale in April 2001 (estimate £30,000 –£34,000). A small gold medal for Nive sold for £6,000 at Sotheby's (estimate £4,000–£5,000). A good sprinkling of Naval and Army GS Medals throughout the year failed to satisfy the insatiable demand and generally sold well above their pre-sale estimates, although who could have predicted the £20,000 paid for the NGS Medal with clasps for 1 June 1794, St Vincent, Nile and Trafalgar which DNW had estimated at £4,500–£5,500 in their April 2001 sale?

Waterloo medals turned up at regular intervals throughout the year, but when no fewer than 20 were included in Spink's sale on May 11, 2001, with estimates in the range £400–£600, any doubts as to the strength of the market were soon dispelled by the fact that all but four of these lots went through the four-figure barrier (and even those four doubled their estimates). The most staggering result was achieved by the medal awarded to Sergeant Joseph Aston which sold for £6,670—11 times the upper pre-sale estimate! Even Crimean medals have had a field day this year, with the more desirable examples also breaking through the £1,000 barrier.

The strong rise in prices for World War I medals continues, perhaps not at the same rate as the Military and Naval General Service Medals, but nevertheless strong. The number of "fresh" groups appearing at auction is much less than a few years ago. The reason for this is obvious; those people who were likely to have disposed of medals inherited from relatives would long since have sold them, whereas those who wished to hang on to them have probably continued to do so as more and more publicity in the national and local press has focused attention on the human interest inherent in even the most mundane of World War I groups. And as attention turns more and more on World War II, in television documentaries, families are more likely to hold on to related memorabilia from this period as well.

On-going interest in the carnage of World War I, especially the terrible battle of the Somme, for example, ensures that medals awarded to servicemen who took part is bound to increase steadily. This is most obvious when it comes to the Memorial Plaques. Two years ago the average price for a plaque relating to the Somme was about £200, but that has now doubled. It is perhaps apposite to add a word of warning regarding the memorial scrolls which accompanied these plaques. There has been a rash of such scrolls lately in apparently excellent condition, usually mounted in contemporary frames. On dismounting them, however, it has been found that many of them are copies and not originals, and it is a sad commentary on individual greed that there are people only too ready to manufacture such things for profit, especially when one considers the sacrifice made by the persons named on the plaques.

Last year we commented on the hardening of the market for World War II groups, if at least one of the medals in the group was named to the recipient. A group of four unnamed medals, unmounted and as issued, but accompanied by an Admiralty condolence slip in respect of a naval airman killed in action, fetched £300 at Spink, against an estimate of £80–£120, showing that even groups without a named medal have a definite value if the provenance can be established.

The definitive website for everyone interested in medals!

www.dnw.co.uk

Whether buying, selling, researching or just browsing, the new DNW site features the most comprehensive and useful suite of numismatic web pages you'll find anywhere – and there's absolutely no charge to use any of the services on offer!

- The largest online numismatic database in the world
- Over 25,000 full medal entries, complete with estimates and prices realised
- Accurate, up to date valuations for all types of medals
- Ultra-sophisticated customised search options
- Regimental and special collections highlighted
- Fully illustrated VC gallery

- The latest news, gossip, comment and opinion in **InterNews**
- Informative articles on a variety of subjects, plus medal rolls, in **InterFormative**
- Keep in touch with fellow enthusiasts on the sophisticated **InterChat** forum
- Match up split groups with the help of the **Reunite** editable database
- Rescue stolen items with the help of the **Recover** searchable database
- Free online identification and valuation service

- View forthcoming auction catalogues and illustrations
- Submit your commission bids online for forthcoming auctions
- All transactions protected by secure encryption technologies, with immediate confirmation

Updated daily – bookmark our site now!

DIX ✠ NOONAN ✠ WEBB

1 Old Bond Street London W1S 4PB
Telephone 020 7499 5022 Fax 020 7499 5023
e-mail: auctions@dnw.co.uk

Q&C
MILITARIA

**22 Suffolk Road, Cheltenham,
Glos GL50 2AQ**
Telephone & Fax (01242) 519815
Answering Machine Outside Hours
Mobile Telephone (07778) 613977
www.qcmilitaria.com
email: john@qc-militaria.freeserve.co.uk

We wish to Buy For Cash

Medals, Orders & Decorations
Helmets & Headwear ,all items of
Uniform, Swords & Bayonets Badges
& Uniform Furniture Military
Memorabilia & Trench Art

Top Prices Paid

Absolute Discretion Assured

Medals mounted for wearing
cased for display & refurbished
miniature medals and mess dress
accoutrements supplied.

We are located on the A40
(Gloucester to Oxford) at
22 Suffolk Road, Cheltenham
We are between the Guild Hair Sylists
and the French Restaurant
Adjacent to the Traffic lights at HSBC
Bank/Gentlemens College on Bath Road
Parking is available in the nearby
Bath Road Car Park @ 20p

Hours of Trading:
Tuesday to Saturday 10.00am to 5.00pm
Other times by
arrangement or coincidence

TOAD HALL MEDALS

REGULAR MEDAL LISTS
EACH WITH SEVERAL HUNDRED
FRESH ITEMS
HIGH PRICES PAID FOR MEDALS
AND COLLECTIONS

**VISIT OUR LARGE WEBSITE
www.toadhallmedals.com**

TOAD HALL MEDALS
**NEWTON FERRERS.
PLYMOUTH, DEVON. PL8 1DH
Tel: 01752 872672 • Fax 01752 872723
E-mail th.medals@virgin.net**

http://www.militaria.co.uk

**JEREMY
TENNISWOOD
MILITARIA**
FOR A WIDE
RANGE OF
BRITISH &
COMMONWEALTH
and FOREIGN
ORDERS;
DECORATIONS;
CAMPAIGN
MEDALS; AND
LONG SERVICE
MEDALS
(Singles & Groups)

**Periodic Medal Lists available. Please
send - UK: £2.00 in loose stamps
Overseas: US$4.00 in notes.**
CREDIT CARDS WELCOMED.

**P. O. BOX 73, ALDERSHOT, HANTS,
GU11 1HJ, GREAT BRITAIN.**
Tel: 0.1252.319791   Fax: 0.1252.342339

Buying • Selling

WORLDWIDE
Orders, Decorations, Medals, Award Documents,
USA & World Coins & Paper Money

– *NEW ITEMS NOW BEING CATALOGUED* –

- Awards & Honours to world famous Astronaut Buzz Aldrin for his 1969 Apollo 11 moon landing
- An important Manhattan Project (Atomic Bomb), Atomic Energy Commission & NASA medal group
- An outstanding explorer's group of medals to Robert English, Captain of the *Bear*, Admiral Perry's vessel during his 2nd Antarctic Voyage of Discovery 1933-35 • Japan Order of The Golden Kite Breast Star
- Collection of Yugoslavia Lands Orders & Medals • Worldwide Orders, Medals, Badges & Documents

Always buying at competitive prices—American, British, German, All European, Asian, Middle Eastern & African Orders & Medals • USA & World Coins & Paper Money

Periodic Orders & Medals price lists issued
For sample copy of our latest issue please send $1.00 postage for USA and $2.00 for overseas

- *30 year Member American Numismatic Asso.*
- *Member Numismatic Literary Guild*
- *Author "Standard Price Guide to World Crowns & Talers 1484-1968"*
- *Member Orders & Medals Society of America*
- *Member Southern California Orders & Medals Soc.*

FRANK DRASKOVIC
P.O. Box 803, Monterey Park, CA 91754-0803, USA. Telephone & Fax 626-281-9281
E-mail: fdraskovic@hotmail.com

III ARM MILITARIA

LINCOLNSHIRE'S LARGEST DEALER SPECIALISING IN CAMPAIGN MEDALS & BRITISH ARMY INSIGNIA

- LARGE RANGE OF VICTORIAN MEDALS
- SOVIET DOCUMENTED AWARDS
- RIBBONS • BOOKS
- INSIGNIA & HEADDRESS DEVICES

FOR A COMPREHENSIVE FREE LIST PLEASE SEND SAE

III Arm Militaria,
PO Box 121 Market Rasen
Lincolnshire LN8 3GF
United Kingdom
Tel: 01673 828081

ACQUISITION OF MEDALS ALWAYS REQUIRED

D. M. D.
Services

Specialists in
Victorian Campaign Medals

Medals and Decorations Bought and Sold

Please send for latest list

6 Beehive Way,
Reigate,
Surrey RH2 8DY,
United Kingdom
Tel/Fax:01737 240080

PETER MORRIS

Dealer in Medals & Coins

MEDALS, MILITARIA, COINS, BANKNOTES ANTIQUITIES

Tel: 020 8313 3410
Fax: 020 8466 8502

Shop hours:

Monday–Friday
10am–6pm

Closed Wednesdays

Saturdays 9am–2pm

**Ask for our latest Medal List via our FREE POST Service
or visit our web-site:
www.petermorris.co.uk or e-mail: info@petermorris.co.uk**

Retail:
1 STATION CONCOURSE
BROMLEY NORTH
BR STATION, KENT

BNTA

Postal:
P.O. BOX 223
BROMLEY, KENT
BR1 4EQ

POSTAL AUCTIONS
PO Box 4087
Hornchurch
Essex
RM11 2BP

EIGHT AUCTIONS OF MEDALS AND ASSOCIATED ITEMS PER YEAR.

The auction catalogues are distributed with the Orders & Medals Research Society Journal and Medal News.

Catalogues can also be obtained by sending a stamped addressed envelope (Internatonal Reply Coupon if overseas) to:

POSTAL AUCTIONS
PO Box 4087, Hornchurch, Essex RM11 2BP

Email: bids@medalauctions.com
website: www.medalauctions.com

Elite-Collections dot com
The Internet medal company

Are you on the net?
Would you like a monthly catalogue emailed to you free of charge?
Do you like personal, absolutely confidential service?
If so, sign up with the original medal e-catalogue company now
Just email your details and collecting requirements to
sales@elite-collections.com
and we will do the rest

We will email you personally when we find something on your wants list for you to consider—no obligation to buy

Non-internet clients are not forgotten
If you send us your details, along with five pounds to cover the postage, we will mail you a copy of the medal catalogue each month. Overseas airmail postage, ten pounds.

Also see our website at
www.elite-collections.com
for our personal details and wants, as well as for medals and related books for sale. Collections large and small purchased at realistic prices—try us, you have nothing to lose.

PO Box 56, Pontypridd CF37 2YL. UK

Beginner beware

Medal collecting has its fair share of pitfalls to trap the unwary. Your best guarantee always is to purchase medals only from reputable dealers who will gladly refund your money should the medal turn out to be not quite what it seems. The main problem arises when you buy medals from general antique shops, street market stalls, swapmeets and collectors' fairs. Despite the Trades Descriptions Act and other legislation in recent years, in practice it is very difficult and expensive to win restitution. It is one thing to study a medal critically in the comfort of one's own home, with all the right tools and reference books at hand; and quite another matter to spot a fake or outright forgery while browsing in a dealer's stock. But a little care, and a better idea of the potential problems, may prevent you from making a costly mistake.

OUTRIGHT FORGERY

The traditional method of producing an outright forgery of a medal was to make moulds from a genuine example and then take casts from it. The most obvious telltale sign of forgery is the metal itself, for forgers seldom took the trouble to get exactly the right composition of alloy. A good example of this is the forgery of the India General Service Medal of 1854 which has a leaden appearance and a peculiarly soapy texture to the touch. On checking the diameter of the suspect medals, using callipers and a half-millimetre scale, it will invariably be found that the diameter is slightly smaller than the genuine medal. This is due to the fact that the plaster used in the mould shrinks slightly as it dries, with the result that any cast made subsequently will be correspondingly smaller and thinner.

Whether the alloy is suspect or not, it is strongly advised that you get into the habit of checking the dimensions of medals, suspension bars and clasps accurately. Both the thickness and diameter of medals should be measured as precisely as possible, the latter being checked at several points—for a reason which will become obvious later.

Apart from alloy and dimensions, the other telltale sign of forgery is the surface condition. Is every detail of the design sharp, or is there evidence of blurring? There are quite fundamental differences in the techniques of production, between a genuinely struck medal and a cast forgery. The latter will usually show some signs of microscopic surface pitting, caused by tiny air bubbles in the molten metal as it cools down. Some forgeries we have examined are actually unbelievably crude, and the wonder is that anyone could be deceived by them—but they frequently are! These forgeries were produced in simple sand moulds which, although lacking the shrinkage factor inherent

in plaster moulds, have a grainy quality. Sometimes attempts will be made to remove this grainy characteristic as well as other surface blemishes, by chasing—an ancient technique of metalsmiths which involves filing and scraping with fine chisels and burins. This technique inevitably leaves very fine marks which are absent in genuinely struck medals. Casts also exhibit fine lines on the rim, where the two halves of the mould join, and although they are invariably filed off this often leaves a slight ridge, often visible by holding the medal with the rim to the light and rotating it slowly.

In more recent years, as the value of medals has soared, forgers have been taking infinitely greater pains, even going to the length of having new dies made (by hubbing from a genuine original) and then striking them. Such struck forgeries are more difficult to detect, but usually there is some subtle difference in the design which betrays their true character. The Air Crew Europe Star, for example, has been a frequent target of the forger, and several counterfeits of varying quality have been recorded. These range from the easily detectable type, with three pearls instead of five on the central arch of the crown, to a very accurate design albeit slightly thinner than the genuine star and having the points noticeably rounded instead of cut square.

Unfortunately with today's computer-aided technology, forgeries are becoming more and more difficult to detect but hopefully the same technology will help us to combat the problem by making simple methods of detection available to everyone.

COPIES

Under this heading come all manner of reproductions and imitations, which are often much harder to detect, especially if their provenance leads you to believe them to be genuine—or at least to be not so wary. It was not uncommon in years gone by, when the

27

wearing of medals was much more frequent than it is today, for generals, admirals, ambassadors and other high officials to have a second set of medals mounted for everyday wear. These copies were often produce by the firms who held the government contracts to manufacture the originals, and they were struck from the same dies, using the same materials. In this case, however, as a precaution, these medals were clearly marked COPY. Where this was stamped in incuse lettering there was little fear of erasure, but where raised capitals were employed these could be filed off. Again, it is advisable to check medals for any evidence of file-marks or erasure on the rim or in the field.

This problem becomes especially acute where gallantry medals and decorations are concerned. It has sometimes been the case that the recipient of a gallantry medal has been compelled, through straitened circumstances, to sell the medal while retaining the campaign medals which made up the rest of the group. Subsequently he obtains an official copy or duplicate medal to complete the set, and in the fulness of time this group comes on the market. In extreme cases the copy decoration may even be detached from the group and sold separately. Thus we have instances of gallantry awards appearing to sell twice over, when in fact only one was the genuine original and the second one was the replacement. This is a potential minefield, for there are also other reasons for replacement medals supplied by the official contractors for legitimate reasons. Gallantry awards, notably the Victoria Cross, have been replaced due to accidental loss or theft, and have then been worn just as proudly by the recipient. At the end of the day, however, the status of these replacements is somewhat less than that of the original medals, and is usually reflected in the market value. The question of status is something of a grey area which only the individual collector can decide for himself.

Campaign and general service medals, issued to serving soldiers to replace those lost or stolen are clearly marked "Replacement" at the time of issue and, as such, are not highly regarded by dealers or collectors. Unfortunately there have been numerous examples in recent years of these replacements having their true identity concealed by erasure. Be on your guard against such medals which appear to have been filed, rubbed or disfigured along the rim where the naming is found, as this could imply that the word "Replacement" has been removed for fraudulent purposes.

FAKES

These are genuine medals which have been tampered with in some way in order to convert a common (and relatively cheap) item into a rarity commanding a greatly enhanced price. Fakery is much harder to detect than forgery and each case has to be examined on its individual merits, but below (and in more depth, with regard to renaming, in the following section: *"Renaming"*) we give a few pointers to look out for.

One common practice is to take a perfectly genuine medal and replace a common campaign clasp by one which is rare. Apart from the fact that the substitute will probably be an out and out forgery, detectable by the factors outlined above, a high-powered magnifier will usually show up evidence of tampering with the rivets securing the clasp to the medal. This in itself is not proof positive of substitution, for clasps can work loose for various reasons; but any sign of tampering with the rivets, or their replacement, should put you immediately on your guard. Examine the rivets closely for signs of file marks, soldering or any other form of tampering.

The chief ploy to improve the value of a medal, however, stems from the British practice of naming campaign medals to their recipients. This has given rise to a form of faking in which a medal named to someone in a plentiful regiment, or to a non-combatant, has had the original name erased by careful filing, and a new name, rank, number and regiment substituted. Some of these fakes were relatively crude in that the original name might be left intact and only the regiment altered; but as medal rolls and regimental muster rolls became more widely available to collectors and military historians, and fakers were forced to give closer attention to adding the name of a serviceman who would theoretically have been awarded such a medal.

This is where a careful measurement of the diameter, from several angles, is vital. Medals should be perfectly round and regular, so that any variation in diameter measured from different points will almost certainly indicate that the rim has been slightly shaved to remove the original impressed lettering. In some cases the original lettering may have been raised; filing this off may not materially affect the diameter, but the substitution of incuse or engraved lettering may be a dead giveaway. It is very important, therefore, to study the detailed catalogues of individual medals, and compare the method of naming with that found on your specimen. Even this is not always foolproof, for replacement medals issued to serving soldiers to make up for lost medals may be named in a manner which differed from the original issue. 19th century campaign medals were not always marked as clearly as they are nowadays to indicate that they were replacements, but the use of different lettering may provide a clue.

Of course, renaming or altering a medal in some way has not always been done to fool the collector; serving servicemen have been guilty of such practices over the years for a variety of reasons!

Any aspect of a medal which appears to differ from the norm should immediately put the collector on his guard. However, it is only fair to point out that many long-running general service medals differed in some subtle way in the fastenings of the clasps over a long period. In this case it is necessary to become fully acquainted with the different styles, including different shapes and sizes of rivets, types of solder and even twisted wire—all of which have been used quite legitimately at various times for the same medal.

Similarly differences in the lettering and numerals inscribed on campaign clasps may not betray the handiwork of the forger or faker, for such subtle variations may merely denote that the clasps were the work of one of the Royal Mint's sub-contractors. For example, India General Service Medals may be found with clasps manufactured at the branch mint in Calcutta, rather than in London. Once again, it is necessary for the collector to study all the available literature in his chosen field and thoroughly familiarise himself with the variants which may quite legitimately arise, as well as the difference between genuine and fake which have been recorded over the years.

RENAMING

Trying to determine whether a medal is correctly named is a problem that every collector has to face at some time or another. When checking for evidence of renaming always examine the medal with the aid of a magnifying glass. It is useful to bear in mind the following points:

1. Generally speaking, it is easier to re-name engraved medals than those that bear impressed namings. An engraved medal is relatively quick and easy to rename as it is necessary to remove less metal to erase the original naming.

    To rename a medal with an impressed naming requires special tools which are not easy to obtain.

    This having been said, it should be pointed out that many of the most notorious cases of renaming (especially with more expensive medals), done with the intention to deceive, have involved impressed medals.

2. Always consider whether the style of naming is correct for the particular medal under consideration, also for the particular clasp(s) concerned and for the regiment, etc. Sometimes medals issued for the same campaign are named in different styles depending on the unit involved and the clasp(s). A good example of this is the India General Service medal 1854–95. Such information can be acquired in part from books and articles, but these can be inaccurate or not sufficiently specialised. The best way to acquire knowledge is by examining as many medals as possible. Always take full advantage of medal fairs, auction viewings, visits to dealers' premises and chances to look at friends' medal collections to enhance your knowledge.

3. Before a medal can be renamed, the original naming must be removed and one can usually see some evidence of this, such as in the form of file marks. Figure 1 shows the results of an attempt to remove a recipient's name from a medal—notice the many scratch marks caused by the file.

Figure 1

Unless the removal of the original naming has been done extremely carefully the edge of the medal may have a "rounded" appearance, instead of being square and flat. Figure 2 shows a renamed medal with edge view silhouette. See how "rounded" the edge is when compared with the flat edge of a correctly named medal in Figure 3.

Figure 2

Figure 3

Figure 4

Figure 5

4. If the suspender on the medal is assumed to be the 12 o'clock position, the naming on most medals appears on the edge between 9 o'clock and 3 o'clock. When the original naming is removed this thins down the rim between these two points. This is well illustrated in Figures 4 and 5. The former (4) shows a renamed medal with a thin rim while the naming has been removed and the latter (5) shows a correct medal with an even rim all round. The removal of the original naming will also reduce the size of the medal and this can be checked by using either a micrometer or a vernier calliper. The diameter of the medal should be measured across the 9 o'clock to 3 o'clock position and then across the 1 o'clock to 7 o'clock position. If the medal is not renamed, the two measurements should be the same. A "suspect" medal can also be checked for size against a known genuine medal, although it should be noted that a random check of say 10 similar medals will show variations in size.

5. Traces of an original naming may be visible under the new naming. Figures 6, 7 and 8 show examples of this. In Figure 6, traces are seen under the new naming and also beyond the end of it. Figure 7 shows the outline of an impressed letter "A" under the new "S" and also shows traces of file marks. Figure 8 has a small impressed "T" appearing between the "L" and "A" of the new naming.

    To recap, always check a medal for the following points
    a. Is it named in the correct style?
    b. Does the edge show file marks?
    c. Is the edge flat?
    d. Is the rim thinned at any point?
    e. Is the diameter the same all round?
    f. Are there traces of the original naming?
    g. Has the medal been checked in all respects with a known correct medal?

A term which often appears in auction house and dealers' lists is "officially corrected" and "corrrected". Normally these expressions refer to instances where a single letter in the naming has been corrected by the issuing authority or by the recipient in order to rectify spelling mistakes, etc. Figures 9 and 10 show examples of "official" corrections. In both cases, traces of file marks can be seen and the corrected letter is impressed more heavily than the other letters.

Examples of privately corrected errors can be seen in Figures 11 and 12, here the new letters have been engraved rather than impressed and so do not match the rest of the naming. Traces of file marks are also visible. Figure 13 shows an example of where the correction is an "addition" due to the recipient's naming being incorrectly spelt. It is corrected by the addition of the letter "E", which is engraved and hence does not match the rest of the impressed naming. The engraved full-stop after the "K" can just be seen beneath the new "E". Figure 14 shows a Naval General Service medal 1793–1840, where the recipient has had his original rank removed and his later rank of "Lieut" added. Again this is engraved and does not match the rest of the naming, which is correctly impressed. Once more, notice the traces of file marks and the original impressed full-stop some way beyond the "Lieut".

These kinds of corrections to namings were necessary because of human error and hence cannot really be classified as renamings.

Why do renamed medals exist on the market? The majority were not produced to deceive medal collectors, but are the result of officers and men losing their own medals and having to find replacements. The obvious and easiest remedy was to buy someone else's medals and have them renamed. Servicemen out to impress their friends and family were not above adding an extra medal to their rows and what better proof of entitlement than to see that the medal had their name on it. Many such medals were renamed by local jewellers.

Most collectors shun renamed medals and they are not usually offered for sale. An "official" correction unfortunately mars the appeal of a medal and hence affects the price. However some medals are very skilfully renamed with the sole intention of deceiving the unwary collector and dealer. This is especially so with rare and, therefore more expensive medals. The best advice is to use the check list given in this article and then, if still in doubt, consult a competent authority.

Figure 6

Figure 7

Figure 8

Figure 9

Figure 10

Figure 11

Figure 12

Figure 13

Figure 14

The definitive website for medals

Whether buying, selling, researching or just browsing, this is where you'll find more of what you're looking for

DNW
DIX · NOONAN · WEBB
AUCTIONEERS AND VALUERS

www.dnw.co.uk

1 Old Bond Street
London W1S 4PB
Tel 020 7499 5022
Fax 020 7499 5023
E-mail: auctions@dnw.co.uk

ORDERS

DECORATIONS

MEDALS

BOUGHT
AND
SOLD

PHILIP
BURMAN

Large and varied selection of Decorations and Medals always in stock

Send large s.a.e. for current list—five lists issued per year

We are always interested in purchasing single items and collections

IMMEDIATE
CASH SETTLEMENT

BLACKBOROUGH END, MIDDLETON, KING'S LYNN, NORFOLK PE32 1SE
Telephone: King's Lynn (01553) 840350
Fax: (01553) 841118
www.military-medals.co.uk

POSTAL AUCTIONS

We hold six Auctions
per year of

MEDALS

Free valuations also given

Please write for your *FREE*
Medal Auction Catalogue

**The Edinburgh Coin Shop
11 West Crosscauseway
EDINBURGH
EH8 9JW**
Tel: 0131 668 2928 or 0131 667 9095
Fax: 0131 668 2926

ALL INCLUSIVE

Bartletts
BATTLEFIELD JOURNEYS

Discover with the specialists, Bartletts Battlefield Journeys, the unique experience of our all inclusive expeditions to the Great War Battlefields in France and Belgium

• Informal, friendly small groups (5-15)
• Individually tailored & researched • Fully escorted by experienced, enthusiastic & dedicated guides
• Journeys of 3,4,5 or 6 days

DISCOVER WWI/WWII HISTORY

• Fine Art Prints • Wartime Posters
• Books • Videos • Study Packs
• Photo Prints • Collectables
Call for a copy of our catalogues or visit our website

ON-LINE ORDERING

Telephone 01507 523128
www.battlefields.co.uk
Chart House, 9 Tudor Park, Horncastle, Lincs LN9 5EZ

Taking
precautions

Like any other form of property, a collection of medals presents its owner with a variety of problems and responsibilities. No one in his right mind would rest easy, knowing that his house or motorcar were not protected by insurance. Indeed, in the latter case, insurance is both a wise precaution and a legal necessity. Yet, how often do we hear of numismatists who possess a really fine, often quite valuable, collection of medals but who have never taken the trouble to get it insured?

The usual argument is that insurance companies place so many obstacles in the way of the insurer, or that premiums are too high, or sometimes that it is just not worth the fuss and bother.

In many cases the antipathy towards insurance stems from a casual attitude. "This is my hobby," they say, "and it's only a bit of fun, a relaxation. If I have to start messing about with such boring matters as insurance, it would rob me of the pleasure of it." This cavalier approach is akin to the attitude of people, on being asked why they have not made a will, responding with some asperity, "Because I'm not at death's door". This completely misses the point, that the main object of making a will is because you have some property and wish to make some provision for its disposal in the (unlikely or hopefully long deferred) event of your death.

The emphasis should be on property and a sense of responsibility for it, rather than dwelling on eventualities that may never happen, or may not occur in the foreseeable future.

So, too, in the matter of insurance. People do not take out house or car insurance because they think their house is going to burn down or that they will be in a motorway pile-up. But these things do happen, and usually without any forewarning. Insurance is one of the methods we adopt to give ourselves some peace of mind.

The argument that premiums are too high is utterly fallacious. At most, they represent a very small percentage of the value of the items insured. It is an amazing fact that some collectors will happily fork out thousands of pounds on a single rarity, yet cavil at paying annual premiums of three figures on a collection worth a hundred times as much.

Normally those companies with whom you have your household contents insured will also extend cover to medal collections, provided that the value of the latter in proportion to other goods and chattels is not above a certain percentage. The practice in this regard varies from one company to another, so it pays to shop around and see what appears to be the most cost-effective deal on offer.

Where a collection of medals is coverable by the normal household policy there is usually a limit on the value of any single item. If you have a few medals which each exceed 10 per cent of the value of the collection as a whole it will usually be necessary to get a special numismatic insurance policy to cover these items adequately. Many of the larger dealers and some auctioneers also act as valuers and insurance brokers, so it is worth while to consult them for precise details of terms and costs in each case.

The insurance company may then require an independent valuation set on the collection, particularly if it is a large and valuable one, and will appoint one of their accredited experts to carry out the assessment. The cost of these valuations is calculated either on the time involved or, more usually, as a percentage of the final value.

Valuations and insurance premiums are not cheap but, with medal thefts on the increase, no collector can afford to do without some safeguard against loss. Money may be small compensation for the loss of a collection which has taken a lifetime to build up and which contains so many irreplaceable items, but it is better than nothing at all and with the insurance money collected one can always start all over again.

In most cases, where the medal collection is of moderate value, no restriction will be placed by the insurance company on how it is stored, but in cases of very valuable collections, or, more likely that relatively small portion of the collection wherein lies the greatest value, the insurer may insist on that part being kept in a fireproof steel safe, or even in a bank vault. This and other aspects of security will be discussed in much greater detail in a subsequent article in this series.

If the collection is a more modest one the insurance company may accept the owner's own valuation. In arriving at this figure it is important to remember that it is the replacement value of the collection which is required. A valuation based on the catalogue prices quoted in the *Medal Yearbook* or other price guides could be regarded as a starting point; on the other hand, some collectors tend to forget that medal values rise steadily and inexorably as the value of money falls, due to inflation, and thus they neglect to keep their valuations up to date.

This leads to the side issue of maintaining records which are invaluable for many purposes other than insurance. Not so long ago, keeping tabs on one's collection was a tedious and time-consuming process, involving notebooks and ledgers in which one could enter the details of each new acquisition, with a description noting the name and personal details of the recipient, bars or clasps and comments on condition or any distinguishing marks, catalogue number where relevant, price paid and date of purchase. A detailed record of this sort served as an inventory and, in the case of probate, would also help to establish whether any items were liable to estate duty.

In recent years, however, home computers have greatly simplified this task, to the point at which it is an easy matter to keep very detailed records and there is now no excuse for not compiling an accurate inventory which can quickly be duplicated in the dread event of burglary. It is also possible to reproduce medals and their ribbons by scanner accurately enough for identification purposes, and this is far cheaper than, and just as effective as, taking photographs of the more important items. Medal photography is a skill in itself, requiring a great deal of time and patience, apart from expensive equipment; so the modern system of digital cameras and computer scanners which enable you to store visual material on floppy disks is extremely useful for this purpose.

In the "bad old days", even the most detailed inventory was probably only revalued every five or six years, but now it is a simple matter to update it annually, thanks to the miracle of the personal computer. It is even possible to build into the program an automatic increase to cope with the annual rate of inflation or according to the Retail Price Index (RPI).

Even if you have not embraced the new technology, some form of inventory is a prerequisite. In its most basic form this might consist of a notebook, giving a brief description of the items, whether individual medals or groups, with catalogue numbers, and condition and physical peculiarities, if any. The date and cost of purchase should also be noted where practicable and such supporting documentation as auction descriptions and auctioneer's or dealer's invoices are useful.

This may not be necessary for items of moderate or low value, but where valuable items are concerned (say from £500 upwards and particularly for items costing £1,000 or more) there is a statutory requirement, under successive Finance Acts, to maintain records. This may become crucial in the event of subsequent disposal and the question of a possible capital gain arises. This is not just a matter of

deducting the purchase price from the eventual selling price, but has to take account of such factors as the length of time the coin was in your possession, and variations in the RPI over that period, to arrive at the true value today, adjusted for inflation over the intervening period. For this reason it is advisable to obtain a bill of sale and to keep a file of all receipts where the sums involved are fairly large.

Apart from their usefulness to the insurance companies, medal inventories are of vital importance to executors. Many collectors, extremely efficient in their business or profession, have unfortunately been quite unbusinesslike where their hobby was concerned. Non-collectors seldom know how much money their partners lavish on their medals. In many cases they have regarded their partner's pastime with amused indulgence, partly condescending and partly tolerant, with little realisation of the value or importance of the asset which is being built up.

Taking out a fully comprehensive insurance policy to safeguard your collection, and revising the contents listing on a regular basis, is a good discipline, not only for the here and now but also for the hereafter.

Few people ever take a real interest in their partner's hobby and consequently when a collector dies, the surviving partner is often at a loss (a) to appreciate the value of the collection and (b) to know what to do with it. If you have spent a lot of money on your medals you owe it to your dependants to make an inventory (a copy of which should be kept with the collection and another filed somewhere safe and separate as a precaution in case of theft). A copy of the inventory should ideally be filed with your will and instructions to your executor regarding the eventual disposal of the collection. If possible, a numismatic executor should be appointed specifically for this purpose. In the "big league" those dealers who have given a great deal of time to building up a collection for a client often act as numismatic executors; but usually some close friend who shares the hobby will suffice. A few numismatic societies even provide a service to the families of deceased members, to ensure that the collection is properly disposed of.

If the collection is to be sold or auctioned off after the death of the owner, written instructions to that effect should be left with the numismatic executor and, if possible, a dealer or auctioneer nominated to handle the negotiations.

INSURANCE FOR COLLECTABLES

This is the name of the special collectables insurance programme that has been developed for Token Publishing specifically for readers of MEDAL NEWS and COIN NEWS, in conjunction with H. W. Wood Ltd (who are registered with the British Insurance and Investment Brokers Association). Offering a specialised insurance policy underwritten by Lloyd's of London at a competitive price from as little as £41.20 per annum for £8,000 cover, each policy is tailored to your own requirements, whether you are a collector or dealer.

For further information contact Carol Hartman at

TOKEN PUBLISHING LTD.
Orchard House, Duchy Road, Heathpark, Honiton, Devon EX14 1YD
Telephone: 01404 46972   e-mail: carol@token-publishing.com

www.medalsonline.co.uk

updated weekly – many illustrations – fastsearch facility

new stock listed here FIRST

www.militarybookworm.co.uk

updated weekly – fastsearch facility

new stock listed here FIRST

NORMAN W. COLLETT

(Medals and Military Bookworm)

P.O. Box 235 - London SE23 1NS

Tel/Fax - (020) 8291 1435

~ Established 1975 ~

VISIT THE H&B MEDALS NEW WEB SITE

WWW.HILTONMEDALS.CO.UK

FULL OF TOP QUALITY BRITISH MEDALS WITH A WIDE SELECTION OF WORLD WAR I, BRITISH GALLANTRY & CAMPAIGN MEDALS

SITE UPDATED REGULARLY

Or contact David Hilton at
Tel: 01925 727035
email: HILTONMEDAL@aol.com
mobile 0771 4174188

GB Militaria

www.gbmilitaria.com

British Medals, Awards and Militaria for Sale.

We specialise in Wants Lists, Medal Mounting and offer a Medal Replacement Service.

We Buy British Medals or sell on a commission basis

Telephone: 0207-704-0634
E-mail info@gbmilitaria.com

Glossary of medal terms

There are a number of words used specifically by the medal collecting hobby, whilst others are borrowed from other areas. Some can cause confusion and many can be misunderstood by the beginner. To help the novice collector DENNIS G. BLAIR has listed many of the words which are regularly used in connection with medals.

Bar
(Sometimes referred to as clasp). An attachment indicating either : (a) campaigns—place, action or date; (b) service—duration or type; (c) gallantry decorations—a subsequent award. Usually attached to the medal suspender or preceding bar but sometimes direct to ribbon as on 1914 Star and WWII Stars.

Beading
String of embossed dots usually lining the rim, as on the Arctic Medal 1818–55.

Boxed
Within the original box of issue.

Brooch (fastening)
For securing a medal to clothing, e.g. buckle, as used with Royal Humane Society medals.

Brooched
A medal spoilt by having a pin soldered to its flan to convert it for wear as a brooch.

Campaign award
Medal to participants in a campaign or battle.

Carriage
Back plate to a bar or clasp to contain the ribbon.

Cartouche
Ornamental plaque containing an inscription as on the Colonial Auxiliary Forces Long Service Medal.

Bars *or* clasps *as affixed to the Crimea Medal (top), and the Indian Mutiny Medal.*

Cast
Technique of forming a medal through the use of a mould and molten metal.

Centre stem
The pivot about which a swivel suspender turns.

Citation
Description of action accompanying an award for bravery.

Clasp
See "bar". Term also used to describe the bottom straight ribbon support used in conjunction with certain awards that have ring attachment, e.g. Victoria Cross.

Claw
Ornate connection between medal flan and suspender via a centre stem.

Clip
Plain link crimped on to a medal rim to which a ring suspender connects, e.g. Waterloo Medal.

Coat of Arms
Heraldic shield, with or without crest, mantling and supporters.

Coinage head
Monarch's portrait as occurring on respective contemporary coins, e.g. George V on the Mercantile Marine Medal 1914–19 obverse.

Commemorative
In honour of an occasion or person, e.g. Visit to Ireland 1900 Medal.

Conjoined
Two overlapping busts, as on the obverse of the Jubilee Medal 1935 (sometimes termed jugate).

Contact mark
Impact scar, usually caused by one medal jangling against another on the wearer's chest.

Converted
Having a pin or clip added to provide direct brooch fixing.

Copy
Replica made to replace a medal lost or stolen.

Cross
Device having four equal arms set at right angles. Most frequent forms being Greek (plain), Maltese (with flared sides and double points to the arms) or pattée (with flared sides).

Cord circlet
Rope like encircling ring as on the Royal Naval Long Service & Good Conduct Medal 2nd type.

Crowned effigy
Portrait of the monarch wearing a crown, as occurring on most British medal obverses.

The Cypher on the Women's Voluntary Service Long Service medal.

Cypher
Desgin comprising a composition of interlocked and over lapping initials e.g. Women's Voluntary Service Long Service Medal.

Decoration
Award for meritorious or gallant conduct, e.g. Distinguished Service Order.

Defective
Not in original state, i.e. incomplete, renamed, damaged or otherwise spoilt.

Device
Symbolic emblem forming part of a design.

Documented
Formally recorded with details.

Duplicate
Official replacement for a lost medal.

Ears
Lugs at the ends of bars to receive a subsequent bar.

Edge
Outer rim of the flan, usually bearing recipient's details.

Edge-knock
Impact scar on the edge.

Efficiency medal
An award in recognition of completion of a set period of competant service.

Emblem attachment
Attachment to the suspension ribbon to indicate class, or other distinction e.g. oak leaf denoting mentioned in despatches.

Embossed
With raised inscription/design.

Enamelled
Inlaid with a fired coloured vitreous coating, as embodied on the neck badge of the Most Eminent Order of the Indian Empire.

Engraved
With an incuse inscription added by hand or machine.

Erased
The deliberate removal of the naming or details from

The exergue *of the China Medal 1900.*

a medal's edge.

Essay Piece
Trial specimen taken during manufacture.

Exergue
Segment below the reverse design often containing the date or an inscription.

Expedition Medals
Issued to those involved in an undertaking such as Polar exploration.

Faked
Having falsified details, e.g. renamed over erasure to convert an apparent common award to a rarity.

Field
Background area of the flan.

Filler Piece
"Temporary" specimen included in a collection pending a replacement proper.

Fishtail bar
Description given to the distinctively-shaped bars of the Second China War and Indian Mutiny medals.

Flan
The "disc body" of a medal.

Flaw
Defect in manufacture.

Forgery
A copy made to deceive.

Frosted
Matt finish often used on the field to contrast with polished highlighting.

Gallantry Award
For bravery, e.g. Military Medal.

Gazetted
Publicised in the *London Gazette*, official journal of the British government.

Ghost dates
Where dates have been officially removed but are still discernible, as on certain early Queen's South Africa Medals.

Grade
The condition in respect of wear. The symbols used are the same as those used for coin grading, e.g. EF, VF, etc.

Group
A number of medals awarded to one person.

The hallmarks *for gold and sterling silver (left) and Britannia silver (right) used by the Assay office in London prior to 1975.*

Hallmark
The official impressed assay mark denoting gold or silver.

Impressed
Indented details applied usually to the edge or a panel on the reverse.

Incuse
Legend or design formed by indentation.

Inscription
Wording as part of or added to the design .

Jewel
Name applied to masonic medals.

Jugate
Another term for conjoined.

K.I.A.
Abbreviation showing that the recipient was "Killed in Action".

Lacquered
Having a coating of clear lacquer added to protect the surface from oxidation.

Late issue
Deferred award (often due to delayed claim); may consequently not possess the original style or naming used.

The laureated *design from the New Zealand Medals 1845–66.*

Laureated
With laurel leaves design, e.g. as on reverse of the New Zealand Medals 1845–66.

Legend
Inscription on medal, usually round the circumference.

Long Service Award
An award for a period of unbroken service, often coupled with the requirement of Good Conduct in continuity.

Loop
Ring affixed to the rim of a medal for ribbon or cord attachment, e.g. as on Coorg Medal 1837.

Lunette contained
Within a watch style casing.

Medalet
Refers to pieces of 25mm diameter or less.

Medalist
A designer or maker of medals.

Medallion
Large piece not intended to be worn; often a prize or commemorative item.

Mention in Despatches
Recorded conduct from the theatre of war.

Miniature Medal
Piece reproduced approximately half full size, worn when full dress is inappropriate.

Moiré
Description given to watered silk ribbon, as used with the South Atlantic Medal.

Monogrammed
Embellished with representative initials, as upon the Second World War stars.

Motto
An inscribed maxim as on the Royal Humane Society medal for life saving.

Mounted
Method of wearing medals (in order of precedence) may be either "standard" whereby medals hang freely, or "royal style" (also termed court style), whereby

Oak leaf *indicating a Queen's Commendation for Valuable Service.*

medals are sewn to a back piece with the ribbons extending below their suspenders.

Named
Having the recipient's name, etc. (usually edge-impressed or engraved).

Native award
Issue to a native as against a member of Home Forces.

Oak leaf
Emblem affixed to the ribbon to indicate extra merit, e.g. "mentioned in despatches".

Obverse
The side on display when being worn, usually bearing the Sovereign's effigy.

Officially corrected
When the name or other details have been amended by the issuing body.

Order
Insignia of certain revered brotherhoods, e.g. Most Honourable Order of the Bath.

Order badges
Insignia emblems worn in the manner of medals, also upon regalia accoutrements.

Ornament
Added embellishment to provide design balance.

Pair
Two medals awarded to one person.

Patinated
Oxidation formed on the surface of bronze and copper medals in particular.

Pattern
Model used to enable the making of moulds and dies.

Peace medal
Unofficial celebratory issue (many made by Local Authorities).

Pierced
With a hole drilled through, usually for unofficial suspension fitting.

Pitted
Surface spoiling by minute holes, caused by chemical attack or contact from another medal.

Planchet
Blank metal disc from which a medal is struck.

Plated
With a thin coating of metal applied, usually silver or gold.

Plugged
Having a hole made good by filling.

Polished
Excessively shined-up, resulting in loss of highlight detail.

Posthumous award
Issued after the death of the award earning person.

Privately engraved
Engraved unofficially.

Prize medal
Award for personal achievement (e.g. academic) or competition success (e.g. sport).

Proficiency medal
Award for achieving a recognised standard in a particular specialisation, e.g. those awarded by the British Red Cross Society.

Radiant star
Formed with emanating rays, as upon the Most Noble Order of the Garter star.

Regimentally named
Engraved or impressed after issue through the recipient's regiment.

Relief
Raised design or legend/inscription.

Renamed
When original naming has been removed and other naming substituted.

Researched
Checked out against roll and records.

Restored
When a defective medal has been fully repaired or any missing parts replaced.

Restrike
Copy produced from original dies subsequent to original issue.

Reverse
The back of a medal not seen when being worn.

Riband bar
Strip (10mm deep) faced with medal ribbons worn to show medals awarded.

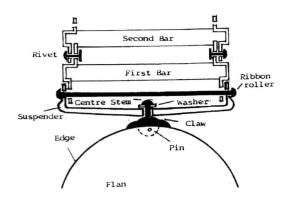

Diagram of medal with swivel suspender, showing assembly of components.

Ribbon
Strip of fabric for suspender attachment, and of respective colour/s to suit each particular medal.

Ribbon roller
The rod of a suspender over which the ribbon passes.

Rim
Raised outer ring to a medal's edge.

Rimless
When the edge is on the same plane as the field, e.g. Victory Medal of World War I.

Roll
Official list of those to whom a medal/bar has been awarded.

Roses
Ornamental florets on certain bars which serve to conceal rivet fixings, as on Indian General Service Medals.

Rosette
Rose emblem attached to ribbons of medals to indicate distinguishing factor, as on the South Atlantic Medal denoting close action involvement.

Roundel
Design contained within a circle, as on the Order of Burma.

Saltire
A diagonal cross, as on the sash badge of the Most Illustrious Order of St Patrick.

Scroll
Ribbon-like device containing an inscription, often a date, as on the 1914 Star.

Series
An ordered succession of medals of like category, e.g. the Indian General Service Medals.

Set
A complete assembly of a theme of collection, e.g. all combinations of bars issued for one campaign.

Shaded ribbon
Description of the colours merging into each other, instead of appearing as separate stripes, e.g. Scinde Campaign medals 1843.

Skeletal
Of open design, e.g. the Territorial Decoration.

Specimen
Medal struck contemporary with the original manufacture but not intended for issue.

Stain
Localised permanent surface discoloration.

Star
Stellar shaped award, e.g. Kimberley Star 1899–1900.

Struck
Technique of medal manufacture by stamping the blank piece between two dies.

Suspender
Means by which a medal is attached to its ribbon. It may be swivel or fixed, straight, horn or scroll shaped, floreate or otherwise ornate.

Tablet
Inscribed plaque panel, often integrated as a base for a design, as on the Queen's Sudan Medal.

Tailor's copy
Also referred as jeweller's copy, a fair reproduction made up as a dress piece.

Temperance medal
Reward for recorded abstinence to encourage continuance.

Toning
The natural darkening of silver occurring with age and exposure.

Tooled
Touch-up work effected with a chasing tool.

Tressure
An ornamental border following the rim as on the reverse of George V Coronation Medals.

Trio
Three medals awarded to the one person and usually referring to First World War medals.

Trophy of arms
Design showing an assembly of armaments representative of the defeated enemy's weaponry.

Uniface
With design on one side only.

Unnamed
Issued without indication of the recipient's name.

Unoffcial issue
Award made by a concern or individual other than that of a fully recognised authority.

Valuation
Estimated cost to purchase from an established dealer.

Verdigris
Damaging greenish deposit which can form on copper in particular.

Veteran's medal
Unofficial appreciation piece to "old soldiers".

Watered
Pattern in silk in which the colours merge e.g. 1914–15 Star and Atlantic Star ribbons.

White metal
Tin or lead alloy used to make cheap production medals from.

Wreath
Representing a ring of foliage, e.g. as on the reverse of the Territorial Force War Medal 1914–19.

NEW BOOK
Gallantry Medals & Decorations of the World

Gallantry Medals and Decorations of the World is the only work dealing with international gallantry awards, past and present.

Fully updated, the book is illustrated throughout and contains a full colour section.

Gallantry Medals is essential for the bookshelf of any militaria collector.

GALLANTRY MEDALS
& DECORATIONS OF THE WORLD
JOHN D. CLARKE

Available now priced £25.00 including FREE Postage & Packing UK/EEC only Non UK/EEC - Airmail £5

To order a copy please:
Tel: 01226 734555/Fax: 01226 734438 or write to:
Pen & Sword Books Ltd, 47 Church Street, Barnsley, South Yorkshire, S70 2AS
Payment can be made by either Credit/Debit Card or by Cheque/Postal Order

Speedbid

www.speedbid.com

www.speedbid.com

M. K. MEDALS

Dealers of Quality Orders, Decorations & Military Medals from all periods

Website updated daily
Collections or singles bought
Part-exchange or low cost
commission sales available
www.mkmedals.co.uk

31 Butlers Grove, Great Linford,
Milton Keynes, Bucks MK14 5DT
Tel: 01908 393383
email: mkmedals@hotmail.com

Send 40p stamp for complimentary list

FRED S. WALLAND

Collections of Unwanted
Medals sold for you in
our monthly Catatlogues.

Hundreds of medals for sale.
Send A5 SAE for
free sample Catalogue.

YEARLY SUBSCRIPTION RATES:
UK & BFPO £7.50
OVERSEAS £15.00

**FRED S. WALLAND
17 GYLLYNGDUNE GDNS,
SEVEN KINGS, ESSEX.
IG3 9HH**

Tel: 020 8590 4389
Fax: 020 8599 9923

Jonathan Collins (MEDALS)
Member OMRS Number 2001
17 Queens Road, Warsash,
Hampshire, SO31 9JY, UK
Tel/Fax: 01489 582222
Email Jonathan@jcollinsmedals.co.uk

Fully Automated Auction Site
– No Insertion Fee –
– No Commission –

Sell your medals & militaria online

www.bids-on.com
Visit my sales site or sell your items
on line 10% commission
Site visited by over 1,000 collectors
every week

www.jcollinsmedals.co.uk

– RESEARCH SERVICE –
a comprehensive research service
for collectors and family historians.
SAE for price list or order on line

www.militaryresearchon.com

A short history of naval medals and decorations 1790-1988

JOHN K. D. COOPER, FRSA

TODAY'S conditions have inevitably led to a standardisation of both decorations and medals as awarded to our now much reduced armed services. The Campaign Service Medal instituted in 1962 is still struck in sterling silver, but that is all it has in common with its illustrious predecessors when the navy and army had their own "campaign" medals and ribbons. This article looks back, not without some nostalgia, to the "glory days" of the British medal and to the history of decorations for gallantry and distinguished service relevant to the Royal Navy.

In the 19th century, a plethora of events occurred in all parts of the world associated with Pax Britannica, the protection of trade and the advancement of the Empire, all intertwined and all dependent upon a large and powerful Royal Navy. By the 1840s, in spite of the protestations of the Iron Duke, it was widely felt that naval and military personnel of all ranks who had participated in any battle, engagement or campaign should be recognised by the award of a wearable medal. Previously, only the soldiery of the East India Company had been so privileged. Senior officers had, of course, been receiving gold medals and decorations, such as the Order of the Bath—which made Nelson a prime target for a French marksman. The battles of the Nile and Trafalgar were among the first to be universally celebrated in this way, but the medals came from private benefactors. Waterloo broke with tradition and silver medals were given to all survivors and, in this instance, next-of-kin, fitted with ring suspensions and ribbon. In the late 1840s, to complement medals already given for the First China Wars in 1840–42 and for campaigns in India and the North West

Frontier from 1839 onwards, a decision was taken to reward survivors of the French Revolutionary and Napoleonic Wars and certain earlier Indian campaigns with medals bearing clasps for individual battles or actions. These were of silver and the same size as the Waterloo Medal, each weighing just under an ounce. They cost the state about 8–10s (40–50p) per man with distinctive ribbons for wearing, and were modest by comparison with the Army Gold Crosses and Medals (or their more discreet naval equivalents) given to senior officers during the same period. Even then, claims had to be made and proved; those who did not apply in time, by May 1st, 1851, the opening day of the Great Exhibition, received no medal. There were no posthumous awards.

The first Naval General Service Medal was thus instituted in 1849–51. Victoria's familiar diademed head by William Wyon appeared on the obverse; an allegory of Britannia ruling the seas, also by Wyon, on the reverse. It was suspended by an appropriate blue and white ribbon with a choice of 231 clasps for actions ranging from HMS *Syren's* boat action of March 15, 1793 (one surviving recipient) to the major engagements of *Trafalgar*, 1805 (1,710 recipients), *Navarino*, 1827 (1,137) and *Syria* in 1840 (7,015). Some British and East India Company naval forces were also entitled to a distinctive Army of India Medal for the First Burma War, 1924–26, fitted with the clasp *Ava*, also issued in 1851. In addition, a further medal was issued for Arctic Discoveries in 1855, retrospective to the year 1818, the first of three issues.

By the time of the Crimean War, the army and navy were receiving campaign medals of the same design and ribbon, usually named to each man. An India General Service Medal was instituted in 1854 for which clasps for *Pegu* (1852–53), *Persia* (1856–57), *Perak* (1875–76), and *Burma* 1885–87, were given to the Royal Navy and, until 1858, the East India Company's naval forces. A South Africa medal was issued in 1853 (for actions from 1834), its design to be re-adopted for the later Zulu Wars of 1877–79, followed soon after by the Crimean War Medal and the Baltic Medal for service against Russia, the

latter medal bestowed entirely upon naval and marine recipients and 102 sappers. The Crimean War also marked a turning point. The Victoria Cross was first awarded for supreme acts of bravery in the field, and all ranks were eligible. Initially, it had a crimson ribbon for the army and a blue ribbon for the navy and marines. A new naval award was made "for conspicuous gallantry" to complement the army's medal "for distinguished conduct" and to add to a lesser medal "for meritorious service". Senior officers continued to receive the gold, later silver-gilt, breast badge of the CB (Companionship of the Bath), or higher grades, until Queen Victoria inaugurated the Distinguished Service Order in 1886, first in gold and again later in silver-gilt for junior officers. As to the Crimea and Baltic campaign medals, so great were the numbers that most naval issues were unnamed but could be engraved privately. Blue jackets and marines selected for shore service were awarded "army" clasps if they had been present at Balaclava or Inkermann, or both, in addition to Sebastopol and naval operations in the Sea of Azoff.

Similar conditions regarding medals prevailed for the Indian Mutiny. Those named to HMS *Shannon* (with clasps usually for *Lucknow* and/or the *Relief of Lucknow*) or to HMS *Pearl* are highly prized. In the Second China Wars, the 1842 medal was re-issued with clasps for the actions at *Canton* and *Fatshan Creek* in 1857, the *Taku Forts* in 1858, and for the second capture of the *Taku Forts* and *Pekin* itself in 1860. The New Zealand Wars of 1840s to the 1860s saw much naval involvement ashore and a medal was awarded in 1869 with each man's years of service in New Zealand die-struck into the design, obviating the need for clasps. Similarly, the Abyssinian War of 1867–68 for which the navy provided not only the usual transport support but also a 100-strong naval rocket party, was honoured with a similar medal but with each recipient's details die-struck in the French style into the centre of the reverse. The Fenian troubles in Canada of 1866–70, in which several RN ships were involved, did not receive medallic recognition (and then only for survivors) until 1899! A medal was struck for the Ashanti Wars of 1873–74 in which there was a strong naval presence. Those present at the final battles near Kumassi ("Coomassie") received a special clasp, HM Ships *Active, Druid* and *Amethyst* being well represented. The same medal was re-issued for most East and West African expeditions, as well as some very small-scale gun-boat actions, from 1887–1900.

The Zulu Wars of 1877–79 saw much naval brigade involvement, principally in the provision of gun crews and rocket parties mainly from HM ships *Active, Tenedos, Boadicea* and *Shah*. A lone naval signaller from HMS *Active* was also present at the Battle of Isandhlwana and died in action.

Some of *Boadicea*'s crew were present during the disastrous 1st Boer War of 1880–81, and were casualties at Majuba Hill. No medals were awarded for this campaign.

The British fleet rarely fired a shot in anger in any of Queen Victoria's wars except in support of land actions, for example, before Sebastopol in 1854–55. The control of Egypt and access to India led to an exception, the bombardment of Alexandria, July 11, 1882. Opposition was slight, but the subsequent battle of Tel-el-Kebir included a full Royal Marine battalion and a naval brigade of 250 men.

Soon after the 1882 campaign, the Royal Navy went on to play an important part in the frustrated campaign to relieve General Gordon in Khartoum during the years 1884–85, all to no avail. The Naval brigade including machine-gun crews distinguished themselves at the battles of El Teb and Tamaai, Kirbekan, Abu Klea and Tofrek, and in the defence of Suakin. There were further actions at Gemaizah in 1888, and at Tokar in 1891, so a wide range of medal clasps could be added to the 1882 medal or to a new undated version. From the 1882 campaign to 1891, the Khedive of Egypt awarded a clumsy bronze star in addition which often pitted the British medals. A new Khedive's silver medal bearing appropriate clasps was issued for the next phase of the Sudanese Wars (1896–99) to accompany a Queen's medal. The navy played a very small role this time, but Commander Colin Keppel, who had distinguished himself in the Nile expedition of 1884–85, and a Lieutenant David Beatty, were among the RN personnel who served valiantly in the Nile gunboats at the battle of Omdurman in 1898.

The East and West Africa Medal referred to above was reintroduced in 1887–8 for actions against the Yonnie tribe in West Africa but received only a dated clasp. In 1890 it also served to celebrate the defeat of the Sultan of Witu in East Africa in a punitive expedition, thus earning around a thousand blue jackets and marines the clasp *Witu 1890*. The same medal then served for several other expeditions until 1900, the Royal Navy being most heavily involved in the Benin Expedition of 1897, receiving 1,500 clasps. On King Edward VII's accession, a new Africa General Service Medal was introduced, the last being issued for the Mau Mau disturbances in Kenya of 1952–56.

The turn of the century witnessed more military and naval activity in the British Empire than at any other time in Queen Victoria's reign. The Boer War was to be "over by Christmas", 1899, but lasted expensively until 1902. Again, naval brigades were landed from a variety of ships to distinguish themselves mainly in the Defence of Ladysmith (which included 175 men from HMS *Powerful)* and the town's relief, involving naval guns being hauled overland and used to great effect. Naval brigades also fought, with the Marines, at Graspan, the Modder River and the Relief of Kimberley and many other engagements. At the same period some naval forces had to be withdrawn to assist in the Relief of Pekin in 1900, for which the same China medal was reinstated from the 1840s and 1857–60 campaigns. Clasps were issued for the taking of the Taku Forts, as before, and a small number for the Defence of Legations given to the RM and RN garrison besieged in Pekin itself. The Navy then had to assist in Jubaland (part of Somalia) during the period 1900–02, in the Gambia and Aro Expeditions of 1901–2, and a series of renewed struggles against the "Mad Mullah" in Somaliland during the years 1902–04 (including the Battle of Illig, 1904), 1908–10, and, finally, 1920.

In 1901, King Edward VII, always very enthusiastic about awards and medals, introduced the Conspicuous Service Cross (recently revived) for junior officers and warrant officers. He also authorized a short-lived Transport Medal for officers of troopships supplied by various shipping lines. Only South Africa and China qualified before the award ceased. The RNR and RNVR received their long service decorations and medals in 1908, the latter featuring a formidable dreadnought on the reverse. A Naval Good Shooting Medal for gun crews was earlier introduced in 1903 only to be discontinued, ironically, on the outbreak of the First World War in 1914.

The reign of King George V began quietly enough with a new Naval General Service Medal. In use until 1962, its first clasp was for anti-piracy activities in the Persian Gulf from 1909 to 1914. The First World War unexpectedly then changed everything. In 1914, the CSC became the DSC and the DSM was introduced, equivalent to the later MM, DFM and AFM. A mention in despatches, similar to the Croix de Guerre in status, was to be recognised with an oak-leaf applied to the relevant medal ribbon. The MSM was widened in scope and, from 1917, the newly introduced Order of the British Empire has sufficed to the present time to reward most non-combattant services.

There was much debate to decide upon medals for the so-called Great War for Civilisation. In the end, only "Pip, Squeak and Wilfred", viz. the 1914 or "Mons" Star or its 1914–15 version, the silver War Medal and the bronze-gilt Victory medals, were approved. The Royal Navy was not pleased and many officers later fitted their dress miniatures with appropriate theatre and battle clasps. The famous Royal Naval Division made up mainly of reservists fought in France and Flanders and received many army gallantry awards. Then there was the irony of the Naval GS Medal being awarded for token operations in Iraq and NW Persia in the period 1919–20, while the troubles in Chinese waters in the 1930s were totally ignored except for some gallantry awards. The Palestine blockades warranted two clasps under King George VI, in the later 1930s and 1940s, similar to the Army and Air Force. As for World War II itself, a series of bronze theatre stars and clasps was awarded to make up for the deficiencies of 1914–1919. To the Naval GS Medal were added further clasps for *SE Asia 1945–46*, *Malaya*, *Yangtze 1949*, *Cyprus*, *Near East*, *Brunei* and *Arabian Peninsula*, as well as to recognise the dangerous tasks of minesweeping and bomb and mine clearance work.

It became increasingly clear by the 1960s that the overlap in the armed services especially in specialist units of mixed recruitment required a change in the award of campaign medals. The Campaign Service Medal of 1962 was, and remains, the solution, familiar to so many in the Royal Navy and Marines today bearing, among others, the clasp for *Northern Ireland*. No longer were there to be distinct ribbons for Navy and Army/RAF except for gallantry and long service awards. At least sterling silver survives as the chosen metal, unlike the 1939–45 cupro-nickel War Medal and Defence Medal or those to be given later for the Korean War and the South Atlantic and Gulf campaigns. Some gallantry and meritorious service awards have been modified in recent years, not without controversy, e.g. the 1974 introduction of the QGM. All the present writer can contribute is a suggestion that ribbons can be altered to indicate new regulations or, failing this, emblems added to ribbons. Both solutions have been adopted in various classes of the Order of the British Empire eg the late BEM, since the mid-1930s revisions.

Surely it is not even now too late to learn from such precedents.

To conclude, a word about medal collecting. It is a fact of life that medals are, and will go on being sold by families in need of money or who are just not interested. And yet most British medals and awards have the distinction of bearing the original recipient's name, unit or ship: a unique heritage. Thousands of what would today be valuable medals have been melted down for a few shillings' or, later, a few pounds' worth of silver. At least this has ceased. However, World War II medals and gallantry awards unnamed as issued are being sold without papers or any other proof of origin. The moral: keep, research and be proud!

www.speedbid.com

YOUR OWN MEDAL AUCTION

WORCESTERSHIRE MEDAL SERVICE LTD

Specialists in Medals and Medal Mounting

56 Broad Street, Sidemoor, Bromsgrove, B61 8LL   Tel: 01527 835375
Fax: 01527 576798   www.worcmedals.com   Email: WMS@WORCMEDALS.COM

Specialists in Ribbons, Full Size and Miniature Medals and Medal Mounting for wear or display

Medals professionally **mounted**, either **Court or Ordinary style**.

We can supply top quality hand made **Storage Cases** for your full size or miniature medals.

Display Cases for wall mounting.

Miniature medals, replacement medals, gold and silver plating, blazer badges.

Catalogues available – no fee, just send SAE

Miniature and full size replacement Medals, Badges, Cases etc.
Ribbons – extensive list of full size and miniature ribbons from around the world

ORDER ONLINE
Use our secure online ordering service
www.worcmedals.com

Please phone or write for catalogue or prices

All major credit cards accepted

ALEC KAPLAN & SON CC

CC Reg No CK 86/00121/23
PO Box 28913, Sandringham, 2131,
Johannesburg, South Africa
E-mail: rhodesia@iafrica.com
Website address: www.medals.co.za

WE BUY AND SELL MILITARY MEDALS AND MILITARIA

✱

WE HOLD AUCTIONS REGULARLY

✱

OUR NEXT AUCTION WILL BE HELD IN NOVEMBER

✱

WE ARE THE SOUTHERN AFRICA SPECIALISTS

~ WRITE FOR A FREE LIST ~

MASONIC WINNERS
OF
THE VICTORIA CROSS
AND
THE GEORGE CROSS

The book *Beyond The Five Points*, based on the researches of the late Phillip May GC, details the 118 Masonic Brethren who have been awarded The Victoria Cross or The George Cross

384pp A4 Hardback with dust jacket £35 sterling (inclusive of post and packing) from

TWIN PILLARS BOOKS
145 Russell Street, KETTERING, Northamptonshire NN16 0EW

Wearing awards

The wearing of Orders, Decorations and Medals is a complex subject too complicated to cover in a publication such as this. However, there a number of questions that collectors frequently ask, so we have attempted to deal with these as fully as possible.

Full-size Awards Mounted for Wear

Orders, decorations and medals are worn on the left breast in a line suspended from a single brooch mount or a rectangular frame (court mounted), the latter gives a firmer grip which occasions less damage than medals hanging more loosely from a brooch. The brooch/frame is covered by the medal ribbons. The most senior medal (see the following Order of Precedence) is furthest from the left shoulder. The obverse of the medals should show (this will usually be the sovereign's head, coat of arms, cypher, etc.).

If more than five medals are worn (three for the Navy), they should not be suspended side by side, but overlapped, the senior medal and ribbon is the one to be positioned so it can be seen completely. Medals should be lined up straight by the bottom rim/point, the length of ribbon should be one and a quarter inches (33mm) from the top of the mount to the first clasp or the suspension, which ever is appropriate (one and three quarters (45mm) for the Navy). Where the awards differ in size then a ribbon adjustment will be necessary to ensure a straight line.

Mentions-in-Despatches emblems should be worn on the relevant campaign medal, for example on the Victory Medal for the First World War and the War Medal 1939–45 for the Second World War. Where a recipient has no relevant campaign medal,

the MID emblem is worn directly on the coat after any medal ribbons, or if no ribbons then in the position of a single ribbon.

There are a number of awards for which the sovereign has granted permission that they be worn on the right breast:

Royal Humane Society Medals
Stanhope Gold Medal
Royal National Lifeboat Institution Medal
Order of St John of Jerusalem Life Saving Medal.

Foreign Order, Decorations and Medals

The British sovereign's subjects are not permitted to accept and wear the orders, decorations and medals of a foreign country of which the sovereign is not head of state. Application can be made for wear and permission is of two types: (a) restricted, that is instructions are given as to the exact occasions on which the award(s) may be worn; (b) unrestricted which allows the item(s) to be worn on all occasions according to the Order of Precedence, that is, generally speaking, arranged after British awards by date—first orders, then decorations, followed by medals (there are exceptions for the members of the armed services serving in an overseas force and receive that country's awards).

Awards are worn on a variety of State, evening or other occasions and the rules governing the wearing of orders according to dress are quite detailed. The subject is covered fully in Medals Will Be Worn *by Lieutenant Colonel Ashley R. Tinson (Token Publishing Ltd., 1999) and in* Spink's Guide to the Wearing of Orders, Decorations and Medals *(Spink, 1990).*

Stephen Wheeler
— MEDALS —

SPECIALIST IN
BRITISH & FOREIGN ORDERS & DECORATIONS

Always keen to purchase, trade, sell all types of World Orders

Please phone me on 020 8464 2068 or 0378 848555 Tuesday–Friday 9.30am–5pm

Or visit my stands in London on **Saturday** at the London Military Market, Angel Arcade, Camden Passage, 8am–1.30pm
or
Monday at the Famous Jubilee Antiques Market Covent Garden, Stand 111, from 8am–2.30pm

~ 20th Year in Business ~

THE LONDON MILITARY MARKET

ANGEL ARCADE, CAMDEN PASSAGE

Every Saturday over 35 stands 8am–2pm

Tel/Fax: 01628 822503
or 01455 556971

BRITANNIA
MEDAL FAIR
At The Victory Services Club
63/79 Seymour Street
Marble Arch, London W2

(2 mins from Marble Arch Underground Station, 5 mins from Paddington Main Line Station or convenient parking)

**2001: Sunday, 25th November
2002: Sunday, 27th January, 24th March, 19th May, 8th Sept, 24th November
(9.30am until 3.00pm)**

Licensed Bar, Hot Meals, Snacks etc.
For further details contact:
BRITANNIA ENTERPRISES
28 Raglan Place,
Burnopfield
Newcastle Upon Tyne
NE16 6NN
Tel: 01207 271869

The order of precedence

The Order of Precedence, or the order in which decorations and medals should be worn in the United Kingdom and the Commonwealth, is set out below, as announced by the Central Chancery of the Orders of Knighthood.

Victoria Cross
George Cross
Most Noble Order of the Garter
Most Ancient and Most Noble Order of the Thistle
Most Illustrious Order of St. Patrick
Knights Grand Cross, The Most Honourable Order of the Bath (GCB)
Order of Merit
Baronet's Badge
Knight Grand Commander, The Most Exalted Order of the Star of India (GCSI)
Knights Grand Cross, The Most Distinguished Order of St. Michael and St. George (GCMG)
Knight Grand Commander, The Most Eminent Order of the Indian Empire (GCIE)
The Order of the Crown of India
Knights Grand Cross, The Royal Victorian Order (GCVO)
Knights Grand Cross, The Most Excellent Order of the British Empire (GBE)
Order of the Companions of Honour (CH)
Knight Commander, The Most Honourable Order of the Bath (KCB)
Knight Commander, The Most Exalted Order of the Star of India (KCSI)
Knight Commander, The Most Distinguished Order of St. Michael and St. George (KCMG)
Knight Commander, The Most Eminent Order of the Indian Empire (KCIE)
Knight Commander, The Royal Victorian Order (KCVO)
Knight Commander, The Most Excellent Order of the British Empire (KBE)
Knight Bachelor's Badge
Companion, The Most Honourable Order of the Bath (CB)
Companion, The Most Exalted Order of the Star of India (CSI)
Companion, The Most Distinguished Order of St. Michael and St. George (CMG)
Companion, The Most Eminent Order of the Indian Empire (CIE)
Commander, The Royal Victorian Order (CVO)
Commander, The Most Excellent Order of the British Empire (CBE)
Distinguished Service Order (DSO)
Lieutenant, The Royal Victorian Order (LVO)
Officer, The Most Excellent Order of the British Empire (OBE)

Imperial Service Order (ISO)
Member, The Royal Victorian Order (MVO)
Member, The Most Excellent Order of the British Empire (MBE)
Indian Order of Merit—Military

DECORATIONS
Conspicuous Gallantry Cross
Royal Red Cross, Class 1
Distinguished Service Cross
Military Cross
Distinguished Flying Cross
Air Force Cross
Royal Red Cross, Class II
Order of British India
Kaisar-I-Hind Medal
Order of St John

GALLANTRY AND DISTINGUISHED CONDUCT MEDALS
Union of South Africa Queen's Medal for Bravery in gold
Distinguished Conduct Medal
Conspicuous Gallantry Medal
Conspicuous Gallantry Medal (Flying)
George Medal
Queen's Police Medal for Gallantry
Queen's Fire Service Medal for Gallantry
Royal West African Frontier Force Distinguished Conduct Medal
King's African Rifles Distinguished Conduct Medal
Indian Distinguished Service Medal
Union of South Africa Queen's Medal for Bravery in silver
Distinguished Service Medal
Military Medal
Distinguished Flying Medal
Air Force Medal
Medal for Saving Life at Sea
Indian Order of Merit (Civil)
Indian Police Medal for Gallantry
Ceylon Police Medal for Gallantry
Sierra Leone Police Medal for Gallantry
Sierra Leone Fire Brigades Medal for Gallantry
Colonial Police Medal for Gallantry
Queen's Gallantry Medal
Royal Victorian Medal (gold, silver and bronze)
British Empire Medal
Canada Medal

Queen's Police Medal for Distinguished Service
Queen's Fire Service Medal for Distinguished Service
Queen's Medal for Chiefs
War Medals, including the UN Medals—in order of
date of campaign for which awarded
Polar Medals—in order of date of award
Imperial Service Medal

POLICE MEDALS FOR VALUABLE SERVICE

Indian Police Medal for Meritorious Service
Ceylon Police Medal for Merit
Sierra Leone Police Medal for Meritorious Service
Sierra Leone Fire Brigades Medal for Meritorious
Service
Colonial Police Medal for Meritorious Service
Badge of Honour

JUBILEE, CORONATION, DURBAR MEDALS

Queen Victoria's Jubilee Medal 1887 (gold, silver and
bronze)
Queen Victoria's Police Jubilee Medal 1887
Queen Victoria's Jubilee Medal 1897 (gold, silver and
bronze)
Queen Victoria's Police Jubilee Medal 1897
Queen Victoria's Commemoration Medal 1900
(Ireland)
King Edward VII's Coronation 1902
King Edward VII's Police Coronation 1902
King Edward VII's Durbar 1903 (gold, silver and
bronze)
King Edward VII's Police Medal 1903 (Scotland)
King's Visit Commemoration Medal 1903 (Ireland)
King George V's Coronation Medal 1911
King George V's Police Coronation Medal 1911
King George V's Visit Police Commemoration Medal
1911 (Ireland)
King George V's Durbar Medal 1911 (gold, silver and
bronze)
King George V's Silver Jubilee Medal 1935
King George VI's Coronation Medal 1937
Queen Elizabeth II's Coronation Medal 1953
Queen Elizabeth II's Silver Jubilee Medal 1977
King George V's Long and Faithful Service Medal
King George VI's Long and Faithful Service Medal
Queen Elizabeth II's Long and Faithful Service
Medal

EFFICIENCY AND LONG SERVICE
DECORATIONS AND MEDALS

Medal for Meritorious Service
Accumulated Campaign Service Medal
The Medal for Long Service and Good Conduct,
Army
Naval Long Service and Good Conduct Medal
Medal for Meritorious Service (Royal Navy 1918–28)
Indian Long Service and Good Conduct Medal (for
Europeans of Indian Army)
Indian Meritorious Service Medal (for Europeans of
Indian Army)
Royal Marines Meritorious Service Medal (1849–1947)
Royal Air Force Meritorious Service Medal 1918–28
Royal Air Force Long Service and Good Conduct
Medal
Ulster Defence Regiment Long Service and Good
Conduct Medal

Indian Long Service and Good Conduct Medal
(Indian Army)
Royal West African Frontier Force Long Service and
Good Conduct Medal
Royal Sierra Leone Military Forces Long Service and
Good Conduct Medal
King's African Rifles Long Service and Good Conduct
Medal
Indian Meritorious Service Medal (for Indian Army)
Police Long Service and Good Conduct Medal
Fire Brigade Long Service and Good Conduct Medal
African Police Medal for Meritorious Service
Royal Canadian Mounted Police Long Service Medal
Ceylon Police Long Service Medal
Ceylon Fire Services Long Service Medal
Sierra Leone Police Long Service Medal
Colonial Police Long Service Medal
Sierra Leone Fire Brigade Long Service Medal
Mauritius Police Long Service and Good Conduct
Medal
Mauritius Fire Service Long Service and Good
Conduct Medal
Mauritius Prisons Service Long Service and Good
Conduct Medal
Colonial Fire Brigades Long Service Medal
Colonial Prison Service Medal
Army Emergency Reserve Decoration
Volunteer Officers' Decoration
Volunteer Long Service Medal
Volunteer Officers' Decoration (for India and the
Colonies)
Volunteer Long Service Medal (for India and the
Colonies)
Colonial Auxiliary Forces Officers' Decoration
Colonial Auxiliary Forces Long Service Medal
Medal for Good Shooting (Naval)
Militia Long Service Medal
Imperial Yeomanry Long Service Medal
Territorial Decoration
Ceylon Armed Service Long Service Medal
Efficiency Decoration
Territorial Efficiency Medal
Efficiency Medal
Special Reserve Long Service and Good Conduct Medal
Decoration for Officers of the Royal Naval Reserve
Decoration for Officers of the Royal Naval Volunteer
Reserve
Royal Naval Reserve Long Service and Good
Conduct Medal
Royal Naval Volunteer Reserve Long Service and
Good Conduct Medal
Royal Naval Auxiliary Sick Berth Reserve Long
Service and Good Conduct Medal
Royal Fleet Reserve Long Service and Good Conduct
Medal
Royal Naval Wireless Auxiliary Reserve Long Service
and Good Conduct Medal
Royal Naval Auxiliary Service Medal
Air Efficiency Award
Ulster Defence Regiment Medal
Queen's Medal (for Champion Shots of the Royal
Navy and Royal Marines)
Queen's Medal (for Champion Shots of the New
Zealand Naval Forces)
Queen's Medal (for Champion Shots in the Military
Forces)

Queen's Medal (for Champion Shots of the Air Force)
Cadet Forces Medal
Coast Guard Auxiliary Service Long Service Medal
Special Constabulary Long Service Medal
Canadian Forces Decoration
Royal Observer Corps Medal
Civil Defence Long Service Medal
Rhodesia Medal
Royal Ulster Constabulary Service Medal
Union of South Africa Commemoration Medal
Indian Independence Medal
Pakistan Medal
Ceylon Armed Services Inauguration Medal
Ceylon Police Independence Medal (1948)
Sierra Leone Independence Medal
Jamaica Independence Medal
Uganda Independence Medal
Malawi Independence Medal

Fiji Independence Medal
Papua New Guinea Independence Medal
Solomon Islands Independence Medal
Service Medal of the Order of St. John
Badge of the Order of the League of Mercy
Voluntary medical Service Medal
Women's Voluntary Service Medal
South African Medal for War Services
Colonial Special Constabulary Medal
Honorary Membership of Commonwealth Orders
    (instituted by the Sovereign, in order of date of award)
Other Commonwealth Members, orders, Decorations
    and Medals (instituted since 1949 otherwise than
    by the Sovereign, and awards by States of
    Malaysia and Brunei in order of date of award)
Foreign Orders in order of date of award
Foreign Decorations in order of date of award
Foreign Medals in order of date of award

THE ORDER IN WHICH CAMPAIGN STARS AND MEDALS AWARDED FOR SERVICE DURING WORLD WAR I AND II ARE WORN

1914 Star with dated "Mons" clasp "15th AUGUST–
    22nd NOVEMBER 1914"
1914 Star
1914/15 Star
British War Medal
Mercantile Marine Medal
Victory Medal
Territorial Force War Medal

1939/45 Star
Atlantic Star
Air Crew Europe Star
Africa Star

Pacific Star
Burma Star
Italy Star
France and Germany Star
Defence Medal
Canadian/Newfoundland Volunteer Service Medal
1939/45 War Medal
1939/45 Africa Service Medal of the Union of South
    Africa
India Service Medal
New Zealand War Service Medal
Southern Rhodesia Service Medal
Australian Service Medal

POST-NOMINAL LETTERS

Recipients of some awards are entitled to use post-nominal letters including the following:

VC	Victoria Cross
GC	George Cross
KG	Knight, Most Noble Order of the Garter
KT	Knight, Most Ancient and Most Noble Order of the Thistle
KP	Knight, Most Illustrious Order of St Patrick
GCB	Knight Grand Cross, The Most Honourable Order of the Bath
OM	Order of Merit
GCSI	Knight Grand Commander, The Most Exalted Order of the Star of India
GCMG	Knight Grant Cross—The Most Distinguished Order of St Michael and St George
GCIE	Knight Grand Commander. The Most Eminent Order of the Indian Empire
CI	The Order of the Crown of India (women only)
GCVO	Knight Grand Cross, The Royal Victorian Order
GBE	Knight Grand Cross, The Most Excellent Order of the British Empire
CH	Order of the Companion of Honour
KCB	Knight Commander, The Most Honourable Order of the Bath

DCB	Dame Commander, The Most Honourable Order of the Bath
KCSI	Knight Commander, The Most Exalted Order of the Star of India
KCMG	Knight Commander, The Most Distinguished Order of St Michael and St George
DCMG	Dame Commander, The Most Distinguished Order of St Michael and St George
KCIE	Knight Commander, The Most Eminent Order of the Indian Empire
KCVO	Knight Commander, The Royal Victorian Order
DCVO	Dame Commander, The Royal Victorian Order
KBE	Knight Commander, The Most Excellent Order of the British Empire
DBE	Dame Commander, The Most Excellent Order of the British Empire
CB	Companion, The Most Honourable Order of the Bath
CSI	Companion, The Most Exalted Order of the Star of India

CMG	Companion, The Most Distinguished Order of St Michael and St George	DCM	Distinguished Conduct Medal (West Africa Frontier Force)
CIE	Companion, The Most Eminent Order of the Indian Empire	DCM	Distinguished Conduct Medal (King's African Rifles)
CVO	Commander, The Royal Victorian Order	IDSM	Indian Distinguished Service Medal
CBE	Commander, The Most Excellent Order of the British Empire	BGM	Burma Gallantry Medal
		DSM	Distinguished Service Medal
DSO	Distinguished Service Order	MM	Military Medal
LVO	Lieutenant, The Royal Victorian Order	DFM	Distinguished Flying Medal
OBE	Officer, The Most Excellent Order of the British Empire	AFM	Air Force Medal
		SGM	Sea Gallantry Medal
QSO	Queen's Service Order (NZ)	IOM	Indian Order of Merit (civil)
ISO	Imperial Service Order	CPM	Colonial Police Medal (gallantry)
MVO	Member, The Royal Victorian Order	QGM	Queen's Gallantry Medal
MBE	Member, The Most Excellent Order of the British Empire	QSM	Queen's Service Medal
		RVM	Royal Victorian Medal
IOM	Indian Order of Merit (military)	BEM	British Empire Medal
OB	Order of Burma (gallantry)	CM/M DU C	Canada Medal
CGC	Conspicuous Gallantry Cross	QPM	Queen's Police Medal (distinguished service)
RRC	Royal Red Cross First Class		
DSC	Distinguished Service Cross	QFSM	Queen's Fire Service Medal (distinguished service)
MC	Military Cross		
DFC	Distinguished Flying Cross	CPMSM	Colonial Police Medal for Meritorious Service
AFC	Air Force Cross		
ARRC	Royal Red Cross, Second Class	MSM	Meritorious Service Medal (Navy, awards up to 20.7.28)
OBI	Order of British India		
OB	Order of Burma (distinguished service)	ERD	Army Emergency Reserve Decoration
AM	Albert Medal	VD	Volunteer Officers' Decoration
DCM	Distinguished Conduct Medal	TD	Territorial Decoration
CGM	Conspicuous Gallantry Medal	ED	Efficiency Decoration
GM	George Medal	RD	Royal Naval Reserve Decoration
KPM	King's Police Medal (gallantry)	VRD	Royal Naval Volunteer Reserve Decoration
QPM	Queen's Police Medal (gallantry)	AE	Air Efficiency Award (officers)
KFSM	King's Fire Service Medal (gallantry)	UD	Ulster Defence Regiment Medal (officers)
QFSM	Queen's Fire Service Medal (gallantry)	CD	Canadian (Forces) Decoration
EM	Edward Medal	QVRM	Queen's Volunter Reserves Medal
		VRSM	Volunteer Reserves Service Medal

Collecting
medal ribbons

There is nothing new or old about collecting medal ribbons, in fact the founders of the present Orders and Medals Research Society originally set out as medal ribbon collectors. The ribbon has, ever since the early 18th century, been an important complement to the medal or badge of an order and its importance has grown over the years. Since those early orders of chivalry when it was deemed necessary to identify the various religious or secular orders one belonged to by the colour of its ribbon, the emphasis has been on the ribbon to identify the order or medal. This practice has continued down through the centuries, even to today when the avid enthusiast can recognise a warriors medals simply by identifying his ribbons.

However, times are changing. The practice of wearing medals is on the decline, reserved only for ceremonial occasions, whilst the wearing of ribbon bars and the awarding of a single campaign or service medal with different ribbons to denote specific operations is on the increase. Our very own Operational Service Medal (OSM), the NATO medal and of course the plethora of United Nations medals are all classic examples of today's expansion of the medal ribbon. There is of course the growing cost of collecting medals and decorations compared to that of medal ribbons. There is also the down side to all of this, as the opportunity to acquire medal ribbons has become a challenge to many, as sources such as tailor's shops, small ribbon manufacturers or numerous regimental or quartermasters stores have all gone into decline, if not altogether vanished.

Before one can collect ribbons properly one must first be able to identify them. It is therefore important to have a reasonable reference library— nothing elaborate or expansive is needed. It is probably wise to start collecting ribbons of the United Kingdom before branching out into those of other countries. There are several good books on the subject and ribbons can be obtained quite easily.

The more one handles ribbons the quicker one starts to get a feel for the subject and gets to know which colours are used by certain countries or organisations, whether they always use silk or fine cottons, prefer moiré (watered) or corded ribbons whether they use wide or narrow ribbons, all are skills one picks up along the way, though sadly this art is slowly dying as the quality of many modern manufactured ribbons is really quite poor compared to the silk watered ribbons of bygone days.

Once over the initial teething problems of deciding how to store ribbons and ultimately mount or display them, the desire to expand and even specialise creeps in. Do you collect ribbons from just one country, state or organisation such as the Red Cross or the United Nations? Campaign medals and their numerous emblems? Famous chests? Regimental battle streamers? Religious or chivalric orders past and present? British or foreign orders and their various rosettes? The choice can be endless. Whatever the path you choose, you will almost certainly have to do a little research to obtain the reason for the award and the colours adopted for the ribbon. In reality, a true ribbon collector will know just as much about the medal or decoration as they will about the ribbon. Depending on the amount of time you have, research can lead you to museums, reading rooms or even portrait galleries, as well as societies such as the Ribbon Branch of the Orders and Medals Research Society. But whatever path is chosen you will be in awe of the sacrifices made by mankind down the centuries.

Miniature medals and decorations

The collecting of miniature medals has gained in popularity over the past few years and as a result groups and single miniatures that were once sold with their full-size counterparts, as an added extra, are now being traded in their own right. The market prices for these attractive and often superbly-produced little pieces are included in the catalogue section. Collectors wishing to learn more about miniature medals are invited to contact the Miniature Medals Branch of the Orders & Medals Research Society whose address can be found opposite.

Miniatures are small versions of orders, decorations and medals designed for formal evening wear. The custom appears to have developed in Continental Europe in the early years of the 18th century, but is now more or less universal, although the actual practice varies from country to country. In the United Kingdom, for example, miniatures are confined to mess kit and evening dress (white tie and tails), whereas in the United States it is quite common to see miniatures worn with dinner jackets. In Europe, miniatures are often worn without ribbons, suspended from a tiny chain, but in Britain and elsewhere miniatures are worn with exact replicas of the appropriate ribbons correspondingly reduced in size.

The scale of miniatures likewise varies from country to country. In Britain miniatures are usually half the size of the full-sized medals, but the Scandinavian countries use a 17mm size, while France and the Low Countries prefer a 14mm size, calculated from the diameter of medals or the badges of orders.

In the 18th and early 19th centuries the breast stars of orders were also worn in miniature, but nowadays only the badges of the orders are miniaturised. In Europe the higher classes of orders are designated by placing wings in silver, gold and silver, or gold, according to the class, below the rosette on the riband of the Officer Class. In Britain, however, miniatures are exact replicas of the badges they represent, and no additional rosettes or emblems are added to the ribands to denote a particular class.

Miniatures differ in one major respect from the full-scale; whereas the latter were produced by specific contractors, the former have been manufactured by many jewellers and goldsmiths. Consequently, the quality may vary considerably, from a very faithful replica (doubtless produced by the same firm that made the originals and using scaled-down dies for the purpose), to quite crude imitations that differ in many details from the full sized version. In many instances, miniature medal groups may be found with the original case as supplied by the jeweller, so that identification is not a problem. Many other groups, however, have long since parted company from their presentation cases, and identification is then only possible from other factors, either stylistic or from marks. Some miniatures are hallmarked (i.e. they bear the punches of an assay office and the mark of the manufacturer), and in such cases the miniature can not only be identified, but even the date of manufacture adduced from the year letter. Not all miniatures by any means are hallmarked, especially if they fall below the statutory minimum weight, so that this aid to identification is not always present.

The value placed on miniatures is governed by condition, of course, but other factors that must be taken into consideration are the provenance and authenticity of the medal or group. Miniatures which are contemporary with the original award are rated more highly than replacements procured many years later. And miniature groups which can definitely be assigned to a particular recipient are worth a premium over those whose original owner cannot be determined. Unlike the full-scale originals, miniatures very seldom bear the name of the recipient. Nevertheless, this is a fascinating aspect of medal collecting, much less expensive than the full-size medals but often as rewarding for the human interest which miniatures represent.

Lets talk miniatures

A cry often heard amongst collectors these days is "Where have all the miniatures gone?" A stroll around the dealers' tables at any medal fair usually provides only a few examples, and these are not always very desirable. Auction houses have, to a certain degree, managed to include some miniature lots in most of their sales, though nothing on the scale of a few years ago. Occasionally a gem does appear—such as the North Borneo General Service Medal which was included in a recent DNW sale. Foreign miniatures, especially those of gold and enamel, have always appealed to a large section of collectors from Europe to North America—and they were favoured with a magnificent chain, in gold, white gold and enamels, offered by Spink in their November 2000 sale (illustrated below). So there is hope yet!

The trend of making up groups continues and whilst harmless in the hands of the creator wishing to replicate a family set of medals, is liable to misrepresentation if and when they subsequently appear on the market, as many of them have done. There is a world of difference between "A group of miniatures *as worn by . . .*" and "The group of miniatures *attributed to . . .*". Unfortunately many single miniatures and clasps are being copied—and very well at that. Experience and, if possible, comparison with the genuine article, will show them up for what they really are. Whilst there is no harm whatever in their being offered for sale as *copies*, passing them off as contemporary originals can result in an expensive mistake for the purchaser.

There is still a wide range differential of pricing amongst dealers, so consult the MEDAL YEARBOOK as a guide, but do remember that the prices given are usually a dealer's selling price.

Mark Cline
Proprietor of MC Miniature Medals

For further information on the collecting of miniature medals, readers are invited to contact:

**The Honorary Secretary
The Miniature Medals Branch
Orders and Medals Research Society
54 Priory Bridge Road
Taunton
Somerset
TA1 1QB**

ACKLEY UNLIMITED

ORDERS. . .

DECORA TIONS. . .

and MEDALS

Bought, Sold or Traded
All Items Guaranteed

FINDER SERVICE • APPRAISALS • LIMITED RESEARCH
• FREE SAMPLE LIST ON REQUEST

(Specify Interests—Want Lists Constantly Checked and Updated)

**P.O. BOX 82144, PORTLAND,
OREGON 97282–0144
U.S.A**

OMSA No. 3848

MCC of C No. 2266

Phone (503) 659-4681

OMRS No. 3134

MINIATURE MEDALS

Exclusively Miniatures

**Extensive stock of all British
Orders, Decorations and Medals**

Send £2 Chq/PO payable to
H. M. G. Cline for sample catalogue

**I am actively seeking to purchase singles,
groups and entire collections, and items
sold by me, willingly re-purchased**

**MC MINIATURE MEDALS
PO BOX 1512,
WARWICK CV35 9YX
Tel/Fax: 01926 651500**

Most major credit cards accepted
Member OMRS, OMSA & MCC of C

LOCKDALES

East Anglia's *Premier* Dealers
& Auctioneers of Collectables

**Do You Want To Get The Best Price For
Your Medals & Militaria?**

Of Course You Do!

Lockdales hold regular auctions of
collectables and have established an extensive
clientele looking for all types of Medals,
Militaria, Cap Badges and associated
Ephemera. We also auction Coins, Banknotes,
Postcards, Stamps and Cigarette/Trade Cards.

We offer extremely competitive rates, whether
you are buying or selling. Just give us a call to
find out how we can help you.

Complimentary catalogue available on request.

Come and visit us at either of our shops
— or visit us in cyberspace at our website
www.lockdales.co.uk

36 Upper Orwell St., Ipswich   01473 218588
168 London Rd., South Lowestoft   01502 568468

Orders
of Chivalry

The most colourful and romantic of all awards are those connected with the orders of chivalry. Many of them have their origins in the Middle Ages, when knights in armour formed the elite fighting force in every European country. This was the period when knights jousted in tournaments as a pastime, between going off to the Holy Land on the wars of Christendom known as the Crusades. This was the era of such popular heroes as Richard the Lionheart, William the Lion, Robert the Bruce, the Black Prince, Pepin of Herstal and John the Blind King of Bohemia. Their exploits have passed into the folklore of Europe, together with the legends of Roland and his Paladins or King Arthur and the Knights of the Round Table.

From the idea of a select band of knights, pledged to the support of a king or an ideal (usually religious), sprang the orders of chivalry. Many of these existed in the Middle Ages but most of them died out as feudalism went into decline. In some cases they survived; in others they disappeared for centuries, only to be resurrected at a later date. Still others were devised and instituted in relatively modern times, and indeed, continue to evolve. For example, Canada instituted the Order of Canada in 1967 and both Australia and New Zealand introduced their own orders in 1975.

In their original form membership of the orders of chivalry were just as highly coveted as they are today, but the insignia was usually simple or even non-existent. The complicated system of insignia which now surrounds these orders is fairly modern, dating from the 16th century or later. Nowadays most orders also exist in several classes, with the insignia becoming increasingly elaborate with each higher class.

Britain's senior order is the Garter, and although it consists of one class only it provides a good example of the pomp and ceremony which often surrounds these awards. It was founded by King Edward III and is said to derive its name from the fact that the King was attending a dance one day, when a lady's garter slipped from her leg and fell to the floor. To save her the embarrassment of retrieving her garter—and thus letting everyone know it was hers—the King himself picked it up and tied it round his own leg. Lest anyone should doubt that it was his garter he said, in court French, "Let evil be to him who evil thinks". From this curious incident came the idea of a very exclusive order of knighthood, consisting of the sovereign and 26 knights.

The insignia of this order consists of a Garter, a mantle of blue velvet lined with taffeta with the star of the Order embroidered on the left breast, a hood of crimson velvet, a surcoat of crimson velvet lined with white taffeta, a hat of black velvet lined with white taffeta, with a plume of white ostrich and black heron feathers fastened by a band of diamonds, a collar of gold composed of buckled garters and lovers' knots with red roses, the George (an enamelled figure of St George slaying the dragon) suspended from the collar, the Lesser George or badge, worn from a broad blue sash passing over the left shoulder to the right hip, and the star, a silver eight-pointed decoration bearing the red cross of St George surrounded by the garter and motto.

The insignia is exceptionally elaborate, the other orders of chivalry varying considerably in their complexity according to the class of the order. The full insignia is only worn on special occasions. In the case of the Garter usually the Lesser George and the breast star are worn on their own.

On the death of a Knight of the Garter the insignia must be returned to the Central Chancery of Orders of Knighthood, and therefore few examples of the Garter ever come on to the market. Those that do are usually examples from the 17th and 18th centuries when regulations regarding the return of insignia were not so strict. In the case of the lesser orders, insignia is returnable on promotion to a higher class. All collar chains are returnable, although that of the Order of St Michael and St George could be retained prior to 1948.

British orders are manufactured by firms holding contracts from the Central Chancery of Orders of Knighthood, and the values quoted in this Yearbook are for the official issues. It should be noted, however, that holders of orders frequently have replicas of breast stars made for use on different uniforms and it is sometimes difficult to tell these replicas from the originals as in many cases the replicas were made by the court jewellers responsible for making the originals. In addition, many jewellers in such European capitals as Vienna, Berlin and Paris have a long tradition of manufacturing the insignia of orders for sale to collectors.

The badges and breast stars of orders of chivalry are very seldom named to the recipient and therefore lack the personal interest of campaign medals and many gallantry awards. For this reason they do not command the same interest or respect of collectors. Nevertheless, in cases where the insignia of orders can be definitely proved to have belonged to some famous person, the interest and value are enhanced. In any case, these orders are invariably very attractive examples of the jeweller's art, and they often possess titles and stories as colourful and romantic as their appearance.

Let us exceed your expectations

A Great War DSO & MC group of 6 to Major W. Gordon, 2nd Bat. Gordon Highlanders. Realised £3,800 14th March 2001

In recent auctions we have continually obtained outstanding prices for Orders, Decorations and Campaign medals, both commoner single medals/groups and more valuable gallantry groups being in great demand.

Consign your medals to Warwick & Warwick and let us exceed your expectations.

Act Now *Telephone us today with details of your property. Write to us, fax us or email us if you prefer. Remember we can be with you in 48 hours.*

Warwick & Warwick

**Warwick & Warwick Limited, Chalon House, Scar Bank, Millers Road, Warwick, England. CV34 5DB.
Tel: 01926–499031. Fax: 01926–491906.
E-mail: info@warwickandwarwick.com**

1. THE MOST NOBLE ORDER OF THE GARTER

Instituted: 1348.

Ribbon: 100mm plain dark blue. Not worn in undress uniform.

Garter: Dark blue velvet. Two versions may be encountered, with embroidered lettering and other details, or with gold lettering, buckle and tab. Worn on the left leg by gentlemen and on the left forearm by ladies.

Collar Chain: Gold composed of alternate buckled garters, each encircling a red enamelled rose, and lovers' knots in gold although sometimes enamelled white.

Collar badge: An enamelled figure of St George fighting the dragon.

Star: Originally always embroidered in metal thread, a style which continues in the mantle to this day. Prior to 1858 knights often purchased metal stars in addition and since that date metal stars have been officially issued. These consist of a silver eight-pointed radiate star bearing in its centre and red cross of St George on a white ground, surrounded by the garter and motto HONI SOIT QUI MAL Y PENSE (evil be who evil thinks).

Sash Badge: The Lesser George, similar to the collar badge but encircled by an oval garter bearing the motto.

KG Star
(a Victorian example)

Comments: *Membership of the Order of the Garter is confined to the reigning sovereign, the Prince of Wales and 25 other Knights, and is the personal gift of the monarch. In addition to the 25 Knights there have, from time to time, been extra Knights, occasionally non-Christians such as the Sultans of Turkey or the Emperor of Japan. The Emperor Hirohito, incidentally had the dubious distinction of being the only person awarded the Garter twice: in 1922 and again in 1971, having forfeited the original award as a result of the Japanese entry into the Second World War in 1941. Sir Winston Churchill was invested with the insignia originally presented in 1702 to his illustrious ancestor, the Duke of Marlborough. All official insignia is returnable to the Central Chancery of Knighthood on the death of the holder. Ladies (other than royalty) are now eligible for the Order.*

Lesser George
(this early example has the garter enamelled in blue)

VALUE:

Collar chain	Rare
Collar badge (the George)	£50,000–100,000*
Star (in metal)	£1500–5000
Star (embroidered)	£400–1000
Mantle star	£500–750
Sash badge (Lesser George)	£3000–40,000
Garter (embroidered)	£350–500
Garter (gold lettering and buckle)	£1200–2500
Miniature	
Star (metal)	£200–250

*Prices are for privately made examples many of which are jewelled and enamelled.

2. THE MOST ANCIENT AND MOST NOBLE ORDER OF THE THISTLE

KT Star

Instituted: 1687.

Ribbon: 100mm plain dark green. Not worn in undress uniform.

Collar Chain: Gold of alternate thistles and sprigs of rue enamelled in proper colours.

Collar Badge: The jewel is a gold and enamelled figure of St Andrew in a green gown and purple surcoat, bearing before him a white saltire cross, the whole surrounded by rays of gold.

Star: Silver, consisting of a St Andrew's cross, with other rays issuing between the points of the cross and, in the centre, on a gold background, a thistle enamelled in proper colours surrounded by a green circle bearing the Latin motto NEMO ME IMPUNE LACESSIT (no one assails me with impunity).

Sash Badge: The medal of the Order is a gold figure of St Andrew bearing before him a saltire cross, surrounded by an oval collar bearing the motto, surmounted by a gold cord fitted with a ring for suspension. Examples are found in plain gold, or with enamelling and/or set with jewels.

Comments: *This order is said to have been founded in AD 787, alluding to barefoot enemy soldiers who cried out when they trod on thistles and thus alerted the Scots of an imminent attack. The order had long been defunct when it was revived by King James VII and II and re-established in December 1703 by Queen Anne. It now consists of the sovereign and 16 Knights, making it the most exclusive of the orders of chivalry. At death, the official insignia is returned to the Central Chancery. Ladies (other than royalty) are now eligible for the Order.*

VALUE:

Collar chain	Rare
Collar badge	Rare
Star (metal)	£1500–4000
Star (embroidered)	£450–650
Mantle star	£500–1000
Sash badge	£5000–8000
Miniature	
Star (metal)	£250–300

Examples of Sash Badges

3. THE MOST ILLUSTRIOUS ORDER OF ST PATRICK

KP Star

Sash badge

Instituted: February 5, 1783.

Ribbon: 100 mm sky-blue. Not worn in undress uniform.

Collar Chain: Gold, composed of five roses and six harps alternating, each tied together with a gold knot. The roses are enamelled alternately white petals within red and red within white.

Collar Badge: An imperial crown enamelled in proper colours from which is suspended by two rings a gold harp and from this a circular badge with a white enamelled centre embellished with the red saltire cross on which is surmounted a green three-petalled shamrock its leaves decorated with gold crowns, the whole surrounded by a gold collar bearing the Latin motto QUIS SEPARABIT (who shall separate us?) with the date of foundation in roman numerals round the foot MDCCLXXXIII.

Star: A silver eight-pointed star, having in its centre, on a white field, the saltire cross of St Parick in red enamel charged with a green trefoil bearing a gold crown on each leaf.

Sash Badge: The saltire cross in red enamel surmounted by a green shamrock with gold crowns as above, surrounded by an oval collar of pale blue with the Latin motto round the top and the date of foundation round the foot, the whole enclosed by a gold and white enamel surround charged with 32 shamrocks.

Comments: *Founded by King George III to reward the loyalty of Irish peers during the American War of Independence, it originally comprised the monarch and 15 Knights. In 1833 it was extended to include the Lord-Lieutenant of Ireland and 22 Knights, with certain extra and honorary knights. Appointments of non-royal Knights to the Order ceased with the partition of Ireland in 1922, although three of the sons of King George V were appointed after that date—the Prince of Wales (1927), the Duke of York (1936) and the Duke of Gloucester (1934). It became obsolete in 1974 with the death of the last holder. All items of official insignia were returned at death. Unlike the other two great orders, the sash for this Order is worn in the manner of the lesser orders, over the right shoulder.*

VALUE:

Collar chain	Rare
Collar badge	£8000–12,000
Star (metal)	£1500–3000
Star (embroidered)	£400–600
Mantle star	£500–1000
Sash badge	£5000–7000
Miniature	
Star (metal)	£200–250

4. THE MOST HONOURABLE ORDER OF THE BATH

GCB Star (Military)

Instituted: 1725.

Ribbon: 38mm.

Collar Chain: Gold composed of nine crowns and eight devices, each consisting of a rose, a thistle and a shamrock issuing from a sceptre all enamelled in their proper colours. The crowns and devices are joined by gold, white-enamelled knots.

Collar Badge: A skeletal gold badge with an oval collar inscribed TRIA JUNCTA IN UNO (three joined in one) in white enamelled letters, enclosing a thistle, rose and shamrock issuing from a sceptre, with a crown above the sceptre and two crowns below, at the sides.

Star: A silver flaming star surmounted by a circular gold band enamelled red bearing the motto round the top and having a laurel spray round the foot, enclosing three gold crowns enamelled in red.

Sash Badge: As the Collar Badge but smaller and without white enamelling.

Comments: *Established by King George I, this was a single-class Order comprising the monarch, a prince of the blood royal, a Great Master and 35 Knights of Companions (KB). It was re-organised at the conclusion of the Napoleonic Wars (see below). Ladies (other than royalty) are now eligible for the Order.*

VALUE:

Collar chain	£18,000–25,000
Collar badge	Rare
Star (metal)	£2000–3500
Star (embroidered)	£400–800
Sash badge	£2000–3000

KNIGHT GRAND CROSS

The Order was re-organised in 1815 in two divisions, Military and Civil. The Military Division had three classes: Knight Grand Cross (GCB), Knight Commander (KCB) and Companion (CB), while the Civil Division continued with the single class of Knight Grand Cross. In 1847 the Civil Division came into line with the Military, and divided into three classes.

Metal: Gold (1815–87): silver-gilt (since 1887).

Collar Badge: The Military Badge is a gold Maltese cross of eight points, each point tipped with a small gold ball, and in each angle between the arms of the cross is a gold lion. In the centre of the cross is a device comprising a rose, thistle and shamrock issuing from a sceptre, and three imperial crowns . This device is surrounded by a red enamelled circle on which appears the Latin motto TRIA JUNCTA IN UNO (three joined in one) in gold lettering. The circle is surrounded by two branches of laurel, enamelled green, and below is a blue enamelled scroll with the German motto ICH DIEN (I serve) in gold.

The Civil Badge is of gold filigree work, and oval in shape. It consists of a bandlet bearing the motto, and in the centre is the usual device of the rose, thistle and shamrock issuing from a sceptre, together with the three crowns.

Star: A gold Maltese cross of the same pattern as the Military Badge, mounted on a silver flaming star (Military); or a silver eight-pointed star with a central device of three crowns on a silver ground, encircled by the motto on a red enamelled ribbon (Civil).

Sash Badges: Similar to the Collar Badges, they were originally made in gold but since 1887 silver-gilt has been substituted.

VALUE:	Military	Civil
Collar chain (gold)	£18,000–25,000	£18,000–25,000
Collar chain (silver gilt)	£8000–10,000	£8000–10,000
Collar badge (gold)	£2000–3500	£800–1000
Star (metal)	£500–1000	£300–400
Star (embroidered)	£300–500	£200–300
Mantle star	£500–700	£400–600
Sash badge (gold)	£1800–3000	£800–1000
Sash badge (gilt)	£800–1000	£400–600

4. THE MOST HONOURABLE ORDER OF THE BATH *continued*

KCB Star (Civil)

GCB Sash badge (Civil)

KCB Neck badge (Military)

KNIGHTS COMMANDERS (KCB) AND COMPANIONS (CB)

Holders of the KCB wear a neck badge suspended by a ribbon as well as a breast star. Prior to 1917 Companions wore a breast badge, the same way as a medal: but in that year it was converted into a neck badge.

Star: (KCB): (Military) a star with the gold Maltese cross omitted, and in the shape of a cross pattée, the three crowns and motto in the centre surrounded by a green enamelled laurel wreath. (Civil) similar but omitting the laurel wreath.

Breast Badge (CB): Similar to the Star but smaller.

Neck Badge (KCB): Similar to the Collar badges of the GCB but smaller, in Military and Civil versions as above.

Neck Badge (CB): Similar to the above, but smaller.

VALUE:

	Military	Miniature	Civil	Miniature
Knight Commander				
Star (metal)	£300–500		£200–400	
Star (embroidered)	£150–400		£100–250	
Neck badge (gold)	£700–1200		£400–500	
Neck badge (gilt)	£350–450		£200–250	
Companion				
Breast badge (gold)	£600–1200	£100–150	£350–400	£80–100
Breast badge (gilt)	£350–450	£30–50	£180–220	£30–50
Neck badge (gilt)	£300–400		£140–180	

5. THE ROYAL GUELPHIC ORDER

Instituted: 1815.
Ribbon: 44mm light blue watered silk.

KNIGHTS GRAND CROSS (GCH)

KCH Star (Military)

Collar Chain: Gold, with lions and crowns alternating, linked by scrolled royal cyphers.

Collar Badge: An eight-pointed Maltese cross with balls on each point and a lion passant gardant in each angle. (Obverse) in the centre, on a ground of red enamel, is a white horse of Hanover surrounded by a circle of light blue enamel with the motto in gold lettering NEC ASPERA TERRENT (difficulties do not terrify). Surrounding this circle is a green enamelled laurel wreath. (Reverse) the monogram GR in gold letters on a red ground, surmounted by the British crown and surrounded by a gold circle with the date of the institution MDCCCXV. In the Military version two crossed swords are mounted above the cross and below a Hanoverian crown. In the Civil version the swords are omited, and the wreath is of oak-leaves instead of laurel.

Star: A radiate star with rays grouped into eight points, the centre being similar to the Collar Badge. Behind the laurel wreathed centre are two crossed swords (Military); in the Civil version the swords are omitted and the wreath is of oak leaves.

Sash Badge: Similar to the Collar Badge but smaller.

Comments: *Founded by HRH the Prince Regent (later King George IV), it took its name from the family surname of the British sovereigns from George I onwards and was awarded by the crown of Hanover to both British and Hanverian subjects for distinguished services to Hanover. Under Salic Law, a woman could not succeed to the Hanoverian throne, so on the death of King William IV in 1837 Hanover passed to Prince Augustus, Duke of Cumberland, and thereafter the Guelphic Order became a purely Hanoverian award.*

VALUE:

	Military	Civil
Collar chain (gold)	£7000–9000	£7000–9000
Collar chain (silver gilt)	£4000–5000	£4000–5000
Collar Chain (copper gilt)	£2000–5000	£2000–3000
Collar badge	£5000–6000	£2500–3500
Star	£1000–2000	£500–1000
Sash badge	£6000–8000	£3000–4000

KNIGHTS COMMANDERS (KCH) AND KNIGHTS (KH)

Knights Commanders wore a neck badge suspended by a ribbon, and a breast star, while Knights wore a breast badge only.

Star: As above, but smaller.
Neck Badge: Similar to the Collar Badge but smaller.
Breast Badge: Two versions, in gold and enamel or silver and enamel.

VALUE:

	Military	Miniature	Civil	Miniature
Star	£600–1000		£400–600	
Neck badge	£1500–2000		£800–1200	
Breast badge (gold)	£800–1200	£250–300	£500–700	£200–250

KH Breast Badge (Military)

6. THE MOST DISTINGUISHED ORDER OF ST MICHAEL AND ST GEORGE

Instituted: 1818.
Ribbon: 38mm three equal bands of Saxon blue, scarlet and Saxon blue.

KNIGHTS GRAND CROSS (GCMG)

Knights Grand Cross wear a mantle of Saxon blue lined with scarlet silk tied with cords of blue and scarlet silk and gold, and having on the left side the star of the Order. The chapeau or hat is of blue satin, lined with scarlet and surmounted by black and white ostrich feathers. The collar, mantle and chapeau are only worn on special occasions or when commanded by the sovereign, but in ordinary full dress the badge is worn on the left hip from a broad ribbon passing over the right shoulder and the star on the left breast.

Collar Chain: Silver gilt formed alternately on lions of England, Maltese crosses enamelled in white, and the cyphers SM and SG with, in the centre, two winged lions of St Mark each holding a book and seven arrows.

Star: A silver star of seven groups of rays, with a gold ray between each group, surmounted overall by the cross of St George in red enamel. In the centre is a representation of St Michael encountering Satan within a blue circular riband bearing the motto AUSPICIUM MELIORIS AEVI (A token of a better age).

Sash Badge: A gold seven-pointed star with V-shaped extremities, enamelled white and edged with gold, surmounted by an imperial crown. In the centre on one side is a representation in enamel of St Michael encountering Satan and on the other St George on horseback fighting the dragon. This device is surrounded by a circle of blue enamel bearing the Latin motto in gold lettering. Silver-gilt was substituted for gold in 1887.

Comments: *Founded by HRH the Prince Regent and awarded originally to citizens of Malta and the Ionian Islands in the Adriatic Sea, both of which had been ceded to Britain during the Napoleonic Wars. The Ionian Islands were transferred to Greece in 1859. Towards the end of the 19th century, however, the Order was awarded to those who had performed distinguished service in the colonies and protectorates of the British Empire and in more recent times it has been widely used as an award to ambassadors and senior diplomats as well as colonial governors. Ladies are now eligible for this Order.*

VALUE:

Collar chain	£1400–1800
Star	£500–600
Sash badge (gold)	£3000–4000
Sash badge (gilt)	£600–800

GCMG Star

6. THE MOST DISTINGUISHED ORDER OF ST MICHAEL AND ST GEORGE *continued*

KCMG Star

KNIGHTS COMMANDERS (KCMG) AND COMPANIONS (CMG)

Knights Commanders wear the badge suspended round the neck from a narrower ribbon of the same colours, and a breast star; Companions wear a neck badge. In undress uniform Knights Grand Cross and Knights Commanders wear the ribbon of Companions of the Order. Prior to 1917 Companions wore a breast badge, worn the same way as a medal, but this was then changed to a neck badge.

Star: A silver eight-pointed star charged with the red St George's cross and having the same central device as the GCMG Star. This was introduced in 1859.

Neck Badge: Similar to the sash badge of the GCMG but smaller. Those worn by KCMG were of gold and enamel until 1887 but silver-gilt and enamel thereafter. The CMG neck badges are invariably of enamel and silver-gilt.

Breast Badge: Similar to the star of the KCMG but smaller and made of gold and enamel till 1887, and silver gilt and enamel from then till 1917.

VALUE:		Miniature
Knight Commander		
Star	£300–400	
Neck badge (gold)	£800–900	
Neck badge (gilt)	£350–450	
Companion		
Breast badge (gold)	£500–600	£80–100
Breast badge (gilt)	£350–400	£30–50
Neck badge (gilt)	£250–350	

7. THE MOST EXALTED ORDER OF THE STAR OF INDIA

Instituted: 1861.
Ribbon: Broad light blue with white edges (GCSI); 50mm plain white (KCSI); 38mm plain white (CSI).

KNIGHTS GRAND COMMANDERS (GCSI)

KCSI Neck badge

The insignia consisted of a gold collar and badge, a mantle of light blue satin with a representation of the star on the left side and tied with a white silk cord with blue and silver tassels. The collar and mantle were only worn on special occasions and in ordinary full dress uniform a GCSI wore the star on the left breast and the badge on the left hip from a broad sash of light blue edged in white.

Collar Chain: Gold formed of lotus flowers, palm branches and united red and white roses.

Badge: An onyx cameo bearing the left-facing bust of Queen Victoria wearing an imperial crown, set in a gold ornamental oval containing the motto of the Order HEAVEN'S LIGHT OUR GUIDE in diamonds, on a pale blue ground surmounted by a five-pointed star in chased silver.

Star: A five-pointed star in diamonds resting on a circular riband of light blue enamel bearing the motto in diamonds, the whole set on a circular star of golden rays.

Comments: *Founded by Queen Victoria a few years after the British Crown took over the administration of India from the Honourable East India Company, it was intended primarily as an award to loyal Indian princes. The highest class was designated Knight Grand Commander, rather than Cross, because the majority of recipient were not Christians (either Hindus or Muslims). The Order at first consisted of the sovereign, a Grand Master (the Viceroy of India), 36 Knights Grand Commanders (18 British and 18 Indian), 85 Knights Commanders and 170 Companions. The GCSI was the most lavish of all British orders. It lapsed in 1947 when the sub-continent attained independence. Until then all insignia of this Order was returnable on the death of recipients. After 1947, however, recipients or their heirs were allowed in certain cases to purchase the star and badges of any of the three applicable classes, but not the collar chain of the Knight Grand Commander.*

VALUE:

Collar chain	Rare
Star and badge	£25,000–30,000

KNIGHTS COMMANDERS (KCSI) AND COMPANIONS (CSI)

Knights Commanders wore a badge round the neck and a star on the left breast, while Companions originally had a breast badge which was transmuted into a neck badge from 1917 onwards.

Star: Similar to that of the GCSI but in silver.

Neck Badge: Similar to the collar badge of the GCSI but smaller and less ornate.

Breast Badge: Similar to the above but smaller and less ornate and fitted with a straight bar suspender. Subtle differences in the ornament at the foot of the blue border and the external ornament at the sides and foot of the oval.

Comments: *The second and third classes of the Order were awarded to Indian and British subjectsof the armed forces and Indian Civil Service for distinguished service of not less than 30 years' duration.*

VALUE:		*Miniature*
Star and Neck badge (KCSI)	£4000–6000	
Breast badge (CSI)	£2500–3000	£180–250 (gold), £100–120 (gilt)
Neck badge (CSI)	£1750–2000	

8. THE MOST EMINENT ORDER OF THE INDIAN EMPIRE

Instituted: 1878.
Ribbon: Broad of imperial purple (GCIE); 50mm imperial purple (KCIE); 38mm imperial purple (CIE).

KNIGHTS GRAND COMMANDERS (GCIE)

KCIE Neck badge

The insignia consisted of a collar, badge and mantle of imperial purple or dark blue satin lined with white silk and fastened with a white silk cord with gold tassels, and having on the left side a representation of the Star of the Order. On ordinary full-dress occasions, however, Knights Grand Commanders wore the badge on the left hip from a broad sash, and a star on the left breast.

Collar Chain: Silver-gilt, composed of elephants, lotus flowers, peacocks in their pride and Indian roses with, in the centre, the imperial crown, the whole linked together by chains.

Badge: A gold five-petalled rose, enamelled crimson and with a green barb between each petal. In the centre is an effigy of Queen Victoria on a gold ground, surrounded by a purple riband originally inscribed VICTORIA IMPERATRIX but from 1901 onwards inscribed IMPERATRICIS AUSPICIIS (under the auspices of the Empress). The letters I N D I A are inscribed on the petals in the first version, but omitted in the second.

Star: Composed of fine silver rays with smaller gold rays between them, the whole alternately plain and scaled. In the centre, within a purple circle bearing the motto and surmounted by the imperial crown in gold, is the effigy of Queen Victoria on a gold ground.

Comments: *Founded by Queen Victoria after assuming the title of Empress of India, it was originally confined to Companions only, together with the Sovereign and Grand Master. Members of the Council of the Governor-General were admitted ex officio as Companions. It was intended for award in respect of meritorious services in India but from the outset it was regarded as a junior alternative to the Star of India. In 1886 the Order was expanded to two classes by the addition of Knights Commanders up to a maximum of 50 in number. In 1887, however, it was again re-organised into three classes: up to 25 Knights Grand Commanders (GCIE), up to 50 Knights Commanders (KCIE) and an unlimited number of Companions (CIE). The Order has been in abeyance since 1947.*

VALUE:

Collar chain	Rare
Star and badge	£4000–5000

KNIGHTS COMMANDERS (KCIE) AND COMPANIONS (CIE)

The insignia of Knights Commanders consisted of a neck badge and a breast star, while that of Companions was originally a breast badge, converted to a neck badge in 1917.

Star: Similar to that of the GCIE but fashioned entirely in silver.

Neck badge: Similar to the collar or sash badge of the GCIE but in correspondingly smaller sizes and differing in minor details.

Breast badge: Similar to the sash badge of the GCIE but differing in minor details, notably the spacing ornament at the foot of the blue circle. Two versions exist, with or without INDIA on the petals of the lotus flower.

VALUE:		*Miniature*
Knights Commanders		
Star and Neck badge	£1400–2000	
Companions		
Breast badge (INDIA)	£800–1000	£150–200 (gold)
Breast badge (smaller, without INDIA)	£400–450	£100–150 (gold), £30–80 (gilt)
Neck badge	£300–350	

9. THE ROYAL FAMILY ORDER

Instituted: 1820.
Ribbon: 50mm sky blue moire (1820); 38mm dark blue bordered by narrow stripes of yellow and broader stripes of crimson with narrow black edges (1902); 50mm pale blue moire (1911); 50mm pink moire (1937); 50mm pale yellow silk moire (1953). These ribbons are tied in a bow and worn on the left shoulder.
Descriptions: An upright oval heavily bordered by diamonds and surmounted by a crown, also embellished in diamonds. The oval contains a miniature portrait of the sovereign in enamels.
Comments: *Awarded to the Queen and female relatives of the reigning monarch. It was instituted by King George IV who conferred such orders on his sister, Princess Charlotte Augusta, wife of Frederick William, King of Wurttemberg, and his niece Princess Augusta Caroline, who married the Grand Duke of Mecklenburg-Strelitz. Queen Victoria instituted a separate Order (see next entry), but this Order was revived by King Edward VII in 1902 and continued by successive sovereigns ever since. Special badges are given to ladies-in-waiting. The insignia of these Family Orders very seldom appear on the market and on account of their immense rarity they are unpriced here.*

VALUE:

George IV	Rare
Edward VIII	Rare
George V	Rare
George VI	Rare
Elizabeth II	Rare
Ladies-in-waiting badges	From £1000

10. THE ROYAL ORDER OF VICTORIA AND ALBERT

Instituted: 1862.
Ribbon: 38mm white moire, in the form of a bow worn on the left shoulder.
Description: An upright oval onyx cameo bearing conjoined profiles of HRH Prince Albert, the Prince Consort and Queen Victoria. The badges of the First and Second Classes are set in diamonds and surmounted by an imperial crown similarly embellished, the badge of the Second Class being rather smaller. The badge of the Third Class is set in pearls, while that of the Fourth Class takes the form of a monogram "V & A" set with pearls and surmounted by an imperial crown.

VALUE:

First Class	£24,000–26,000
Second Class	£16,000–18,000
Third Class	£10,000–12,000
Fourth Class	£4000–5000

11. THE IMPERIAL ORDER OF THE CROWN OF INDIA

Instituted: January 1, 1878.
Ribbon: 38mm light blue watered silk with narrow white stripes towards the edges, formed in a bow worn on the left shoulder.
Description: A badge consisting of the royal and imperial monogram VRI in diamonds, turquoises and pearls, surrounded by an oval frame and surmounted by a jewelled imperial crown.
Comments: *Awarded by Queen Victoria to the princesses of the royal and imperial house, the wives or other female relatives of Indian princes and other Indian ladies, and of the wives or other female relatives of any of the persons who had held or were holding the offices of Viceroy and Governor-General of India, Governors of Madras or Bombay, or of Principal Secretary of State for India, as the sovereign might think fit to appoint. This order, conferred on females only, became obsolete in 1947.*

VALUE:

Breast badge	£6000–10,000

12. THE ROYAL VICTORIAN ORDER

Instituted: April 1896.
Ribbon: Dark blue with borders of narrow red, white and red stripes on either side.

KNIGHTS GRAND CROSS AND DAMES GRAND CROSS (GCVO)

The insignia consists of a mantle of dark blue silk, edged with red satin, lined with white silk, and fastened by a cordon of dark blue silk and gold; a gold collar and a badge, worn only on special occasions. Knights wear the badge on the left hip from a broad ribbon worn over the right shoulder, with a star on the left breast, while Dames wear a somewhat narrower ribbon over the right shoulder with the badge, and a star similar to that of the Knights. Dames' insignia are smaller than those of the Knights.

Collar: Silver gilt composed of octagonal pieces and oblong perforated and ornamental frames alternately linked together with gold. The pieces are edged and ornamented with gold, and each contains on a blue-enamelled ground a gold rose jewellerd with a carbuncle. The frames are gold and each contains a portion of inscription VICTORIA BRITT. DEF. FID. IND. IMP. in letters of white enamel. In the centre of the collar, within a perforated and ornamental frame of gold, is an octagonal piece enamelled blue, edged with red, and charged with a white saltire, superimposed by a gold medallion of Queen Victoria's effigy fromwhich is suspended the badge.

Badge: A white-enamelled Maltese cross of eight points, in the centre of which is an oval of crimson enamel bearing the cypher VRI in gold letters. Encircling this is a blue enamel riband with the name VICTORIA in gold letters, and above this is the imperial crown enamelled in proper colours.

Star: Of chipped silver of eight points on which is mounted a white-enamelled Maltese cross with VRI in an oval at the centre.

Comments: *Awarded for extraordinary, important or personal services to the sovereign of the Royal Family. Ladies became eligible for the Order in 1936. Most of the badges of the Royal Victorian Order are numbered on the reverse and are returnable on promotion. Honourary awards are unnumbered.*

VALUE:

	Knights	Dames
Collar	£5000–6000	£6000–7000
Star and Badge	£900–1200	£1000–1200

KNIGHTS COMMANDERS (KCVO), DAMES COMMANDERS (DCVO), COMMANDERS (CVO), LIEUTENANTS (LVO) AND MEMBERS (MVO)

The insignia of the Second, Third, Fourth and Fifth Classes follows the usual pattern. Knights wear a neck badge and a breast star, Dames a breast star and a badge on the left shoulder from a ribbon tied in a bow, Commanders the same neck badge (men) or shoulder badge (women), Lieutenants a somewhat smaller breast badge worn in line with other medals and decorations (men) or a shoulder badge (women) and Members breast or shoulder badges in frosted silver instead of white enamel. The two lowest classes of the Order were originally designated member Fourth Class or member Fifth Class (MVO), but in 1984 the Fourth Class was renamed Lieutenant (LVO) and the Fifth Class simply Member (MVO).

GCVO star

VALUE:

	Gentlemen	*Miniature*	Ladies
Neck badge and breast star	£400–600		£500–600
Neck badge (CVO)	£300–350	£30–50	£400–450
Breast or shoulder badge (LVO)	£200–250	£30–50	£250–300
Breast or shoulder badge (MVO)	£190–230	£15–25	£220–250

13. ROYAL VICTORIAN MEDAL

Instituted: April 1896.
Ribbon: As for the Royal Victorian Order (above); foreign Associates, however, wear a ribbon with a central white stripe added.
Metal: Silver-gilt, silver or bronze.
Size: 36mm.
Description: (Obverse) the effigy of the reigning sovereign; (reverse) the royal cypher on an ornamental shield within a laurel wreath.
Comments: *Awarded to those below the rank of officers who perform personal services to the sovereign or to members of the Royal Family. Originally awarded in silver or bronze, a higher class, in silver-gilt, was instituted by King George V. Only two medals (both silver) were issued in the brief reign of King Edward VIII (1936) and only four bronze medals were issued in the reign of King George VI. Any person in possession of the bronze medal to whom a silver medal is awarded, can wear both, and the silver-gilt medal in addition if such be conferred upon him or her. Clasps are awarded for further services to each class of the medal, while the medals may be worn in addition to the insignia of the Order if the latter is subsequently conferred. To distinguish between British and foreign recipients, King George VI decreed in 1951 that the ribbon worn by the latter should have an additional stripe, these recipients to be designated Associates. In 1983 the order for wearing this medal was altered, and it was no longer to be worn after campaign medals but took precedence over them.*

VALUE:

	Silver-gilt	Miniature	Silver	Miniature	Bronze	Miniature
Victoria	—	£45–50	£120–150	£25–35	£85–100	£25–35
Edward VII	£250–300		£120–150	£15–20	£85–100	£20–30
George V	£250–300		£100–125	£10–15	£250–300	£15–20
Edward VIII	—		Rare		—	
George VI	£120–140		£100–125	£10–15	Rare	£10–15
Elizabeth II	£140–160		£130–150	£10–15	£145–180	£10–15

14. THE ROYAL VICTORIAN CHAIN

Instituted: 1902.
Ribbon: None.
Metal: Silver gilt
Description: A chain consisting of three Tudor roses, two thistles, two shamrocks and two lotus flowers (the heraldic flowers of England, Scotland, Ireland and India respectively), connected by a slender double trace of gold chain. At the bottom of the front loop is a centre piece consisting of the royal cypher in enamel surrounded by a wreath and surmounted by a crown. From this centrepiece hangs a replica of the badge of a Knight Grand Cross of the Royal Victorian order. Ladies were the insignia in the form of a shoulder badge suspended from a miniature chain with links leading to a rose, thistle, shamrock and lotus. An even more elaborate collar, with diamonds encrusting the crown and cypher, was adopted in 1921 and there is a ladies' version of this as well.
Comments: *Sometimes regarded as the highest grade of the Royal Victorian Order, it is actually a quite separate Order and was introduced by King Edward VII for conferment as a special mark of the sovereign's favour, and then only very rarely, upon Royalty, or other especially distinguished personages, both foreign and British.*

VALUE

	Gentlemen	Ladies
Chain (1902–21)	Rare	Rare
Chain with diamonds	Rare	Rare

15. ORDER OF MERIT

Order of Merit obverse

Order of Merit reverse

Instituted: 1902.

Ribbon: 50mm half blue, half crimson.

Metal: Gold.

Size: Height 50mm; max. width 35mm.

Description: A pattée convexed cross, enamelled red, edged blue. (Obverse) FOR MERIT in the centre surrounded by a white band and a laurel wreath enamelled in proper colours. (Reverse) the royal cypher in gold on a blue ground with a white surround and a laurel wreath as above. The cross is surmounted by a Tudor crown to which is attached a ring for suspension. Naval and military recipients have crossed swords in the angles of the cross.

Comments: *This highly prestigious Order consists of the sovereign and a maximum of 24 members in one class only. There is, however, no limit on the number of foreign honorary members, although only ten have so far been admitted to the Order. It was intended for award to those whose achievements in the fields of art, music and literature were outstanding, but it was later extended to naval and military leaders in wartime. To date, fewer than 160 awards have been made, including a mere five ladies, from Florence Nightingale (1907) to Baroness Thatcher. The insignia of those appointed since 1991 have to be returned on the death of the recipient. The insignia of members appointed prior to that date is retained, but understandably few items have come on to the market.*

VALUE:

	Military	Civil
Edward VII	£5000–6000	£3500–4500
George V	£5000–6000	£3000–4000
George VI	Rare	£4000–5000
Elizabeth II	Rare	£3500–4500
Miniature (crude example)		£100–150

16. THE MOST EXCELLENT ORDER OF THE BRITISH EMPIRE

GBE Star (2nd type)

Instituted: June 1917.

Ribbon: 38mm originally purple, with a narrow central scarlet stripe for the Military Division; rose-pink edged with pearl grey, with a narrow central stripe of pearl-grey for the Military Division (since 1936). A silver crossed oakleaf emblem for gallantry was instituted in 1957.

Comments: *Founded by King George V during the First World War for services to the Empire at home, in India and in the overseas dominions and colonies, other than those rendered by the Navy and Army, although it could be conferred upon officers of the armed forces for services of a non-combatant character. A Military Division was created in December 1918 and awards made to commissioned officers and warrant officers in respect of distinguished service in action. The insignia of the Civil and Military Divisions is identical, distinguished only by the respective ribbons.*

KNIGHTS AND DAMES GRAND CROSS (GBE)

The insignia includes a mantle of rose-pink satin lined with pearl-grey silk, tied by a cord of pearl-grey silk, with two rose-pink and silver tassels attached. On the left side of the mantle is a representation of the star of the First Class of the Order. The mantle, collar and collar badge are only worn on special occasions. In dress uniform, however, the badge is worn over the left hip from a broad (96mm) riband passing over the right shoulder, while Dames wear the badge from a narrower (57mm) ribbon in a bow on the left shoulder; both with the breast star of the Order.

Collar: Silver-gilt with medallions of the royal arms and of the royal and imperial cypher of King George V alternately linked together with cables. In the centre is the imperial crown between two sea lions. The collar for Dames is somewhat narrower than that for Knights.

Badge: A cross patonce in silver-gilt the arms enamelled pearl-grey. In the centre, within a circle enamelled crimson, the figure of Britannia, replaced since 1936 by the conjoined left-facing crowned busts of King George V and Queen Mary, surrounded by a circle inscribed FOR GOD AND THE EMPIRE.

Star: An eight-pointed star of silver chips on which is superimposed the enamelled medallion as for the badge (Britannia or George V and Queen Mary). The star worn by Dames is smaller.

CBE Badge (2nd type)

VALUE:	1st type Britannia	2nd type King and Queen
Knights Grand Cross		
Collar	£5000–6000	£5000–6000
Badge and star	£900–1000	£1000–1200
Dames Grand Cross		
Collar	£6000–7000	£6000–7000
Badge and star	£1000–1200	£1200–1400

16. THE MOST EXCELLENT ORDER OF THE BRITISH EMPIRE *continued*
KNIGHTS COMMANDERS (KBE),
DAMES COMMANDERS (DBE),
COMMANDERS (CBE) AND
MEMBERS (MBE)

KBE Star

The insignia of these four Classes follows the same pattern as other Orders. Both Britannia and King and Queen medallion types have been issued.

Star: A star of four large points and four minor points in chipped silver, with the enamelled medallion superimposed. The star worn by Dames is smaller.

Neck Badge: Similar to the badge of the GBE but smaller and worn from a 44mm ribbon round the neck (men) or from a shoulder bow (ladies). Worn by KBE, DBE and CBE.

Breast Badge: As above, but in silver-gilt (OBE) or frosted silver (MBE), with shoulder versions for ladies, worn with a 38mm ribbon.

Gallantry Award: An emblem of silver crossed oak leaves was added to the ribbon of the CBE, OBE and MBE (1957–74).

VALUE:	1st type Britannia	Miniature	2nd type King&Queen	Miniature
Badge and Star (KBE,)	£500–550		£500–550	
Badge and Star (DBE)	£500–550		£500–550	
Neck badge (CBE)	£160–180	£15–20	£160–180	£15–20
Shoulder badge (CBE)	£160–180		£160–180	
Breast badge (OBE)	£75–85	£10–15	£75–85	£10–15
Shoulder badge (OBE)	£75–85		£75–85	
Breast badge (MBE)	£75–85	£8–10	£75–85	£8–10
Shoulder badge (MBE)	£75–85		£75–85	

OBE badge (silver-gilt) and reverse of the MBE badge (frosted silver).

Ribbons: (top to bottom) OBE (Civil) 1st type, OBE (Civil) 2nd type, OBE (Military) 1st type and OBE (Military) 2nd type.

17. MEDAL OF THE ORDER OF THE BRITISH EMPIRE

Civil ribbon

Instituted: June 1917.

Ribbon: 32mm plain purple (Civil), with a narrow scarlet central stripe (Military).

Medal: Silver.

Size: 30mm.

Description: (Obverse) a seated figure of Britannia facing right, her left arm extended and her right holding a trident, with the inscription FOR GOD AND THE EMPIRE round the upper part of the circumference; (reverse) the royal and imperial cypher GRI surmounted by a Tudor crown, the whole enclosed in a cable circle. Fitted with a plain ring for suspension.

Comments: *Instituted as a lower award connected with the Order, it consisted originally of a Civil Division, but a Military Division, distinguishable solely by the ribbon, was added in December 1918. This medal was issued unnamed but many were subsequently engraved or impressed on the rim privately. Fewer than 2000 medals were awarded before they were discontinued in 1922.*

VALUE:

		Miniature
Medal unnamed as issued	£85–100	£30–40
Military award with named medal group	£150–200	
Civil award with supporting documents	£120–160	

18. EMPIRE GALLANTRY MEDAL

1st type rev.

Instituted: December 29, 1922.

Ribbon: Originally plain purple (Civil), with a thin scarlet central stripe (Military; from July 1937 rose-pink with pearl-grey edges (Civil) and a central pearl-grey stripe (Military). A silver laurel branch was added to the ribbon (1933), with a smaller version for wear on the ribbon alone.

Metal: Silver.

Size: 36mm.

Description: (Obverse) the seated figure of Britannia, her left hand resting on a shield and her right holding a trident, with a blazing sun upper right. The words FOR GOD AND THE EMPIRE inscribed round the upper part of the circumference, with FOR in the wave lower left above the exergue which bears the word GALLANTRY. (Reverse) 1st type has six lions passant gardant, with the Royal cypher in the centre surmounted by an imperial crown. The George VI issue has four lions, two either side and round the foot, in two concentric arcs, the words INSTITUTED BY KING GEORGE V. It is suspended from a straight bar ornamented with laurel leaves. Named in seriffed capitals engraved round the rim.

Comments: *This medal, officially known as the Medal of the Order of the British Empire for Gallantry, replaced the Medal of the Order of the British Empire and was awarded for specific acts of gallantry. It was abolished on the institution of the George Cross in September 1940, while it was announced in the London Gazette of April 22, 1941 that a recipient still living on September 24, 1940 should return it to the Central Chancery of the Orders of Knighthood and become a holder of the George Cross instead. Not all EGMs, however, were exchanged or returned. Only 130 medals were issued, 64 being civil, 62 military and 4 honorary.*

VALUE:

		Miniature
George V	£3000–3500	£40–50
George VI	£3000–3500	£30–40

19. BRITISH EMPIRE MEDAL

BEM (MIlitary) 2nd type

Instituted: December 1922.
Ribbon: As above, but without the silver laurel branch.
Metal: Silver.
Size: 36mm.
Description: As above, but with the words MERITORIOUS SERVICE in the exergue. Suspended from a straight bar ornamented with oak leaves. A silver bar decorated with oak leaves was introduced in March 1941 for further acts, and is denoted by a silver rosette on the ribbon worn on its own. An emblem of crossed silver oak leaves was introduced in December 1957 to denote a gallantry award, a smaller version being worn on the ribbon alone. Named in engraved capitals round the rim.
Comments: *Formally entitled the Medal of the Order of the British Empire for Meritorious Service, it is generally known simply as the British Empire Medal. It is awarded for meritorious service by both civil and military personnel. The medal may be worn even if the recipient is promoted to a higher grade of the Order. The gallantry awards, instituted in December 1957, ceased in 1974 on the introduction of the Queen's Gallantry Medal. No British awards have been made for the BEM since 1995 but Commonwealth awards are still being made.*

VALUE:

	Military	Civil	Miniature
George V	£150–180	£100–120	£10–15
George VI GRI cypher	£120–175	£80–90	£10–15
George VI GVIR cypher	£120–175	£80–90	£10–15
Elizabeth II	£120–175	£90–100	£10–15
Elizabeth II with gallantry emblem	£300–600	£250–350	

19A. QUEEN'S VOLUNTEER RESERVES MEDAL

Instituted: 1999.
Ribbon: Dark green with three narrow gold stripes.
Metal: Silver.
Size: 36mm.
Description: (Obverse) effigy of Queen Elizabeth II; (reverse) five ribbons containing the words THE QUEEN'S VOLUNTEER RESERVES MEDAL. The medal is fitted with a large ring for suspension.
Comments: *Awarded to men and women of any rank in the volunteer reserves of all three services, in recognition of outstanding service which formerly would have merited an award within the Order of the British Empire. Holders are entitled to the post-nominal letters QVRM.*

VALUE: — *Miniature £10–15*

20. THE ORDER OF THE COMPANIONS OF HONOUR

Instituted: June 1917
Ribbon: 38mm carmine with borders of gold thread.
Metal: Silver gilt.
Size: Height 48mm; max. width 29mm.
Description: An oval badge consisting of a medallion with an oak tree, a shield bearing the royal arms hanging from one branch, and on the left a knight armed and in armour, mounted on a horse. The badge has a blue border with the motto IN ACTION FAITHFUL AND IN HONOUR CLEAR in gold letters. The oval is surmounted by an imperial crown. Gentlemen wear the badge round their necks, while ladies wear it from a bow at the left shoulder.
Comments: *Instituted at the same time as the Order of the British Empire, it carries no title or precedence althought the post-nominal letters CH are used. The Order consists of the sovereign and one class of members. Not more than 50 men or women who have rendered conspicuous service of national importance were admitted, but in 1943 this was increased to 65. The Order is awarded in Britain and the Commonwealth on a quota basis: UK (45), Australia (7), New Zealand (2), other countries (11). It is awarded for outstanding achievements in the arts, literature, music, science, politics, industry and religion.*

VALUE

Gentlemen	£1800–2000
Ladies	£1800–2000
Uniface miniature	£100–150

21. THE BARONET'S BADGE

Instituted: 1629
Ribbon: 30mm orange watered silk (Nova Scotia); 44mm orange bordered with narrow blue edges (other Baronets).
Metal: Gold or silver-gilt.
Size: Height 55mm; max. width 41mm(Nova Scotia) or 44mm (later badges).
Description: An upright oval badge with a plain ring suspension. The badge of the Baronets of Nova Scotia was originally skeletal, with a shield bearing the lion rempant of Scotland, decorated with pearls and enamels, surmounted by a Scottish crown and surrounded by a blue border inscribed in gold FAX MENTIS HONESTAE GLORIA. The remaining badges (authorised in 1929) have a solid ground and a central shield with the red hand of Ulster surmounted by a crown and a border of gold and blue enamel decorated with roses (England), shamrocks (Ireland), roses and thistles combined (Great Britain) or roses, thistles and shamrocks combined (United Kingdom). Engraved on the reverse with the recipient's title and date of creation.
Comments: *By Letter Patent of 1611 James I created Baronets whose knighthood became hereditary. In 1624, to raise money independently of Parliament, James I sold grants of land in Nova Scotia (New Scotland) to Scotsmen. In 1625 Charles I conferred on the holders of this land the title and dignity of Baronets of Nova Scotia with the title of Sir, and decreed that they should wear round their necks "an orange tawny ribbon whereon shall be pendent an escutcheon". After the Union with England (1707) English and Scottish baronetcies ceased to be created, being replaced by baronetcies of Great Britain. Irish baronetcies continued to be created until 1801 after which all new creations were of the United Kingdom.*

Baronet's badge—United Kingdom

VALUE:	Gold	Silver-gilt
Nova Scotia, 18th–early 19th centuries	£1500–3000	£500–800
Nova Scotia, late 19th and 20th centuries	£1400–1600	£400–600
England (rose surround)	£700–900	£400–600
Ireland (shamrock surround)	£700–900	£400–600
Great Britain (roses and thistles)	£700–900	£400–600
United Kingdom (roses, thistles and shamrocks)	£700–900	£400–600

22. THE KNIGHT BACHELOR'S BADGE

Instituted: April 21, 1926.
Ribbon: 38mm scarlet with broad yellow borders.
Metal: Silver-gilt and enamels. Some pre-war breast badges in base metal.
Size: Height 81mm; max. width 60mm. Reduced in 1933 and 1973.
Description: An upright oval medallion enclosed by a scroll, bearing a cross-hilted sword, belted and sheathed, pommel upwards, between two spurs, rowels upwards, the whole set about with the sword-belt.
Comments: *The title Knight Bachelor (KB) was introduced by King Henry III to signify a battelier (one who fought in battle). The badge was authorised by King George V in response to a request from the Imperial Society of Knights Bachelors who wished to have a distinctive badge denoting their rank. The original badge was of the dimensions given above and affixed to the breast by means of a pin on the reverse. This badge was reduced in size in 1933 and again in 1973 when it was fitted with a ring for suspension by a ribbon round the neck.*

VALUE:

		Miniature
First type (1929)	£200–220	£30–40
Smaller type (1933)	£200–220	(Skeletal type
Neck badge (1974)	£300–350	£20–35)

Knight Bachelor's badge

23. THE ORDER OF ST JOHN

Breast star

Shoulder badge

Instituted: May 14, 1888.

Ribbon: Plain black watered silk. Sash ribbons for Bailiffs, 100mm; Dames Grand Cross, 65mm. Ribbons for Chaplains and Knights, 50mm; Dames 32mm in a bow. Ribbons for Commanders, Officers and Serving Brothers, 38mm for men and 32mm for ladies. Donats have a white central stripe.

Metal: Gold, silver-gilt and silver, or base metal.

Sash badge: An eight-pointed gold Maltese cross in white enamel with two lions and two unicorns in the angles. Confined to Bailiffs and Dames Grand Cross.

Neck badge: Worn by Knights of Justice and Chaplains in gold and Knights of Grace and Commanders (Brothers) in silver. These neck badges are all of the same size.

Star: The eight-pointed Maltese cross in white enamel without the lions and unicorns (Grand Cross and Justice) or with lions and unicorns (Grace and Sub-Prelate). A sub-Prelate is an Order Chaplain (so his badge is included above) who holds high rank in the Church as distinct from the Order.

Shoulder badge: Worn by Dames of Justice in gold and Dames of Grace, Commanders (Sisters) and Officers (Sisters) in silver. The badge is the same size for Dame and Commander but smaller for Officers.

Breast badges: Officers (Brothers) is the Order badge with animals, in silver (1926–36) and in silver and enamel subsequently. Those worn by Serving Brothers, and as shoulder badges by Serving Sisters, have undergone six main phases:

> 1892–1939: a circular badge with crosses and animals raised above the surface of the medal.
>
> 1939–1949: circular skeletal badge with ring suspension and the eight-point cross set in a silver rim.
>
> 1949–1974: the first badge resumed.
>
> 1974–1984: a badge of the same design but with the cross and animals flush with their background.
>
> 1984–1991: the cross and animals in white metal, slightly smaller than the Officer (Brother) cross and the whole convex on the obverse.
>
> Since 1991: Cross and animals thicker, with each arm raised and shaped on both sides of a central channel, the whole in rhodium.

Donats' badges: Gold, silver or bronze, consisting of the badge of the Order with the upper arm of the cross replaced by an ornamental piece of metal for suspension.

Comments: *The Most Venerable Order of the Hospital of St John of Jerusalem was incorporated by Royal Charter of Queen Victoria and granted the epithet Venerable in 1926 and Most in 1955; despite its title, it has no connection with the Knights Hospitallers of Jerusalem, who were subsequently based at Rhodes and Malta and are now located at Rome. In 1926 the Order was reorganised into five Classes like certain other Orders. A sixth class was added later. Both men and women are eligible for membership. Her Majesty the Queen is the Sovereign Head of the Order. Next in authority is the Grand Prior, followed by Bailiffs and Dames Grand Cross, Chaplains, Knights and Dames of Justice, Knights and Dames of Grace, Commanders, Officers, Serving Brothers and Sisters and Esquires. Associates are people who are not citizens of the United Kingdom, the British Commonwealth or the Republic of Ireland, or are non-Christians, who have rendered conspicuous service to the Order and may be attached to any grade of the Order. They wear the insignia of that grade, at one time distinguished only by a central narrow white stripe on the ribbon, but now all ribbons are identical. Donats are people who have made generous contributions to the funds of the Order. They are not enrolled as members of the Order but receive badges in gold, silver or bronze. The category of Associate was abolished in 1999, all Associates being regraded as Members.*

VALUE:

	Gold	Silver/Gilt	Bronze	Miniature
Bailiff badge and star	£1500–2250	£800–1000	—	
Dame Grand Cross	£1500–2000	£500–600	—	
Knight of Justice neck badge and star	£800–900	£400–500	£150–250	
Dame of Justice shoulder badge and star	£800–900	£400–500	£200–300	
Knight of Grace neck badge and star	—	£350–400	£150–250	
Dame of Grace shoulder badge and star	—	£350–400	£150–250	
Commander (Brother) neck badge	—	£130–180	£60–80	
Commander (Sister) shoulder badge	—	£35–50	£30–50	
Officer breast badge, plain silver	—	£35–50	—	£10–15
Office breast badge, enamelled	—	£45–65	£30–50	£15–20
Officer (Sister) enamelled badge	—	£45–65	£30–50	
Serving Brother/Sister 1926–39	—	£50–75	£30–50	£10–12
Serving Brother/Sister 1939–49	—	£45–65	£40–60	£10–12
Serving Brother/Sister 1949–	—	—	£30–50	
Donat's badge	£80–100	£45–55	£30–40	£25–30

NEATE MILITARIA
& ANTIQUES

SPECIALISTS IN MEDALS

MEMBER: O.M.R.S., O.M.S.A.,
M.M.S.S.A., M.C.C.of C.

P.O. Box 3794,
Preston St. Mary, Sudbury,
CO10 9PX, United Kingdom
Telephone: (01787) 248168
Fax: (01787) 248363
Email:gary@neatemedals.co.uk
Business Hours:
Monday–Friday, 9am to 6pm

Proprietor: Gary C. Neate

Catalogues available.
Subscription per annum:
£6.00 U.K. £10.00 Rest of the World.

Sample copy available
free on request

Website:www.neatemedals.co.uk
Updated weekly, secure server for
credit card ordersby
Visa/Mastercard/Switch etc

SERIOUS BUYERS OF ALL MEDALS

WANTED

(All in groups of 5 medals or more)

1. GC, to RAF, Aircrew
2. GM, to RCAF, RNZAF, or RAF, Aircrew
3. DSO , to R. A. Air Observation Post
4. DFC, to Australian Flying Corps
5. DFM, to Post War Army Air Corps or RNZAF
6. QGM, to Para Regiment
7. MBE, (1st Pattern) to a pilot
8. MVO or LVO to a pilot
9. GALLANTRY GROUPS TO RHODESIANS
   (Pairs or groups)
   — a premium will be paid for any of the above —

Jonathan Pittaway
South Africa
pittaway@iafrica.com

27–31 – 3051697 (Work)
27– 31–3045890 (Fax)
27–31–3120674 (Home)
27–83–660 0000 (Mobile)

LIVERPOOL MEDAL COMPANY

THE LARGEST AND BEST SELECTION OF ORDERS, MEDALS AND DECORATIONS OF THE WORLD ON OFFER FOUR TIMES A YEAR

IF BUYING

Quarterly catalogues issued containing 4000–5000 British and World Orders, Medals and Decorations plus miniatures and related books.
Large S.A.E. for sample copy.

IF SELLING

We are keen and competitive purchasers of all medals and decorations, Single pieces or entire collections.

Quick decision and payment

LIVERPOOL MEDAL COMPANY

42 BURY BUSINESS CENTRE
KAY STREET, BURY, LANCS BL9 6BU

PHONE: 0161 763 4610/2 FAX: 0161 763 4963

Visit our interactive web-site at www.liverpoolmedals.co.uk

Decorations

The award of decorations for distinguished military service is an ancient institution. In his *Antiquities of the Jews*, the historian Josephus relates that, in the third century BC, King Alexander was so pleased with Jonathan the High Priest that he sent him a gold button as a mark of favour for his skill in leading the Jews in battle. Subsequently Jonathan was presented with a second gold button for his gallant conduct in the field, making these incidents among the earliest recorded for which specific military awards were granted. The award of jewels, gold buttons and badges for valour was carried on in most European countries on a sporadic basis but the present system of decorations is essentially a modern one dating back no farther than the middle of the seventeenth century. Earlier medals were quasi-commemorative and include the famous Armada Medal of 1588. A few medals in silver or gold were awarded to officers for distinguished service during the English Civil War, although the first "official" rewards in Britain were probably those issued by Parliament to naval officers following their victories over the Dutch fleet in 1653.

Decorations may be divided into those awarded for individual acts of heroism and those conferred in recognition of distinguished military, political or social service. In general terms collectors prefer a decoration awarded for bravery in the field rather than a political honour given automatically to a civil servant, just because he happens to have been in a particular grade for a certain number of years. The debasement of civil awards, such as the OBE and MBE, is reflected in the relative lack of interest shown by collectors.

It is generally true to say that military decorations are more desirable, but it is important to note that one decoration may be more highly prized than another, while the same decoration may well be more valuable to collectors when issued in one period rather than in another. At one extreme is the greatly coveted Victoria Cross, only 1354 of which (including three bars) have been awarded since its inception. VCs won during the Crimean War (111 awarded) are usually less highly regarded than Crosses awarded during the First World War, where, although numerically greater (633) they were far more dearly won. Second World War Crosses are correspondingly more expensive as only 182 were awarded and even now comparatively few of them have ever come on to the market. Today, while pre-1914 Crosses would rate at least £10,000 and those from the First World War slightly more, Second World War Crosses start around £20,000 but have been known to fetch several times as much, depending on the precise circumstances and the branch of the services.

At the other extreme is the Military Medal, of which no fewer than 115,589 were awarded during the First World War alone. For this reason a MM from this period can still be picked up for under £100, whereas one from the Second World War would usually fetch about four times as much, and awards made during the minor campaigns of the 1930s or the Korean War often rate at least ten times as much.

The value of a decoration, where its provenance can be unquestionably established, depends largely on the decoration itself, whether awarded to an officer or an enlisted man, the individual circumstances of the award, the campaign or action concerned, the regiment, unit or ship involved, and the often very personal details of the act or acts of bravery. These factors are extraordinarily difficult to quantify, hence the frequent large discrepancies in the prices fetched by decorations at auction.

The addition of even relatively common decorations, such as the Military Cross or the Military Medal to the average First World War campaign medal group, invariably enhances its value very considerably while the addition of bars for subsequent awards likewise rates a good premium. Decorations awarded to officers tend to fetch more than those awarded to other ranks, mainly because they are proportionately rarer but also because it is usually easier to trace the career details of an officer.

Sometimes the rank of the recipient may have a bearing on the demand for a particular decoration: e.g. Military Crosses awarded to warrant officers are scarcer than those awarded to subalterns and captains. The branch of the armed services may also have some bearing. Thus a Military Medal awarded to a member of the RAF rates far higher than one awarded to a soldier, while a medal awarded to a seaman in one of the naval battalions which fought on the Western Front is also equally desirable.

Initially the Distinguished Service Order could be won by commissioned officers of any rank but after 1914, when the Military Cross was instituted, it was usually restricted to officers of field rank. DSOs awarded to lieutenants and captains in the Army in both World Wars are therefore comparatively rare and invariably expensive, usually as they were awarded for acts of heroism which in earlier campaigns might have merited the VC.

The opportunity for individual acts of bravery varied

from service to service, and in different conflicts. Thus sailors in the Second World War generally had less scope than air crew. Consequently specifically naval awards, such as the Conspicuous Gallantry Medal and the Distinguished Service Cross, are much more scarce than the corresponding RAF awards for Conspicuous Gallantry and the Distinguished Flying Cross.

The addition of bars to gallantry decorations greatly enhances the scarcity and value of such medals. The VC, for example, has been won by only three men on two occasions; none of these VC and bar combinations has ever come on the market, but should one come up for sale, it is certain that the price would be spectacular. The average First World War MM is today worth around £60, but with a bar for second award its value immediately jumps to about three times as much, while MMs with two or more bars are very much more expensive.

It is important to note that in some cases (the DSO for example) decorations were issued unnamed; for this reason the citation or any other supporting documents relevant to the award should be kept with the decoration wherever possible to confirm its attribution.

Engraving of Gallantry Decorations

After the special investiture for the South Atlantic campaign held on February 8, 1983, the question as to why certain awards were engraved with the date only was raised within the Ministry of Defence. A joint service working party considered the matter and recommended that procedures for all decorations and medals for gallantry in the face of the enemy and for the Air Force Cross when awarded for a specific act of gallantry should be brought into line. A submission was accordingly made to the Queen by the Committee on the Grant of Honours, Decorations and Medals and in April 1984 Her Majesty approved the following:

(i)   That the Distinguished Service Cross, Military Cross, Distinguished Flying Cross and Air Force Cross when awarded for gallantry should be engraved with the personal details of the recipient with effect from January 1, 1984.
(ii) That there should be no retrospection;
(iii) That the badge of a Companion of the Distinguished Service Order should not be engraved (in common with the badges of other orders); and
(iv) That the Royal Red Cross (RRC and ARRC) and the Air Force Cross when awarded for meritorious service should not be engraved.

Condition

The same terms are applied to describe the condition of medals and decorations as apply to coins, although the wear to which they are put is caused by other factors. In modern times, when the number of occasions on which medals are worn are relatively few and far between, the condition of most items will be found to be Very Fine (VF) to Extremely Fine (EF). Indeed, in many cases, the medals may never have been worn at all. A good proportion of Second World War medals and decorations are found in almost mint condition as they were not issued till long after the war, by which time their recipients had been demobilised. In some cases they even turn up still in the original cardboard box in which they were posted to the recipients or their next-of-kin.

Before the First World War, however, the wearing of medals was customary on all but the most informal occasions and when actually serving on active duty. Thus medals could be, and often were, subject to a great deal of wear. Medals worn by cavalrymen are often found in poor condition, with scratches and edge knocks occasioned by the constant jangling of one medal against another while on horseback. Often the medals in a group have an abrasive effect on each other. For this reason the Queen's Medal for Egypt (1882) is comparatively rare in excellent condition, as it was usually worn in juxtaposition to the bronze Khedive's Star whose points were capable of doing considerable damage to its silver companion. Apart from these factors it should also be remembered that part of the ritual of "spit and polish" involved cleaning one's medals and they were therefore submitted to vigorous cleaning with metal polish over long periods of service.

For these reasons medals are often sold by dealers "as worn"—a euphemism which conceals a lifetime of hardy service on the chest of some grizzled veteran. Because of the strong personal element involved in medal-collecting, however, genuine wear does not affect the value of a medal to the same degree that it would in other branches of numismatics. There is a school of thought which considers that such signs enhance the interest and value of a medal or group.

This line of thinking also explains the controversy over medal ribbons. Some military outfitters still carry extensive stocks of medal ribbons covering every campaign from Waterloo onwards, so that it is a very easy matter to obtain a fresh length of ribbon for any medal requiring it, and there is no doubt that the appearance of a piece is greatly improved by a clean, bright new ribbon. On the other hand, that ribbon was not the one actually worn by Corporal Bloggs on parade and, to the purist, it would spoil the total effect of the medal. Some collectors therefore retain the original ribbon, even though it may be faded and frayed. As ribbons are things which one cannot authenticate, however, there seems to be little material benefit to be gained from clinging rigidly to a tattered strip of silk when an identical piece can be obtained relatively cheaply. In reality, most collectors compromise by obtaining new ribbons while preserving the old lengths out of sentiment.

Pricing

The prices quoted are *average* figures for medals and decorations as individual items. Combinations with other decorations and campaign medals will produce a value usually well in excess of the aggregate of the individual items. Value will depend to a large extent on the personal factors and circumstances of the award, but where general factors are involved (e.g. the design of the medal, the period of issue or the campaign concerned, or in some cases the branch of the services) these are itemised separately. "—" indicates that either no examples have come onto the market or no examples have been issued. The figure in brackets (where available) is the *approximate* number awarded.

In the lists which follow, it should be assumed that decorations were instituted by Royal Warrant, unless otherwise stated.

24. THE VICTORIA CROSS

Instituted: January 1856.

Ribbon: Crimson. Originally naval crosses used a blue ribbon, but since 1918 the crimson (Army) ribbon has been used for all awards. A miniature cross emblem is worn on the ribbon alone in undress uniform.

Metal: Bronze, originally from Russian guns captured in the Crimea. Modern research, however, reveals that guns captured in other conflicts, e.g. China, have also been used at various periods.

Size: Height 41mm; max. width 36mm.

Description: A cross pattée. (Obverse) a lion statant gardant on the royal crown, with the words FOR VALOUR on a semi-circular scroll. (Reverse) a circular panel on which is engraved the date of the act for which the decoration was awarded. The Cross is suspended by a ring from a seriffed "V" attached to a suspension bar decorated with laurel leaves. The reverse of the suspension bar is engraved with the name, rank and ship, regiment or squadron of the recipient.

Comments: *Introduced as the premier award for gallantry, available for all ranks, to cover all actions since the outbreak of the Crimean War in 1854, it was allegedly created on the suggestion of Prince Albert, the Prince Consort. Of the 1354 awards since 1856, 832 have gone to the Army, 107 to the Navy, 31 to the RAF, ten to the Royal Marines and four to civilians. Second award bars have been awarded three times. The facility for posthumous awards, made retrospective to 1856, began in 1902 and was confirmed in 1907, while the early practice of forfeitures (eight between 1863 and 1908) was discontinued after the First World War.*

VALUE:	Royal Navy/Army	RFC/RAF	Miniature
1856–1914 (522)	£30,000–50,000	—	£50–80
1914–18 (633)	£50,000–65,000	£80,000–120,000	£20–30
1920–45 (187)	£75,000–85,000	£65,000–120,000	£20–30
post-1945 (12)	From £50,000	—	£10–20

NB These prices can only be construed as a general guide. Quite a few awards would exceed these price ranges, particularly Commonwealth examples or those appertaining to well known actions.

Number One for Quality
Number One for Results

To achieve the very best prices for your orders, decorations and medals, contact
Nimrod Dix or Pierce **N**oonan today

DIX • NOONAN • WEBB
DNW
AUCTIONEERS AND VALUERS

No. 1 Old Bond Street
London W1S 4PB
Tel 020 7499 5022
Fax 020 7499 5023
E-mail: auctions@dnw.co.uk

www.dnw.co.uk

25. NEW ZEALAND CROSS

Instituted: 10 March 1869 (by an Order in Council, Wellington).
Ribbon: 38mm crimson.
Metal: Silver with gold appliqué.
Size: Height 52mm; max. width 38mm.
Description: A silver cross pattée with a six-pointed gold star on each
limb. In the centre are the words NEW ZEALAND within a gold
laurel wreath. The cross is surmounted by a gold Tudor crown
which is attached by a ring and a seriffed "V" to a silver bar
ornamented with gold laurel leaves, through which the ribbon
passes. The recipient's name and details are engraved on the reverse.
Comments: *The rarest of all gallantry awards, it was conferred for bravery
during the second series of Maori Wars (1860-72). Only 23 Crosses were
awarded, the last being authorised in 1910. This medal was called into
being solely because local volunteer forces were not eligible for the VC.
Replicas of the Cross have been authorised by the New Zealand
government.*

| VALUE: | £15,000–20,000 | *Miniature £250–750* |
| | Official copy £650–750 | **(depending on the quality which is extremely varied)** |

26. GEORGE CROSS

Instituted: 24 September 1940.
Ribbon: 38mm dark blue. A silver miniature cross emblem is worn on
the ribbon alone.
Metal: Silver.
Size: Height 48mm; max. width 45mm.
Description: A plain bordered cross with a circular medallion in the
centre depicting the effigy of St George and the Dragon after
Benedetto Pistrucci, surrounded by the words FOR GALLANTRY.
In the angle of each limb is the Royal cypher GVI. The plain reverse
bears in the centre the name of the recipient and date of the award.
The Cross hangs by a ring from a bar adorned with laurel leaves.
Comments: *The highest gallantry award for civilians, as well as for
members of the armed forces in actions for which purely military honours
would not normally be granted. It superseded the Empire Gallantry
Medal whose holders were then required to return it and receive the GC in
exchange. By Warrant of December 1971 suviving recipients of the Albert
and Edward Medals were also invited to exchange their awards for the
GC—a move which created a controversy which is still continuing,
particularly among those who received the Albert Medal. Perhaps the
most famous Cross was that conferred on the island of Malta in
recognition of its gallantry during the Second World War. Apart from
exchange awards, between 1940 and 1947 the GC was awarded to 102 men
and four women; since 1947 a further 40 awards have been made. To date
no second award bars have been awarded. Since its inception in 1940 the
George Cross has been awarded 153 times, including four women. In
addition, 112 Empire Gallantry medallists, 64 Albert medallists and 68
Edward medallists who were eligible to exchange their awards for the GC
have increased the total to 397. Most awards were made during World
War II but it should be noted that since 1947 the GC has been awarded
only 41 times (including one woman and the collective award to the
Royal Ulster Constabulary, conferred by Her Majesty the Queen at
Hillsborough Castle on 12 April 2000, the most recent award).*

VALUE:

Service awards 1940 to date	£6500–9000
Civilian awards 1940 to date	£2500–3500
Service exchange pre-1940	£2500–3000
Civilian exchange pre-1940	£2500–3000
Miniature	£10-15

26A. CONSPICUOUS GALLANTRY CROSS

Instituted: October 1993.
Ribbon: White with blue edges and a red central stripe.
Metal: Silver.
Size: Max. width 36mm
Description: A cross pattée imposed on a wreath of laurel, with the royal crown in a circular panel in the centre. Suspended by a ring from a plain suspension bar.
Comments: *As part of the decision to remove distinctions of rank in awards for bravery this decoration replaced the DSO for gallantry as well as the Conspicuous Gallantry Medal and the Distinguished Conduct Medal. It was first awarded in 1995 to Corporal Wayne Mills of the Duke of Wellington's Regiment and in 1996 to Colour Sergeant Peter Humphreys of the Royal Welch Fusiliers, both for gallantry in action during service with the UN Peacekeeping Forces in Bosnia. Two awards were made in respect of gallantry by members of the SAS and SBS in Sierra Leone in May–June 2000.*

VALUE:	Rare	*Miniature*	£15–18

27. DISTINGUISHED SERVICE ORDER

Instituted: 1886.
Ribbon: 29mm crimson with dark blue edges.
Metal: Originally gold; silver-gilt (since 1889).
Size: Height 44mm; max. width 41.5mm.
Description: A cross with curved ends, overlaid with white enamel. (Obverse) a green enamel laurel wreath enclosing an imperial crown; (reverse) the royal monogram within a similar wreath. It is suspended from its ribbon by a swivel ring and a straight laureated bar. Additional awards are denoted by bars ornamented by a crown. Silver rosettes on the ribbon alone are worn in undress uniform. Since its inception, the DSO has been issued unnamed, but since 1938 the year of award has been engraved on the reverse of the lower suspension bar as well as the reverse of the bars for second or subsequent awards.
Comments: *Intended to reward commissioned officers below field rank for distinguished service in time of war, and for which the VC would not be appropriate. Previously the CB had sometimes been awarded to junior officers, although intended mainly for those of field rank. It was also available to officers in both the other armed services. In September 1942 the regulations were relaxed to permit award of the DSO to officers of the Merchant Navy who performed acts of gallantry in the presence of the enemy. As a result of the 1993 Review of gallantry awards and resultant changes to the operational gallantry award system, the DSO is now awarded for "Leadership" only— theoretically to all ranks (it is not awarded posthumously). It has been replaced by the Conspicuous Gallantry Cross as the reward for gallantry.*

VALUE:	Unnamed single	Attributable group	*Miniature*
Victoria, gold (153)	£1500–2000	£3500–5000	£80–100
Victoria, silver-gilt (1170)	£700–800	£2000–5000	£60–80
Edward VII (78)	£1000–1200	£3500–5500	£80–100 (gold)
George V (9900)	£525–575	£850–1500	£25 (gilt), £50 (gold)
George VI 1st type 1938–48 (4880)	£650–750	£2000–2500	£40 (gilt)
George VI 2nd type 1948–52 (63)	£800–1200	£3500–4500	£40 (gilt)
Elizabeth II (110)	£1000–1500	£3500–5000	£30

28. IMPERIAL SERVICE ORDER

Instituted: August 1902.

Ribbon: 38mm three equal sections of crimson, blue and crimson.

Metal: Silver with gold overlay.

Size: Height 61mm; max. width 55mm.

Description: The badge consists of a circular gold plaque bearing the royal cypher and surrounded by the words FOR FAITHFUL SERVICE. This plaque is then superimposed on a seven-pointed silver star surmounted by a crown and ring for suspension. The badge of the ISO awarded to women is similar but has a laurel wreath instead of the star-shaped base.

Comments: *Instituted by King Edward VII as a means of rewarding long and faithful service in the Administrative and Clerical grades of the Civil Service at home and overseas. Women were admitted to the order in 1908. The order was awarded after at least 25 years service at home, 20 years and 6 months (India) and 16 years in the tropics, but in exceptional cases awards were made for "eminently meritorious service" irrespective of qualifying period. No UK awards have been made since 1995 but some Commonwealth awards continue to this day.*

VALUE:

			Miniature
Edward VII	Gentleman (489)	£100–150	£25–30
	Lady (3)	£350–400	£50–60
George V	Gentleman (909)	£120–130	£20–25
	Lady (2)	£360–400	£45–50
George VI	Gentleman (608)	£120–130	£15–20
	Lady (8)	£350–400	£30–35
Elizabeth II	Gentleman (2,153)*	£120–150	£10–15
	Lady (114)*	£280–350	£20–25

*1953–94

29. IMPERIAL SERVICE MEDAL

Instituted: August 1902.

Ribbon: Same as above.

Metal: Silver and bronze.

Description: Originally similar to the ISO but with a silver plaque and bronze star or wreath. In 1920 the ISM was transformed into a circular medal of silver with the sovereign's effigy on the obverse and a reverse depicting a naked man resting from his labours, with FOR FAITHFUL SERVICE in the exergue.

Comments: *Instituted at the same time as the ISO but intended for junior grades of the Civil Service.*

VALUE:

		Miniature
Edward VII, 1903–10 (c. 4,500) Star (Gentleman)	£45–55	£15–20
Wreath (Lady)	£200–250	£30–40
George V, 1911-20 (c. 6,000) Star (Gentleman)	£40–45	£12–15
Wreath (Lady)	£250–300	£30–40
George V Circular type		
Coinage profile, 1920–31 (c. 20,000)	£12–15	£10–12
Crowned bust, 1931–37 (c. 16,000)	£12–15	£10–12
George VI		
Crowned bust INDIAE:IMP, 1938–48 (c. 36,000)	£12–15	£8–10
Crowned bust FID:DEF, 1949–52 (c. 16,000)	£12–15	£8–10
Elizabeth II		
Tudor crown BRITT:OMN, 1953–54 (c. 9,000)	£12–15	£8–10
Tudor crown DEI:GRATIA, 1955– (c. 150,000)	£12–15	£8–10

30. INDIAN ORDER OF MERIT

Instituted: 1837 (by the Honourable East India Company).

Ribbon: Dark blue with crimson edges (military) or crimson with dark blue edges (civil).

Metal: Silver and gold.

Size: Height 41mm; max. width 40mm.

Description: An eight-pointed star with a circular centre surrounded by a laurel wreath and containing crossed sabres and the relevant inscription. The star is suspended by a curvilinear suspension bar. The different classes were denoted by the composition of the star, noted below.

Comments: *The oldest gallantry award of the British Empire, it was founded in 1837 by the Honourable East India Company. Twenty years later it became an official British award when the administration of India passed to the Crown after the Sepoy Mutiny. Originally known simply as the Order of Merit, it was renamed in 1902 following the introduction of the prestigious British order of that name. There were three classes of the order, promotion from one class to the next being the reward for further acts of bravery. A civil division (also in three classes) was introduced in 1902. Ten years later the military division was reduced to two classes, when troops of the Indian Army became eligible for the VC. The civil division became a single class in 1939 and the military in 1945. Both divisions came to an end with the British Raj in 1947.*

VALUE:

Military Division	
1837-1912 Reward of Valor	
1st class in gold (42)	£1400–1600
2nd class in silver and gold (130)	£450–650
3rd class in silver (2740)	£250–450
1912-39 Reward of Valor	
1st class in silver and gold (26)	£750–1000
2nd class in silver (1215)	£250–450
1939-44 Reward for Gallantry	
1st class in silver and gold (2)	Rare
2nd class in silver (332)	£400–650
1945-47 Reward for Gallantry (44mm diameter)	£800–1000
Civil Division	
1902-39 For Bravery (35mm diameter)	
1st class in gold (0)	—
2nd class in silver and gold (0)	—
3rd class in silver (39)	£600–800
1939-47 For Bravery (26mm diameter)	
Single class (10)	Rare
Miniature	£150–250

NB These prices represent unattributable pieces. Values can climb rapidly when in company with related campaign medals, particularly for the Victorian era.

www.speedbid.com

YOUR OWN MEDAL AUCTION

31. ROYAL RED CROSS

First Class obverse

2nd Class reverse

Instituted: 27 April 1883.

Ribbon: 25mm dark blue edged with crimson, in a bow.

Metal: Gold (later silver-gilt) and silver.

Size: Height 41mm; max. width 35mm.

Description: (Obverse) The *1st class* badge was originally a gold cross pattée, enamelled red with gold edges, but from 1889 silver-gilt was substituted for gold. At the centre was a crowned and veiled portrait, with the words FAITH, HOPE and CHARITY inscribed on three arms, and the date 1883 on the lower arm. Subsequently the effigy of the reigning monarch was substituted for the allegorical profile; (reverse) crowned royal cypher. *2nd Class:* in silver, design as the 1st class but the inscriptions on the arms appear on the reverse. Awards from 1938 have the year of issue engraved on the reverse of the lower arm.

Comments: *This decoration had the distinction of being confined to females until 1976. It is conferred on members of the nursing services regardless of rank. A second class award was introduced in November 1915. Bars for the first class were introduced in 1917. Holders of the second class are promoted to the first class on second awards. Holders of the first class decoration are known as Members (RRC) while recipients of the second class are Associates (ARRC).*

VALUE:	First class (RRC)	Miniature	Second class (ARRC)	Miniature
Victoria, gold	£1000–1200	—	—	£90–100
Victoria, silver-gilt	£400–500	—	—	£60–70
Edward VII, gold	£500–550	—	—	£90–100
George V	£230–250	£20–30	£75–85	£10–20
George V, with bar	£300–350		—	
George VI GRI	£250–300	£20–30	£130–150	£10–20
George VI GVIR	£300–350	£20–30	£150–180	£10–20
Elizabeth II	£300–350	£20–30	£140–150	£10–20

32. DISTINGUISHED SERVICE CROSS

Instituted: June 1901.

Ribbon: 36mm three equal parts of dark blue, white and dark blue.

Metal: Silver.

Size: Height 43mm; max. width 43mm.

Description: A plain cross with rounded ends. (Obverse) crowned royal cypher in the centre, suspended by a ring; (reverse) plain apart from the hallmark. From 1940 onwards the year of issue was engraved on the reverse of the lower limb.

Comments: *Known as the Conspicuous Service Cross when instituted, it was awarded to warrant and subordinate officers of the Royal Navy who were ineligible for the DSO. In October 1914 it was renamed the Distinguished Service Cross and thrown open to all naval officers below the rank of lieutenant-commander. Bars for second awards were authorised in 1916 and in 1931 eligibility for the award was enlarged to include officers of the Merchant Navy. In 1940 Army and RAF officers serving aboard naval vessels also became eligible for the award. Since 1945 fewer than 100 DSCs have been awarded. As a result of the 1993 Review of gallantry awards and resultant changes to the operational gallantry award system, this award is now available to both officers and other ranks, the DSM having been discontinued.*

VALUE:	Unnamed single	Attributable group	Miniature
Edward VII	Rare	£5000–7000	£150–200
George V	£375–400	£600–650	£15–20
George VI GRI	£380–400	£500–600	£12–15
George VI GVIR	Rare	£2000–2500	£25–30
Elizabeth II	Rare	£2000–3000	£10–12

33. MILITARY CROSS

Instituted: 31 December 1914.
Ribbon: 38mm three equal bars of white, deep purple and white.
Metal: Silver.
Size: Height 46mm; max. width 44mm.
Description: An ornamental cross with straight arms terminating in broad finials decorated with imperial crowns. The royal cypher appears at the centre and the cross is suspended from a plain silver suspension bar.
Comments: *There was no gallantry award, lesser than the VC and DSO, for junior Army officers and warrant officers until shortly after the outbreak of the First World War when the MC was instituted. Originally awarded to captains, lieutenants and warrant officers of the Army (including RFC), it was subsequently extended to include equivalent ranks of the RAF when performing acts of bravery on the ground and there was even provision for the Royal Naval Division and the Royal Marines during the First World War. Awards were extended to majors by an amending warrant of 1931. Bars for second and subsequent awards have a crown at the centre. The MC is always issued unnamed, although since about 1938 the reverse of the cross or bar is officially dated with the year of issue. As a result of the 1993 Review of gallantry awards and resultant changes to the operational gallantry award system, this award is now available to both officers and other ranks, the Military Medal having been discontinued.*

VALUE:	Unnamed single	Attributable group	*Miniature*
George V 1914-1920 (37,000)	£280–300	£550–1000	£15–20
George V 1914-1920 one bar (3000)	£400–450	£1000–1400	
George V 1914-1920 two bars (170)	£600–700	£2500–3500	
George V 1914-1920 three bars (4)	Rare	Rare	
George V 1921-1936 (350)	Rare	£800–1000	
George V 1921-1936 one bar (31)	Rare	£1200–1600	
George VI GRI 1939-1946 (11,000)	£300–350	£800–1200	£10–15
George VI GRI one bar (500)	£450–550	£1800–2500	
George VI GVIR (158)	Rare	£2000–2500	£10–15
Elizabeth II	£500–600	£3000–3500	£8–10
Elizabeth II one bar	Rare	Rare	

34. DISTINGUISHED FLYING CROSS

Instituted: June 1918.
Ribbon: 30mm diagonal alternate stripes of white and deep purple.
Metal: Silver.
Size: Height 60mm; max. width 54mm.
Description: (Obverse) a cross flory terminating with a rose, surmounted by another cross made of propeller blades charged in the centre with a roundel within a laurel wreath. The horizontal arms bear wings and the crowned RAF monogram at the centre; (reverse) the royal cypher above the date 1918. The cross is suspended from a bar decorated with a sprig of laurel.
Comments: *Established for officers and warrant officers of the RAF in respect of acts of valour while flying in active operations against the enemy. The DFC is issued unnamed, but Second World War crosses usually have the year of issue engraved on the reverse of the lower limb. As a result of the 1993 Review of gallantry awards and resultant changes to the operational gallantry award system, this award is now available to both officers and other ranks, the Distinguished Flying Medal having been discontinued.*

VALUE:	Unnamed single	Attributable group	*Miniature*
George V 1918-20 (1100)	£550–600	£1000–1200	£20–25
George V 1918-20 one bar (70)	£700–800	£2500–3500	
George V 1918-20 two bars (3)	Rare	Rare	
George V 1920-36 (130)	Rare	£1500–2000	
George V 1920-36 one bar (20)	Rare	£2800–4000	
George V 1920-36 two bars (4)	Rare	Rare	
George VI GRI 1939-45 (20,000)	£450–550	£1200–3500	£15–20
George VI 1939-45 one bar (1550)	£650–750	£2000–4000	
George VI 1939-45 two bars (42)	Rare	£4000–6000	
George VI GVIR 1948-52 (65)	Rare	£2000–3000	£15–20
Elizabeth II (260)	Rare	£2000–4000	£12–15

(in silver add £5)

35. AIR FORCE CROSS

Instituted: June 1918.
Ribbon: 30mm originally horizontal but since June 1919 diagonal alternate stripes of white and crimson.
Metal: Silver.
Size: eight 60mm; max. width 54mm.
Description: (Obverse) the cross consists of a thunderbolt, the arms conjoined by wings, base bar terminating in a bomb, surmounted by another cross of aeroplane propellers, the finials inscribed with the royal cypher. A central roundel depicts Hermes mounted on a hawk bestowing a wreath; (reverse) the royal cypher and the date 1918.
Comments: *This decoration, awarded to officers and warrant officers of the RAF, was instituted in June 1918 for gallantry on non-operational missions and for meritorious service on flying duties. Since the 1993 Review of gallantry awards it is now available to all ranks (the Air Force Medal having been discontinued) for non-operational gallantry in the air only (no longer for meritorious service also).*

VALUE:	Unnamed single	Attributable group	*Miniature*
George V 1918-20 (680)	£550–600	£900–1000	£15–20
George V 1918-20 one bar (12)	Rare	Rare	
George V 1918-20 two bars (3)	Rare	Rare	
George V 1920-36 (160)	Rare	£800–1000	
George VI GRI (2000)	£550–600	£800–1000	£15–20
George VI one bar (26)	£550–600	£1400–1600	
George VI two bars (1)	Rare	Rare	
George VI GVIR (980)	£550–650	£900–1200	£15–20
Elizabeth II	£550–650	£900–1200	£10–12

(in silver add £5)

36. ORDER OF BRITISH INDIA

Instituted: 1837 by the Honourable East India Company.
Ribbon: Worn around the neck, the base colour of the ribbon was originally sky blue but this was altered to crimson in 1838, allegedly because the hair oil favoured by Indians of all classes would soon have soiled a light ribbon. From 1939 onwards the first class ribbon had two thin vertical lines of light blue at the centre, while the second class ribbon had a single vertical line. Originally these distinctive ribbons were only worn in undress uniform (without the insignia itself), but from 1945 they replaced the plain crimson ribbons when worn with the decoration.
Metal: Gold.
Size: Height 42mm; max. width 38mm.
Description: The first class badge consists of a gold star with a crown between the upper two points and a blue enamelled centre bearing a lion surrounded by the words ORDER OF BRITISH INDIA enclosed in a laurel wreath. The second class badge is smaller, with dark blue enamel in the centre and with no crown.
Comments: *Intended for long and faithful service by native officers of the Indian Army, it was thrown open in 1939 to officers of the armed forces, frontier guards, military police and officers of the Indian native states. There were two classes, promotion to the first being made from the second. Recipients of both classes were entitled to the letters OBI after their names, but holders of the first class had the rank of Sardar Bahadur, while those of the second were merely Bahadur. A few awards were made by Pakistan to British officers seconded to the Pakistani forces at the time of independence.*

VALUE:		*Miniature*
1st class, light blue centre and dark blue surround	£400–450	£150–200
1st class, sky blue centre and surround (1939)	£400–450	£150–200
2nd class	£400–450	£150–200

NB The prices quoted are for unattributable awards.

37. ORDER OF BURMA

Instituted 1940.
Ribbon: 38mm dark green with light blue edges.
Metal: Gold.
Size: Height 52mm; max. width 38mm.
Description: The badge consists of a gold-rayed circle with a central roundel charged with a peacock in his pride azure, surmounted by an imperial crown.
Comments: *Instituted by King George VI, three years after Burma became independent of British India. Only 24 awards were made, to Governor's Commissioned Officers for long, faithful and honourable service in the army, frontier force and military police of Burma. By an amendment of 1945 the order could also be awarded for individual acts of heroism or particularly meritorious service. It was abolished in 1947.*

VALUE: £3500–4500   *Miniature* £150–200

38. KAISAR-I-HIND MEDAL

Instituted: May 1900.
Ribbon: 37mm bluish green.
Metal: Gold, silver or bronze.
Size: Height 61mm; max. width 34mm.
Description: An oval badge surmounted by the imperial crown. (Obverse) the royal cypher set within a wreath; (reverse) FOR PUBLIC SERVICE IN INDIA round the edge and KAISAR-I-HIND (Emperor of India) on a scroll across the centre against a floral background.
Comments: *Queen Victoria founded this medal for award to those, regardless of colour, creed or sex, who had performed public service in India. Originally in two classes George V introduced a 3rd Class in bronze. The medals were originally large and hollow but were changed to smaller in diameter and solid during the reign of George V.*

Victoria obv.

VALUE:	1st class (gold)	*Miniature*	2nd class (silver)	*Miniature*	3rd class (bronze)
Victoria	£600–700	£120–150	£200–250	£80–100	—
Edward VII	£600–650	£120–150	£180–220	£80–100	—
George V 1st	£500–600	£50–100	£150–180	£25–50	—
George V 2nd	£450–500	£50–100	£120–130	£25–50	£80–100
George VI	£500–600	£120–150	£120–140	£50–80	£80–100

Victoria rev.

George VI   *obv.*

rev.

39. ALBERT MEDAL

Instituted: 7 March 1866.

Ribbons: Originally 16mm blue with two white stripes (gold 1st class), changed on introduction of the 2nd class to 35mm blue with four white stripes. The 2nd class remained 16mm blue with two white stripes until 1904 when it was changed to 35mm blue with two white stripes. For the gold 1st class medal the ribbon was 35mm crimson with four white stripes, that for the 2nd class originally 16mm crimson with two white stripes, changing in 1904 to a 35mm ribbon.

Metal: Gold (early issues gold and bronze); bronze.

Size: Height 57mm; max. width 30mm.

Description: The badge consists of an oval enclosing the entwined initials V and A. The sea medals have, in addition, an anchor. The oval is enclosed by a bronze garter with the words FOR GALLANTRY IN SAVING LIFE, with AT SEA or ON LAND as appropriate, and enamelled in blue or crimson respectively. The whole is surmounted by a crown pierced by a ring for suspension. The first class medal was originally worked in gold and bronze and later in gold alone, the second class in bronze alone.

Comments: *Named in memory of the Prince Consort who died in 1861, this series of medals was instituted for gallantry in saving life at sea. An amendment of 1867 created two classes of medal and ten years later awards were extended to gallantry in saving life on land. In 1917 the title of the awards was altered, the first class becoming the Albert Medal in Gold and the second class merely the Albert Medal. It was last awarded to a living recipient in April 1943, the last posthumous award being in May 1945. The last bronze medal awarded to a living recipient was in January 1949, and posthumous in August 1970. In 1949 the Medal in Gold was abolished and replaced by the George Cross and henceforward the Albert Medal (second class) was only awarded posthumously. In 1971 the award of the medal ceased and holders were invited to exchange their medals for the George Cross. Of the 64 eligible to exchange, 49 did so.*

VALUE:

	Civilian	Service	Miniature
Gold Sea (25)	£3500–4500	£4500–5500	£40–60*
Bronze Sea (216)	£2200–2500	£2500–3000	£30–50
Gold Land (45)	£2500–3000	£3000–4000	£40–60*
Bronze Land (282)	£2000–2500	£2000–2500	£30–50

*assumed gilt

40. UNION OF SOUTH AFRICA KING'S/ QUEEN'S MEDAL FOR BRAVERY (WOLTEMADE MEDAL)

Instituted: 1939 by the Government of the Union of South Africa.

Ribbon: Royal blue with narrow orange edges.

Metal: Gold or silver.

Size: 37mm.

Description: (Obverse) an effigy of the reigning sovereign; (reverse) a celebrated act of heroism by Wolraad Woltemade who rescued sailors from the wreck of the East Indiaman *De Jong Thomas* which ran aground in Table Bay on 17 June 1773. Seven times Woltemade rode into the raging surf to save fourteen seamen from drowning, but on the eighth attempt both rider and horse perished.

Comments: *This medal was awarded to citizens of the Union of South Africa and dependent territories who endangered their lives in saving the lives of others. It was awarded very sparingly, in gold or silver.*

VALUE: **George VI Gold (1)** Rare
George VI Silver (34) Rare
Elizabeth II Silver (1) Rare

41. DISTINGUISHED CONDUCT MEDAL

1st type obv.

Instituted: 1854.
Ribbon: 32mm crimson with a dark blue central stripe.
Metal: Silver.
Size: 36mm.
Description: (Obverse) originally a trophy of arms but, since 1902, the effigy of the reigning sovereign; (reverse) a four-line inscription across the field FOR DISTINGUISHED CONDUCT IN THE FIELD.
Comments: *The need for a gallantry medal for other ranks was first recognised during the Crimean War, although previously the Meritorious Service Medal (qv) had very occasionally been awarded for gallantry in the field. The medals have always been issued named, and carry the number, rank and name of the recipient on the rim, together with the date of the act of gallantry from 1881 until about 1901. Bars are given for subsequent awards and these too were dated from the first issued in 1881 until 1916 when the more usual laurelled bars were adopted. Since 1916 it has ranked as a superior decoration to the Military Medal. As a result of the 1993 Review of gallantry awards and resultant changes to the operational gallantry award system, the decoration has been replaced by the Conspicuous Gallantry Cross.*

VALUE:

Crimea (800)	£600–4000
Indian Mutiny (17)	£5500–7000
India general service 1854-95	£1500–3000
Abyssinia 1867-8 (7)	£2000–3000
Ashantee 1873-4 (33)	£1800–2000
Zulu War 1877-9 (16)	£3000–7000
Afghanistan 1878-80 (61)	£1800–2500
First Boer War 1880-1 (20)	£2500–5000
Egypt & Sudan 1882-9 (134)	£2500–3000
India 1895-1901	£1500–2200
Sudan 1896-7	£1500–5500
Second Boer War 1899-1902 (2090)	£500–1200
Boxer Rebellion 1900	£3000–7000
Edward VII	Many rarities
George V 1st type (25,000)	£350–1000
George V 2nd type 1930-7 (14)	£2500–3500
George VI, IND IMP 1937-47	£2400–4000
George VI, 2nd type 1948-52 (25)	£3000–4000
Elizabeth II, BR: OMN:	£3000–4000
Elizabeth II, DEI GRATIA	£3000–6000
Miniature	
Victoria	£40–50
Edward VII	£25–30
George V	£15–20
George VI	£10–15
Elizabeth II	£10–15

42. DISTINGUISHED CONDUCT MEDAL (DOMINION & COLONIAL)

Instituted: 31 May 1895.
Ribbon: 32mm crimson with a dark blue central stripe.
Metal: Silver.
Size: 36mm.
Description: As above, but the reverse bears the name of the issuing country or colony round the top.
Comments: *A separate DCM for warrant officers, NCOs and men of the colonial forces. Medals were struck for the Cape of Good Hope, Natal, New Zealand, New South Wales, Queensland, Tasmania, Natal and Canada, but only the last two actually issued them and the others are known only as specimens.*

VALUE:

Victoria Canada (1)	Rare
Victoria Natal (1)	Rare
Edward VII Natal (9)	Rare

43. DISTINGUISHED CONDUCT MEDAL (KAR & WAFF)

Instituted: early 1900s.
Ribbon: Dark blue with a central green stripe flanked by crimson stripes.
Metal: Silver.
Size: 3mm.
Description: As no. 42, with either King's African Rifles or West Africa Frontier Force around the top of the reverse.
Comments: *Separate awards for gallantry were instituted in respect of the King's African Rifles (East Africa) and the West Africa Frontier Force (Nigeria, Sierra Leone, Gambia and the Gold Coast). These were issued until 1942 when they were superseded by the British DCM.*

VALUE:	Attributable groups
Edward VII KAR (2)	Rare
Edward VII WAFF (55)	Rare
George V KAR (190)	£600–800
George V WAFF (165)	£600–800

44. CONSPICUOUS GALLANTRY MEDAL

Instituted: 1855.
Ribbon: 31mm white (RN) or sky blue (RAF) with dark blue edges.
Metal: Silver.
Size: 36mm.
Description: (Obverse) the effigy of the reigning monarch; (reverse) the words FOR CONSPICUOUS GALLANTRY in three lines within a crowned laurel wreath.
Comments: *Conceived as the naval counterpart to the DCM, it was instituted for award to petty officers and seamen of the Royal Navy and to NCOs and other ranks of the Royal Marines. Originally awarded only for gallantry during the Crimean War, it was revived in 1874 to recognise heroism during the Ashantee War and has since been awarded, albeit sparingly, for other wars and campaigns. The Crimean issue utilised the dies of the Meritorious Service Medal which had the date 1848 below the truncation of the Queen's neck on the obverse. The raised relief inscription MERITORIOUS SERVICE on the reverse was erased and the words CONSPICUOUS GALLANTRY engraved in their place. When the decoration was revived in 1874 a new obverse was designed without a date while a new die, with the entire inscription in raised relief, was employed for the reverse. In 1943 the CGM was extended to NCOs and other ranks of the RAF. Both naval and RAF medals are identical, but the naval medal has a white ribbon with dark blue edges, whereas the RAF award has a pale blue ribbon with dark blue edges. It ranks as one of the rarest decorations: the only three medals issued in the present reign were awarded to an airman in the RAAF for gallantry in Vietnam (1968), to Staff-Sergeant James Prescott, RE, during the South Atlantic War (1982) (posthumous) and to CPO Diver Philip Hammond, RN, during the Gulf War (1991). As a result of the 1993 Review and resultant changes to the operational gallantry award system, the decoration has been replaced by the Conspicuous Gallantry Cross.*

VALUE:	Attributable groups
Victoria 1st type (11)	£3500–4500
Victoria 2nd type (51)	£3000–5000
Edward VII (2)	£8000–9000
George V (110)	£2500–4000
George VI Navy (72)	£3000–10,000
George VI RAF (111)	£4500–6500
Elizabeth II (3)	Rare
Miniature	
Victoria	£50–80
Edward VII	£50–80
George V	£20–30
George VI	£15–20
Elizabeth II	£15–20

45. GEORGE MEDAL

Instituted: 1940.

Ribbon: 32mm crimson with five narrow blue stripes.

Metal: Silver.

Size: 36mm.

Description: (Obverse) the effigy of the reigning monarch; (reverse) St George and the Dragon, modelled by George Kruger Gray, after the bookplate by Stephen Gooden for the Royal Library, Windsor.

Comments: *Awarded for acts of bravery where the services were not so outstanding as to merit the George Cross. Though primarily a civilian award, it has also been given to service personnel for heroism not in the face of the enemy. Of the approximately 2000 medals awarded, 1030 have been to civilians.*

VALUE:	Civilian	Service
George VI 1st type 1940-47	£750–1000	£1000–1400
George VI 2nd type 1948-52	£750–1000	£1100–1500
Elizabeth II 1st type 1953	£800–1000	£1200–1700
Elizabeth II 2nd type	£900–1100	£1400–1800

Miniature	
George VI	£10–15 (Silver £20–25)
Elizabeth II	£10–15 (Silver £20–25)

46. KING'S POLICE MEDAL

Instituted: 7 July 1909.

Ribbons: 36mm Originally deep blue with silver edges, but in 1916 a central silver stripe was added. Gallantry awards have thin crimson stripes superimposed on the silver stripes.

Metal: Silver.

Size: 36mm.

Description: (Obverse) the monarch's effigy; (reverse) a standing figure with sword and shield inscribed TO GUARD MY PEOPLE. The first issue had a laurel spray in the exergue, but in 1933 two separate reverses were introduced and the words FOR GALLANTRY or FOR DISTINGUISHED SERVICE were placed in the exergue.

Comments: *Instituted to reward "courage and devotion to duty" in the police and fire services of the UK and overseas dominions. Recognising the bravery of the firemen during the Blitz, the medal was retitled the King's Police and Fire Services Medal in 1940, but no change was made in the design of the medal itself. From 1950, the gallantry medals were only awarded posthumously and all medals were discontinued in 1954 when seperate awards were established for the two services (see numbers 47 and 48).*

VALUE:		*Miniature*
Edward VII (100)	£600–800	£25–30
George V 1st type coinage head (1900)	£225–300	£20–25
George V 2nd type crowned head	£250–350	£20–25
George V for Gallantry (350)	£450–650	£15–20
George V for Distinguished Service	£225–250	£15–20
George VI 1st type for Gallantry (440)	£550–650	£10–15
George VI 2nd type for Gallantry (50)	£800–1000	£10–15
George VI 1st type for Distinguished Service	£200–250	£10–15
George VI 2nd type for Distinguished Service	£200–250	£10–15

47. QUEEN'S POLICE MEDAL

Instituted: 19 May 1954.
Ribbon: Three silver stripes and two broad dark blue stripes.
Metal: Silver.
Size: 36mm.
Description: (Obverse) effigy of the reigning sovereign; (reverse) a standing figure (as on the KPM) but the laurel spray has been restored to the exergue and the words FOR GALLANTRY or FOR DISTINGUISHED POLICE SERVICE are inscribed round the circumference.
Comments: *The QPM for Gallantry has been effectively redundant since November 1977 when it was made possible to award the George Medal posthumously. Prior to this the QPM was the posthumous equivalent of the GM for police officers.*

VALUE:

Elizabeth II for Gallantry (23)	£800–1200
Elizabeth II for Distinguished Service (1100)	£350–450
Miniature	£10–15

48. QUEEN'S FIRE SERVICE MEDAL

Instituted: 19 May 1954.
Ribbon: Red with three yellow stripes (distinguished service) or similar, with thin dark blue stripes bisecting the yellow stripes (gallantry).
Metal: Silver.
Size: 36mm
Description: (Obverse) effigy of the reigning monarch; (reverse) standing figure with sword and shield (as on KPM), laurel spray in the exergue, and inscription round the circumference FOR GALLANTRY or FOR DISTINGUISHED FIRE SERVICE.

VALUE:

Elizabeth II for Gallantry	Rare
Elizabeth II for Distinguished Service	£550–650
Miniature	£10–12

49. KING'S POLICE MEDAL (SOUTH AFRICA)

Instituted: 24 September 1937.
Ribbon: Silver with two broad dark blue stripes. Red stripes are added for gallantry awards.
Metal: Silver.
Size: 36mm.
Description: (Obverse) effigy of George VI and title including the words ET IMPERATOR (1937-49), George VI minus IMPERATOR (1950-52) and Queen Elizabeth II (1953-60). (Reverse) as UK (no. 47 above) but inscribed in English and Afrikaans. Inscribed FOR BRAVERY VIR DAPPERHEID or FOR DISTINGUISHED SERVICE VIR VOORTREFLIKE DIENS.
Comments: *Awarded to members of the South Africa Police for courage and devotion to duty. In 1938 it was extended to cover the constabulary of South West Africa.*

VALUE:

George VI 1st type 1937-49	
for Gallantry (10)	Rare
for Distinguished Service (13)	Rare
George VI 2nd type 1950-52	
for Distinguished Service (13)	Rare
Elizabeth II 1953-60	
for Gallantry (20)	Rare
Elizabeth II 1953-69	
for Distinguished Service (3)	Rare

50. EDWARD MEDAL (MINES)

Instituted: July 1907.
Ribbon: Dark blue edged with yellow.
Metal: Silver or bronze.
Size: 33mm.
Description: (Obverse) the monarch's effigy; (reverse) a miner rescuing a stricken comrade, with the caption FOR COURAGE across the top (designed by W. Reynolds-Stephens).
Comments: *Awarded for life-saving in mines and quarries, in two grades: first class (silver) and second class (bronze). Interestingly, the cost of these medals was borne not by the State but from a fund created by a group of philanthropic individuals led by A. Hewlett, a leading mine-owner. Medals were engraved with the names of the recipient from the outset, but since the 1930s the date and sometimes the place of the action have also been inscribed. Since 1949 the medal was only granted posthumously and in 1971 living recipients were invited to exchange their medals for the GC, under Royal Warrant of 1971. Two silver and seven bronze medallists elected not to do so. This is one of the rarest gallantry awards, only 77 silver and 318 bronze medals having been granted since its inception.*

VALUE:	Silver	Bronze
Edward VII	£750–850	£650–750
George V 1st type	£750–850	£750–800
George V 2nd type	£1200–1500	£750–850
George VI 1st type	£1500–1800	£1200–1400
George VI 2nd type	—	Rare
Elizabeth II	Not issued	From £1800
Miniature		
Edward VII	£60–80	
George V	£50–60	
George VI	£70–80	

51. EDWARD MEDAL (INDUSTRY)

1st type rev.

2nd type rev.

Instituted: December 1909.
Ribbon: As above.
Metal: Silver or bronze.
Size: 33mm.
Description: (Obverse) effigy of the reigning monarch; (reverse) originally a worker helping an injured workmate with a factory in the background and the words FOR COURAGE inscribed diagonally across the top. A second reverse, depicting a standing female figure with a laurel branch and a factory skyline in the background, was introduced in 1912.
Comments: *Awarded for acts of bravery in factory accidents and disasters. Like the Mines medal it was also available in two classes, but no first class medals were awarded since 1948. Since 1949 the medal was only granted posthumously and in 1971 living recipients were invited to exchange their medals for the GC, under Royal Warrant of 1971. A total of 25 silver and 163 bronze awards have been issued. Two awards were made to women, the rarest gallantry award to a lady.*

VALUE:	Silver	Bronze
Edward VII	Rare	Rare
George V 1st Obv, 1st Rev	—	£1500–1800
George V 1st Obv, 2nd Rev	£1400–1500	£800–1000
George V 2nd Obv, 2nd Rev	Rare	£1200–1400
George VI 1st type	—	£1000–1200
George VI 2nd type	Not issued	Rare
Elizabeth II 1st type	Not issued	Rare
Elizabeth II 2nd type	Not issued	Rare
Miniature		
George V	£60–80	
George VI (modern)	£15–20	

52. INDIAN DISTINGUISHED SERVICE MEDAL

Instituted: 25 June 1907.

Ribbon: Crimson with broad dark blue edges.

Metal: Silver.

Size: 36mm.

Description: (Obverse) the sovereign's effigy; (reverse) the words FOR DISTINGUISHED SERVICE in a laurel wreath.

Comments: *Awarded for distinguished service in the field by Indian commissioned and non-commissioned officers and men of the Indian Army, the reserve forces, border militia and levies, military police and troops employed by the Indian Government. An amendment of 1917 extended the award to Indian non-combatants engaged on field service, bars for subsequent awards being authorised at the same time. It was formally extended to the Royal Indian Marine in 1929 and members of the Indian Air Force in 1940. Finally it was extended in 1944 to include non-European personnel of the Hong Kong and Singapore Royal Artillery although it became obsolete in 1947.*

VALUE:

		Miniature
Edward VII (140)	£500–650	£50–70
George V KAISAR-I-HIND (3800)	£150–250	£30–40
George V 2nd type (140)	£350–550	£30–40
George VI (1190)	£300–650	£20–30

53. BURMA GALLANTRY MEDAL

Instituted: 10 May 1940.

Ribbon: Jungle green with a broad crimson stripe in the centre.

Metal: Silver.

Size: 36mm.

Description: (Obverse) the effigy of King George VI; (reverse) the words BURMA at the top and FOR GALLANTRY in a laurel wreath.

Comments: *As Burma ceased to be part of the Indian Empire in April 1937 a separate gallantry award was required for its armed services. The Burma Gallantry Medal was awarded by the Governor to officers and men of the Burma Army, frontier forces, military police, Burma RNVR and Burma AAF, although by an amendment of 1945 subsequent awards were restricted to NCOs and men. The medal became obsolete in 1947 when Burma became an independent republic and left the Commonwealth. Just over 200 medals and three bars were awarded, mainly for heroism in operations behind the Japanese lines.*

VALUE: *Miniature*
£2000–3000   £35–50

54. DISTINGUISHED SERVICE MEDAL

Instituted: 14 October 1914.
Ribbon: Dark blue with two white stripes towards the centre.
Metal: Silver.
Size: 36mm.
Description: (Obverse) the sovereign's effigy; (reverse) a crowned wreath inscribed FOR DISTINGUISHED SERVICE.
Comments: *Awarded to petty officers and ratings of the Royal Navy, NCOs and other ranks of the Royal Marines and all other persons holding corresponding ranks or positions in the naval forces, for acts of bravery in face of the enemy not sufficiently meritorious to make them eligible for the CGM. It was later extended to cover the Merchant Navy and Army, the WRNS and RAF personnel serving aboard ships in the Second World War. Of particular interest and desirability are medals awarded for outstanding actions, e.g. Jutland, Q-Ships, the Murmansk convoys, the Yangtze incident and the Falklands War. First World War bars for subsequent awards are dated on the reverse, but Second World War bars are undated. As a result of the 1993 Review of gallantry awards and resultant changes to the operational gallantry award system, this award has been replaced by the DSC which is now available* both *to officers and other ranks.*

VALUE:

		Miniature
George V uncrowned head 1914-30 (4100)	£450–1000	£15–18
George VI IND IMP 1938-49 (7100)	£450–750	£10–15
George VI 2nd type 1949-53	£1200–2000	£10–15
Elizabeth II BR OMN 1953-7	£2000–3000	£8–10
Elizabeth II 2nd type	£2000–4000	£8–10

55. MILITARY MEDAL

Instituted: 25 March 1916.
Ribbon: Broad dark blue edges flanking a central section of three narrow white and two narrow crimson stripes.
Metal: Silver.
Size: 36mm.
Description: (Obverse) the sovereign's effigy—six types; (reverse) the crowned royal cypher above the inscription FOR BRAVERY IN THE FIELD, enclosed in a wreath.
Comments: *Awarded to NCOs and men of the Army (including RFC and RND) for individual or associated acts of bravery not of sufficient heroism as to merit the DCM. In June 1916 it was extended to women, two of the earliest awards being to civilian ladies for their conduct during the Easter Rising in Dublin that year. Some 115,600 medals were awarded during the First World War alone, together with 5796 first bars, 180 second bars and 1 third bar. Over 15,000 medals were conferred during the Second World War, with 177 first bars and 1 second bar. About 300 medals and 4 first bars were awarded for bravery in minor campaigns between the two world wars, while some 932 medals and 8 first bars have been conferred since 1947. As a result of the 1993 Review of gallantry awards and resultant changes to the operational gallantry award system, this award has been replaced by the MC which is now available* both *to officers and other ranks.*

VALUE:

		Miniature
George V uncrowned head 1916-30		
Corps/RA—single	£150–180*	£10–12
in group	£180–200	
Regiment—single	£200–240	
in group	£260–350	
named to a woman	£800–1500	
George V crowned head 1930-38	£2500–4000	£15–20
George VI IND IMP 1938-48	£750–1200	£8–10
George VI 2nd type 1948-53	£1200–2000	£8–10
Elizabeth II BR: OMN 1953-8	£2500–3000	£8–10
Elizabeth II 2nd type	£2500–6000	£8–10

*Groups to RFC and RND will be considerably higher.

56. DISTINGUISHED FLYING MEDAL

Instituted: 1918.

Ribbon: Originally purple and white horizontal stripes but since 1919 thirteen narrow diagonal stripes alternationg white and purple.

Metal: Silver.

Size: 42mm tall; 34mm wide.

Description: An oval medal, (obverse) the sovereign's effigy; (reverse) Athena Nike seated on an aeroplane, with a hawk rising from her hand. Originally undated, but the date 1918 was added to the reverse with the advent of the George VI obverse. The medal is suspended by a pair of wings from a straight bar.

Comments: *Introduced at the same time as the DFC, it was awarded to NCOs and men of the RAF for courage or devotion to duty while flying on active operations against the enemy. During the Second World War it was extended to the equivalent ranks of the Army and Fleet Air Arm personnel engaged in similar operations. First World War medals have the names of recipients impressed in large seriffed lettering, whereas Second World War medals are rather coarsely engraved. Approximately 150 medals have been awarded since 1945. As a result of the 1993 Review of gallantry awards and resultant changes to the operational gallantry award system, this award has been replaced by the DFC which is now available both to officers and other ranks.*

Example of WWI impressed naming

WWII engraved naming

VALUE:

		Miniature
George V uncrowned head 1918-30 (105)	£1200–2000	£15–18
George V crowned head 1930-38	£2500–3500	£25–30
George VI IND IMP 1938-49 (6500)	£900–2000	£8–10
George VI 2nd type 1949-53	£2000–2500	£8–10
Elizabeth II	£2000–2750	£8–10

(in silver add £5)

57. AIR FORCE MEDAL

Instituted: 1918.

Ribbon: Originally horizontal narrow stripes of white and crimson but since July 1919 diagonal narrow stripes of the same colours.

Metal: Silver.

Size: 42mm tall; 32mm wide.

Description: An oval medal with a laurel border. (Obverse) the sovereign's effigy; (reverse) Hermes mounted on a hawk bestowing a laurel wreath. The medal is suspended by a pair of wings from a straight bar, like the DFM.

Comments: *Instituted at the same time as the AFC, it was awarded to NCOs and men of the RAF for courage or devotion to duty while flying, but not on active operations against the enemy. About 100 medals and 2 first bars were awarded during the First World War, 106 medals and 3 bars between the wars and 259 medals during the Second World War. After the 1993 Review of gallantry awards the AFM was discontinued; the AFC is now available both to officers and other ranks.*

VALUE:

		Miniature
George V uncrowned head 1918-30	£1000–1400	£12–15
George V crowned head 1930-38	£2000–3000	£20–25
George VI IND IMP 1939-49	£1000–1200	£8–10
George VI 2nd type 1949-53	£1000–1200	£8–10
Elizabeth II	£1000–1200	£8–10

(in silver add £5)

58. CONSTABULARY MEDAL (IRELAND)

1st type obv.

Instituted: 1842.

Ribbon: Originally light blue, but changed to green in 1872.

Metal: Silver.

Size: 36mm.

Description: (Obverse) a crowned harp within a wreath of oak leaves and shamrocks, with REWARD OF MERIT round the top and IRISH CONSTABULARY round the foot. In the first version the front of the harp took the form of a female figure but later variants had a plain harp and the shape of the crown and details of the wreath were also altered. These changes theoretically came in 1867 when the Constabulary acquired the epithet Royal, which was then added to the inscription round the top, although some medals issued as late as 1921 had the pre-1867 title. (Reverse) a wreath of laurel and shamrock, within which are engraved the recipient's name, rank, number, date and sometimes the location of the action.

Comments: *Originally awarded for gallantry and meritorious service by members of the Irish Constabulary. From 1872, however, it was awarded only for gallantry. It was first conferred in 1848 and became obsolete in 1922 when the Irish Free State was established. Bars for second awards were authorised in 1920. About 315 medals and 7 bars were awarded (or, in some cases, second medals—the records are inconclusive), mostly for actions in connection with the Easter Rising of 1916 (23) or the subsequent Anglo-Irish War of 1920 (180) and 1921 (55).*

2nd type obv.

VALUE:		Miniature
First type	Rare	—
Second type	£800–1200	£150–200

59. INDIAN POLICE MEDAL

1st type

Instituted: 23 February 1932.

Ribbon: Crimson flanked by bands of dark blue and silver grey. From 1942 onwards an additional silver stripe appeared in the centre of the ribbon intended for the gallantry medal.

Metal: Bronze.

Size: 36mm.

Description: (Obverse) the King Emperor; (reverse) a crowned wreath inscribed INDIAN POLICE, with the words FOR DISTINGUISHED CONDUCT across the centre. In December 1944 the reverse was re-designed in two types, with the words FOR GALLANTRY or FOR MERITORIOUS SERVICE in place of the previous legend.

Comments: *Intended for members of the Indian police forces and fire brigades as a reward for gallantry or meritorious service. The medal became obsolete in 1950 when India became a republic.*

VALUE:		Miniature
George V	£200–300	£20–25
George VI Distinguished Conduct	£250–300	£20–25
George VI for Gallantry	£300–400	£20–25
George VI for Meritorious Service	£200–300	£20–25

2nd type (after 1944)

60. BURMA POLICE MEDAL

Instituted: 14 December 1937.
Ribbon: A wide central blue stripe flanked by broad black stripes and white edges.
Metal: Bronze.
Size: 36mm.
Description: (Obverse) the effigy of George VI; (reverse) similar to the Indian medal (first type)and inscribed FOR DISTINGUISHED CONDUCT, irrespective of whether awarded for gallantry or distinguished service.
Comments: *Introduced following the separation of Burma from India, it was abolished in 1948. All ranks of the police, frontier force and fire brigades, both European and Burmese, were eligible.*

VALUE:		MIniature
For Gallantry (53)	£750–1000	£20–25
For Meritorious Service (80)	£600–800	£10–15

61. COLONIAL POLICE MEDAL

Instituted: 10 May 1938.
Ribbon: Blue with green edges and a thin silver stripe separating the colours, but the gallantry award had an additional thin red line through the centre of each green edge stripe.
Metal: Silver.
Size: 36mm.
Description: (Obverse) the sovereign's effigy; (reverse) a policeman's truncheon superimposed on a laurel wreath. The left side of the circumference is inscribed COLONIAL POLICE FORCES and the right either FOR GALLANTRY or FOR MERITORIOUS SERVICE.
Comments: *Intended to reward all ranks of the police throughout the Empire for acts of conspicuous bravery or for meritorious service. The number to be issued was limited to 150 in any one year. Only 450 were awarded for gallantry, whilst almost 3000 were issued for meritorious service.*

VALUE:		Miniature
George VI GRI for Gallantry	£600–1200	£10–12
George VI GRI for Meritorious Service	£280–350	£12–15
George VI GVIR for Gallantry	£700–1000	£12–15
George VI GVIR for Meritorious Service	£280–350	£12–15
Elizabeth II 1st type for Gallantry	£700–1000	£15–20
Elizabeth II 1st type for Meritorious Service	£280–350	£15–20
Elizabeth II 2nd type for Gallantry	£700–1000	£15–20
Elizabeth II 2nd type for Meritorious Service	£280–350	£15–20

62. COLONIAL FIRE BRIGADE MEDAL

Instituted: 10 May 1938.
Ribbon: As above.
Metal: Silver.
Size: 36mm.
Description: (Obverse) the effigy of the reigning sovereign; (reverse) a fireman's helmet and axe, with the inscription COLONIAL FIRE BRIGADES FOR GALLANTRY or FOR MERITORIOUS SERVICE.
Comments: *As No. 59 this medal was intended to reward all ranks of the Colonial fire brigades but very few were awarded for gallantry.*

VALUE:		Miniature
George VI GRI for Gallantry	Rare	£12–15
George VI GRI for Meritorious Service	Rare	£12–15
George VI GVIR for Gallantry	Rare	£12–15
George VI GVIR for Meritorious Service	£300–500	£12–15
Elizabeth II 1st type for Gallantry	From £750	£10–12
Elizabeth II 1st type for Meritorious Service	£300–500	£10–12
Elizabeth II 2nd type for Gallantry	£400–600	£10–12
Elizabeth II 2nd type for Meritorious Service	£250–350	£10–12

63. QUEEN'S GALLANTRY MEDAL

Instituted: 20 June 1974.
Ribbon: Blue with a central pearl-grey stripe bisected by a narrow rose-pink stripe.
Metal: Silver.
Size: 36mm.
Description: (Obverse) the Queen's effigy; (reverse) an imperial crown above THE QUEEN'S GALLANTRY MEDAL flanked by laurel sprigs.
Comments: *Awarded for exemplary acts of bravery. Although intended primarily for civilians, it is also awarded to members of the armed forces for actions which would not be deemed suitable for a military decoration. With the introduction of the QGM the gallantry awards in the Order of the British Empire came to an end. To date, about 1,000 QGMs have been awarded, including 18 bars. A bar is added for a second award. A post-1990 SAS QGM and bar group sold at a recent auction for £26,000.*

VALUE: *Miniature*
    Service award   £1400–2000   £10–12
    Civilian award   £600–800

64. ALLIED SUBJECTS' MEDAL

Instituted: November 1920.
Ribbon: Bright red with a light blue centre, flanked by narrow stripes of yellow, black and white (thus incorporating the Belgian and French national colours).
Metal: Silver or bronze.
Size: 36mm.
Description: (Obverse) the effigy of King George V; (reverse) designed by Edmund Dulac, the female allegory of Humanity offering a cup to a British soldier resting on the ground, with ruined buildings in the background.
Comment: *Shortly after the cessation of the First World War it was proposed that services rendered to the Allied cause, specifically by those who had helped British prisoners of war to escape, should be rewarded by a medal. The decision to go ahead was delayed on account of disagreement between the War Office and the Foreign Office, but eventually the first awards were announced in November 1920, with supplementary lists in 1921 and 1922. Medals were issued unnamed and almost half of the total issue, namely 56 silver and 247 bronze medals, were issued to women.*

VALUE: *Miniature*
    Silver (134)   £500–700   £35–40
    Bronze (574)   £300–400   £40–45

NB These prices are for unattributable awards.

65. KING'S MEDAL FOR COURAGE IN THE CAUSE OF FREEDOM

Instituted: 23 August 1945
Ribbon: White with two narrow dark blue stripes in the centre and broad red stripes at the edges.
Metal: Silver.
Size: 36mm.
Description: (Obverse) the crowned profile of King George VI; (reverse) inscribed, within a chain link, THE KING'S MEDAL FOR COURAGE IN THE CAUSE OF FREEDOM.
Comments: *Introduced to acknowledge acts of courage by foreign civilians or members of the armed services "in the furtherance of the British Commonwealth in the Allied cause" during the Second World War. Like its First World War counterpart, it was intended mainly to reward those who had assisted British escapees in enemy-occupied territories. About 3200 medals were issued, commencing in 1947.*

VALUE: £250–300 (unattributable)   *Miniature* £30–40

66. KING'S MEDAL FOR SERVICE IN THE CAUSE OF FREEDOM

Instituted: 23 August 1945.
Ribbon: White with a central red bar flanked by dark blue stripes.
Metal: Silver.
Size: 36mm.
Description: (Obverse) effigy of King George VI; (reverse) a medieval warrior in armour carrying a broken lance, receiving nourishment from a female.
Comments: *Introduced at the same time as the foregoing, it was intended for foreign civilians who had helped the Allied cause in other less dangerous ways, such as fund-raising and organising ambulance services. 2490 medals were issued.*

VALUE:	£200–250 (unattributable)	*Miniature*	£15–20

67. SEA GALLANTRY MEDAL

Instituted: 1855, under the Merchant Shipping Acts of 1854 and 1894.
Ribbon: Bright red with narrow white stripes towards the edges.
Metal: Silver or bronze.
Size: 58mm or 33mm.
Description: (Obverse) Profile of Queen Victoria; (reverse) a family on a storm-tossed shore reviving a drowning sailor. Both obverse and reverse were sculpted by Bernard Wyon.
Comments: *Exceptionally, this group of medals was authorised not by Royal Warrant but by Parliamentary legislation, under the terms of the Merchant Shipping Acts of 1854 and 1894. The 1854 Act made provision for monetary rewards for life saving at sea, but in 1855 this was transmuted into medals, in gold, silver or bronze, in two categories, for gallantry (where the rescuer placed his own life at risk) and for humanity (where the risks were minimal). The gold medal, if ever awarded, must have been of the greatest rarity. These medals, issued by the Board of Trade, were 58mm in diameter and not intended for wearing. The only difference between the medals lay in the wording of the inscription round the circumference of the obverse. In 1903 Edward VII ordered that the medal be reduced to 1.27 inches (33mm) in diameter and fitted with a suspension bar and ribbon for wearing. Both large and small medals were always issued with a minimum of the recipient's name and date of issue round the rim. The last medal was awarded in 1980. Only one second award clasp has ever been issued—that to Ch.Off James Whiteley in 1921.*

VALUE:

	Silver	Bronze	*Miniature*
Victoria Gallantry	£400–500	£300–400	£100–150
Victoria Humanity (to 1893)	Rare	Rare	
Edward VII Gallantry (large)	£1400–1800	£1200–1400	
Edward VII Gallantry (small)	£450–600	£400–450	£100–150
Edward VII (2nd small type)	£450–600	£400–450	
George V	£350–450	£250–400	£50–75
George VI 1st type	Rare	Rare	
George VI 2nd type	—	Rare	
Elizabeth II	Rare	Rare	

68. SEA GALLANTRY MEDAL (FOREIGN SERVICES)

Instituted: 1841.

Ribbon: Plain crimson till 1922; thereafter the same ribbon as the SGM above.

Metal: Gold, silver or bronze.

Size: 36mm or 33mm.

Description: The large medal had Victoria's effigy (young head) on the obverse, but there were five reverse types showing a crowned wreath with PRESENTED BY (or FROM) THE BRITISH GOVERNMENT inside the wreath. Outside the wreath were the following variants:

1. Individually struck inscriptions (1841-49 but sometimes later).
2. FOR SAVING THE LIFE OF A BRITISH SUBJECT (1849-54)
3. FOR ASSISTING A BRITISH VESSEL IN DISTRESS (1849-54)
4. FOR SAVING THE LIVES OF BRITISH SUBJECTS (1850-54)

There are also unissued specimens or patterns with a Latin inscription within the wreath VICTORIA REGINA CUDI JUSSIT MDCCCXLI.

The small medal, intended for wear, has five obverse types combined with four reverse types: as 2 above (1854-1906), as 3 above (1854-1896), as 4 above (1854-1926), or FOR GALLANTRY AND HUMANITY (1858 to the present day).

Comments: *Although intended to reward foreigners who rendered assistance to British subjects in distress some early awards were actually made for rescues on dry land. Originally a special reverse was struck for each incident, but this was found to be unnecessarily expensive, so a standard reverse was devised in 1849. Medals before 1854 had a diameter of 45mm and were not fitted with suspension. After 1854 the diameter was reduced to 33mm and scrolled suspension bars were fitted. Of the large medals about 100 gold, 120 silver and 14 bronze were issued, while some 10 gold and 24 bronze specimens have been recorded.*

Type 4 rev.

VALUE:

	Gold	Silver	Bronze
Victoria large	Rare	£400–500	£400–500
Victoria small	£1000–1200	£250–350	—
Edward VII	£1000–1500	£400–500	—
George V	£1000–1200	£250–350	—
George VI	—	Rare	—
Elizabeth II	Rare	Rare	—
Miniature			£60–80

69. BRITISH NORTH BORNEO COMPANY'S BRAVERY CROSS

Instituted: 1890 by the British North Borneo Company.

Ribbon: Yellow watered silk.

Metal: Silver or bronze.

Size: 36mm.

Description: The cross pattée has a central medallion bearing a lion passant gardant with the Company motto PERGO ET PERAGO (I carry on and accomplish) within a garter. The arms of the cross are inscribed BRITISH NORTH BORNEO with FOR BRAVERY in the lower limb.

Comments: *Both silver and bronze crosses were manufactured by Joseph Moore of Birmingham. Both silver and bronze medals were issued unnamed. The only genuine striking of silver medals bears the Birmingham hallmark for 1890. Examples with the word STERLING on the reverse are modern copies. The reverse of the bronze medal is smooth, with no marks.*

VALUE:

Silver	£300–350
Bronze	£150–200

70. KING'S MEDAL FOR NATIVE CHIEFS

Instituted: 1920.
Ribbon: Yellow with two white central stripes (silver-gilt) or a single white stripe (silver).
Metal: Silver or silver-gilt.
Size: 40mm x 34mm (oval) or 36mm (circular).
Description: Originally an oval badge with collar. (Obverse) the crowned effigy of the monarch; (reverse) a warship, symbolic of imperial power.

Comments: *Various large silver medals were struck for award to native chiefs in various parts of the world, from the eighteenth century onwards, and of these the awards to American Indian chiefs are probably the best known. In 1920, however, a standard King's Medal for Chiefs was instituted. It was awarded exceptionally in silver-gilt (first class), and usually in silver (second class). The oval medal was worn round the neck from a silver collar. The more modern issues, however, are smaller and intended for wear with a ribbon from the breast. The medal is normally returned on the death of the recipient.*

VALUE:	Silver-gilt	Silver
George V		
First (couped) type	£800–1000	£700–800
Second (larger bust) type	£750–1000	£650–750
George VI	£800–1000	£500–600
Elizabeth II		
First type	£800–1000	£600–700
Second (small) type	£250–300	£200–250

Mentions and Commendations

A description of the various emblems denoting Mentions in Despatches and King's (or later Queen's) Commendations was published as a Supplement to the *London Gazette,* July 27, 1951. A special clasp to signify a Mention in Despatches was instituted during the First World War and continued to be awarded for active service up to August 10, 1920. It was worn on the ribbon of the Victory Medal (no. 170) and consisted of a bronze spray of oak leaves.

For Mentions in Despatches after August 10, 1920, or a King's Commendation for brave conduct or valuable service in the air, a bronze emblem consisting of a single oak leaf was worn on the appropriate medal ribbon, either a General Service Medal or the War Medal, 1939–45. King's or Queen's Commendations for brave conduct or valuable service in the air, in cases where no campaign or war medal was awarded, were worn on the breast in the position where an appropriate medal ribbon would have been worn, generally on the uniform tunic after any medal ribbons.

King's or Queen's Commendations in respect of bravery, granted to civilians for acts during or since the Second World War, are denoted by a silver emblem in the form of a spray of laurel leaves (this was originally a plastic oval badge). For service during the Second World War this emblem was worn on the ribbon of the Defence Medal (no. 185). Where no medal was awarded, it was sewn directly on to the coat, after any medal ribbons.

For civilians the King's or Queen's Commendation for Valuable Service in the Air, during the Second World War and subsequently, consisted of an oval silver badge, worn on the coat below any medals or medal ribbons, or in civil airline uniform, on the panel of the left breast pocket.

The emblems denoting Mentions and Commendations were revised on August 12, 1994, as shown in the table below.

Mention in Despatches emblem 1914-1920

Mention in Despatches emblem 1920–94

FOR GALLANTRY			FOR VALUABLE SERVICE
IN ACTION WITH THE ENEMY (ALL ENVIRONMENTS)	NOT IN ACTION WITH THE ENEMY or OUT OF THEATRE (EXCEPT FLYING)	NOT IN ACTION WITH THE ENEMY or OUT OF THEATRE (FLYING)	IN-THEATRE BUT NOT IN ACTION WITH THE ENEMY
MENTION IN DESPATCHES	QUEEN'S COMMENDATION FOR BRAVERY	QUEEN'S COMMENDATION FOR BRAVERY IN THE AIR	QUEEN'S COMMENDATION FOR VALUABLE SERVICE
A single oak leaf in SILVER	A spray of laurel leaves in SILVER	A new emblem in SILVER	A spray of oak leaves in SILVER

ROMSEY MEDALS

MEMBERS OF THE O.M.R.S. and L.A.P.A.D.A.

Gallantry and Campaign Medals
urgently required,
Singles and collections.
Medals must be in good condition
and correctly named

Why not visit our showroom,
open by appointment only

Alternatively an enquiry or wants list will be dealt
with on a personal basis

Medal Consultant James R. Bullock
Proprietor Trevor R. Cambridge

**PO Box 169, Romsey
SO51 6XU
Tel: 01794 324488 (day), 01794 322125 (eves.)
Fax: 01794 324411
E-mail: post@romseymedals.co.uk
Web site www.romseymedals.co.uk**

Campaign medals

The evolution of medals struck to commemorate, and later to reward participants in, a battle or campaign was a very gradual process. The forerunner of the modern campaign medal was the Armada Medal, cast in gold or silver, which appears to have been awarded to naval officers and distinguished persons after the abortive Spanish invasion of 1588. The obverse bears a flattering portrait of Queen Elizabeth (thought to have been designed by Nicholas Hilliard, the celebrated miniaturist) with a Latin inscription signifying "enclosing the most precious treasure in the world" (i.e. the Queen herself). On the reverse, the safety of the kingdom is represented by a bay tree growing on a little island, immune from the flashes of lightning which seem to strike it. This medal, and a similar type depicting the Ark floating calmly on a stormy sea, bore loops at the top so that a chain or cord could be passed through it for suspension from the neck of the recipient.

The Civil War produced a number of gallantry medals, mentioned in the previous section; but in 1650 Parliament authorised a medal which was struck in silver, bronze or lead to celebrate Cromwell's miraculous victory over the Scots at Dunbar. This was the first medal granted to all the participants on the Parliamentary side, and not restricted to high-ranking officers, or given for individual acts of heroism.

The Dunbar Medal thus established several useful precedents, which were eventually to form the criteria of the campaign medal as we know it today. After this promising start, however, the pattern of medals and their issue were much more restrictive. Naval medals were struck in gold for award to admirals and captains during the First Dutch War (1650–53), while the battle of Culloden (1746) was marked by a medal portraying the "Butcher" Duke of Cumberland, and granted to officers who took part in the defeat of the Jacobites.

In the second half of the eighteenth century there were a number of medals, but these were of a private or semi-official nature. The Honourable East India Company took the lead in awarding medals to its troops. These medals were often struck in two sizes and in gold as well as silver, for award to different ranks. The siege of Gibraltar (1779–83) was marked by an issue of medals to the defenders, but this was made on the initiative (and at the expense) of the garrison commanders, Generals Eliott and Picton, themselves.

During the French Revolutionary and Napoleonic Wars several medals were produced by private individuals for issue to combatants. Alexander Davison and Matthew Boulton were responsible for the medals granted to the officers and men who fought the battles of the Nile (1798) and Trafalgar (1805). Davison also produced a Trafalgar medal in pewter surrounded by a copper rim; it is recorded that the seamen who received it were so disgusted at the base metal that they threw it into the sea! At the same time, however, Government

recognition was given to senior officers who had distinguished themselves in certain battles and engagements and a number of gold medals were awarded. The events thus marked included the capture of Ceylon (1795–96) and the battles of Maida, Bagur and Palamos.

Towards the end of the Napoleonic Wars an Army Gold Medal was instituted in two sizes—large (generals) and small (field officers). Clasps for second and third battles and campaigns were added to the medal, but when an officer became eligible for a third clasp the medal was exchanged for a Gold Cross with the names of the four battles engraved on its arms. Clasps for subsequent campaigns were then added to the cross (the Duke of Wellington receiving the Gold Cross with nine clasps). A total of 163 crosses, 85 large and 599 small medals was awarded, so that, apart from their intrinsic value, these decorations command very high prices when they appear in the saleroom.

The first medal awarded to all ranks of the Army was the Waterloo Medal, issued in 1816 shortly after the battle which brought the Napoleonic Wars to an end. No action was taken to grant medals for the other campaigns in the Napoleonic Wars until 1847 when Military and Naval General Service Medals were awarded retrospectively to veterans who were then still alive. As applications were made, in some cases, in respect of campaigns more than fifty years earlier, it is hardly surprising that the number of medals awarded was comparatively small, while the number of clasps awarded for certain engagements was quite minute. The Military General Service Medal was restricted to land campaigns during the Peninsular War (1808–13), the American War (1812–14) and isolated actions in the West Indies, Egypt and Java, whereas the Naval GSM covered a far longer period, ranging from the capture of the French frigate La Cleopatra by HMS Nymphe in June 1793, to the naval blockade of the Syrian coast in 1840,

111

during the British operations against Mehemet Ali. Thus Naval Medals with the clasp for Syria are relatively plentiful (7057 awarded) while in several cases clasps were awarded to one man alone, and in seven cases there were no claimants for clasps at all. It is worth bearing in mind that applications for the medals and clasps resulted mainly from the publicity given by printed advertisements and notices posted up all over the country. With the poor general standard of literacy prevalent at the time, many people who were entitled to the medals would have been quite unaware of their existence.

The Naming of Medals

The Military and Naval GSMs, with their multitudinous combinations of clasps, have long been popular with collectors, but the other campaign medals of the past century and a half have a strong following as well. With the exception of the stars and medals awarded during the Second World War, all British campaign medals have usually borne the name of the recipient and usually his (or her) number, rank and regiment, unit or ship as well. This brings a personal element into the study of medals which is lacking in most other branches of numismatics. The name on a medal is very important for two reasons. It is a means of testing the genuineness, not only of the medal itself, but its bar combination, and secondly it enables the collector to link the medal not only with the man who earned it, but with his unit or formation, and thus plays a vital part in the development of naval or military history, if only a small part in most cases.

Much of the potential value of a medal depends on the man who won it, or the unit to which he belonged. To form a coherent collection as opposed to a random accumulation of medals, the collector would be well advised to specialise in some aspect of the subject, restricting his interests perhaps to one medal (the Naval GSM) or a single group (British campaigns in India), or to medals awarded to the men of a particular regiment. The information given on the rim or back of a medal is therefore important in helping to identify it and assign it to its correct place. Even this has to be qualified to some extent. Some regiments are more popular than others with collectors and much depends on the part, active or passive, played by a unit in a particular battle or campaign for which the medal was awarded. Then again, the combination of event with the corps or regiment of the recipient must also be considered.

At one extreme we find the Royal Regiment of Artillery living up to its motto *Ubique* (everywhere) by being represented in virtually every land action (and not a few naval actions, as witness the Atlantic Star worn by former Maritime Gunners), so that a comprehensive collection of medals awarded to the RA would be a formidable feat.

At the other extreme one finds odd detachments, sometimes consisting of one or two men only, seconded from a regiment for service with another unit. The Indian GSM, with bar for Hazara (1891), is usually found named to personnel of the 11th Bengal Lancers and various battalions of the Bengal Infantry, but according to the medal rolls it was also given to six men of the 2nd Manchester Regiment, two men of the Queen's Regiment and one each to troopers of the 2nd and 7th Dragoon Guards. Whereas a specimen of the IGS medal with this bar is not hard to find named to a soldier in one of the Bengal units, it constitutes a major rarity when awarded to one of the "odd men" and its value is correspondingly high.

As the personal details given on a medal regarding the recipient are so important, it is necessary for the collector to verify two facts—that the person whose name is on the medal was actually present at the action for which either the medal or its bars were awarded, and secondly, that the naming of the bar and the attachment of the bars is correct and not tampered with in any way. As regards the first, the Public Record Office at Kew, London is a goldmine of information for all naval and military campaigns. Apart from despatches, reports and muster rolls covering the actions, there are the medal rolls compiled from the applications for medals and bars. Transcriptions of the medal rolls are held by regimental museums and also by such bodies as the Military Historical Association and the Orders and Medals Research Society. Details of these and other clubs and societies devoted to medal collecting can be found in the later chapters.

The presence of a name on the roll does not mean that a medal or clasp was inevitably awarded; conversely authenticated medals are known to exist named to persons not listed on the medal roll. There are often divergences between the muster and medal rolls. Moreover, discrepancies in the spelling of recipients' names are not uncommon and bars are sometimes found listed for regiments which were not even in existence when the battle was fought! This is explained, however, by the fact that a man may have been serving with one unit which took part in the campaign and subsequently transferred to another regiment. When claiming his medal he probably gave his *present* unit, rather than the one in which he was serving at the time of the action.

Unfortunately cases of medals having been tampered with are by no means rare, so it is necessary to be able to recognise evidence of fakery. A favourite device of the faker is to alter the name and personal details of the recipient and to substitute another name in order to enhance the medal's value. This is done simply by filing the inscription off the rim and adding a new one. In order to check for such alterations a similar medal of proven genuineness should be compared with a pair of fine callipers. Take the measurements at several points round the rim so that any unevenness should soon be apparent.

We cannot stress too much the importance of being closely familiar with the various styles of naming medals. Over the past 150 years an incredible variety of lettering—roman, italic, script, sans-serif, seriffed in all shapes and sizes—has been used at one time or another. In some cases the inscription was applied by impressing in raised relief; in others the inscription was punched in or engraved by hand. If a medal is normally impressed and you come across an engraved example you should immediately be on your guard. This is not an infallible test, however, as medals have been known with more than one style of naming, particularly if duplicates were issued at a much later date to replace medals lost or destroyed.

A rather more subtle approach was adopted by some fakers in respect of the Naval GSM. The three commonest clasps—*Algiers* (1362), *Navarino* (1137) and *Syria* (7057)—were awarded to many recipients possessing common names such as Jones or Smith which can be matched with recipients of some very rare clasps. In the case of the Naval GSM the ship on which the recipient served is not given, thus aiding the fraudulent substitution of clasps. It is necessary, therefore, to check the condition of clasps, even if the naming appears to be correct. Points to watch for are file or solder marks on the rivets which secure the clasps to each other and to the suspender of the medal. This test is not infallible as clasps *do* occasionally work loose if subject to constant wear (particularly if the recipient was a cavalryman, for obvious reasons). But clasps whose rivets appear to have been hammered should automatically be suspect, until a check of the medal rolls pass them as authentic. Examples of the earlier medals, particularly those awarded to officers, may be found with unorthodox coupling. Major L. L. Gordon, in his definitive work *British Battles and Medals*, mentions a Naval GSM awarded to one of his ancestors, with clasps for *Guadaloupe* and *Anse la Barque* in a large rectangular style which must have been unofficial. The medal is quite authentic, so it must be presumed that officers were allowed a certain degree of latitude in the manner in which they altered their medals.

Medals with clasps awarded for participation in subsequent engagements are invariably worth much more than the basic medal. In general, the greater number of clasps, the more valuable the medal, although, conversely, there are a few instances in which single-clasp medals are scarcer than twin-clasp medals. There is no short answer to this and individual rare clasps can enhance the value of an otherwise common medal out of all proportion. Thus the Naval GSM with clasp for *Syria* currently rates £350–400, but one of the two medals known to have been issued with the *Acheron* clasp of 1805 would easily rate twelve times as much. Again, relative value can only be determined by reference to all the circumstances of the award.

The person to whom a medal was issued has considerable bearing on its value. If the recipient belonged to a regiment which played a spectacular part in a battle, this generally rates a premium. The rank of the recipient also has some bearing; in general the higher the rank, the more valuable the medal. Medals to commissioned officers rate more than those awarded to NCOs and other ranks, and the medals of British servicemen rate more as a rule than those awarded to native troops. Medals granted to women usually command a relatively good premium. Another grim aspect is that medals issued to personnel who were wounded or killed in the campaign also rate more highly than those issued to servicemen who came through unscathed.

With the collector of British campaign medals the person to whom the medal was awarded tends to become almost as important as the medal itself. It is often not sufficient to collect the medal and leave it at that. The collector feels that he must investigate it and delve into the archives to find out all that he can about the recipient. The Public Record Office and regimental museums have already been mentioned, but do not overlook the usefulness of such reference tools as the monumental Mormon International Genealogical Index (now on microfiche and available in good public libraries and county record offices). All of these should help you to flesh out the bare bones of the details given in the muster and medal rolls.

Medal Groups

Apart from the combination of clasps on a medal and the significance of the recipient, there is a third factor to be considered in assessing the value of medals, namely the relationship of one medal to another in a group awarded to one person. Just as the number of clasps on a medal is not in itself a significant factor, so also the number of medals in a group is not necessarily important *per se*. Groups of five or more medals, whose recipient can be identified, are by no means uncommon. For example, a fairly common five medal group would consist of 1914–15 Medal, War Medal and Victory Medal (for the First World War) and the Defence Medal and War Medal (for the Second World War). Thousands of men served throughout the first war to do duty, in a less active role, during a part at least of the second, long enough to qualify for the latter pair of medals.

It should be noted that none of the medals awarded for service in the Second World War was named to the recipient, so that groups comprising such medals alone cannot be readily identified and are thus lacking in the interest possessed by those containing named medals. Six-medal groups for service in the Second World War are not uncommon, particularly the combination of 1939–45 Star, Africa Star, Italy Star, France and Germany Star, Defence Medal and War Medal awarded to Army personnel who served from any time up to late 1942 and took part in the campaigns of North Africa and Europe.

Conversely it would be possible for troops to have served over a longer period and seen more action, and only been awarded the 1939–45 Star, Burma Star (with Pacific bar) and the War Medal. Naval groups consisting of the 1939–45 Star, Atlantic Star (with bar for France and Germany), Italy Star and War Medal are less common and therefore more desirable (with, of course, the rider that it must be possible to identify the recipient), while the most desirable of all is the three-medal group of 1939–45 Star (with Battle of Britain bar), Air Crew Europe Star (with bar for France and Germany) and the War Medal. Such a group, together with a Distinguished Flying Cross awarded to one of The Few, is a highly coveted set indeed, providing, as always, that one can prove its authenticity. In any event, the addition of a named medal to a Second World War group (e.g. a long service award, a gallantry medal, or some other category of medal named to the recipient), together with supporting collateral material (citations, log-books, pay-books, service records, newspaper cuttings, etc), should help to establish the provenance of the group.

71. LOUISBURG MEDAL

Date: 1758.

Campaign: Canada (Seven Years War).

Branch of Service: British Army and Navy.

Ribbon: 32mm half yellow, half black, although not originally intended for wear and therefore not fitted with suspension or ribbon.

Metals: Gold, silver or bronze.

Size: 42mm.

Description: (Obverse) the globe surrounded by allegorical figures of victory and flanked by servicemen; (reverse) burning ships in the harbour.

Comments: *More in the nature of a decoration, this medal was only given to certain recipients for acts of bravery or distinguished service in the capture in July 1758 of Louisburg in Canada during the Seven Years War. James Wolfe and Jeffrey Amherst commanded the land forces and Edward Boscawen the fleet.*

VALUE:

Gold	Rare
Silver	£2000–4000
Bronze	£800–1100

72. CARIB WAR MEDAL

Date: 1773.

Campaign: Carib rebellion, St Vincent.

Branch of Service: Local militia or volunteers.

Ribbon: None.

Metal: Silver.

Size: 52mm.

Description: (Obverse) bust of George III in armour; (reverse) Britannia offering an olive branch to a defeated Carib, the date MDCCLXXIII in the exergue.

Comments: *The Legislative Assembly of St Vincent in the West Indies instituted this award to members of the militia and volunteers who served in the campaign of 1773 which put down a native rebellion that had been fomented by the French.*

VALUE:

Silver	£800–900

73. DECCAN MEDAL

Date: 1784.

Campaign: Western India and Gujerat 1778-84.

Branch of Service: HEIC forces.

Ribbon: Yellow cord.

Metals: Gold or silver.

Size: 40.5mm or 32mm.

Description: (Obverse) a rather languid Britannia with a trophy of arms, thrusting a laurel wreath towards a distant fort. (Reverse) an inscription in Farsi signifying "As coins are current in the world, so shall be the bravery and exploits of these heroes by whom the name of the victorious English nation was carried from Bengal to the Deccan. Presented in AH 1199 [1784] by the East India Company's Calcutta Government".

Comments: *The first medals struck by order of the Honourable East India Company were conferred on Indian troops for service in western India and Gujerat under the command of Warren Hastings. They were struck at Calcutta in two sizes; both gold and silver exist in the larger size but only silver medals in the smaller diameter.*

VALUE:

40.5mm gold	£4000–6000
40.5mm silver	£1200–1500
32mm silver	£650–850

74. DEFENCE OF GIBRALTAR

Date: 1783.

Eliott's medal   Picton's medal

Campaign: Siege of Gibraltar 1779-83.
Branch of Service: British and Hanoverian forces.
Ribbon: None.
Metal: Silver.
Size: 59mm (Picton) and 49mm (Eliott).
Description: Eliott's medal was confined to the Hanoverian troops, hence the reverse inscribed BRUDERSCHAFT (German for "brotherhood") above a wreath containing the names of the three Hanoverian commanders and General Eliott. The obverse, by Lewis Pingo, shows a view of the Rock and the naval attack of 13 September 1782 which was the climax of the siege. Picton's medal, awarded to the British forces, has a larger than usual diameter, with a map of the Rock on the obverse and a 22-line text—the most verbose British medal—above a recumbent lion clutching a shield bearing the castle and key emblem of Gibraltar on the reverse.
Comments: *Several medals of a private nature were struck to commemorate the defence of Gibraltar during the Franco-Spanish siege of 1779–83, but those most commonly encountered are the silver medals which were provided by George Augustus Eliott and Sir Thomas Picton, the military commanders.*

VALUE:

Picton medal	£450–550
Eliott medal	£400–500

75. MYSORE MEDAL

Date: 1792.
Campaign: Mysore 1790-92.
Branch of Service: HEIC forces.
Ribbon: Yellow cord.
Metal: Gold or silver.
Size: 43mm or 38mm.
Description: (Obverse) a sepoy of the HEIC Army holding British and Company flags over a trophy of arms with the fortress of Seringapatam in the background; (reverse) a bilingual inscription (in English and Farsi). The medal has a ring for suspension round the neck by a cord.
Comments: *Indian officers and men who served under Marquis Cornwallis and Generals Abercromby and Meadows received this medal for service in the campaign which brought about the downfall of Tippoo Sultan of Mysore.*

VALUE:

43mm gold (subadars)	£5000–7000
43mm silver (jemadars)	£1000–1200
38mm silver (other ranks)	£600–700

76. ST VINCENTS BLACK CORPS MEDAL

Date: 1795.
Campaign: Carib rebellion 1795.
Branch of Service: Local militia volunteers.
Ribbon: None.
Metal: Bronze.
Size: 48.5mm.
Description: (Obverse) the winged figure of Victory brandishing a sword over a fallen foe who has abandoned his musket; (reverse) native holding musket and bayonet, BOLD LOYAL OBEDIENT around and H.G.FEC. in exergue.
Comments: *Awarded to the officers and NCOs of the Corps of Natives raised by Major Seton from among the island's slaves for service against the rebellious Caribs and French forces.*

VALUE:

Bronze	Rare

77. CAPTURE OF CEYLON MEDAL

Date: 1796.
Campaign: Ceylon 1795.
Branch of Service: HEIC forces.
Ribbon: Yellow cord.
Metal: Gold or silver.
Size: 50mm.
Description: The plain design has an English inscription on the obverse, and the Farsi equivalent on the reverse.
Comments: *Awarded for service in the capture of Ceylon (Sri Lanka) from the Dutch during the French Revolutionary Wars. It is generally believed that the gold medals were awarded to Captains Barton and Clarke while the silver medals went to the native gunners of the Bengal Artillery.*

VALUE:

Gold (2)	—
Silver (121)	£750–850

78. DAVISON'S NILE MEDAL

Date: 1798.   **Campaign:** Battle of the Nile 1798.
Branch of Service: Royal Navy.
Ribbon: None, but unofficially 32mm, deep navy blue.
Metal: Gold, silver, gilt-bronze and bronze.   **Size:** 47mm.
Description: (Obverse) Peace caressing a shield decorated with the portrait of Horatio Nelson; (reverse) the British fleet at Aboukir Bay.
Comments: *Nelson's victory at the mouth of the Nile on 1 August 1798 was celebrated in a novel manner by his prize agent, Alexander Davison, whose name and London address appear in the edge inscription of the medal designed by Kuchler. Originally issued without a suspender, many recipients added a ring to enable the medal to be worn. Admiral Nelson's medal was stolen in 1900 and is believed to have been melted down. If it ever came on the market and proved to be genuine the price would undoubtedly be in the £40,000–50,000 price range. Prices quoted below are for unnamed specimens, contemporary engraved medals are usually worth about twice as much.*

VALUE:

Gold (Nelson and his captains)	£4000–6000	Gilt-bronze (petty officers)	£275–300
Silver (junior officers)	£500–600	Bronze (ratings)	£150–200

79. SERINGAPATAM MEDAL

Date: 1808.   **Campaign:** Seringapatam, India, 1799.
Branch of Service: HEIC forces.
Ribbon: 38mm gold.
Metal: Gold, silver-gilt, silver, bronze and pewter.   **Size:** 48mm or 45mm.
Description: (Obverse) the British lion defeating Tiger of Mysore (Tippoo Sultan) with the date of the capture of the fortress IV MAY MDCCXCIX (1799) in the exergue; (reverse) the assault on Seringapatam.
Comments: *The British and native troops who took part in the renewed campaign against Tippoo Sultan were awarded this medal in 1808 in various metals without suspension (a number of different types of suspenders and rings were subsequently fitted by individual recipients). The medal was designed by Kuchler and struck in England and Calcutta, the latter version being slightly smaller. There are several different strikings of these medals.*

VALUE:

Gold 48mm (113)	£3000–4000	Silver 45mm	£300–350
Gold 45mm	£2500–3000	Bronze 48mm (5000)	£200–240
Silver-gilt 48mm (185)	£500–550	Pewter 48mm (45,000)	£200–220
Silver 48mm (3636)	£450–500		

80. EARL ST. VINCENT'S MEDAL

Date: 1800.   **Campaign:** Mediterranean.
Branch of Service: Royal Navy.
Ribbon: None.
Metal: Gold or silver.   **Size:** 48mm.
Description: (Obverse) left-facing bust of the Earl in Admiral's uniform; (reverse) a sailor and marine.
Comments: *A private medal presented by Earl St Vincent, when he struck his flag and came ashore in 1800, to the petty officers and men of his flagship* Ville de Paris *as a token of appreciation to his old shipmates. Contemporary engraved and named pieces with researched provenance are worth at least twice as much as unnamed specimens.*

VALUE:
Gold	£3000–4000
Silver	£350–450

81. EGYPT MEDAL 1801

Date: 1801.   **Campaign:** Egypt 1801.
Branch of Service: HEIC forces.
Ribbon: Yellow cord.
Metal: Gold or silver.   **Size:** 48mm.
Description: (Obverse) a sepoy holding a Union Jack, with an encampment in the background. A four-line Farsi text occupies the exergue; (reverse) a warship and the Pyramids.
Comments: *Issued by the Honourable East India Company to British and Indian troops in the Company's service who took part in the conquest of Egypt under Generals Baird and Abercromby.*

VALUE:
Gold (16)	Rare
Silver (2200)	£600–700

82. SULTAN'S MEDAL FOR EGYPT

Date: 1801.
Campaign: Egypt 1801.
Branch of Service: British forces.
Ribbon: The gold medals were originally suspended by gold hook and chain as shown. The silver medals were hung from a sand-coloured ribbon.
Metals: Gold or silver.
Size: Various (see below).
Description: The very thin discs have an elaborate arabesque border enclosing the *toughra* or sign manual of the Sultan.
Comments: *This medal was conferred by Sultan Selim III of Turkey on the British officers and NCOs who took part in the campaign against the French. It was produced in five gold versions for award to different ranks of commissioned officers, as well as one in silver for award to sergeants and corporals.*

VALUE:

Gold 54mm studded with jewels	Rare
Gold 54mm plain	£3000–3500
Gold 48mm	£2000–2300
Gold 43mm	£1400–1600
Gold 36mm	£1000–1350
Silver 36mm	£600–700
Miniature	
Gold	£100–150
Silver	£50–80

83. HIGHLAND SOCIETY'S MEDAL FOR EGYPT 1801

Date: 1801.
Campaign: Egypt 1801.
Branch of Service: British forces.
Ribbon: None.
Metals: Gold, silver and bronze.
Size: 49mm.
Description: The medal was designed by Pidgeon. (Obverse) the right-facing bust of General Sir Ralph Abercromby, with a Latin inscription alluding to his death in Egypt; (reverse) a Highlander and the date 21 MAR. 1801 with the Gaelic inscription NA FIR A CHOISIN BUAIDH (These are the heroes who achieved victory in Egypt).
Comments: *The Highland and Agricultural Society (now Royal) was founded in 1784 to promote the development of agriculture in Scotland generally and the Highlands in particular. General Abercromby (born at Tullibody, 1734) commanded the British expedition to Egypt, and the landing at Aboukir Bay on 2 March 1801 in the face of strenuous French opposition, is justly regarded as one of the most brilliant and daring exploits of all time. The French made a surprise attack on the British camp on the night of 21 March and Abercromby was struck by a ricochet; he died aboard the flagship seven days later. Medals in gold were presented to the Prince Regent and Abercromby's sons, but silver and bronze medals were later struck and awarded to senior officers of the expedition as well as soldiers who had distinguished themselves in the campaign.*

VALUE:

Gold	—
Silver	£500–600
Bronze	£200–250

84. BOULTON'S TRAFALGAR MEDAL

Date: 1805.
Campaign: Battle of Trafalgar 1805.
Branch of Service: Royal Navy.
Ribbon: None, but unofficially 32mm navy blue (originally issued without suspension).
Metals: Gold, silver, white metal, gilt-bronze or bronze.   **Size:** 48mm.
Description: (Obverse) bust of Nelson; (reverse) a battle scene.
Comments: *Matthew Boulton of the Soho Mint, Birmingham, struck this medal on his own initiative for presentation to the survivors of the battle of Trafalgar. It was awarded in white metal, but bronze and gilt-bronze specimens also exist. It was subsequently restruck on at least two occasions, the first and second strikings have the inscription impressed in large capitals around the rim TO THE HEROES OF TRAFALGAR FROM M:BOULTON, the last having the inscription omitted. As the original dies were used for each striking, they had to be polished before reuse, so the fine detail on Nelson's uniform and in the battle scene is less pronounced in the second and subsequent strikings. Examples of the original striking can sometimes be found engraved in various styles, but great care should be taken over checking the authenticity of such pieces. All gold specimens are restrikes. Silver medals were not awarded but were later ordered from Boulton or his descendants by officers who wished to have a medal to form a group with the 1848 NGS.*

VALUE:

Gold (c. 1905)	£1000	Gilt-bronze	£500–700
Silver (1820–50)	£1000–1500	Bronze	£150–300
White metal	£150–300		

NB These prices are based on medals ssued from the original striking and are dependent on attribution.

85. DAVISON'S TRAFALGAR MEDAL

Date: 1805.
Campaign: Battle of Trafalgar 1805.
Branch of Service: Royal Navy.
Ribbon: None, but unofficially 32mm navy blue.
Metal: Pewter with a copper rim.   **Size:** 52mm.
Description: (Obverse) bust of Nelson; (reverse) a man-of-war with an appropriate biblical quotation from Exodus "The Lord is a Man-of-War".
Comments: *Alexander Davison, Nelson's prize agent, had this medal struck for award to the ratings of HMS* Victory *who took part in the battle.*

VALUE: £850–1000

86. CAPTURE OF RODRIGUEZ, ISLE OF BOURBON AND ISLE OF FRANCE

Date: 1810.
Campaign: Indian Ocean 1809-10.
Branch of Service: HEIC forces.
Ribbon: Yellow cord.
Metal: Gold or silver.
Size: 49mm.
Description: (Obverse) a sepoy in front of a cannon with the Union Jack; (reverse) a wreath with inscriptions in English and Farsi.
Comments: *The East India Company awarded this medal to native troops of the Bengal and Bombay Armies for the capture of three French islands in the Indian Ocean (the latter two being better known today as Mauritius and Reunion) between July 1809 and December 1810.*

VALUE:
Gold (50)	£4000–6000
Silver (2200)	£650–850

87. BAGUR AND PALAMOS MEDAL

Date: 1811.
Campaign: Peninsular War 1810.
Branch of Service: Royal Navy.
Ribbon: Red with yellow edges.
Metal: Gold or silver.
Size: 45mm.
Description: (Obverse) the conjoined crowned shields of Britain and Spain in a wreath with ALIANZA ETERNA (eternal alliance) round the foot; (reverse) inscription in Spanish GRATITUDE OF SPAIN TO THE BRAVE BRITISH AT BAGUR 10 SEPT. 1810, PALAMOS 14 SEPT. 1810.
Comments: *Awarded by the Spanish government to the crews of the British warships* Ajax, Cambrian *and* Kent *who landed at Bagur and Palamos to seize French ships. The British force was, in fact, driven back with very heavy losses.*

VALUE:
Gold (8)	£3000–4000
Silver (600)	£600–800

88. JAVA MEDAL

Date: 1811.
Campaign: Java 1811.
Branch of Service: HEIC forces.
Ribbon: Yellow cord.
Metals: Gold or silver.
Size: 49mm.
Description: (Obverse) the assault on Fort Cornelis; (reverse) inscriptions in English and Farsi.
Comments: *Awarded by the HEIC for the seizure of Java from the Dutch. The 750 British officers and men who took part in the operation were not only awarded this medal but were eligible for the Military GSM with Java clasp, issued 38 years later. Senior officers of the Company were given the gold medal, while junior officers, NCOs and sepoys received the silver version.*

VALUE:
Gold (133)	£3500–4500
Silver (6519)	£650–850

89. NEPAUL MEDAL

Date: 1816.
Campaign: Nepal 1814-16.
Branch of Service: HEIC native troops.
Ribbon: Yellow cord.
Metal: Silver.
Size: 51mm.
Description: (Obverse) a fortified mountain-top with a cannon in the foreground; (reverse) Farsi inscription.
Comments: *This medal marked the campaign to pacify Nepal led by Generals Marley, Ochterlony and Gillespie (the last named being killed in action). At the conclusion of the war Ochterlony began recruiting Gurkha mercenaries, a policy which has continued in the British Army to this day. The clasp "Nepaul" was granted with the Army of India Medal to British forces in 1851.*

VALUE: £650–750

90. CEYLON MEDAL

Date: 1818.
Campaign: Ceylon (Sri Lanka) 1818.
Branch of Service: British and HEIC forces.
Ribbon: 38mm deep navy blue.
Metal: Gold or silver.
Size: 35mm.
Description: The very plain design has "Ceylon 1818" within a wreath (obverse) and REWARD OF MERIT at top and bottom of the reverse, the personal details being engraved in the centre.
Comments: *Awarded by the Ceylon government for gallant conduct during the Kandian rebellion. Only selected officers and men of the 19th, 73rd and 83rd Foot, the 1st and 2nd Ceylon Regiments and 7th, 15th and 18th Madras Native Infantry received this medal.*

VALUE:

Gold (2)	—
Silver (45)	£1500–2000

91. BURMA MEDAL

Date: 1826.
Campaign: Burma 1824-26.
Branch of Service: HEIC native forces.
Ribbon: 38mm crimson edged with navy blue.
Metals: Gold or silver.
Size: 39mm.
Description: (Obverse) the Burmese elephant kneeling in submission before the British lion; (reverse) the epic assault on Rangoon by the Irrawaddy Flotilla.
Comments: *Granted to native officers and men who participated in the campaign for the subjugation of Burma. This was the first of the HEIC campaign medals in what was to become a standard 1.5 inch (38mm) diameter. The medal was fitted with a large steel ring for suspension and issued unnamed. British troops in this campaign were belatedly (1851) given the clasp "Ava" to the Army of India Medal.*

VALUE:

		Miniature
Gold (750)	£2000–2500	—
Silver-gilt	£450–500	—
Silver (24,000)	£450–550	£250–300

92. COORG MEDAL

Date: 1837.
Campaign: Coorg rebellion 1837.
Branch of Service: HEIC loyal Coorg forces.
Ribbon: Yellow cord.
Metals: Gold, silver or bronze.
Size: 50mm.
Description: (Obverse) a Coorg holding a musket, with kukri upraised; (reverse) weapons in a wreath with the inscription FOR DISTINGUISHED CONDUCT AND LOYALTY TO THE BRITISH GOVERNMENT COORG APRIL 1837, the equivalent in Canarese appearing on the obverse.
Comments: *Native troops who remained loyal during the Canara rebellion of April-May 1837 were awarded this medal by the HEIC the following August. Bronze specimens were also struck but not officially issued and may have been restrikes or later copies. Bronzed and silvered electrotype copies are also known.*

VALUE:

Gold (44)	£4000–6000
Silver (300)	£650–850
Bronze	£200–300

93. NAVAL GOLD MEDAL

Date: 1795.
Campaign: Naval actions 1795-1815.
Branch of Service: Royal Navy.
Ribbon: 44mm white with broad dark blue edges.
Metal: Gold.
Size: 51mm and 38mm.
Description: The medals were glazed on both sides and individually engraved on the reverse with the name of the recipient and details of the engagement in a wreath of laurel and oak leaves. (Obverse) the winged figure of Victory bestowing a laurel wreath on the head of Britannia standing in the prow of a galley with a Union Jack shield behind her, her right foot on a helmet, her left hand holding a spear.
Comments: *Instituted in 1795, a year after Lord Howe's naval victory on "the glorious First of June", this medal was awarded continually till 1815 when the Order of the Bath was expanded into three classes. Large medals were awarded to admirals and small medals went to captains. As medals were awarded for separate actions it was possible for officers to wear more than one; Lord Nelson himself had three. Two miniatures are recorded and would probably fetch at least £1000 if they came onto the market.*

VALUE:

Large medal (22)	From £25,000
Small medal (117)	From £15,000

94. NAVAL GENERAL SERVICE MEDAL

Date: 1847.

Campaign: Naval battles and boat actions 1793-1840.

Branch of Service: Royal Navy.

Ribbon: 32mm white with dark blue edges.

Metal: Silver.

Size: 36mm.

Description: (Obverse) the Young Head profile of Queen Victoria by William Wyon; (reverse) Britannia with her trident seated on a sea horse.

Clasps: No fewer than 230 different clasps for major battles, minor engagements, cutting-out operations and boat service were authorised. These either have the name or date of the action, the name of a ship capturing or defeating an enemy vessel, or the words BOAT SERVICE followed by a date. No fewer than 20,933 medals were awarded but most of them had a single clasp. Multi-clasp medals are worth very considerably more. The greatest number of clasps to a single medal was seven (two awards made); four medals had six clasps and fourteen medals had five clasps. For reasons of space only those clasps which are met with fairly often in the salerooms are listed below. At the other end of the scale it should be noted that only one recipient claimed the clasps for *Hussar* (17 May 1795), *Dido* (24 June 1795), *Spider* (25 August 1795), *Espoir* (7 August 1798), *Viper* (26 December 1799), *Loire* (5 February 1800), *Louisa* (28 October 1807), *Carrier* (4 November 1807), *Superieure* (10 February 1809), *Growler* (22 May 1812) and the boat actions of 15 March 1793, 4 November 1803, 4 November 1810 and 3-6 September 1814. In several cases no claimants came forward at all. The numbers of clasps awarded are not an accurate guide to value, as some actions are rated more highly than others, and clasps associated with actions in the War of 1812 have a very strong following in the USA as well as Britain. Clasps for famous battles, such as Trafalgar, likewise command a high premium out of all proportion to the number of clasps awarded. A medal to HMS *Victory* would be worth in excess of £5000.

Comments: *Instituted in 1847 and issued to **surviving** claimants in 1848, this medal was originally intended to cover naval engagements of the French Revolutionary and Napoleonic Wars (1793-1815) but was almost immediately extended to cover all naval actions of a more recent date, down to the expedition to Syria in 1840. It was fitted with a straight suspender.*

VALUE (major actions):

Fleet Actions

1 June 1794 (540)	£800–1000
14 March 1795 (95)	£1200–1500
23 June 1795 (177)	£800–1000
St Vincent (348)	£800–1000
Camperdown (298)	£1000–1200
Nile (326)	£800–1000
12 Octr 1798 (78)	£1500–2000
Egypt (618)	£600–800
Copenhagen (555)	£800–1000
Gut of Gibraltar (142)	£120–1500
Trafalgar (1710)	£2000–2500
4 Novr 1805 (296)	£800–1000
St Domingo (396)	£700–800
Martinique (486)	£550–650
Basque Roads (529)	£750–800
Guadaloupe (483)	£550–650
Java (665)	£600–650
St Sebastian (293)	£750–800
Algiers (1328)	£450–550
Navarino (1142)	£600–650
Syria (6978)	£350–400

Miniature

Without clasp	£100–150, for each clasp add £50+ depending on the action.

Ship Actions

Mars 21 April 1798 (26)	£2000–2500
Lion 15 July 1798 (23)	£2000–2500
Acre 30 May 1799 (41)	£2500–2000
London 13 March 1806 (27)	£2000–2500
Curacao 1 Jany 1807 (65)	£1500–2000
Stately 22 March 1808 (31)	£2000–2500
Lissa (124)	£800–1000
Shannon with Chesapeake (42)	£4000–5000
Gluckstadt 5 Jany 1814 (44)	£1500–2000
Gaieta 24 July 1815 (88)	£1000–1200

Boat Service

16 July 1806 (51)	£1200–1500
1 Novr 1809 (110)	£800–1000
28 June 1810 (25)	£1400–1700
29 Sepr 1812 (25)	£1400–1700
8 Ap and May 1813 (57)	£2000–2300
2 May 1813 (48)	£1200–1500
8 April 1814 (24)	£2300–2600
24 May 1814 (12)	£2000–2300
14 Decr 1814 (205)	£900–1100

95. ARMY GOLD CROSS

Date: 1813.

Campaigns: Peninsular War and War of 1812.

Branch of Service: British Army.

Ribbon: 38mm crimson edged with dark blue.

Metal: Gold. **Size:** 38mm.

Description: A cross pattée with a laurel border having a rose at the centre on each of the four flat ends. At the centre of the cross appears a British lion statant. The scrolled top of the cross is fitted with an elaborate ring decorated with laurel leaves looped through a plain swivel ring fitted to the suspender. The arms of the cross on both obverse and reverse bear the names of four battles in relief.

Clasps: Large borders of laurel leaves enclosing the name of a battle in raised relief within an elliptical frame, awarded for fifth and subsequent battles.

Comments: *Arguably the most prestigious award in the campaign series, the Army Gold Cross was approved by the Prince Regent in 1813. It was granted to generals and officers of field rank for service in four or more battles of the Peninsular War. Three crosses had six clasps, two had seven, while the Duke of Wellington himself had the unique cross with nine clasps, representing participation in thirteen battles.*

VALUE:

Gold cross without clasp (61)	From £25,000
Miniature	£350–450

Battle of Vimiera.

96. MAIDA GOLD MEDAL

Date: 1806.
Campaign: Peninsular War, Battle of Maida 1806.
Branch of Service: British Army.
Ribbon: 38mm crimson edged with navy blue.
Metal: Gold. **Size:** 39mm.
Description: (Obverse) laureated profile of George III; (reverse) winged figure of Victory hovering with a laurel wreath over the head of Britannia, shield upraised, in the act of throwing a spear. The name and date of the battle appears on Britannia's left, with the *trinacria* or three-legged emblem on the right.
Clasps: None.
Comments: *This small gold medal was authorised in 1806 and awarded to the thirteen senior officers involved in the battle of Maida in Calabria when a small British force under General Sir John Stuart defeated a much larger French army with heavy loss. A small unknown number of gold and silver specimens are known to exist.*

VALUE: from £25,000

97. ARMY GOLD MEDAL

Date: 1810.
Campaigns: Peninsular War 1806-14 and War of 1812.
Branch of Service: British Army.
Ribbon: 38mm crimson edged with navy blue.
Metal: Gold.
Size: 54mm and 33mm.
Description: (Obverse) Britannia seated on a globe, holding a laurel wreath over the British lion and holding a palm branch in her left hand while resting on a shield embellished with the Union Jack. The name of the first action is generally engraved on the reverse.
Clasps: For second and third actions.
Comments: *The Maida medal (no. 96) established a precedent for the series of medals instituted in 1810. The name of the battle was inscribed on the reverse, usually engraved, though that for Barossa was die-struck. These medals were struck in two sizes, the larger being conferred on generals and the smaller on officers of field rank. Second or third battles were denoted by a clasp appropriately inscribed, while those who qualified for a fourth award exchanged their medal and bars for a gold cross. The award of these gold medals and crosses ceased in 1814 when the Companion of the Bath was instituted.*

VALUE:
	Large medal	From £16,000
	Small medal	From £7000

98. MILITARY GENERAL SERVICE MEDAL

Date: 1847.

Campaigns: French Revolutionary and Napoleonic Wars 1793-1814.

Branch of Service: British Army.

Ribbon: 31mm crimson edged with dark blue.

Metal: Silver.

Size: 36mm.

Description: (Obverse) the Wyon profile of Queen Victoria; (reverse) a standing figure of the Queen bestowing victor's laurels on a kneeling Duke of Wellington. The simple inscription TO THE BRITISH ARMY appears round the circumference, while the dates 1793-1814 are placed in the exergue. Despite this, the earliest action for which a clasp was issued took place in 1801 (Abercromby's Egyptian campaign).

Clasps: Only 29 battle or campaign clasps were issued but multiple awards are much commoner than in the naval medal, the maximum being fifteen. While it is generally true to say that multi-clasp medals are worth more than single-clasp medals, there are many in the latter category (noted below) which command higher prices. The figures quoted below are based on the commonest regiments. Clasps awarded to specialists and small detached forces rate more highly than medals to the principal regiment in a battle or campaign. In particular, it should be noted that one naval officer, Lieut. Carroll, received the Military GSM and clasp for Maida, while a few other officers of the Royal Navy and Royal Marines received the medal with the clasps for Guadaloupe, Martinique or Java, and these, naturally, are now very much sought after. Paradoxically, the clasps for Sahagun and Benevente alone are very much scarcer than the clasp inscribed Sahagun and Benevente, awarded to surviving veterans who had participated in both battles. The clasps are listed below in chronological order. Medals to officers rate a premium.

Comments: *Like the Naval GSM, this medal was not sanctioned till 1847 and awarded the following year. Unlike the Naval medal, however, the Military GSM was confined to land actions up to the defeat of Napoleon in 1814 and the conclusion of the war with the United States. The regiment is now having a bearing on price, with medals to the 52nd, 88th or 95th Foot worth a good premium.*

VALUE:

Egypt	£600–700	Chateauguay	£1900–2000
Maida	£600–700	Chrystler's Farm	£1800–2200
Roleia	£700–800	Vittoria	£500–600
Vimiera	£500–550	Pyrenees	£500–600
Sahagun	£1000–1100	St Sebastian	£550–650
Benevente	£4500–5500	Nivelle	£500–550
Sahagun and Benevente	£1000–1100	Nive	£500–600
Corunna	£550–600	Orthes	£500–600
Martinique	£550–650	Toulouse	£500–600
Talavera	£500–550	2 clasps	£550–600
Guadaloupe	£550–600	3 clasps	£600–700
Busaco	£550–600	4 clasps	£700–800
Barrosa	£550–600	5 clasps	£800–900
Fuentes D'Onor	£550–600	6 clasps	£900–1000
Albuhera	£600–700	7 clasps	£950–1100
Java	£600–700	8 clasps	£1100–1250
Ciudad Rodrigo	£500–600	9 clasps	£1300–1550
Badajoz	£600–650	10 clasps	£1600–1800
Salamanca	£550–650	11 clasps	£1850–2300
Fort Detroit	£1800–2200	12 or more clasps	From £2500

Miniature without clasp   £100–150, for each clasp add £50+ depending on the action.

99. WATERLOO MEDAL

Date: 1815.
Campaign: Waterloo 1815.
Branch of Service: British Army.
Ribbon: 38mm, crimson edged in dark blue.
Metal: Silver.
Size: 37mm.
Description: (Obverse) the profile of the Prince Regent; (reverse) the seated figure of Victory above a tablet simply inscribed WATERLOO with the date of the battle in the exergue.
Comments: *This was the first medal awarded and officially named to all ranks who took part in a particular campaign. It was also issued, however, to those who had taken part in one or more of the other battles of the campaign, at Ligny and Quatre Bras two days earlier. The ribbon was intended to be worn with an iron clip and split suspension ring but many recipients subsequently replaced these with a more practical silver mount which would not rust and spoil the uniform. Some 39,000 medals were issued. The value of a Waterloo medal depends to a large extent on the regiment of the recipient. Medals awarded to those formations which saw the heaviest action and bore the brunt of the losses are in the greatest demand, whereas medals named to soldiers in General Colville's reserve division which did not take part in the fighting, are the least highly rated.*

VALUE:

Heavy Cavalry	£1200–1500
Scots Greys	£2200–2500
Light Cavalry	£1000–1100
Royal Artillery	£800–900
Royal Horse Artillery	£900–100
Foot Guards	£1000–1200
1st, 27th, 28th, 30th, 42nd, 44th, 52nd, 73rd, 79th, 92nd, 95th Foot	£1100–1500
Other Foot regiments	£800–1000
Colville's division (35th, 54th, 59th, 91st Foot)	£800–1000
King's German Legion	£700–800
Miniature	£50–200

100. BRUNSWICK MEDAL FOR WATERLOO

Date: 1815.
Campaign: Battle of Waterloo 1815.
Branch of Service: Brunswick troops.
Ribbon: Cream with light blue stripes towards the edges.
Metal: Bronze.
Description: (Obverse) Duke Friedrich Wilhelm of Brunswick who was killed in the battle; (reverse) a wreath of laurel and oak leaves enclosing the German text "Braunschweig Seinen Kriegern" (Brunswick to its warriors) and the names of Quatre Bras and Waterloo.
Comments: *The Prince Regent authorised this medal for issue to the contingent from the Duchy of Brunswick.*

VALUE: £300–350

101. HANOVERIAN MEDAL FOR WATERLOO

Date: 1815.
Campaign: Battle of Waterloo 1815.
Branch of Service: Hanoverian troops.
Ribbon: Crimson edged with light blue.
Metal: Silver.
Description: (Obverse) the Prince Regent, his name and title being rendered in German. (Reverse) a trophy of arms below the legend HANNOVERSCHER TAPFERKEIT (Hanoverian bravery), with the name and date of the battle wreathed in the centre.
Comments: *The Prince Regent authorised this medal on behalf of his father George III in his capacity as Elector of Hanover and this was conferred on survivors of the battle. Suspension was by iron clip and ring similar to the British Waterloo Medal.*

VALUE: £350–450

102. NASSAU MEDAL FOR WATERLOO

Date: 1815.
Campaign: Battle of Waterloo 1815.
Branch of Service: Nassau forces.
Ribbon: Dark blue edged in yellow.
Metal: Silver.
Size: 25mm.
Description: (Obverse) Duke Friedrich of Nassau; (reverse) the winged figure of Victory crowning a soldier with laurels, the date of the action being in the exergue.
Comments: *Friedrich Duke of Nassau distributed this medal on 23 December 1815 to all of his own troops who had been present at the battle.*

VALUE: £220–260

103. SAXE-GOTHA-ALTENBURG MEDAL

Date: 1815.
Campaign: Germany and Waterloo 1814-15.
Branch of Service: Saxe-Gotha-Altenburg Foreign Legion.
Ribbon: Green with black edges and gold stripes.
Metal: Gilt bronze or bronze.
Size: 42mm.
Description: (Obverse) a crown with the legend IM KAMPFE FUER DAS RECHT (in the struggle for the right); (reverse) an ornate rose motif with the name of the duchy and the dates of the campaign in roman numerals.
Comments: *Gilded medals were issued to officers, but other ranks received a bronze version.*

VALUE:
    Gilt-bronze   £260–300
    Bronze   £240–280

104. ARMY OF INDIA MEDAL

Date: 1851.

Campaigns: India 1803–26.

Branch of Service: British and HEIC troops.

Ribbon: 32mm pale blue.

Metal: Silver.

Size: 35mm.

Description: (Obverse) the Wyon profile of Queen Victoria; (reverse) the seated figure of Victory beside a palm tree, with a wreath in one hand and a laurel crown in the other. The medal is fitted with an ornamental scroll suspender.

Clasps: The medal was not awarded without a campaign clasp and, unusually, in multi-clasp medals, the last clasp awarded was mounted closest to the medal itself, so that the battle roll has to be read downwards. There were two dies of the reverse, leading to the long- or short-hyphen varieties, both of comparable value. In all, some 4500 medals were awarded, but there is a very wide divergence between the commonest and rarest bars. Multi-clasp medals are rare, and medals awarded to Europeans are much scarcer than those to Indian troops.

Comments: *The last of the medals authorised in connection with the Napoleonic Wars, it was instituted and paid for by the Honourable East India Company in March 1851 for award to surviving veterans of the battles and campaigns in India and Burma between 1803 and 1826. Despite the dates 1799–1826 in the exergue, the medal was in fact awarded for service in one or other of four wars: the Second Mahratta War (1803–4), the Nepal War (1814–16), the Pindaree or Third Mahratta War (1817–18) and the Burmese War (1824–26), together with the siege of Bhurtpoor (1825–26). The medal is scarce, and examples with the clasps for the Second Mahratta War are much sought after, partly because few veterans were still alive 48 years after the event to claim their medals, and partly because of the war's association with Arthur Wellesley, the Duke of Wellington, who died in the very year in which the medal was awarded. Medals to the Royal Navy with the Ava clasp are very rare.*

Rev. die a, short hyphen

Rev. die b, long hyphen

VALUE:

Prices for medals bearing the following clasps are for European recipients. Medals to Indians are generally less expensive.

Allighur (66)	£2500–3000
Battle of Delhi (40)	£3000–3500
Assye (87)	£2500–3000
Asseerghur (48)	£3000–3500
Laswarree (100)	£2000–2500
Argaum (126)	£2500–3000
Gawilghur (110)	£2500–3000
Defence of Delhi (5)	Rare
Battle of Deig (47)	£2800–3500
Capture of Deig (103)	£2300–2800
Nepaul (505)	£800–1000
Kirkee (5)	Rare
Poona (75)	£2000–2500
Kirkee and Poona (88)	£2000–2500
Seetabuldee (2)	Rare
Nagpore (155)	£1600–2000
Seetabuldee and Nagpore (21)	Rare
Maheidpoor (75)	£1500–2000
Corygaum (4)	Rare
Ava (2325)	£650–750
Bhurtpoor (1059)	£750–850
2 clasps (300)	Rare
3 clasps (150)	Rare
4 clasps (23)	Rare
5 or more clasps (10 x 5, 2 x 6, 1 x 7)	Rare
Glazed gilt specimen	£400
*Miniature**	
One clasp Ava	£100–150
Further clasps	£100–150 each

*Note there are many silver reproductions and clasps on the market, value £10–20.

105. GHUZNEE MEDAL

Date: 1839.
Campaign: Ghuznee 1839.
Branch of Service: British and HEIC forces.
Ribbon: 35mm half crimson, half dark green.
Metal: Silver.
Size: 37mm.
Description: (Obverse) the impressive gateway of the fortress of Ghuznee; (reverse) a mural crown enclosed in a laurel wreath with the date of capture.
Comments: *This was the second medal awarded for a particular campaign (after Waterloo) and was granted to both British and Indian troops who took part in the assault on Ghuznee in July 1839 which brought the first Afghan War to a close, overthrew the pro-Russian Dost Mohamed and restored Shah Soojah who instituted the Order of the Dooranie Empire (awarded to British generals and field officers) in appreciation. The Ghuznee medal was issued unnamed by the Honourable East India Company, but many recipients subsequently had their names impressed or engraved in various styles. No clasps were issued officially, but unauthorised clasps are occasionally encountered.*

VALUE:

British recipient	£350–450
Indian recipient	£250–300
Unnamed as issued	£200–250
Miniature	£150–300

106. ST. JEAN D'ACRE MEDAL

Date: 1840.
Campaign: Syria 1840.
Branch of Service: Royal Navy, Royal Marines and British Army.
Ribbon: Red with white edges.
Metal: Gold, silver or copper (bronzed).
Size: 30mm.
Description: (Obverse) a fortress flying the Ottoman flag, with six five-pointed stars round the top. A commemorative inscription and date in Arabic appear at the foot; (reverse) the Toughra of the Sultan in a laurel wreath.
Comments: *Awarded by the Sultan of Turkey to British, Austrian and Turkish forces under Sir Charles Napier, taking part in the liberation of this important city on the Syrian coast after eight years of Egyptian occupation. The medal has a plain ring suspension. The clasp "Syria" to the Naval GSM was awarded in 1848 in respect to this operation, and this medal generally accompanies the St Jean d'Acre medal.*

VALUE:

		Miniature
Gold (captains and field officers)	£500–700	—
Silver (junior officers)	£150–200	£150–200
Copper (petty officers, NCOs and other ranks)	£70–90	—

107. CANDAHAR, GHUZNEE, CABUL MEDAL

Date: 1842.
Campaign: Afghanistan 1841–42.
Branch of Service: British and HEIC troops.
Ribbon: 40mm watered silk of red, white, yellow, white and blue.
Metal: Silver.
Size: 35mm.
Description: Although the medals have a uniform obverse, a profile of the Queen captioned VICTORIA VINDEX, reverses are inscribed with the names of individual battles, or combinations thereof, within wreaths surmounted by a crown.
Comments: *The Honourable East India Company instituted this series of medals in 1842 for award to both HEIC and British troops who took part in the First Afghan War. The issue of this medal to units of the British Army, to Europeans serving in the Company's forces, and to Indian troops is further complicated by the fact that unnamed medals are generally common. In addition, the medal for Cabul is known in two versions, with the inscription CABUL or CABVL, the latter being a major rarity as only fifteen were issued. Beware of modern copies of the Candahar and Cabul medals.*

VALUE:	Imperial Regiments	Indian Units	Unnamed
Candahar	£450–550	£250–300	£220–250
Cabul	£300–350	£200–250	£180–230
Cabvl (15)	Rare	Rare	Rare
Ghuznee/Cabul	£500–600	£300–350	£200–250
Candahar/Ghuznee/ Cabul	£400–500	£250–300	£200–240
Miniature	from £200		

108. JELLALABAD MEDALS

Type 2 rev.

Type 1 obv.

Date: 1842.
Campaign: Afghanistan 1841-42.
Branch of Service: British and HEIC forces.
Ribbon: 44mm watered silk red, white, yellow, white and blue.
Metal: Silver.
Size: 39mm and 35mm.
Description: There are two different types of this medal, awarded by the HEIC to surviving defenders of the fortress of Jellalabad between 12 November 1841 and 7 April 1842. The first, struck in Calcutta, has a mural crown and JELLALABAD on the obverse, with the date of the relief of the garrison on the reverse; the second type shows the Wyon profile of Victoria (obverse) and the winged Victory with mountain scenery in the background and JELLALABAD VII APRIL round the top and the year in roman numerals in the exergue (reverse).
Comment: *The first type, struck in Calcutta, was considered to be unsuitable and holders were invited to exchange their medals for the second, more attractive, issue which was produced in London, although very few recipients took up the offer. The latter type was also awarded to the next of kin of soldiers killed in action.*

VALUE:	Imperial Regiments	Indian Units	Unnamed	*Miniature*
First type (Crown)	£450–550	£350–450	£350–400	£150–250
Second type (Victory)	£600–800	—	£450–550	£150–250

109. MEDAL FOR THE DEFENCE OF KELAT-I-GHILZIE

Date: 1842.
Campaign: Afghanistan 1842.
Branch of Service: European and native troops, HEIC.
Ribbon: 40mm watered silk red, white, yellow, white and blue.
Metal: Silver.
Size: 36mm.
Description: (Obverse) a shield bearing the name of the fort, surmounted by a mural crown and encircled by laurels; (reverse) a trophy of arms above a tablet inscribed INVICTA (unbeaten) and the date in roman numerals.
Comments: *Awarded to those who took part in the defence of the fort at Kelat-i-Ghilzie in May 1842, it is the rarest medal of the First Afghan War. No British imperial regiments took part, but 55 Europeans in the Company's service received the medal. It was also awarded to 877 native troops (including a contingent supplied by Shah Soojah) but few of their medals appear to have survived.*

VALUE:

European recipients	£4500–5500
Indian recipients	£1800–2300
Unnamed	£800–1000
Miniature	£250–300

110. CHINA WAR MEDAL

Issued reverse

Date: 1842.
Campaign: China 1841-42.
Branch of Service: British and HEIC forces.
Ribbon: 39mm crimson with yellow edges.
Metal: Silver.
Size: 36mm.
Description: The medal has the usual Wyon obverse, but the reverse was to have shown a British lion with its forepaws on a dragon. This was deemed to be offensive to the Chinese and was replaced by an oval shield bearing the royal arms and a palm treeflanked by a capstan, anchor and naval cannon representing the Royal Navy (left) and a field gun, drum and regimental flag representing the Army (right), with the Latin motto ARMIS EXPOSCERE PACEM (to pray for peace by force of arms) round the top and CHINA 1842 at the foot.
Comments: *Originally intended for issue to all ranks of the Honourable East India Company, it was subsequently awarded by the British government in 1843 to all who had taken part in the campaign in China popularly known as the First Opium War which ended with the seizure of Nanking.*

VALUE:

Royal Navy	£275–325
Indian and Bengal marine units	£240–300
British imperial regiments	£260–325
Indian Army	£220–250
Specimens of the original reverse	From £500
Miniature	£150–250

133

111. SCINDE MEDAL

Date: 1843.
Campaign: Scinde 1843.
Branch of Service: HEIC forces and 22nd Foot.
Ribbon: 44mm watered silk red, white, yellow, white and blue.
Metal: Silver.
Size: 36mm.
Description: The usual Wyon profile obverse was married to three different reverse types showing a crowned laurel wreath inscribed with the name of one or two campaigns and the date.
Comments: *Authorised in September 1843, this silver medal marked Sir Charles Napier's conquest of Scinde. The two major battles in the campaign, at Meeanee and Hyderabad, accomplished the complete rout of the forces of the Amirs of Scinde. The medals were originally issued with steel suspenders but the commanding officer of the 22nd Foot had the medals awarded to his men fitted with silver suspenders, at his own expense. Medals to the Indus Flotilla are particularly sought after by collectors.*

VALUE:

	22nd Foot	Indian units	HEIC ships
Meeanee	£650–950	£300–400	£1100–1500 (38)
Hyderabad	£600–750	£250–275	£1100–1500 (52)
Meeanee/Hyderabad	£550–650	£250–275	
Miniature	£150–250		

112. GWALIOR STAR

Date: 1843.
Campaign: Gwalior 1843.
Branch of Service: British and HEIC forces.
Ribbon: 44mm watered silk red, white, yellow, white and blue.
Metals: Bronze, with a silver centre.
Size: Max. width 45mm; max. height 52mm.
Description: Six-pointed bronze star with a silver centre star. The silver stars in the centre bear the name of one or other of the battles and the date 29 December 1843 on which both battles were fought. The plain reverse bears the name and regiment of the recipient.
Comments: *Bronze from guns captured at the battles of Maharajpoor and Punniar during the Gwalior campaign was used in the manufacture of these stars, thus anticipating the production of the Victoria Cross in the same manner. They were presented by the Indian government to all ranks who took part in these actions. When first issued, these stars were fitted with hooks to be worn like a breast decoration, but later ornate bar or ring suspensions were fitted to individual fancy and worn with the standard Indian ribbon of the period.*

VALUE:

		Miniature
Maharajpoor	£300–375	£100–150
Punniar	£325–400	£150–200

*Awards to Indian recipients are usually somewhat less.

113. SUTLEJ MEDAL

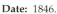

Date: 1846.

Campaign: Sutlej 1845-46.

Branch of Service: British and HEIC forces.

Ribbon: Dark blue with crimson edges.

Metal: Silver.

Size: 36mm.

Description: (Obverse) Wyon profile of Queen Victoria; (reverse) standing figure of Victory holding aloft a laurel crown, with a pile of captured weapons at her feet. The legend ARMY OF THE SUTLEJ appears round the top. The medal was fitted with an ornamental scroll suspender.

Clasps: Mounted above the suspender with roses between: Ferozeshuhur, Aliwal or Sobraon.

Comments: *The practice of issuing medals inscribed with different battles now gave way to the style of medals with specific battle or campaign clasps which set the precedent for the Naval and Military GSMs and later awards. As a compromise, however, the exergue of the reverse bears the name and date of the action for which the medal was first granted, and thus several different types are known.*

VALUE:	British regiments	Europeans in HEIC units	Indian units
Moodkee	£200–250	£150–200	£125–150
Moodkee 1 clasp	£250–300	£185–250	£165–185
Moodkee 2 clasps	£375–420	£250–285	£225–285
Moodkee 3 clasps	£550–620	£450–550	£310–350
Ferozeshuhur	£200–225	£155–225	£145–180
Ferozeshuhur 1 clasp	£280–300	£185–235	£185–220
Ferozeshuhur 2 clasps	£350–400	£310–350	£225–285
Aliwal	£200–220	£165–185	£145–180
Aliwal 1 clasp	£225–280	£220–250	£165–185
Sobraon	£275–320	£185–225	£125–150
Glazed gilt specimen	£275–320		
Miniature	£100–150, for each clasp add £50		

114. PUNJAB MEDAL

Date: 1849.

Campaign: Punjab 1848-49.

Branch of Service: British and HEIC forces.

Ribbon: Dark blue with yellow stripes towards the edges.

Metal: Silver.

Size: 36mm.

Description: (Obverse) Wyon profile of Queen Victoria; (reverse) Sir Walter Gilbert receiving the Sikh surrender. TO THE ARMY OF THE PUNJAB appears round the top and the year in roman numerals in the exergue. The medal has a scroll suspender.

Clasps: Mooltan, Chilianwala, Goojerat. Unusually the clasps read downwards from top to bottom

Comments: *This medal was granted to troops taking part in the campaigns which ended in the annexation of the Punjab. Unlike the Sutlej medal, however, this silver medal had a standard design. Large numbers of this medal were awarded to native troops, however many were melted down and therefore surprisingly few remain on the market in comparison with medals to European recipients.*

VALUE:	British units	Europeans in HEIC units	Indian units
No clasp	£155–190	£125–165	£100–125
Mooltan	£190–240	£185–220	£125–150
Chilianwala	£200–250	£185–220	£125–150
Goojerat	£190–220	£185–220	£150–175
Mooltan/Goojerat	£300–350	£245–285	£185–225
Chilianwala/Goojerat	£300–350	£245–285	£185–225
24th Foot casualty at Chilianwala	£650–750	—	—
Glazed gilt specimen	£250–320		
Miniature	£50–75, for each clasp add £25		

115. SOUTH AFRICA MEDAL

Date: 1854.

Campaigns: Southern Africa 1834–53.

Branch of Service: Royal Navy and Army.

Ribbon: Gold with broad and narrow deep blue stripes towards each end.

Metal: Silver.

Size: 36mm.

Description: (Obverse) Wyon profile of Queen Victoria; (reverse) a British lion drinking at a waterhole beside a protea shrub, the date 1853 being in the exergue.

Clasps: None.

Comments: *Authorised in November 1854, this medal was awarded in respect of three campaigns in southern Africa: 1834–35, 1846–47 and 1850–53, but as the medal was issued with a standard reverse and no campaign clasps it is impossible to tell when and where the recipient served without reference to the medal rolls. The majority of recipients were British troops but several hundred sailors of the Royal Navy also received the medal and a much smaller number of local forces. Of particular interest are medals awarded to men who survived the sinking of the troopship* Birkenhead *on its way to the Eastern Cape from Simons Town.*

VALUE:

	1834–35	1846–47	1850–53
British Army	£275–325	£225–275	£220–250
Royal Navy	—	£275–300	£200–235
HMS *Birkenhead*			From £500
Local forces	£275–325	£245–285	£200–235
Miniature	£50–65	£50–65	£50–65

116. SIR HARRY SMITH'S MEDAL FOR GALLANTRY

Date: 1851.

Campaign: Eighth Kaffir War 1850-51.

Branch of Service: Cape Mounted Rifles.

Ribbon: Dark blue with crimson edges.

Metal: Silver.

Size: 34mm.

Description: (Obverse) British lion passant gardant with a laurel wreath over its head; date 1851 in the exergue. (Reverse) PRESENTED BY round top and FOR GALLANTRY IN THE FIELD round the foot. HIS EXCELLENCY SIR H. G. SMITH and the name of the recipient appear across the centre.

Comments: *Sir Harry Smith (1787–1860) served with distinction in the Kaffir War of 1834–35, gained his KCB in the Gwalior campaign and a baronetcy for his decisive victory at Aliwal in the Sikh War. In 1847 he returned to South Africa as governor of Cape Colony. Although short of troops he conducted the eighth Frontier War (1850–53) with great resourcefulness but was recalled to England in 1852 before the Xhosas had been subdued. Harrismith in the Orange Free State was named in his honour, while Ladysmith in Natal was named after his beautiful and spirited Spanish wife Juanita, the forces' sweetheart of her day. Sir Harry had this medal struck at his own expense and awarded to troopers of the Cape Mounted Rifles who took part in the epic ride through the enemy lines from Fort Cox to Kingwilliamstown in 1851. Only 31 medals were presented, of which 22 are believed to be still extant.*

VALUE:

Unnamed	£1500–1800
Named	£2000–3000

117. INDIA GENERAL SERVICE MEDAL

Date: 1854.

Campaigns: Indian 1854-95.

Branch of Service: British and Indian forces.

Ribbon: Three crimson and two dark blue bars of equal width.

Metal: Silver or bronze.

Size: 36mm.

Description: (Obverse) Wyon profile of Queen Victoria; (reverse) Victory crowning a semi-nude seated warrior.

Clasps: 24 (see below).

Comments: *This medal was the first of five general service medals issued to cover minor campaigns in India. It was instituted in 1854 and continued for forty-one years, retaining the original Wyon profile of Queen Victoria throughout the entire period. Although the medal itself is quite common, some of its clasps are very rare, notably* Kachin Hills 1892–93 *awarded to the Yorkshire Regiment and* Chin Hills 1892–93 *awarded to the Norfolk Regiment. The maximum number of clasps to one medal recorded is seven. At first the medal was awarded in silver to all ranks regardless of race or branch of the services, but from 1885 onwards it was issued in bronze to native support personnel such as bearers, sweepers and drivers.*

VALUE:

	RN/RM	British Army	Indian Army	Bronze
Pegu	£115–135	£125–145	—	—
Persia	—	£125–145	£75–85	—
North West Frontier	—	£125–145	£65–75	—
Umbeyla	—	£120–130	£75–85	—
Bhootan	—	£125–140	£65–75	—
Looshai	—	—	£115–125	—
Perak	£115–150	£140–160	£85–110	—
Jowaki 1877–78	—	£120–130	£75–85	—
Naga 1879–80	—	—	£140–175	—
Burma 1885–87	£90–120	£90–110	£60–70	£50–60
Sikkim 1888	—	£130–150	£70–85	£80–100
Hazara 1888	—	£120–140	£95–110	£75–90
Burma 1887–89	—	£90–110	£55–65	£60–70
Burma 1887–9	—	£110–125	—	—
Chin Lushai 1889–90	—	£130–150	£65–75	£110–130
Lushai 1889–92	—	£320–350	£125–165	£170–190
Samana 1891	—	£120–140	£65–75	£60–70
Hazara 1891	—	£110–125	£55–65	£50–60
NE Frontier 1891	—	£130–150	£55–65	£80–90
Hunza 1891	—	—	£190–220	£350–380
Burma 1889–92	—	£100–120	£70–80	£50–60
Chin Hills 1892-93	—	£600–700	£115–140	£320–350
Kachin Hills 1892-93	—	£500–600	£190–220	£700–750
Waziristan 1894–95	—	£110–125-	£55–65	£40–50

Miniature
£20–30, for each clasp add £10 (*Hunza, Chin Hills* and *Kachin Hills* clasps are rare)

118. BALTIC MEDAL

Date: 1856.
Campaign: Baltic Sea 1854–55.
Branch of Service: Royal Navy, Royal Marines and Royal Sappers and Miners.
Ribbon: Yellow with light blue edges.
Metal: Silver.
Size: 36mm.
Description: (Obverse) Wyon profile of Queen Victoria; (reverse) Britannia seated on a plinth decorated by a cannon, with a coastal scene in the background and BALTIC round the top.
Comments: *Authorised in 1856, this medal was granted to officers and men of the Royal Navy and Royal Marines for operations against Russia in the Baltic at the same time as the war in the Crimea. It was also awarded to about 100 members of the Royal Sappers and Miners engaged in the demolition of Russian fortifications of Bomarsund and Sveaborg. Medals were generally issued unnamed but often privately named afterwards, the exception being medals to the Sappers and Miners which were officially impressed.*

VALUE:

Unnamed	£100–120
Privately named	£100–120
Officially impressed to Sappers and Miners	£800–1000
Miniature	£15–20

119. CRIMEA MEDAL

Date: 1854.
Campaign: Crimea 1854–56.
Branch of Service: British Army, Navy and Marines.
Ribbon: Pale blue with yellow edges.
Metal: Silver.
Size: 36mm.
Description: (Obverse) Wyon profile of Queen Victoria; (reverse) a Roman soldier, armed with circular shield and short sword, being crowned by a flying Victory.
Clasps: Unusually ornate, being shaped like oak leaves with acorn finials: Alma, Inkerman, Azoff, Balaklava, Sebastopol, but the maximum found on any medal is four. Unofficial clasps for Traktir, Mamelon Vert, Malakoff, Mer d'Azoff and Kinburn are sometimes found on medals awarded to French troops.
Comments: *Medals may be found unnamed, unofficially or regimentally named, or officially impressed. Medals awarded to participants in the most famous actions of the war—the Thin Red Line (93rd Foot) and the Charge of the Light and Heavy Brigades—rate a very high premium. The prices quoted are for medals officially impressed to the Army. Clasps awarded to the Royal Navy and Royal Marines (Azoff, Balaklava, Inkerman, Sebastopol) rate a good premium, especially those named to personnel on board HM Ships* London, Niger, Rodney *and* Wasp.

VALUE:	Unnamed	Engraved	Regimentally impressed	Officially impressed Army
No clasp	£70–90	£75–100	£80–100	£100–150
Alma	£120–140	£100–120	£120–140	£160–180
Inkerman	£100–120	£100–120	£100–120	£150–170
Azoff	£140–160	£180–200	—	£400–500
Balaklava	£100–120	£110–130	£150–200	£200–250
93rd Foot*	—	£350–400	£600–700	£900–1000
Heavy Brigade*	—	£350–400	£500–600	£800–950
Light Brigade (Charger)*	—	£1200–1500	£1400–1800	£5000–6000
Sebastopol	£80–115	£90–120	£100–125	£120–160
2 clasps	£140–160	£130–150	£135–165	£170–200
3 clasps	£200–240	£200–250	£220–250	£300–350
4 clasps	£250–280	£250–300	£250–300	£500–550
Miniature	£15–20, for each clasp add £10			

It is always difficult to price scarce or rare medals such as those marked as we have seen many engraved or Depot-style impressing that were probably named in the past 30 to 40 years. Also an engraved Crimea, together with a Mutiny and/or LS&GC would be worth considerably more than the prices indicated. Buyer beware!

120. TURKISH CRIMEA MEDAL

Date: 1855.

Campaign: Crimea 1855-56.

Branch of Service: British, French and Sardinian forces.

Ribbon: Crimson with green edges.

Metal: Silver.

Size: 36mm.

Description: (Obverse) a cannon, weapons and the four Allied flags with the name and date in the exergue; (reverse) the Toughra and Arabic date according to the Moslem calendar.

Clasps: None.

Comments: *Instituted by the Sultan of Turkey, this silver medal was conferred on troops of the three Allies who fought in the Crimea. The obverse types differed in the arrangement of the flags, corrsponding with the inscription in English, French or Italian in the exergue. Although the medals were intended to be issued to British, French and Sardinian troops respectively, they were issued haphazardly due to the British version being lost at sea. They were unnamed, but many were privately engraved or impressed later. Dangerous copies, emanating from the West Country of the UK is known to be circulating.*

VALUE:

			Miniature
CRIMEA (British Issue)		£75–85	£20–25
LA CRIMEE (French Issue)		£125–185	Rare
LA CRIMEA (Sardinia Issue)		£65–75	£10–15

121. INDIAN MUTINY MEDAL

Date: 1858.

Campaign: Sepoy mutiny, India 1857-58.

Branch of Service: British Army, Navy and Indian forces. It was also awarded to many civilians who took part in suppressing the Mutiny.

Ribbon: White with two red stripes.

Metal: Silver.

Size: 36mm.

Description: (Obverse) Wyon profile of Queen Victoria; (reverse) the standing figure of Britannia bestowing victor's laurels, with the British lion alongside. INDIA appears round the top with the dates 1857-1858 in the exergue.

Clasps: Delhi, Defence of Lucknow, Relief of Lucknow, Lucknow, Central India. The maximum recorded for a single medal is four (Bengal Artillery) or three (imperial troops, 9th Lancers).

Comments: *This medal was awarded to troops who took part in operations to quell the Sepoy mutiny which had been the immediate cause of the uprising, although it also served to focus attention on the Honourable East India Company's conduct of affairs and led directly to the transfer of the administration of India to the Crown. Medals with the clasp for the defence of Lucknow awarded to the original defenders rate a considerable premium, as do medals awarded to members of the Naval Brigade which witnessed most of the fighting in the mopping-up operations. Medals to Indian recipients although scarcer on the market, generally bring a little less than their British counterparts. Four-clasp medals to the Bengal Artillery bring from £800 if verified.*

VALUE:

	British Navy	British Army	Miniature
No clasp	£400–500*	£125–160	£15–20
Delhi	—	£180–200	£25–30
Defence of Lucknow			
original defender	—	£650–800	£35–45
first relief force	—	£350–400	
Relief of Lucknow	£500–600	£180–200	£25–30
Lucknow	£500–600	£180–200	£25–30
Central India	—	£160–190	£25–30, add
2 clasps	£600–700	£250–300	£10 for each
3 clasps (9th Lancers)	—	£600–700	additional clasp

*The 66 medals to HMS Shannon and the 253 to HMS Pearl rate an even higher premium.

122. SECOND CHINA WAR MEDAL

Date: 1861.

Campaign: Second China War 1857-60.

Branch of Service: British Army and Navy.

Ribbon: 33mm crimson with yellow edges.

Metal: Silver.

Size: 36mm.

Description: As the First China War Medal (no. 110), but without the year 1842 at the foot.

Clasps: Fatshan 1857, Canton 1857, Taku Forts, Pekin 1860.

Comments: *This medal was awarded to British sevicemen who took part, alongside the French, in the campaign against China which had been provoked by hostile acts against European nationals. The Royal Navy, under Admiral Sir Michael Seymour, destroyed a Chinese flotilla at Fatshan Creek, preparing the way for the attack on Canton whose capture brought the first phase to an end in June 1858. Reinforcements were meanwhile diverted to help put down the Indian mutiny. Fighting broke out again and this time large numbers of troops were involved in the assault on the Taku forts and the sack of Pekin (Beijing). Examples of the China medal of 1842, with or without clasps for 1857-60, have been recorded to recipients who fought in the Second China War. Medals may be found unnamed or with names officially engraved (Indian Army) or impressed (British Army, Indian Navy). Although those to the Navy were all issued unnamed, they are occasionally encountered unofficially named. Awards to Army and Navy personnel are other factors governing values.*

VALUE:	Unnamed	Army/Navy officially impressed	*Miniature*
No clasp	£90–120	£115–130	£18
China 1842	Rare	Rare	—
Fatshan 1857	£110–125	£145–175	£45
Canton 1857	£110–125	£150–185	£35
Taku Forts 1858	£110–125	£145–175	£30
Taku Forts 1860	£110–125	£150–185	£40
Pekin 1860	£110–125	£150–180	£30
2 clasps	£150–195	£225–275	£55
3 clasps	£175–220	£375–450	£65
4 clasps	£225–250		
5 clasps	£265–300		

123. NEW ZEALAND MEDALS

Date: 1869.
Campaigns: First and Second Maori Wars 1845–47 and 1860–66.
Branch of Service: Army, Navy and local volunteers.
Ribbon: Blue with a central orange stripe.
Metal: Silver.
Size: 36mm.
Description: (Obverse) Veiled head of Queen Victoria. (Reverse) Date
of service in a wreath, with NEW ZEALAND round the top and
VIRTUTIS HONOR (honour of valour) round the foot. Suspender
ornamented with New Zealand wattle.
Comments: *These medals were unusual in having the recipient's dates of
service die-struck on the centre of the reverse, though medals were also
issued without dates. As the medal was only awarded to surviving
veterans, the numbers issued in respect of the earlier conflict are
understandably small. Many of the dates are very scarce, especially those
issued to naval personnel in the first war. Only naval personnel received
dated medals in the first war.*

VALUE:	Army	Navy/Royal Marines
First war		
Undated	£300–350	—
1845–46 (155)	—	£325–360
1845–47 (36)	—	£375–425
1846–47 (69)	—	£475–525
1846 (10)	—	£575–625
1847 (20)	£500–575	£465–500
Second war		
Undated	£150–200	—
1860	£600–670	Rare
1860-61	£375–400	£275–350
1860-63	From £1550	—
1860-64	£225–275	—
1860-65	£245–295	—
1860-66	£225–275	—
1861	Rare	—
1861-63	Rare	—
1861-64	£250–325	—
1861-65	Rare	—
1861-66	£220–255	—
1862-66	Rare	—
1863	£265–300	Rare
1863-64	£240–285	£255–300
1863-65	£225–275	Scarce
1863-66	£225–275	Rare
1864	£235–285	Rare
1864-65	£220–255	—
1864-66	£220–255	—
1865	£285–345	£380–450
1865-66	£220–255	—
1866	£220–255	—
Miniature		
Undated	£60–65	
Dated	£80+	

124. ABYSSINIAN WAR MEDAL

Date: 1869.
Campaign: Abyssinia (Ethiopia) 1867–68.
Branch of Service: Royal Navy, British and Indian Armies.
Ribbon: Red with broad white edges.
Metal: Silver.
Size: 33mm diameter.
Description: (Obverse) the veiled portrait of Victoria framed by a zigzag pattern with floral ornament alternating with the letters of the name ABYSSINIA. The recipient's name and unit were embossed in the centre of the reverse except most to Indian troops which were impressed. Suspension is by a ring via a large crown standing proud from the top of the medal.
Clasps: None.
Comments: *The imprisonment of British subjects by King Theodore of Abyssinia precipitated a punitive expedition under General Sir Robert Napier involving ships of the Royal Navy, a naval brigade and troops of the British and Indian armies. Because casualties were unusually light (only two killed and 27 wounded), medals from this campaign are not so highly rated as those from other nineteenth century wars.*

VALUE:

British troops	£220–250
Royal Navy	£220–250
RN Rocket Brigade	£400–450
Indian troops	£120–150
Miniature	£55–65

125. CANADA GENERAL SERVICE MEDAL

Date: 1899.
Campaign: Canada 1866–70.
Branch of Service: Royal Navy, British Army and Canadian units.
Ribbon: Red, white and red.
Metal: Silver.
Size: 36mm.
Description: (Obverse) crowned and veiled Old Head bust of Queen Victoria by Sir Thomas Brock (reflecting the very late issue of the medal). (Reverse) Canadian flag surrounded by maple leaves.
Clasps: Fenian Raid 1866, Fenian Raid 1870, Red River 1870.
Comments: *This medal was not authorised until January 1899, thirty years after the event, and was issued by the Canadian government to British and Canadian local forces who took part in operations to put down the Fenian raids of 1866 and 1870 and the Red River rebellion of the latter year. Of the 16,100 medals awarded, 15,000 went to local forces. Naval medals command a premium.*

VALUE:

	Canadian forces	British Army	Royal Navy	*Miniature*
Fenian Raid 1866	£170–200	£200–240	£220–250	£60
Fenian Raid 1870	£170–200	£200–240	£300–400	£65
Red River 1870	£600–650	£650–800	£850–1000	£85
2 clasps	£220–250	—	—	£80
3 clasps	Rare	—	—	—

126. ASHANTEE MEDAL

Date: 1874.
Campaign: Gold Coast 1873–74.
Branch of Service: Royal Navy, Army and native troops.
Ribbon: Orange with black stripes at the sides and two narrow black stripes towards the centre.
Metal: Silver.
Size: 36mm.
Description: The obverse and reverse are similar to the East and West Africa Medal of 1887–1900, differing solely in thickness and the method of naming. The veiled profile of Victoria graces the obverse while the reverse, designed by Sir Edwin Poynter, shows a skirmish in the jungle between British soldiers and Ashantee warriors.
Clasps: Coomassie.
Comments: *All ranks who took part in operations against King Kalkali of Ashantee, Gold Coast, were awarded this medal, approved in June 1874. The campaign lasted only four weeks but was fought with great ferocity and resulted in the award of four VCs. There was also a very high incidence of sickness and disease among the troops, notably the naval contingent. Unusually the medals are named in engraved capitals filled in with black.*

VALUE:

	Navy	Army	Natives	Miniature
No clasp	£120–140	£140–180	£75–100	£30
Coomassie	£240–280	£300–320	£125–160	£65

127. SOUTH AFRICA MEDAL

Date: 1879.
Campaign: South Africa 1877-79.
Branch of Service: Royal Navy, Army and colonial units.
Ribbon: As no. 115.
Metal: Silver.
Size: 36mm.
Description: The same design as no. 115, except that the date 1853 in the exergue is replaced by a Zulu shield and four crossed assegais.
Clasps: 1877, 1877–8, 1877–9, 1877–8–9, 1878, 1878–9, 1879.
Comments: *The campaign began in 1877 with an attack on the Fingoes by the Galeka and Gaika tribes and culminated in the showdown between the Zulus and the British when Lord Chelmsford's column was annihilated at Isandhlwana. When the 3000 Zulus advanced on Rorke's Drift, however, they were checked with heavy losses by a tiny garrison of 139 men. During the defence no fewer than eleven VCs were won—the largest number for a single action. The campaign concluded with the defeat of Dinizulu and his warriors at Ulundi.*

VALUE:

	Navy	Army	Colonial	Miniature
No clasp	£125–150	£135–175	£120–145	£25
1877	—	Rare	£1250–1500	—
1877–8	£450–550	£250–325	£250–275	£40
1877–9	—	Unique	£4500–6000	—
1877–8–9	£400–475	£275–300	£200–250	£35
1878	—	£285–325	£220–275	£40
1878–9	—	£275–300	£220–275	£35
1879	£200–220	£255–285	£200–250	£35

Isandhlwana casualty	£2000–3500	
Rorke's Drift participant	From £7500	

128. AFGHANISTAN MEDAL

Date: 1881.
Campaign: Afghanistan 1878–80.
Branch of Service: British and Indian Armies.
Ribbon: Dark green with broad crimson edges.
Metal: Silver or bronze.
Size: 36mm.
Description: (Obverse) veiled profile of Queen Victoria. (Reverse) a column on the march, with an elephant carrying cannon. The dates 1878–79–80 appear in the exergue.
Clasps: Ali Musjid, Peiwar Kotal, Charasia, Kabul, Ahmed Kel, Kandahar. Maximum number of clasps per medal is four.
Comments: *This medal was awarded to all who took part in the campaigns against Afghanistan known as the Second Afghan War. In 1877 the Amir refused to accept a British resident and the following year raised an army which began harrassing the Indian frontier. A treaty with Russia, however, granting it protective rights in Afghanistan, precipitated an armed response from Britain. In 1880 General Roberts led a column from Kabul to Kandahar to relieve General Burrows and the resulting battle led to the defeat of the Afghans and the conclusion of the war. Medals awarded to the 66th Foot (Berkshire regiment) and E Battery of B Brigade, Royal Artillery rate a high premium as these units sustained the heaviest casualties at the battle of Maiwand in July 1880.*

VALUE:	British units	Indian units	*Miniature*
No clasp bronze	—	£140–180	—
No clasp silver	£90–100	£40–60	£20
Ali Musjid	£140–180	£60–80	£30
Peiwar Kotal	£150–200	£60–80	£40
Charasia	£140–180	£60–80	£30
Kabul	£140–180	£60–80	£25
Ahmed Khel	£140–180	£60–80	£30
Kandahar	£140–180	£60–80	£30
2 clasps	£200–240	£70–95	£50
3 clasps	£300–325	£110–135	£65
4 clasps	£375–500	£150–200	£80
Maiwand casualties:			
66th Foot	£750–850	—	
E Bty, B Bde RHA	£750–850	—	

129. KABUL TO KANDAHAR STAR

Date: 1881.
Campaign: Afghanistan 1878–80.
Branch of Service: British and Indian Armies.
Ribbon: Watered silk red, white, yellow, white and blue.
Metal: Bronze from captured guns.
Size: Height 60mm, width 45mm.
Description: (Obverse) a rayed five-pointed star surmounted by a crown with a ring for suspension. The centre is inscribed KABUL TO KANDAHAR with 1880 at the foot and the VRI monogram of the Queen Empress in the centre. Stars were either issued unnamed, or had the recipient's name impressed (to British) or engraved (to Indian troops) on the reverse.
Clasps: None.
Comments: *This star, struck by Jenkins of Birmingham, was awarded to those who took part in the epic 300-mile march from the Afghan capital to Kandahar, led by General Roberts to relieve the beleaguered forces of General Burrows.*

VALUE:

Unnamed	£80–95
Impressed (British troops)	£145–165
Engraved (Indian troops)	£100–135
Miniature	£40–65

Maiwand (see no. 128)

130. CAPE OF GOOD HOPE GENERAL SERVICE MEDAL

Date: 1900.
Campaign: Uprisings in Transkei, Basutoland and Bechuanaland 1880-97.
Branch of Service: Local forces and volunteers.
Ribbon: Dark blue with a central yellow stripe.
Metal: Silver.
Size: 36mm.
Description: (Obverse) Jubilee bust of Queen Victoria by Sir Joseph Boehm; (reverse) arms of Cape Colony.
Clasps: Transkei, Basutoland, Bechuanaland.
Comments: *Instituted by the Cape government, this medal acknowledged service in putting down the Transkei (1880-1) and Bechuana (1896-7) rebellions and dealing with the unrest that erupted sporadically in Basutoland for much of this period. The medal was awarded, with one or more campaign clasps, to local forces and volunteer regiments. Ten medals were, however, officially awarded without a clasp.*

VALUE:

		Miniature
Transkei (1070)	£250–280	£50
Basutoland (2150)	£140–160	£50
Bechuanaland (2580)	£140–160	£45
2 clasps	£230–260	£65
3 clasps (23)	Rare	—
No clasp	Very rare	

131. EGYPT MEDAL 1882–89

Dated rev.

Undated rev.

Date: 1882.

Campaign: Egypt 1882–89.

Branch of Service: Royal Navy and Army.

Ribbon: Three blue and two white stripes.

Metal: Silver.

Size: 36mm.

Description: (Obverse) the veiled profile of Queen Victoria; (reverse) the Sphinx.

Clasps: 13, listed below. Maximum number for one medal is 7, but only one such award was made. Common two-clasp combinations are denoted below by /.

Comments: *British involvement in Egypt deepened after the opening of the Suez Canal in 1869, many British officers being seconded to the Khedive's Army. When the Army mutinied in 1882 and triggered off a general anti-European uprising, an Anglo-French expedition was mounted. Subsequently the French withdrew before a landing was effected. Trouble erupted in the Sudan (under Anglo-Egyptian administration) in 1884 where General Gordon was besieged at Khartoum. Further campaigns aimed at the overthrow of the Mahdi and the reconquest of the Sudan. These prolonged operations created immense logistical problems. Nile transportation in particular was a matter resolved only when Canadian voyageurs were recruited to handle the river-boats. In addition, a contingent of troops from New South Wales "answered the Empire's call" and medals awarded to them for the Suakin campaign of 1885 are much sought after. Except where noted, the prices quoted below are for medals awarded to British Army personnel. Medals awarded to Indian or Egyptian troops are generally worth about 25 per cent less than comparable awards to British Army units.*

VALUE:		*Miniature*
No clasp (dated)	£70–85	£15
No clasp (undated)	£70–85	£20
Alexandria 11th July	£120–140	£22
Tel-el-Kebir	£120–140	£22
El-Teb	£160–200	£35
Tamaai	£170–210	£30
El-Teb/Tamaai	£160–200	£30
Suakin 1884	£130–150	£25
The Nile 1884-85	£130–150	£25
The Nile 1884-85/Abu Klea	£450–550	£30
The Nile 1884-85/Kirbekan	£160–180	£30
Suakin 1885	£130–150	£25
Suakin 1885/Tofrek	£200–220	£35
Gemaizah 1888	£150–180	£40
Toski 1889	£200–250	£50
2 clasps	£160–180	£40
3 clasps	£220–260	£50
4 clasps	£340–380	£60
5 clasps	£450–550	—
Canadian boatmen	£900–1000	
NSW units (Suakin 1885)	From £700	

132. KHEDIVE'S STAR

Date: 1882.
Campaign: Egypt 1892-91.
Branch of Service: Royal Navy and Army.
Ribbon: 37mm deep blue.
Metal: Bronze.
Size: Height 60mm; width 45mm.
Description: A five-pointed star with a circular centre showing the Sphinx and Pyramids surrounded by a band inscribed EGYPT followed by a year round the top, with 'Khedive of Egypt' and the year in the Moslem calendar in Arabic at the foot. (Reverse) the Khedive's monogram surmounted by a crown. The star is suspended by a ring from an ornamental clasp in the centre of which is a star and crescent.
Clasps: Tokar.
Comments: *This star, struck by Jenkins of Birmingham, was conferred by Khedive Tewfik of Egypt on those who qualified for the Egypt medal and it was invariably worn alongside, to the detriment of the silver medal which suffered abrasion from the points of the star. There was also an undated version found with or without a campaign clasp for Tokar, awarded in 1891. These stars were issued unnamed.*

VALUE:		Miniature
1882	£45–50	£10
1884	£50–55	£12
1884-86	£45–55	£12
Undated	£65–75	£12
Undated with Tokar bar	£120–140	£60

133. GENERAL GORDON'S STAR FOR THE SIEGE OF KHARTOUM

Date: 1884.
Campaign: Mahdist uprising, Sudan 1884.
Branch of Service: British and Sudanese forces.
Ribbon: Deep blue (?).
Metal: Silver or pewter.
Size: Height 80mm; maximum width 54mm.
Description: Star with three concentric circles and seven groups of rays on which are superimposed seven crescents and stars. Suspension by a ring from a Crescent and Star ornament.
Clasps: None.
Comments: *To boost the morale of the defenders Charles Gordon, commanding the garrison at Khartoum, had this star cast locally in a sand mould, using his own breast star of the Order of Mejidieh as the model. Exceptionally, recipients had to purchase their medals, the proceeds going to a fund to feed the poor.*

VALUE:	
Silver gilt	£900–1200
Silver	£600–800
Pewter	£400–500

134. NORTH WEST CANADA MEDAL

Date: 1885.

Campaign: Riel's rebellion 1885.

Branch of Service: Mainly local forces.

Ribbon: Blue-grey with red stripes towards the edges.

Metal: Silver.

Size: 36mm.

Description: (Obverse) bust of Queen Victoria; (reverse) the inscription NORTH WEST CANADA 1885 within a frame of maple leaves.

Clasps: Saskatchewan,

Comments: *Paradoxically, while the medal for the Fenian Raids of 1866–70 was not sanctioned till 1899, this medal for service in the North West was authorised immediately after the conclusion of operations against the Metis led by Louis Riel. It was issued unnamed, with or without the clasp for Saskatchewan where the bulk of the action took place. Of particular interest are medals to officers and men aboard the steamship* Northcote *involved in a boat action; exceptionally, their medals were impressed. Other medals may be encountered with unofficial naming. The medal was awarded to sixteen British staff officers but the majority of medals (5600 in all) went to local forces.*

VALUE:		*Miniature*
No clasp	£200–250	£35
Saskatchewan	£500–550	£65
Northcote recipient	£800–1000	

135. ROYAL NIGER COMPANY'S MEDAL

Date: 1899.

Campaign: Nigeria 1886–97.

Branch of Service: Officers and men of the Company's forces.

Ribbon: Three equal stripes of yellow, black and white.

Metal: Silver or bronze.

Size: 39.5mm.

Description: (Obverse) the Boehm bust of Queen Victoria; (reverse) the Company's arms in a laurel wreath.

Clasps: Nigeria 1886-97 (silver), Nigeria (bronze).

Comments: *This medal was issued in silver to Europeans and bronze to natives for service in the vast territories administered by the Royal Niger chartered company. Silver medals were impressed in capitals, but those in bronze were more usually stamped with the recipient's service (constabulary) number. Specimens of both versions were later struck from the original dies but these lack name or number.*

VALUE:		*Miniature*
Silver named (85)	£2000–2500	
Original Silver specimen	£80–100	£130–150
Bronze named (250)	£450–500	
Original Bronze specimen	£60–80	

136. IMPERIAL BRITISH EAST AFRICA COMPANY'S MEDAL

Date: 1890.
Campaign: East Africa (Kenya and Uganda) 1888–95.
Branch of Service: Company forces.
Ribbon: Plain blue.
Metal: Silver.
Size: 39mm.
Description: (Obverse) the Company badge, a crowned and radiant sun, with a Suaheli inscription in Arabic round the foot signifying "the reward of bravery"; (reverse) plain except for a wreath. Suspension is by a plain ring or an ornamental scroll.
Comments: *The rarest of the medals awarded by the chartered companies, this medal was originally intended solely as a gallantry award; but after the BEA Company was wound up in 1895 further issues were authorised by the Foreign Office for service in Witu (1890) and the Ugandan civil war (1890-91). Less than thirty medals are known.*

VALUE: From £600   *Miniature* £200–250

137. EAST AND WEST AFRICA MEDAL

Date: 1892.
Campaigns: East and West Africa 1887–1900.
Branch of Service: Royal Navy, Army and native forces.
Ribbon: As 126.
Metal: Silver or bronze.
Size: 36mm.
Description: As for the Ashantee Medal (q.v.), distinguished only by its clasps.
Clasps: 21 (see below). A 22nd operation (Mwele, 1895–96) was denoted by engraving on the rim of the medal.
Comments: *This medal was awarded for general service in a number of small campaigns and punitive expeditions. Though usually awarded in silver, it was sometimes struck in bronze for issue to native servants, bearers and drivers. British regiments as such were not involved in any of the actions, but individual officers and NCOs were seconded as staff officers and instructors and their medals bear the names of their regiments. Units of the Royal Navy were also involved in many of the coastal or river actions. Especially sought after are naval medals with the bar for Lake Nyassa 1893 in which the ships* Pioneer *and* Adventure *were hauled in sections overland through 200 miles of jungle.*

VALUE:

	Royal Navy	Europeans	Natives	*Miniature*
1887–8	£390–500	£190–160	£110–140	£40
Witu 1890	£140–160	£150–180	£90–110	£40
1891–2	£180–200	£160–180	£110–140	£40
1892 (8)	£770–990	£180–200	£110–140	£40
Witu August 1893	£170–200	—	£130–150	£60
Liwondi 1893	£1650–2200	—	—	—
Juba River 1893	£1650–2200	—	—	—
Lake Nyassa 1893	£1650–2200	—	—	—
1893–94	£660–880	£160–180	£100–120	£50
Gambia 1894	£160–180	—	£110–140	£45
Benin River 1894	£160–180	£140–160	£100–120	£40
Brass River 1895	£200–220	—	—	£45
M'wele 1895–6	£110–140	£110–140	£90–110	£100
1896–98	—	£330–390	£170–220	£30
Niger 1897	—	£280–330	£170–220	£30
Benin 1897	£130–150	£110–140	£160–220	£35
Dawkita 1897	£880–1100	Rare	Rare	—
1897–98	—	£140–170	£130–140	£40
1898	£660–880	£150–180	£130–150	£40
Sierra Leone 1898–99	£150–190	£140–170	£90–110	£30
1899	£880–1100	£240–270	£160–180	£35
1900	—	£220–245	£140–160	£35

138. BRITISH SOUTH AFRICA COMPANY'S MEDAL

1st type rev.

Mashonaland (2nd) rev.

Date: 1896.
Campaign: South Africa 1890-97.
Branch of Service: British Army and colonial units.
Ribbon: Seven equal stripes, four yellow and three dark blue.
Metal: Silver.
Size: 36mm.
Description: (Obverse) the Old Head bust of Queen Victoria; (reverse) a charging lion impaled by a spear, with a mimosa bush in the background and a litter of assegais and a shield on the ground.
Clasps: Mashonaland 1890, Matabeleland 1893, Rhodesia 1896, Mashonaland 1897.
Comments: *Originally instituted in 1896 for award to troops taking part in the suppression of the Matabele rebellion, it was later extended to cover operations in Rhodesia (1896) and Mashonaland (1897). The medal, as originally issued, had the inscription MATABELELAND 1893 at the top of the reverse. The medal was re-issued with RHODESIA 1896 or MASHONALAND 1897 inscribed on the reverse, but holders of medals for their first campaign only added clasps for subsequent campaigns. Rather belatedly, it was decided in 1927 to issue medals retrospectively for the Mashonaland campaign of 1890; in this instance the name and date of the campaign were not inscribed on the reverse though the details appeared on the clasp. An unusually ornate suspender has roses, thistles, shamrocks and leeks entwined. Only two medals are known with all four clasps, while only fifteen medals had three clasps.*

VALUE:

		Miniature
Mashonaland 1890	£600–700	£30
Matabeleland 1893	£200–220	£30
with 1 clasp	£280–320	£50
with 2 clasps	£450–550	£65
Rhodesia 1896	£200–220	£30
with 1 clasp	£300–350	£50
Mashonaland 1897	£220–250	£30

139. HUNZA NAGAR BADGE

Date: 1891.
Campaign: Hunza and Nagar 1891.
Branch of Service: Jammu and Kashmir forces.
Ribbon: Large (46mm x 32mm) with a broad red diagonal band and white centre stripe and green upper left and lower right corners.
Metal: Bronze.
Size: 55mm x 27mm.
Description: A uniface rectangular plaque featuring three soldiers advancing on the crenellated hill fort of Nilt, with mountains in the background. The inscription HUNZA NAGAR 1891 appears lower right. It was intended to be worn as a brooch at the neck but subsequently many were fitted with a suspender for wear with a red and green ribbon.
Clasps: None.

Comments: *Gurney of London manufactured this badge which was awarded by the Maharajah of Jammu and Kashmir to his own troops who served in the operation against the border states of Hunza and Nagar and qualified for the Indian general service medal with clasp for Hunza 1891. The punitive expedition was led by Colonel A. Durand in response to the defiant attitude of the Hunza and Nagar chiefs towards the British agency at Gilgit.*

VALUE: £450–500

140. CENTRAL AFRICA MEDAL

Date: 1895.
Campaigns: Central Africa 1891–98.
Branch of Service: Mainly local forces.
Ribbon: Three equal stripes of black, white and terracotta representing the Africans, Europeans and Indians.
Metal: Silver or bronze.
Size: 36mm.
Description: Obverse and reverse as the East and West Africa (Ashantee) medal, distinguished only by its ribbon.
Clasps: Originally issued without a clasp but one for Central Africa 1894–98 was subsequently authorised.
Comment: *Though generally issued in silver, a bronze version was awarded to native servants. The first issue of this medal had a simple ring suspension and no clasp. For the second issue a clasp, Central Africa 1894–98 was authorised and the medal was issued with a straight bar suspender, which is very rare.*

VALUE:

		Miniature
Without clasp (ring)	£300–375	£80
Clasp and ring suspension	£350–400	—
Clasp and bar suspension	£550–650	£40
Bronze	From £1000	—

141. HONG KONG PLAGUE MEDAL

Date: 1894.
Campaign: Hong Kong, May-September 1894.
Branch of Service: Royal Navy, Royal Engineers, KSLI and local personnel.
Ribbon: Red with yellow edges and two narrow yellow stripes in the centre.
Metal: Silver.
Size: 36mm.
Description: (Obverse) a Chinese lying on a trestle table being supported by a man warding off the winged figure of Death while a woman tends to the sick man. The year 1894 appears on a scroll in the exergue, while the name of the colony in Chinese pictograms is inscribed on the left of the field. (Reverse) inscribed PRESENTED BY THE HONG KONG COMMUNITY round the circumference, and FOR SERVICES RENDERED DURING THE PLAGUE OF 1894 in seven lines across the centre. It was fitted with a plain ring for suspension.
Clasps: None.
Comments: *The colonial authorities in Hong Kong awarded this medal to nurses, civil servants, police, British Army and Royal Navy personnel who rendered assistance when the crown colony was stricken by a severe epidemic of bubonic plague in May 1894. Despite stringent measures, over 2500 people died in the ensuing three months. About 400 medals were issued in silver and awarded to 300 men of the King's Shropshire Light Infantry, 50 petty officers and ratings of the Royal Navy and NCOs and other ranks of the Royal Engineers, as well as about the same number of police and junior officials, while 45 were struck in gold for award to officers, nursing sisters and senior officials.*

VALUE:

		Miniature
Gold (45)	From £4000	—
Silver (400)	£1200–1500	£50–65

142. INDIA MEDAL

Date: 1896.
Campaign: India 1895–1902.
Branch of Service: British and Indian forces.
Ribbon: Crimson with two dark green stripes.
Metal: Silver or bronze.
Size: 36mm.
Description: Issued with two different obverses, portraying Queen Victoria (1895–1901) and King Edward VII in field marshal's uniform (1901–02). (Reverse) British and Indian soldiers supporting a standard.
Clasps: Seven, mainly for actions on the North West Frontier (see below).
Comments: *This medal replaced the India GSM which had been awarded for various minor campaigns over a period of four decades from 1854. Combatant troops were given the medal in silver but native bearers and servants received a bronze version. Although the clasp Waziristan 1901–2 is rare to British recipients it was awarded to a number of regiments.*

VALUE:

	British regiments	Indian	Bronze	Miniature
Defence of Chitral 1895	—	£700–800	Rare	£60
Relief of Chitral 1895	£85–95	£50–60	£50–60	£20
Punjab Frontier 1897-98	£80–90	£50–60	£65–75	£15
pair with Malakand 1897	£90–100	£60–75	£60–70	£20–25
pair with Samana 1897	£90–100	£60–75	£70–80	£20–25
pair with Tirah 1897-98	£100–110	£50–65	£50–60	£20–25
Waziristan 1901-2	£255–300	£70–80	£60–70	£20–25
3 clasps	£150–165	£85–115	£80–115	£50–60
4 clasps	—	£115–130	—	£60–80

143. JUMMOO AND KASHMIR MEDAL

Date: 1895.
Campaign: Defence of Chitral 1895.
Branch of Service: Native levies.
Ribbon: White with red stripes at the edges and a broad central green stripe.
Metal: Bronze, silver.
Size: 35mm high; 38mm wide.
Description: This medal, by Gurney of London, has a unique kidney shape showing the arms of Jummoo (Jammu) and Kashmir on the obverse. (Reverse) a view of Chitral fort with troops in the foreground.
Clasps: Chitral 1895.
Comments: *Awarded by the Maharajah of Jummoo (Jammu) and Kashmir to the Indian troops who participated in the defence of Chitral (a dependency of Kashmir) during the siege of 4 March to 20 April by Chitralis and Afghans led by Umra Khan and Sher Afzul.*

VALUE:

Named	£350–400
Unnamed	£240–280
Silver	Rare

144. ASHANTI STAR

Date: 1896.
Campaign: Gold Coast 1896.
Branch of Service: British forces.
Ribbon: Yellow with two black stripes.
Metal: Bronze.
Size: 44mm.
Description: A saltire cross with a four-pointed star in the angles, surmounted by a circular belt inscribed ASHANTI 1896 around a British crown. The plain reverse is simply inscribed FROM THE QUEEN.
Clasps: None.
Comments: *Issued unnamed, but the colonel of the West Yorkshire Regiment had the medals of the second battalion engraved at his own expense. Some 2000 stars were awarded to officers and men serving in the expedition led by Major-General F.C. Scott against the tyrannical King Prempeh. It is believed that the star was designed by Princess Henry of Battenberg whose husband died of fever during the campaign.*

VALUE:

Unnamed	£130–150
Named to West Yorkshire Regiment	£280–325
Miniature	£35–40

INTERIOR OF CHITRAL FORT

(see nos. 142 & 143)

145. QUEEN'S SUDAN MEDAL

Date: 1899.
Campaign: Reconquest of the Sudan 1896–97.
Branch of Service: Royal Navy, Army and local forces.
Ribbon: Half-yellow and half-black representing the desert and the Sudanese nation, divided by a thin crimson stripe representing the British forces.
Metal: Silver or bronze.
Size: 36mm.
Description: (Obverse) the Jubilee bust of Queen Victoria. (Reverse) a seated figure of Victory holding palms and laurels with flags in the background, the word SUDAN appearing on a tablet at her feet.
Clasps: None.
Comments: *Unusually, no clasps were granted for individual actions which included the celebrated battle of Omdurman in which young Winston Churchill charged with the cavalry. Medals named to the 21st Lancers are especially desirable on that account.*

VALUE:

Bronze named	£160–180
Silver named to British Regt	£165–185
Indian Regt	£125–140
21st Lancers (confirmed charger)	From £900
RN/RM (46)	£700–950
Miniature	£25–30

146. KHEDIVE'S SUDAN MEDAL 1896–1908

(reverse)

Date: 1897.
Campaign: Sudan 1896-1908.
Branch of Service: Royal Navy and British and Egyptian Armies.
Ribbon: 38mm yellow with a broad central deep blue stripe, symbolising the desert and the River Nile.
Metal: Silver or bronze.
Size: 39mm.
Description: (Obverse) an elaborate Arabic inscription translating as 'Abbas Hilmi the Second' and the date 1314 (AD 1897); (reverse) an oval shield surrounded by flags and a trophy of arms. Bar suspender.
Clasps: Fifteen (see below) but medals with more than the two clasps 'The Atbara' and 'Khartoum' are unusual. Inscribed in English and Arabic.
Comments: *Instituted by the Khedive of Egypt in February 1897 and granted to those who served in the reconquest of Dongola province in the Sudan (1896-8) as well as in subsequent operations for the pacification of the southern provinces. It was awarded to officers and men of the British and Egyptian Armies and Royal Navy personnel who served on the Nile steamboats. In addition, the crews of the Royal Naval ships HMS* Melita *(139) and HMS* Scout *(149) were awarded silver medals with no clasps for Dongola 1896 (but were* not *awarded the Queen's Sudan Medal 1896–98). Medals to Royal Naval personnel with clasps are rare and command a high premium: Hafir (16), The Atbara (6), Sudan 1897 (12), Khartoum (33), Gedaref (9), Gedid (5) and Sudan 1899 (6).*

VALUE:

		Miniature			*Miniature*
No clasp silver	£70–80	£20	Jerok	£100–110	£45
No clasp silver (RN)	£150–200	—	Nyam-Nyam	£120–130	£40
No clasp bronze	£80–90	—	Talodi	£120–130	£45
Firket	£100–110	£30	Katfia	£120–130	£45
Hafir	£100–110	£30	Nyima	£110–120	£35
Abu Hamed	£100–110	£35			
Sudan 1897	£100–110	£35	2 clasps	£120–130	Add £10–15
The Atbara	£100–110	£25	3 clasps	£130–150	per clasp
Khartoum	£120–130	£25	4 clasps	£150–170	
Gedaref	£100–110	£40	5 clasps	£160–180	
Gedid	£100–110	£40	6 clasps	£170–190	
Sudan 1899	£100–110	£25	7 clasps	£190–220	
Bahr-el-Ghazal 1900–2	£135–165	£45	8 clasps	£220–260	

147. EAST AND CENTRAL AFRICA MEDAL

Date: 1899.
Campaigns: East and Central Africa 1897–99.
Branch of Service: British, Indian and local forces.
Ribbon: Half yellow, half red.
Metal: Silver or bronze.
Size: 36mm.
Description: (Obverse) the Jubilee bust of Queen Victoria; (reverse) a standing figure of Britannia with the British lion alongside.
Clasps: Five (see below).
Comments: *Instituted for service in operations in Uganda and the southern Sudan, it was awarded in silver to combatants and in bronze to camp followers. Most of the medals were awarded to troops of the Uganda Rifles and various Indian regiments. The few British officers and NCOs were troop commanders and instructors seconded from their regiments and their medals are worth very much more than the prices quoted, which are for native awards.*

VALUE:

	Europeans	Natives	Miniature
No clasp silver	—	£220–240	£30–35
Lubwa's (with clasp Uganda 1897-98)	—	£330–390	£40–45
Uganda 1897-98	£350–400	£300–360	£40–45
1898 (silver)	—	£300–360	£40–45
1898 (bronze)	—	£420–600	—
Uganda 1899	—	£300–360	£35–40

147A. UGANDA STAR

Instituted: 1897–98.
Campaign: Mutiny of Sudanese troops in Uganda.
Branch of Service: African civilians and soldiers.
Ribbon: None.
Metal: Silver.
Description: An eight-pointed uniface star surmounted by a crown, with the dates 1897 and 1898 on a circular rim enclosing the Old Head or Veiled Bust of Queen Victoria. Brooch-mounted. Manufactured by Carrington of London and issued in a blue plush-lined case.
Comments: *This award, approved by the Foreign Office and sanctioned by Queen Victoria, acknowledged the loyalty of African tribal leaders but, in a few cases, was also awarded to Sudanese troops (one, in fact, a Tunisian) who fought gallantly in quelling the serious mutiny of Sudanese troops of the Uganda Rifles. It was for this action that British, Indian and Local forces were awarded the East and Central Africa Medal with the bar for Lubwa's (see above). Only 39 stars were awarded.*

VALUE: From £2500

148. BRITISH NORTH BORNEO COMPANY'S MEDALS

1st type obv.

1st type rev.

Date: 1897.

Campaign: North Borneo 1897–1915.

Branch of Service: Company forces.

Ribbon: (i) 36mm gold watered silk, (ii) 32mm yellow with maroon edges and a central blue stripe (Punitive Expeditions and Rundum) or (iii) 32mm yellow with a central green stripe (Tambunan).

Metal: Silver or bronze.

Size: 39mm.

Description: (Obverse) the Company arms; (reverse) the British lion standing in front of a bush adorned by the Company flag, with a small wreath in the exergue.

Clasps: Four (see below).

Comments: *This series of medals was made by the British North Borneo Company for service in what is now Sabah. The medals, struck by Spink and Son of London, were issued in silver and bronze (except for Rundum) to British and Bornean officials, Sikh troops and a small number of servants. The first obverse showed the Company arms with supporters, crest and motto. This medal was issued unnamed and unnumbered. Specimens from the original dies are known with the S of Spink or Son erased and the word "Copy" on the rim. The medal was re-issued for a second expedition in 1898 and on this occasion it was named and numbered to the recipient. For a third expedition, in 1899–1900, the second obverse was used, showing the Company shield without supporters, motto or crest, but inscribed BRITISH NORTH BORNEO and with the date 1900 round the foot. This was used in conjunction with a new reverse showing the Company crest, two arms supporting a flag. This medal had a yellow ribbon with a central green stripe. In 1915 an expedition to raise the siege of Rundum was marked by the issue of a silver medal, similar to the 1897 medal but only struck in silver and fitted with a Rundum clasp.*

VALUE:

	Silver	Bronze	Miniature
Punitive Expedition (1897)	£60–80	£40–60	£80–100
Punitive Expeditions (1898)	£70–80	£40–60	£45
Tambunan	£70–80	£50–60	£45
Rundum	£80–100	—	£50
Originally named and numbered	from £1500	£650–850	

2nd type obv.

2nd type rev.

149. SULTAN OF ZANZIBAR'S MEDAL

Date: 1896.
Campaign: East Africa 1896.
Branch of Service: Sultan's forces.
Ribbon: Plain bright scarlet.
Metal: Silver.
Size: 36mm.
Description: (Obverse) a facing bust of Sultan Hamid bin Thwain surrounded by a Suaheli inscription in Arabic; (reverse) same inscription set in four lines.
Clasps: Pumwani, Jongeni, Takaungu, Mwele (inscribed only in Arabic).
Comments: *Awarded to the Zanzibari contingent who served under Lieut. Lloyd-Matthews RN in East Africa alongside British and Imperial forces.*

VALUE: £300–400   *Miniature*   £80–100

150. QUEEN'S SOUTH AFRICA MEDAL

1st type rev.

Date: 1899.
Campaign: Anglo-Boer War 1899-1902.
Branch of Service: British and Imperial forces.
Ribbon: Red with two narrow blue stripes and a broad central orange stripe.
Metal: Silver or bronze.
Size: 36mm.
Description: (Obverse) the Jubilee bust of Queen Victoria; (reverse) Britannia holding the flag and a laurel crown towards a large group of soldiers, with warships offshore. The words SOUTH AFRICA are inscribed round the top.
Clasps: 26 authorised but the maximum recorded for a single medal is nine to the Army and eight to the Navy.
Comments: *Because of the large number of British and imperial forces which took part and the numerous campaign and battle clasps awarded, this is one of the most popular and closely studied of all medals, offering immense scope to the collector. A total of 178,000 medals were awarded. Numerous specialist units were involved for the first time, as well as locally raised units and contingents from India, Canada, Australia and New Zealand. Of particular interest are the medals awarded to war correspondents and nurses which set precedents for later wars. Although nurses received the medal they were not issued with clasps to which they were entitled. A small number of bronze medals without a clasp were issued to bearers and servants in Indian units. The original issue of the QSA depicts Britannia's outstretched hand pointing towards the R of AFRICA and bears the dates 1899–1900 on the reverse field. Less than 70 of these were issued to Lord Strathcona's Horse who had returned to Canada before the war ended, but as the war dragged on the date was removed before any other medals were issued, although some medals can be found with a "ghost" of this date still to be seen. On the third type reverse there is again no date but Britannia's hand points towards the F. The prices for clasps given below are for clasps issued in combination with others. Some clasps are much scarcer when issued singly than combined with other clasps and conversely some clasps are not recorded on their own. Verified ten-clasp medals to South African units are known.*

continued overleaf

150. QUEEN'S SOUTH AFRICA MEDAL *continued*

VALUE:

	RN	British	SA/Indian	Aus/NZ	Canadian
No clasp bronze	—	—	£100–120	—	—
No clasp silver	£80–100	£40–50	£75–100	£85–95	£120–130
Cape Colony	£150–200	£50–60	£45–55	£50–55	£120–130
Rhodesia	£1000	£120–150	£110–120	£165–220	£290–310
Relief of Mafeking	—	—	£160–180	£145–180	£385–410
Defence of Kimberley	—	£125–150	£110–120	—	—
Talana	—	£150–180	£110–150	—	—
Elandslaagte	—	£135–155	£240–300	—	—
Defence of Ladysmith	£220–250	£90–110	£85–100	—	—
Belmont	£180–220	£70–90	—	£200–220	—
Modder River	£180–220	£70–90	—	£200–220	—
Tugela Heights	£350–500	£60–70	—	—	—
Natal	£250–300	£75–100	£75–85	—	£210–220
Relief of Kimberley	£750–900	£65–75	£50–60	£110–130	—
Paardeberg	£180–220	£60–70	£65–75	£100–110	£140–150
Orange Free State	£160–180	£45–55	£45–50	£55–65	£130–150
Relief of Ladysmith	£250–400	£65–75	£75–85	—	—
Driefontein	£180–200	£50–60	—	£45–55	£200–220
Wepener	—	£280–350	£265–300	—	—
Defence of Mafeking	—	—	£780–960	—	—
Transvaal	£450–600	£45–55	£45–55	£55–70	£200–220
Johannesburg	£180–200	£55–65	£60–75	£55–70	£130–140
Laing's Nek	£500–650	£65–80	—	—	—
Diamond Hill	£200–220	£65–75	£65–75	£70–85	£200–220
Wittebergen	£1000	£55–65	£110–120	£75–85	—
Belfast	£200–220	£70–80	£60–75	£70–85	£130–150
South Africa 1901	£60–75	£45–55	£50–60	£70–85	£150–160
South Africa 1902	£750–850	£45–55	£50–60	£70–85	£130–140
2 clasps	£180–200	£50–60	£50–60	£100–110	£130–140
3 clasps	£250–280	£65–85	£60–75	£110–140	£130–140
4 clasps	£800–350	£65–90	£60–85	£140–180	£150–160
5 clasps	£380–450	£80–125	£65–90	£170–220	£220–240
6 clasps	£560–650	£115–135	£120–160	£270–330	£270–330
7 clasps	£650–800	£185–255	£215–305	£495–660	—
8 clasps	£850–1100	£455–555	£530–605	—	—
Relief dates on reverse	—	—	—	—	£2090–2400
Nurses	—	£150–205	—	—	—
War Correspondents	—	£1205–1505	—	—	—

Miniature
From £10 with no clasp to £45 with 6 fixed clasps—"slip-on" style clasps approx. 20% less.

2nd type rev.

3rd type rev.

151. QUEEN'S MEDITERRANEAN MEDAL

Date: 1899.
Campaign: Mediterranean garrisons 1899-1902.
Branch of Service: British militia forces.
Ribbon: Red with two narrow dark blue stripes and a central broad orange stripe (as for Queen's South Africa Medal).
Metal: Silver.
Size: 36mm.
Description: Similar to the Queen's South Africa Medal but inscribed MEDITERRANEAN at the top of the reverse.
Clasps: None.
Comments: *Awarded to officers and men of the militia battalions which were sent to Malta and Gibraltar to take over garrison duty from the regular forces who were drafted to the Cape.*

VALUE:

Silver (5000)	£180–200	*Miniature*	£45–55

152. KING'S SOUTH AFRICA MEDAL

Date: 1902.
Campaign: South Africa 1901–02.
Branch of Service: British and imperial forces.
Ribbon: Three equal stripes of green, white and orange.
Metal: Silver.
Size: 36mm.
Description: (Obverse) bust of King Edward VII in field marshal's uniform; (reverse) as for Queen's medal.
Clasps: Two: South Africa 1901, South Africa 1902.
Comments: *This medal was never issued without the Queen's medal and was awarded to all personnel engaged in operations in South Africa in 1901–02 when fighting was actually confined to numerous skirmishes with isolated guerrilla bands. Very few medals were awarded to RN personnel as the naval brigades had been disbanded in 1901. Apart from about 600 nurses and a few odd men who received the medal without a clasp, this medal was awarded with two clasps—most men were entitled to both clasps, single clasp medals being very rare. Only 137 were awarded to New Zealand troops.*

VALUE:

No clasp (nurses)	£75–100
1901 / 1902 (RN) (33)	£750–1000
1901 / 1902 (Army)	£40–55
1901 / 1902 (Canada)	£50–60
1901 / 1902 (Aus)	£40–50
1901 / 1902 (NZ)	£300–350
1901 / 1902 (South African units)	£80–100
1901 alone	From £100
1902 alone	From £100

Miniature £10   2-clasps £12–15

153. ST JOHN AMBULANCE BRIGADE MEDAL FOR SOUTH AFRICA

Date: 1902.
Campaign: South Africa 1899–1902.
Branch of Service: St John Ambulance Brigade.
Ribbon: Black with narrow white edges.
Metal: Bronze.
Size: 37mm.
Description: (Obverse) King Edward VII; (reverse) the arms of the Order with a legend in Latin, SOUTH AFRICA and the dates 1899 and 1902.
Clasps: None.
Comments: *Issued by the Order of St John of Jerusalem to the members of its ambulance brigade who served during the Boer War or who played an active part in the organisation, mobilisation and supply roles. Medals were engraved on the edge with the recipient's name and unit. It is most often associated with the two South Africa medals, but fourteen members who went on from South Africa to serve during the Boxer Rebellion were also awarded the China Medal.*

VALUE: Bronze (1,871)   £220–250   *Miniature*   £50–60

154. KIMBERLEY STAR

Date: 1900.
Campaign: Defence of Kimberley 1899–1902.
Branch of Service: British and local forces.
Ribbon: Half yellow, half black, separated by narrow stripes of red, white and blue.
Metal: Silver.
Size: Height 43mm; max. width 41mm.
Description: A six-pointed star with ball finials and a circular centre inscribed KIMBERLEY 1899–1900 with the civic arms in the middle. (Reverse) plain, but for the inscription MAYOR'S SIEGE MEDAL 1900. Suspended by a plain ring from a scrolled bar.
Clasps: None
Comments: *The Mayor and council of Kimberley awarded this and the following medal to the defenders of the mining town against the Boer forces. Two medals were struck in gold but about 5000 were produced in silver. Those with the "a" Birmingham hallmark for 1900 rate a premium over stars with later date letters.*

VALUE:
hallmark "a"	£125–140
later date letters	£120–130

Miniature	£80–100s

155. KIMBERLEY MEDAL

Date: 1900.
Campaign: Defence of Kimberley 1899–1900.
Branch of Service: Local forces.
Ribbon: As above.
Metal: Silver
Size: 38mm.
Description: (Obverse) the figure of Victory above the Kimberley Town Hall, with the dates 1899–1900 in the exergue. (Reverse) two shields inscribed INVESTED 15 OCT. 1899 and RELIEVED 15 FEB. 1900. The imperial crown appears above and the royal cypher underneath, with the legend TO THE GALLANT DEFENDERS OF KIMBERLEY round the circumference.
Clasps: None.
Comments: *Although awarded for the same purpose as the above, this silver medal is a much scarcer award.*

VALUE:
Silver	£500–650

156. YORKSHIRE IMPERIAL YEOMANRY MEDAL

Date: 1900.
Campaign: South Africa 1900–02.
Branch of Service: Yorkshire Imperial Yeomanry.
Ribbon: Yellow.
Metal: Silver.
Size: 38mm.
Description: Three versions were produced. The first two had the numeral 3 below the Prince of Wales's feathers and may be found with the dates 1900–1901 or 1901–1902, while the third type has the figures 66, denoting the two battalions involved. The uniform reverse has the white rose of Yorkshire surmounted by an imperial crown and enclosed in a laurel wreath with the legend A TRIBUTE FROM YORKSHIRE.
Clasps: None.
Comments: *Many medals wre produced locally and awarded to officers and men of county regiments. The medals struck by Spink and Son for the Yorkshire Imperial Yeomanry, however, are generally more highly regarded as they were much more extensively issued, and therefore more commonly met with, than the others.*

VALUE:

3rd Battalion 1900–1901	£80–100
3rd Battalion 1901–1902	£80–100
66th Battalion 1900–1901	£120–150

157. MEDAL FOR THE DEFENCE OF OOKIEP

Date: 1902.
Campaign: Defence of Ookiep 1902.
Branch of Service: British and colonial forces.
Ribbon: Dark brown with a central green stripe.
Metal: Silver or bronze.
Size: 36mm.
Description: (Obverse) a miner and copper-waggon, with the Company name and date of foundation (1888) round the circumference; (reverse) a thirteen-line text. Fitted with a scroll suspender.
Clasps: None.
Comments: *Commonly known as the Cape Copper Co. Medal, this medal was awarded by the Cape Copper Company to those who defended the mining town of Ookiep in Namaqualand when it was besieged from 4 April to 4 May 1902 by a Boer commando led by Jan Christian Smuts, later Field Marshal, Prime Minister of South Africa and a member of the Imperial War Cabinet. The defence was conducted by Lieut. Colonel Sheldon, DSO and Major Dean, the Company's manager. The garrison consisted of 206 European miners, 660 Cape Coloureds, 44 men of the 5th Warwickshire militia and twelve men of the Cape Garrison Artillery.*

VALUE:

Silver (officers)	£1500–2000
Bronze (other ranks)	£500–600

158. CHINA WAR MEDAL 1900

Date: 1901.
Campaign: Boxer Rebellion 1900.
Branch of Service: British and imperial forces.
Ribbon: Crimson with yellow edges.
Metal: Silver or bronze.
Size: 36mm.
Description: (Obverse) bust of Queen Victoria; (reverse) trophy of arms, similar to the 1857-60 China Medal but inscribed CHINA 1900 at the foot.
Clasps: Taku Forts, Defence of Legations, Relief of Pekin.
Comments: *Instituted for service during the Boxer Rebellion and the subsequent punitive expeditions, this medal was similar to that of 1857-60 with the date in the exergue altered to 1900. There are three types of naming: in small, impressed capitals for European troops, in large impressed capitals for naval recipients, and in engraved cursive script for Indian forces. The medal was issued in silver to combatants and in bronze to native bearers, drivers and servants. The international community was besieged by the Boxers, members of a secret society, aided and abetted by the Dowager Empress. The relieving force, consisting of contingents from Britain, France, Italy, Russia, Germany and Japan, was under the command of the German field marshal, Count von Waldersee. The British Legation Guard, comprising 80 Royal Marines and a number of 'odd men', won the clasp for Defence of Legations, the most desirable of the campaign bars in this conflict.*

VALUE:

	Royal Navy	Army	Indian units	*Miniature*
Silver no clasp	£110–130	£100–120	£60–80	£15–20
Bronze no clasp	—	—	£70–90	—
Taku Forts	£300–320	—	—	£20–25
Defence of Legations	£3000–4000	—	—	£50–60
Relief of Pekin (silver)	£220–250	£300–400	£160–180	£20–25
Relief of Pekin (bronze)	—	—	£150–175	—
2 clasps	£400–450	—	—	£40–50
No-clasp medal to a nurse	£1000–1500			
To a War correspondent	£1000–1500			

159. TRANSPORT MEDAL

Date: 1903.
Campaigns: Boer War 1899-1902 and Boxer Rebellion 1900.
Branch of Service: Mercantile Marine.
Ribbon: Red with two blue stripes.
Metal: Silver.
Size: 36mm.
Description: (Obverse) bust of King Edward VII in the uniform of an Admiral of the Fleet; (reverse) HMS *Ophir* below a map of the world.
Clasps: S. Africa 1899-1902, China 1900.
Comments: *The last of the medals associated with the major conflicts at the turn of the century, it was instituted for award to the officers of the merchant vessels used to carry troops and supplies to the wars in South Africa and China.*

VALUE:

		Miniature
South Africa 1899–1902 (1219)	£260–280	£40–60
China 1900 (322)	£380–420	£50–70
Both clasps (178)	£450–550	£80–100

160. ASHANTI MEDAL

Date: 1901.
Campaign: Gold Coast 1900.
Branch of Service: British and local forces.
Ribbon: Black with two broad green stripes.
Metal: Silver or bronze.
Size: 36mm.
Description: (Obverse) bust of King Edward VII in field marshal's uniform. (Reverse) a lion on the edge of an escarpment looking towards the sunrise, with a native shield and spears in the foreground. The name ASHANTI appeared on a scroll at the foot.
Clasps: Kumassi.
Comments: *A high-handed action by the colonial governor provoked a native uprising and the siege of the garrison at Kumassi. The medal was awarded to the defenders as well as personnel of the two relieving columns. Very few Europeans were involved as most were in South Africa fighting the Boers. The medal was awarded in silver to combatants and bronze to native transport personnel and servants.*

VALUE:

	Silver	Bronze	*Miniature*
No clasp	£150–170	£250–300	£20–25
Kumassi	£320–350	Rare	£40–50

161. AFRICA GENERAL SERVICE MEDAL

Date: 1902.
Campaigns: Minor campaigns in Africa 1902 to 1956.
Branch of Service: British and colonial forces.
Ribbon: Yellow with black edges and two thin central green stripes.
Metal: Silver or bronze.
Size: 36mm.
Description: (Obverse) effigies of Edward VII, George V and Elizabeth II; (reverse) similar to that of the East and Central Africa medal of 1897–99, with AFRICA in the exergue.
Clasps: 34 awarded in the reign of Edward VII, ten George V and only one Elizabeth II (see below).
Comments: *This medal replaced the East and West Africa Medal 1887–1900, to which 21 clasps had already been issued. In turn, it remained in use for 54 years, the longest-running British service medal. Medals to combatants were in silver, but a few bronze medals were issued during the 1903–04 operations in Northern Nigeria and the Somaliland campaigns of 1902 and 1908 to transport personnel and these are now much sought after, as are any medals with the effigy of George V on the obverse. With the exception of the 1902–04 Somali campaign and the campaign against the Mau Mau of Kenya (1952–56) European troops were not involved in any numbers, such personnel consisting mostly of detached officers and specialists.*

VALUE:

	RN	British units	African/Indian regiments
N. Nigeria	—	—	£120–140
N. Nigeria 1902	—	—	£110–130
N. Nigeria 1903	—	—	£100–120
N. Nigeria 1903-04	—	—	£150–170
N. Nigeria 1903-04 (bronze)	—	—	£130–150
N. Nigeria 1904	—	—	£130–150
N. Nigeria 1906	—	—	£130–150
S. Nigeria	—	—	£180–200
S. Nigeria 1902	—	—	£130–150
S. Nigeria 1902-03	—	—	£130–150

continued overleaf

161. AFRICA GENERAL SERVICE MEDAL *continued*

S. Nigeria 1903	—	—	£120–140
S. Nigeria 1903-04	—	—	£150–170
S. Nigeria 1904	—	—	£120–140
S. Nigeria 1904-05	—	—	£150–170
S. Nigeria 1905	—	—	£250–300
S. Nigeria 1905-06	—	—	£140–160
Nigeria 1918	—	—	£110–130
East Africa 1902	—	—	£300–350
East Africa 1904	—	—	£170–190
East Africa 1905	—	—	£170–190
East Africa 1906	—	—	£170–190
East Africa 1913	—	—	£180–220
East Africa 1913-14	—	—	£170–190
East Africa 1914	—	—	£180–220
East Africa 1915	—	—	£200–250
East Africa 1918	—	—	£170–190
West Africa 1906	—	—	£170–190
West Africa 1908	—	—	£180–220
West Africa 1909-10	—	—	£180–200
Somaliland 1901	—	—	£250–300
Somaliland 1901 (bronze)	—	—	£200–250
Somaliland 1902-04	£95–110	£80–100	£50–60
Somaliland 1902-04 (bronze)	—	—	£220–250
Somaliland 1908-10	£95–110	—	£65–75
Somaliland 1908-10 (bronze)	—	—	£80–90
Somaliland 1920	£180–200	—	£80–90
as above but RAF	—	£320–350	—
Jidballi (with Somaliland 1902–04)	—	£150–180	£110–130
Uganda 1900	—	—	£170–190
B.C.A. 1899-1900	—	—	£120–150
Jubaland	£200–220	—	£90–110
Jubaland (bronze)	—	—	£275–325
Jubaland 1917-18	—	—	£160–180
Jubaland 1917-18 (bronze)	—	—	£125–150
Gambia	£600–800	—	£180–200
Aro 1901-1902	£500–650	—	£130–150
Lango 1901	—	—	£200–250
Kissi 1905	—	—	£350–400
Nandi 1905-06	—	—	£80–120
Shimber Berris 1914-15	—	—	£200–220
Nyasaland 1915	—	—	£120–150
Kenya	£350–500	£50–70	£40–50
Kenya (to RAF)	—	£55–65	—
2 clasps	£80–120	£100–150	£100–250
3 clasps	—	—	£200–400
4 clasps	—	—	£300–450
5 clasps	—	—	£350–500
6 clasps	—	—	£350–550

Medal to War Correspondent	£1200–1500

Miniature
    Range from £10 to £60 depending upon clasp. "Slip-on" clasps are approx. 20% cheaper. Add £5 for each additional clasp.

162. TIBET MEDAL

Date: 1905.
Campaign: Tibet 1903–04.
Branch of Service: British and Indian regiments.
Ribbon: Green with two white stripes and a broad maroon central stripe.
Metal: Silver or bronze.
Size: 36mm.
Description: (Obverse) bust of King Edward VII; (reverse) the fortified hill city of Lhasa with TIBET 1903–04 at the foot.
Clasps: Gyantse.
Comments: *The trade mission led by Colonel Sir Francis Younghusband to Tibet was held up by hostile forces, against whom a punitive expedition was mounted in 1903. This medal was awarded mainly to Indian troops who took part in the expedition, camp followers being awarded the medal in bronze. A clasp was awarded to those who took part in the operations near Gyantse beteen 3 May and 6 July 1904.*

VALUE:

	British	Indian	Bronze	*Miniature*
Without clasp	£300–400	£150–200	£85–100	£30–40
Gyantse	£500–600	£250–300	£190–220	£50–60

163. NATAL REBELLION MEDAL

Date: 1907.
Campaign: Natal 1906.
Branch of Service: Local forces.
Ribbon: Crimson with black edges.
Metal: Silver.
Size: 36mm.
Description: (Obverse) right-facing profile of King Edward VII. (Reverse) an erect female figure representing Natal with the sword of justice in her right hand and a palm branch in the left. She treads on a heap of Zulu weapons and is supported by Britannia who holds the orb of empire in her hand. In the background, the sun emerges from behind storm clouds.
Clasp: 1906.
Comments: *The Natal government instituted this medal for services in the operations following the Zulu rebellion. Local volunteer units bore the brunt of the action and it is interesting to note that one of the recipients was Sergeant-Major M. K. Gandhi who later led India to independence.*

VALUE:

		Miniature
without clasp (2000)	£80–110	£15–20
clasp 1906 (8000)	£120–140	£30–40
Natal Naval Corps		
without clasp (67)	£150–200	
clasp 1906 (136)	£250–300	

163A. MESSINA EARTHQUAKE COMMEMORATIVE MEDAL

Date: 1908.
Campaign: Messina earthquake relief.
Branch of Service: Royal Navy.
Ribbon: Green with white edges and central white stripe.
Metal: Silver.
Size: 31.5mm.
Description: (Obverse) left-facing profile of King Victor Emanuel III; (reverse) A wreath of oak leaves within which are the words MEDAGLIA COMMEMORATIVA/TERREMOTO CALABRO SICULO 28 DICEMBRE 1908.
Comments: *The King of Italy rewarded Royal Naval and other personnel who went to the aid of victims of the tragic earthquake that hit Messina in December 1908 with this silver medal. Officers and men serving on certain ships were eligible for the award as well as members of the Mercantile Marine and others who were engaged in relief operations. The Admiralty's published list of RN ships is as follows: HMS Duncan, HMS Euralyus, HMS Exmouth, HMS Lancaster, HMS Minerva and HMS Sutlej. However 52 medals were also awarded to personnel from HMS Boxer, which was omitted from the original list and a further 35 medals were awarded to the officers and men of HMS Philomel who had actually* 'been engaged in work which was directly attributable to the rescue operations'. *The medal was issued unnamed. In addition to the commemorative medal a special Messina Earthquake Merit Medal was awarded in two sizes (40mm and 30mm) bronze, silver and gold to organisations, vessels and various key individuals who played a part in the rescue operations.*

VALUE:

		Miniature
Unattributed single medal	£80–100	£20–30
Royal Navy (c. 3500)	£120–160	
Royal Marines (481)	£140–180	
Mercantile Marine (c. 400)	£140–180	
Other	Rare	

Aftermath of the earthquake, Messina.

164. INDIA GENERAL SERVICE MEDAL

Date: 1909.

Campaigns: India 1908 to 1935.

Branch of Service: British and Indian forces.

Ribbon: Green with a broad blue central band.

Metal: Silver.

Size: 36mm.

Description: Three obverse types were used: Edward VII (1908–10), George V Kaisar-i-Hind (1910–30) and George V Indiae Imp (1930–35). (Reverse) the fortress at Jamrud in the Khyber Pass, with the name INDIA in a wreath at the foot.

Clasps: Fourteen, some in bronze (see below).

Comments: *This medal was awarded for a number of minor campaigns and operations in India before and after the First World War. The medals were struck at the Royal Mint in London and by the Indian government in Calcutta, the only difference being in the claw suspenders, the former being ornate and the latter plain. Medals with the bars North West Frontier 1908 and Abor 1911–12 were also issued in bronze to native bearers.*

VALUE:

	British Army	RAF	Indian regiments	*Miniature*
NW Frontier 1908	£65–85	—	£40–50	£20
bronze	—	—	£50–65	—
Abor 1911–12	—	—	£140–180	£20
bronze	—	—	£250–300	—
Afghanistan NWF 1919	£40–60	£100–120	£18–25	£15
*Mahsud 1919–20 & Waziristan 1919–21	£90–100	£120–150	£35–45	£15
Malabar 1921–22	£100–120	—	£35–55	£30
Waziristan 1921–24	£35–45	£70–90	£20–35	£15
Waziristan 1925	—	£500–600	—	£15
NW Frontier 1930–31	£35–45	£70–80	£20–30	£15
Burma 1930–32	£50–60	Rare	£25–30	£15
Mohmand 1933	£100–120	£200–230	£25–35	£15
NW Frontier 1935	£50–60	£100–120	£25–30	£15

*Usually found in combination with Waziristan 1919-21, but 10 medals were awarded either with this clasp alone or with the Afghanistan NWF clasp.

165. KHEDIVE'S SUDAN MEDAL 1910

Date: 1911.
Campaign: Sudan 1910 to 1922
Branch of Service: British and Egyptian forces.
Ribbon: Black with thin red and green stripes on either side.
Metal: Silver or bronze.
Size: 36mm.
Description: (Obverse) an Arabic inscription signifying the name of Khedive Abbas Hilmi and the date 1328 in the Moslem calendar (1910 AD). He was deposed in December 1914 when Egypt was declared a British protectorate, and succeeded by his nephew who was proclaimed Sultan. Sultan Hussein Kamil changed the Arabic inscription and date to AH 1335 (1916–17) on later issues of the medal. (Reverse) a lion poised on a plinth with the sunrise in the background.
Clasps: 16, inscribed in English and Arabic.
Comments: *Introduced in June 1911 as a replacement for the previous Khedive's Sudan medal of 1896–1908, it was awarded for minor operations in the southern Sudan between 1910 and 1922. The silver medal was issued with clasps to combatants, and without a clasp to non-combatants, while the bronze version was granted to camp followers. The medal is usually found unnamed although a few British recipient's medals are found named in small impressed capitals or arabic script. The prices below are for unnamed examples.*

VALUE:

Silver without clasp type I	£100–120		
Silver without clasp type II	£130–150	Darfur 1916	£220–250
Bronze without clasp type I	£400–450	Fasher	£220–240
Bronze without clasp type II	£160–180	Lau Nuer	£240–260
Atwot	£220–240	Nyima 1917-18	£220–240
S. Kordofan 1910	£220–240	Atwot 1918	£220–240
Sudan 1912	£240–260	Garjak Nuer	£240–260
Zeraf 1913-14	£260–280	Aliab Dinka	£260–280
Mandal	£260–280	Nyala	£260–280
Miri	£260–280	Darfur 1921	£280–320
Mongalla 1915-16	£260–280	2 clasps	£280–300

Miniature
Silver £20. Prices for clasps vary between £10 and £30.

The Camel Corps in the Sudan.

FIRST WORLD WAR MEDALS

The various combinations of WWI medals that are found makes them still fairly easy to value. There are however large differences in price when it comes to casualties, for example medals to those who were killed on the first day of the battle of the Somme command a far higher price than to someone who was killed several days before. Regiments also alter the price greatly. Purchasing the medals, plaque and scroll is far harder than ever before. Scrolls and plaques tended to become separated from the medals as relatives generally did not view them with as great a significance as the medals.

Valuations for casualty groups are usually made without including the Memorial Scroll. For those fortunate to have the scroll with their group of medals then add £25 minimum to the group.

166. 1914 STAR

Date: 1917.
Campaign: France and Belgium 1914.
Branch of Service: British forces.
Ribbon: Watered silk red, white and blue.
Metal: Bronze.
Size: Height 50mm; max. width 45mm.
Description: A crowned four-pointed star with crossed swords and a wreath of oak leaves, having the royal cypher at the foot and a central scroll inscribed AUG NOV 1914. Uniface, the naming being inscribed incuse on the plain reverse.
Clasps: 5th Aug. –22nd Nov. 1914. The clasp was sewn on to the ribbon of the medal, the first of this type. A silver rosette is worn on the ribbon strip if the bar is awarded.
Comments: *Awarded to all those who had served in France and Belgium between 5 August and 22 November 1914. In 1919 King George V authorised a clasp bearing these dates for those who had actually been under fire during that period. The majority of the 400,000 recipients of the star were officers and men of the prewar British Army, the "Old Contemptibles" who landed in France soon after the outbreak of the First World War and who took part in the retreat from Mons, hence the popular nickname of Mons Star by which this medal is often known.*

VALUE:

		Miniature
1914 Star	£35–55	£2–3
With "Mons" clasp	£65–75	£3–4
To RN or RM	£40–60	
1914 Star trio	from £65	
Trio with plaque (no. 172)	from £125	

167. 1914–15 STAR

Date: 1918.
Campaign: First World War 1914–15.
Branch of Service: British and imperial forces.
Ribbon: Watered silk red, white and blue (as above).
Metal: Bronze.
Size: Height 50mm; max. width 45mm.
Description: As above, but AUG and NOV omitted and scroll across the centre inscribed 1914–15.
Clasps: None.
Comments: *Awarded to those who saw service in any theatre of war between 5 August 1914 and 31 December 1915, other than those who had already qualified for the 1914 Star. No fewer than 2,350,000 were awarded, making it the commonest British campaign medal up to that time.*

VALUE:

1914–15 Star	£15–20	*Miniature*	£2–3
1914–15 Star trio			
Corps	from £35		
Regiments	from £45		
Trio with plaque (no. 172)	from £110		

169

168. BRITISH WAR MEDAL 1914–20

Date: 1919.
Campaign: First World War, 1914–20.
Branch of Service: British and imperial forces.
Ribbon: Orange watered centre with stripes of white and black at each side and borders of royal blue.
Metal: Silver or bronze.
Size: 36mm.
Description: (Obverse) the uncrowned left-facing profile of King George V by Sir Bertram Mackennal. (Reverse) St George on horseback trampling underfoot the eagle shield of the Central Powers and a skull and cross-bones, the emblems of death. Above, the sun has risen in victory. The figure is mounted on horseback to symbolise man's mind controlling a force of greater strength than his own, and thus alludes to the scientific and mechanical appliances which helped to win the war.
Clasps: None.
Comments: *This medal was instituted to record the successful conclusion of the First World War, but it was later extended to cover the period 1919–20 and service in mine-clearing at sea as well as participation in operations in North and South Russia, the eastern Baltic, Siberia, the Black Sea and Caspian. Some 6,500,000 medals were awarded in silver, but about 110,000 in bronze were issued mainly to Chinese, Indian and Maltese personnel in labour battalions. It was originally intended to award campaign clasps, but 79 were recommended by the Army and 68 by the Navy, so the scheme was abandoned as impractical. The naval clasps were actually authorised (7 July 1920) and miniatures are known with them, though the actual clasps were never issued.*

VALUE:

		Miniature
Silver (6,500,000)	£10–12	£3–4
Bronze (110,000)	£60–65	£10–15
BWM/Victory pair		
Corps	from £15	
Regiments	from £20	
Pair with plaque (no. 172)	from £80	

169. MERCANTILE MARINE WAR MEDAL

Date: 1919.
Campaign: First World War 1914–18.
Branch of Service: Mercantile Marine.
Ribbon: Green and red with a central white stripe, symbolising port and starboard navigation lights.
Metal: Bronze.
Size: 36mm.
Description: (Obverse) Mackennal profile of King George V; (reverse) a steamship ploughing through an angry sea, with a sinking submarine and a sailing vessel in the background, the whole enclosed in a laurel wreath.
Clasps: None.
Comments: *Awarded by the Board of Trade to members of the Merchant Navy who had undertaken one or more voyages through a war or danger zone.*

VALUE:

Bronze (133,000)	£22–26	*Miniature*	£3–5
BWM/Mercantile Marine pair	from £30		

170. VICTORY MEDAL

Date: 1919.
Campaign: First World War 1914–19.
Branch of Service: British forces.
Ribbon: 38mm double rainbow (indigo at edges and red in centre).
Metal: Yellow bronze.
Size: 36mm.
Description: (Obverse) the standing figure of Victory holding a palm branch in her right hand and stretching out her left hand. (Reverse) a laurel wreath containing a four-line inscription THE GREAT WAR FOR CIVILISATION 1914–1919.
Clasps: None.
Comments: *Issued to all who had already got the 1914 or 1914–15 Stars and most of those who had the British War Medal, some six million are believed to have been produced. It is often known as the Allied War Medal because the same basic design and double rainbow ribbon were adopted by thirteen other Allied nations (though the USA alone issued it with campaign clasps). The Union of South Africa produced a version with a reverse text in English and Dutch (not Afrikaans as is often stated).*

VALUE:

British pattern	£6–10
South African pattern	£12–15
Miniature	
Normal	£2–3
"CIVILIZATION" variety	£3–4

171. TERRITORIAL FORCE WAR MEDAL

Date: 1919.
Campaign: First World War 1914–19.
Branch of Service: Territorial forces.
Ribbon: Watered gold silk with two dark green stripes towards the edges.
Metal: Bronze.
Size: 36mm.
Description: (Obverse) effigy of King George V; (reverse) a wreath enclosing the text FOR VOLUNTARY SERVICE OVERSEAS 1914–19.
Clasps: None.
Comments: *Granted to all members of the Territorial Force embodied before 30 September 1914, who had completed four years service by that date, and who had served outside the United Kingdom between 4 August 1914 and 11 November 1918. Those who had already qualified for the 1914 or 1914–15 Stars, however, were excluded. Only 34,000 medals were awarded, making it by far the scarcest of the First World War medals. The value of individual medals depends on the regiment or formation of the recipient.*

VALUE:

Infantry	£80–90
RA, RE or support units	£70–85
Yeomanry	£140–180
RFC or RAF	£300–400
Nursing sisters	£150–200
Miniature	£5–6

172. MEMORIAL PLAQUE

Date: 1919.
Campaign: First World War.
Branch of Service: British forces.
Ribbon: None.
Metal: Bronze.
Size: 120mm.
Description: The plaque shows Britannia bestowing a laurel crown on a rectangular tablet bearing the full name of the dead in raised lettering. In front stands the British lion, with dolphins in the upper field, an oak branch lower right, and a lion cub clutching a fallen eagle in the exergue. The inscription round the circumference reads HE (or SHE) DIED FOR FREEDOM AND HONOVR. A parchment scroll was issued with each plaque giving the deceased's name and unit.
Comments: *Awarded to the next of kin of those who lost their lives on active service during the War. Plaques issued to the Army and the Navy can usually be differentiated by the size of the H in "HE". Those issued to the Navy have a narrower H when compared with the H of "HONOUR", whereas those to the Army are of equal size.*

VALUE: He died (1,355,000)   From £30   She died (600)   From £1000   Parchment scroll   (male) £20–30
(female) £400–600

172A. SILVER WAR BADGE

Date: 12 September 1916.
Campaign: First World War.
Ribbon: None.
Metal: Silver.
Size: 33mm.
Description: A brooch-mounted circular badge with the crowned royal monogram in the centre and edge inscription FOR KING AND EMPIRE + SERVICES RENDERED +.
Comments: *Awarded to service personnel who sustained a wound or contracted sickness or disability in the course of the war as a result of which they were invalided out. It was worn on the lapel in civilian clothes. Each badge was numbered on the reverse. The purpose of the badge was to prevent men of military age but not in uniform from being harassed by women pursuing them with white feathers.*

VALUE: £10–20   *Miniature:*   ££10–15

172B. CEYLON VOLUNTEER SERVICE MEDAL

Date: 1919.
Campaign: First World War.
Branch of Service: Ceylon volunteer forces.
Ribbon: None.
Metal: Bronze.
Size: 48mm x 44mm.
Description: An upright oval medal. (Obverse) a seated female figure bestowing a laurel crown on a kneeling soldier, with a radiant sun on the horizon; above, a six-line inscription: PRESENTED BY THE GOVERNMENT OF CEYLON TO THOSE WHO VOLUNTARILY GAVE THEIR SERVICES OVERSEAS IN THE GREAT WAR OF with the dates 1914 1919 in two lines on the right of the field; (reverse) the winged figure of Victory seated on a throne above a tablet inscribed with the name of the recipient.
Comments: *Awarded to the 450 volunteers from the Ceylon forces who served abroad during the war. Ceylon (now Sri Lanka) was the only British colony to issue such a medal for war service.*

VALUE: £100–200

173. NAVAL GENERAL SERVICE MEDAL 1915–62

Date: 1915.

Campaigns: Naval actions 1915 to 1962.

Branch of Service: Royal Navy.

Ribbon: White with broad crimson edges and two narrow crimson stripes towards the centre.

Metal: Silver.

Size: 36mm.

Description: (Obverse) effigy of the reigning monarch (see below). (Reverse) Britannia and two seahorses travelling through the sea.

Clasps: Seventeen (see below).

Comments: *Instituted for service in minor operations for which no separate medal might be issued, it remained in use for almost half a century. In that period five different obverses were employed: George V (1915-36), George VI Ind Imp (1936-49), George VI Fid Def (1949-52), Elizabeth II Br Omn (1952-53) and Elizabeth II Dei Gratia (1953-62). Medals issued with the first clasp include the name of the recipient's ship but this lapsed in later awards. The Malaya clasp was issued with three types of medal: the George VI Fid Def and Elizabeth II Dei Gratia being the most common, the Elizabeth II Br Omn type being awarded mainly to SBS for special duties. The clasp Bomb & Mine Clearance 1945–46 is very rare as it was apparently only awarded to the Royal Australian Navy.*

VALUE:		*Miniature*
Persian Gulf 1909-1914		*(in silver add £5)*
RN (7,127)	£70–80	
Army (37)	£250–300	£10
Iraq 1919-20 (116)	£800–1000	£15
NW Persia 1919-20 (4)*	Rare	£15
Palestine 1936-39 (13,600)	£60–75	£10
SE Asia 1945-46 (2,000)	£100–135	£10
Minesweeping 1945-51 (4,750)	£90–100	£10
Palestine 1945-48 (7,900)	£65–75	£10
Malaya (George VI, Elizabeth II		
2nd type) (7,800)	£65–75	£10
(Elizabeth II 1st type)	£120–135	£10
Yangtze 1949 (1,450)	£300–350	£10
to HMS *Amethyst*	£600–800	
Bomb and Mine Clearance		
1945-53 (117)	£450–475	£10
Bomb and Mine Clearance 1945–56	Very rare	—
Bomb and Mine Clearance		
Mediterranean (60)	£900–1000	£10
Cyprus (4,300)	£80–90	£10
Near East (17,800)	£60–65	£10
Arabian Peninsula (1,200)	£160–180	£10
Brunei (900)	£140–160	£10

* The clasp NW Persia 1920 was withdrawn in favour of the clasp NW Persia 1919–20. Recipients were supposed to return their first clasp in exchange for the latter.

Visit

www.tokenpublishing.com

you'll be glad you did

174. GENERAL SERVICE MEDAL 1918–62

Date: 1923.
Campaigns: Minor campaigns 1918 to 1962.
Branch of Service: Army and RAF.
Ribbon: Purple with a central green band.
Metal: Silver.
Size: 36mm
Description: (Obverse) five different effigies of the reigning monarch (see preceding entry). (Reverse) a standing figure of Victory in a Greek helmet and carrying a trident, bestowing palms on a winged sword.
Clasps: Sixteen (see below).
Comments: *Awarded to military and RAF personnel for numerous campaigns and operations that fell short of full-scale war. It did not cover areas already catered for in the Africa and India general service medals.*

VALUE:

	British units	RAF	Indian and local units	Miniature (in silver add £5)
S. Persia (Brit. officers)	£140–170	Rare	£30–40	£12
Kurdistan	£65–75	£130–150	£30–35	£12
Iraq	£40–50	£130–15 0	£25–35	£10
N.W. Persia	£65–75	£180–220	£30–35	£10
Southern Desert Iraq	—	£250–275	£80–100	£10
Northern Kurdistan	£150–175	£650–850	£120–150	£10
Palestine	£40–50	£35–40	£30–35	£10
S.E. Asia 1945-46	£60–70	£60–65	£25–35	£10
Bomb and Mine Clearance 1945-49	£300–340	£300–340	—	£10
Bomb and Mine Clearance 1945-56	£400–500	£400–500	—	£10
Palestine 1945-48	£35–40	£35–50	£25–30	£10
Malaya (George VI)	£35–40	£35–40	£25–30	£10
Malaya (Elizabeth II)	£35–40	£35–40	£25–30	£10
Cyprus	£35–45	£35–45	£25–30	£10
Near East	£50–60	£50–60	—	£10
Arabian Peninsular	£40–45	£40–45	£30–35	£10
Brunei	£140–150	£110–120	£60–80	£10

175. INDIA GENERAL SERVICE MEDAL 1936–39

Date: 1938.
Campaign: India 1936–39.
Branch of Service: British and Indian Armies and RAF.
Ribbon: Grey flanked by narrow red stripes, with broad green stripes at the edges.
Metal: Silver.
Size: 36mm
Description: (Obverse) crowned effigy of King George VI; (reverse) a tiger with the word INDIA across the top.
Clasps: North-West Frontier 1936–37, North-West Frontier 1937–39.
Comments: *The fifth and last of the IGS series, it was introduced when the change of effigy from George V to George VI became necessary, anticipating a similarly long life. It was not awarded after the outbreak of the Second World War, while the partition and independence of the Indian sub-continent afterwards rendered it obsolete. The medal was struck at the Royal Mint, London for award to British Army troops and RAF personnel, but the Calcutta Mint struck the medals awarded to the Indian Army.*

VALUE:	British Army	RAF	Indian Army	Miniature
North West Frontier				
1936-37	£60–80	£80–90	£25–30	£12
1937-39	£60–80	£80–90	£25–30	£12
2 clasps	£80–90	£120–140	£30–40	£15

Cherat as sketched by Lt C. A. Souper, RA (later Captain, Army Pay Corps), November 1880.

176. NORTH BORNEO GENERAL SERVICE MEDAL

Date: 1937.

Campaign: British North Borneo 1937-41.

Branch of Service: British North Borneo Company Staff, Constabulary and Residents.

Ribbon: Half dark green, half yellow for general awards, with provision for a thin red central stripe in the case of awards for bravery.

Metal: Silver.

Size: 37mm.

Description: (Obverse) the seated figure of Britannia with shield and trident, and a laurel spray in the exergue; (reverse) the arms of the Company.

Clasps: None.

Comments: *Although it could be granted for meritorious service or individual acts of gallantry, as a rule it was granted for at least eighteen years service. The medal was no longer awarded after the Japanese occupation of North Borneo, January 19, 1942. 50 medals were manufactured in 1937. Between 1937 and 1941 a total of 44 were awarded, including one for bravery (1939). In 1947 one officially-named medal was issued to replace one lost during the Japanese occupation. Total issued was therefore 45, and all were officially named prior to issue.*

VALUE: £1500–2000   *Miniature:*   £80–100

176A. SUDAN DEFENCE FORCE GENERAL SERVICE MEDAL

Instituted: November 1933.

Campaign: Minor campaigns in the Sudan after 1933.

Branch of Service: Sudan Defence Force (SDF) and Police.

Ribbon: Central stripe of royal blue, edged by two yellow stripes and two black stripes at the edges.

Metal: Silver.

Size: 36mm.

Description: (Obverse) the seal of the Governor-General of the Sudan; (reverse) a stationary group of Sudanese soldiers, with "The Sudan" in Arabic below.

Clasps: None.

Comments: *The medal was awarded on the recommendation of the Kaid el'Amm (SDF Commander) to native personnel of the SDF, Police and other approved Sudanese who served in the field on such operations as might be considered by the Governor-General as being of sufficient importance to warrant the grant of the medal. It was also awarded for action against Italian forces in the southern Sudan from June 1940 to November 1941. Only 700 were issued.*

VALUE: £150–£200

SECOND WORLD WAR STARS

Eight different campaign stars were issued for the Second World War. Apart from some Commonwealth issues, these were issued unnamed. It was decided that the maximum number of stars that could be earned by any one person was five, while those who qualified for more received a clasp to be sewn on the ribbon of the appropriate star. Only one clasp per ribbon was permitted which was the first to be earned after qualifying for that star.

Thus the stars could bear the following clasps:

1 1939-45 (Battle of Britain)
2 Atlantic (Air Crew Europe or France and Germany)
3 Air Crew Europe (Atlantic or France and Germany)
4 Africa (North Africa 1942-43, 8th Army or 1st Army)
5 Pacific (Burma)
6 Burma (Pacific)
7 Italy
8 France and Germany (Atlantic)

The ribbons are believed to have been designed by King George VI personally and have symbolic significance in each case.

When ribbons alone are worn, the clasp is denoted by a silver rosette, the Battle of Britain being represented by a gilt rosette. As the clasps were sewn on to the ribbon and the stars issued unnamed, it is difficult to put valuations on examples with campaign clasps, however, the prices quoted are for medals with the *original* clasps. When purchasing expensive groups it is advisable that the medals be supported by documentary provenance or form part of a group in which at least one of the medals is named to the recipient.

Many of the medals and stars of the Second World War are still being produced, therefore there are a number of different die varieties available. There are also a number of dangerous forgeries in existence so care should be taken when purchasing expensive items.

177. 1939–1945 STAR

Date: 1945.
Campaign: Second World War 1939–45.
Branch of Service: British and Commonwealth forces.
Ribbon: Equal stripes of dark blue, red and light blue symbolising the Royal Navy, Army and RAF respectively.
Metal: Bronze.
Size: Height 44mm; max. width 38mm.
Description: The six-pointed star has a circular centre with the GRI/VI monogram, surmounted by a crown and inscribed THE 1939-1945 STAR round the foot.
Clasps: Battle of Britain, sewn directly on to the ribbon.
Comments: *The first in a series of eight bronze stars issued for service in the Second World War, it was awarded to personnel who had completed six months' service in specified operational commands overseas, between 3 September 1939 and 2 September 1945, though in certain cases the minimum period was shortened. Any service curtailed by death, injury or capture also qualified, as did the award of a decoration or a mention in despatches. The clasp awarded to RAF aircrew for action during the Battle of Britain was denoted by a gilt rosette when the ribbon was worn alone.*

VALUE:		*Miniature*
1939-45 Star	£10–12	£3–5
With Battle of Britain clasp	£400–450	£8

178. ATLANTIC STAR

Campaign: Atlantic 1939-45.
Branch of Service: Mainly Royal and Commonwealth Navies.
Ribbon: Watered silk blue, white and green representing the ocean.
Metal: Bronze.
Size: Height 44mm; max. width 38mm.
Description: As above, but inscribed THE ATLANTIC STAR.
Clasps: Air Crew Europe, France and Germany.
Comments: *This star was awarded in the Royal Navy for six months' service afloat between 3 September 1939 and 8 May 1945 in the Atlantic or home waters, and to personnel employed in the convoys to North Russia and the South Atlantic. Personnel must have already qualified for the 1939–45 Star with the qualifying period for this not counting towards the Atlantic Star. Merchant Navy personnel also qualified, as did RAF and Army (maritime gunners and air crews—the latter only requiring 2 months service) who served afloat. In the case of Merchant seamen who served in the last six months of operational service up to 8 May 1945, the Atlantic Star was awarded but not the 1939–45 Star. Entitlement to the France and Germany or Air Crew Europe stars was denoted by clasps to that effect, if the Atlantic Star was previously awarded.*

VALUE:

		Miniature
Atlantic Star	£25–30	£3
Air Crew Europe clasp	£50–60	£8
France and Germany clasp	£35–40	£6

179. AIR CREW EUROPE STAR

Campaign: Air operations over Europe 1939-44.
Branch of Service: RAF and Commonwealth aircrew.
Ribbon: Pale blue (the sky) with black edges (night flying) and a narrow yellow stripe on either side (enemy searchlights).
Metal: Bronze.
Size: Height 44mm; max. width 38mm.
Description: As above, but inscribed THE AIR CREW EUROPE STAR.
Clasps: Atlantic or France and Germany.
Comments: *Awarded for operational flying from UK bases over Europe, for a period of two months between 3 September 1939 and 4 June 1944. Entitlement to either the Atlantic Star or France and Germany Star was denoted by the appropriate bar. This star is by far the most coveted of all the Second World War stars. Officially named, stars to South Africans are the rarest of all the Second World War medals.*

VALUE:

		Miniature
Air Crew Europe Star	£100–120	£3
Atlantic Clasp	£150–155	£6
France and Germany Clasp	£110–120	£6

180. AFRICA STAR

Campaign: Africa 1940-43.
Branch of Service: British and Commonwealth forces.
Ribbon: Pale buff symbolising the sand of the desert, with a broad red central stripe, a dark blue stripe on the left and a light blue stripe on the right symbolising the three services.
Metal: Bronze.
Size: Height 44mm; max. width 38mm.
Description: As above, but inscribed THE AFRICA STAR.
Clasps: North Africa 1942-43, 8th Army, 1st Army.
Comments: *Awarded for entry into an operational area in North Africa between 10 June 1940 (the date of Italy's declaration of war) and 12 May 1943 (the end of operations in North Africa), but service in Abyssinia (Ethiopia), Somaliland, Eritrea and Malta also qualified for the award. A silver numeral 1 or 8 worn on the ribbon denoted service with the First or Eighth Army between 23 October 1942 and 23 May 1943. A clasp inscribed North Africa 1942-43 was awarded to personnel of the Royal Navy Inshore Squadrons and Merchant Navy vessels which worked inshore between these dates. RAF personnel also qualified for this clasp, denoted by a silver rosette on the ribbon alone.*

VALUE:

		Miniature
Africa Star	£12–15	£3
8th Army clasp	£18–22	£8
1st Army clasp	£18–22	£8
North Africa 1942-43 clasp	£18–22	£10

181. PACIFIC STAR

Campaign: Pacific area 1941-45.
Branch of Service: British and Commonwealth forces.
Ribbon: Dark green (the jungle) with a central yellow stripe (the beaches), narrow stripes of dark and light blue (Royal Navy and RAF) and wider stripes of red (Army) at the edges.
Metal: Bronze.
Size: Height 44mm; max. width 38mm.
Description: As above, but inscribed THE PACIFIC STAR.
Clasps: Burma.
Comments: *Awarded for operational service in the Pacific theatre of war from 8 December 1941 to 15 August 1945. Service with the Royal and Merchant navies in the Pacific Ocean, Indian Ocean and South China Sea and land service in these areas also qualified. Personnel qualifying for both Pacific and Burma Stars got the first star and a clasp in respect of the second.*

VALUE:		*Miniature*
Pacific Star	£25–30	£3
Burma clasp	£35–40	£6

182. BURMA STAR

Campaign: Burma 1941-45.
Branch of Service: British and Commonwealth forces.
Ribbon: Three equal bands of dark blue (British forces), red (Commonwealth forces) and dark blue. The dark blue bands each have at their centres a stripe of bright orange (the sun).
Metal: Bronze.
Size: Height 44mm; max. width 38mm.
Description: As above, but inscribed THE BURMA STAR.
Clasps: Pacific
Comments: *Qualifying service in the Burma campaign counted from 11 December 1941 and included service in Bengal or Assam from 1 May 1942 to 31 December 1943, and from 1 January 1944 onwards in these parts of Bengal or Assam east of the Brahmaputra. Naval service in the eastern Bay of Bengal, off the coasts of Sumatra, Sunda and Malacca also counted.*

VALUE:		*Miniature*
Burma Star	£20–28	£3
Pacific Clasp	£30–35	£6

183. ITALY STAR

Campaign: Italy 1943-45.
Branch of Service: British and Commonwealth forces.
Ribbon: Five equal stripes of red, white, green, white and red (the Italian national colours).
Metal: Bronze.
Size: Height 44mm; max. width 38mm.
Description: As above, but inscribed THE ITALY STAR.
Clasps: None.
Comments: *Awarded for operational service on land in Italy, Sicily, Greece, Yugoslavia, the Aegean area and Dodecanese islands, Corsica, Sardinia and Elba at any time between 11 June 1943 and 8 May 1945.*

VALUE:		*Miniature*
Italy Star	£12–15	£3

184. FRANCE AND GERMANY STAR

Date: 1945.

Campaign: France and Germany 1944-45.

Branch of Service: British and Commonwealth forces.

Ribbon: Five equal stripes of blue, white, red, white and blue (the national colours of the United Kingdom, France and the Netherlands).

Metal: Bronze.

Size: Height 44mm; max. width 38mm.

Description: As above, but inscribed THE FRANCE AND GERMANY STAR.

Clasps: Atlantic.

Comments: *Awarded for operational service in France, Belgium, the Netherlands or Germany from 6 June 1944 to 8 May 1945. Service in the North Sea, English Channel and Bay of Biscay in connection with the campaign in northern Europe also qualified. Prior eligibility for the Atlantic or Air Crew Europe Stars entitled personnel only to a bar for France and Germany. Conversely a first award of the France and Germany Star could earn an Atlantic bar.*

VALUE:		Miniature
France and Germany Star	£18–20	£3
Atlantic Clasp	£70–80	£6

185. DEFENCE MEDAL

Date: 1945.

Campaign: Second World War 1939-45.

Branch of Service: British and Commonwealth forces.

Ribbon: Two broad bars of green (this green and pleasant land) superimposed by narrow stripes of black (the black-out), with a wide band of orange (fire-bombing) in the centre.

Metal: Cupro-nickel or silver.

Size: 36mm.

Description: (Obverse) the uncrowned effigy of King George VI; (reverse) two lions flanking an oak sapling crowned with the dates at the sides and wavy lines representing the sea below. The words THE DEFENCE MEDAL appear in the exergue.

Clasps: None.

Comments: *Awarded to service personnel for three years' service at home or six months' service overseas in territories subjected to air attack or otherwise closely threatened. Personnel of Anti-Aircraft Command, RAF ground crews, Dominion forces stationed in the UK, the Home Guard, Civil Defence, National Fire Service and many other civilian units* qualified for the medal. The medal was generally issued unnamed in cupro-nickel, but the Canadian version was struck in silver.*

VALUE:		Miniature
Cupro-nickel	£14–16	£8
Silver (Canadian)	£15–18	£12

*The definitive list of eligible recipients was published by the Ministry of Defence in 1992—Form DM1/DM2 and Annexe. This lists 50 different organisations and 90 sub-divisions of eligible personnel.

186. WAR MEDAL 1939–45

Date: 1945.
Campaign: Second World War 1939-45.
Branch of Service: British and Commonwealth forces.
Ribbon: Narrow red stripe in the centre, with a narrow white stripe on either side, broad red stripes at either edge and two intervening stripes of blue.
Metal: Cupro-nickel or silver.
Size: 36mm.
Description: (Obverse) effigy of King George VI; (reverse) a triumphant lion trampling on a dragon symbolising the Axis powers.
Clasps: None.
Comments: *All fulltime personnel of the armed forces wherever they were serving, so long as they had served for at least 28 days between 3 September 1939 and 2 September 1945 were eligible for this medal. It was granted in addition to the campaign stars and the Defence Medal. A few categories of civilians, such as war correspondents and ferry pilots who had flown in operational theatres, also qualified. No clasps were issued with this medal but a bronze oak leaf denoted a mention in despatches. The medal was struck in cupro-nickel and issued unnamed, but those issued to Australian and South African personnel were officially named. The Canadian version of the medal was struck in silver.*

VALUE:		Miniature
Cupro-nickel	£10–12	£8
Named (Australian or South African)	£10–12	
Silver (Canadian)	£10–15	£12

186A. KING'S BADGE FOR WAR SERVICE

Date: 1945.
Campaign: Second World War.
Ribbon: None.
Metal: Silver.
Size: 26mm.
Description: A circular buttonhole badge with the crowned monogram GRI in script capitals in the centre, inscribed FOR LOYAL SERVICE.
Comments: *Awarded to personnel who did not qualify for one or other of the service medals or campaign stars, and who had been invalided out of the services. The badges are not numbered or named.*

VALUE: £10–12

187. INDIA SERVICE MEDAL

Date: 1945.
Campaign: India 1939-45.
Branch of Service: Indian forces.
Ribbon: Dark blue with two wide and one central thin pale blue stripes.
Metal: Cupro-nickel.
Size: 36mm.
Description: (Obverse) the effigy of the King Emperor; (reverse) a map of the Indian sub-continent with INDIA at the top and 1939-45 at foot.
Clasps: None.
Comments: *Awarded to officers and men of the Indian forces for three years' non-operational service in India. In effect, it took the place of the Defence Medal in respect of Indian forces.*

VALUE: £10–12   *Miniature*   £10–12

188. CANADIAN VOLUNTEER SERVICE MEDAL

Date: 1943.

Campaign: Second World War 1939-45.

Branch of Service: Canadian forces.

Ribbon: Narrow stripes of green and red flanking a broad central stripe of dark blue.

Metal: Silver.

Size: 36mm.

Description: (Obverse) seven men and women in the uniforms of the various services, marching in step; (reverse) the Canadian national arms.

Clasps: Maple leaf. A clasp inscribed DIEPPE and surmounted by the Combined Operations emblem, was instituted in 1994 for award to all servicemen who took part in the Dieppe raid of 1942.

Comments: *Awarded for eighteen months' voluntary service in the Canadian forces. The clasp denoted overseas service. The seven marching personnel are based on real people taken from National Defence photographs, representing the land, sea and air forces plus a nurse. The individuals are: first row: centre, 3780 Leading Seaman P. G. Colbeck, RCN; left, C52819 Pte D. E. Dolan, 1 Can. Para Bn; right, R95505 F/Sgt K. M. Morgan, RCAF. Second row: centre, W4901 Wren P. Mathie, WRCNS; left, 12885 L/Cpl J. M. Dann, CWAC; right, W315563 LAW O. M. Salmon, RCAF; back row: Lt N/S E. M. Lowe, RCAMC.*

VALUE:		*Miniature*
Silver medal	£14–16	£8
Maple leaf clasp	£18–22	£12
Dieppe clasp	£35–45	£15

188A. CANADIAN MEMORIAL CROSS

Instituted: 1914.

Branch of Service: Relative of Canadian forces.

Ribbon: Violet 11mm (ring suspension), 32mm (bar suspension).

Metal: Dull silver.

Size: 32mm.

Description: A Greek cross with the royal Cypher at the centre, superimposed on another with arms slightly flared at the ends. Maple leaves adorn three of the arms while the top arm has a crown surmounted by a suspension ring. (Reverse): details of the award. Four versions of the cross exist: the original, with GVR cypher (1914–19), with GVIR cypher and ring suspension (1940–45), GVIR cypher with suspension bar (1945–52) and an EIIR version for Korea and later conflicts.

Comments: *Issued to wives and mothers of servicemen who had died during World War I. A second version was introduced in August 1940 for award to widows and mothers of World War II servicemen, but this was extended to include those of merchant seamen and civilian firefighters. Newfoundland service personnel became eligible after April 1, 1949.*

VALUE:	
GVR, ring suspension	From £50
GVIR, ring suspension	From £50
GVIR, bar suspension	From £60
EIIR, bar suspension	From £120

189. AFRICA SERVICE MEDAL

Date: 1943.
Campaign: Second World War 1939-45.
Branch of Service: South African forces.
Ribbon: A central orange stripe, with green and gold stripes on either side.
Metal: Silver.
Size: 36mm.
Description: (Obverse) depicts a map of the African Continent; (reverse) bears a leaping Springbok. Inscribed AFRICA SERVICE MEDAL on the left and AFRIKADIENS-MEDALJE on the right.
Clasps: None.
Comments: *Awarded to Union service personnel who served at home and abroad during the War for at least thirty days. Medals were fully named and gave the service serial number of the recipient, prefixed by various letters, for example N (Native Military Corps), C (Cape Corps), M (Indian and Malay Corps), etc., no prefix indicated a white volunteer.*

VALUE:
    Silver medal (190,000)   £10–12   *Miniature* £10

190. AUSTRALIA SERVICE MEDAL

Date: 1949.
Campaign: Second World War 1939-45.
Branch of Service: Australian forces.
Ribbon: A broad central band of khaki bordered in red, with a dark blue and a light blue bar at either edge.
Metal: Cupro-nickel.
Size: 36mm.
Description: (Obverse) the effigy of King George VI; (reverse) the Australian arms supported by a kangaroo and an emu.
Clasps: None.
Comments: *Awarded to all Australian personnel who had seen eighteen months' overseas or three years' home service. The medals were named to the recipients. In the case of Army personnel, their service numbers were prefixed by the initial of their state: N (New South Wales), Q (Queensland), S (South Australia), T (Tasmania), V (Victoria) and W (Western Australia). In 1999 the time served for eligibility was reduced.*

VALUE:
    Cupro-nickel medal (180,000)   £30–35 *Miniature* £12

191. NEW ZEALAND WAR SERVICE MEDAL

Date: 1946.
Campaign: Second World War 1939-45.
Branch of Service: New Zealand forces.
Ribbon: Black with white edges.
Metal: Cupro-nickel.
Size: 36mm.
Description: (Obverse) effigy of King George VI; (reverse) the text FOR SERVICE TO NEW ZEALAND 1939-45 with a fern leaf below. Suspension was by a pair of fern leaves attached to a straight bar.
Clasps: None.
Comments: *Issued unnamed, to all members of the New Zealand forces who completed one month full-time or six months part-time service between September 1939 and September 1945. It was also named to casualties and those killed in action.*

VALUE:
    Cupro-nickel medal (240,000)   £18–20   *Miniature* £7

191A. NEW ZEALAND MEMORIAL CROSS

Instituted: 1960.
Campaign: Second World War, 1939–45.
Branch of Service: Relatives of New Zealand forces.
Ribbon: 12mm royal purple
Metal: Dull Silver.
Size: 32 mm.
Description: A cross surmounted by a St Edward Crown, with fern leaves on each arm, in the centre, within a wreath, the Royal Cypher; (reverse) details of the person in respect of whose death the cross is granted.
Comments: *Originally granted to the next-of-kin of persons who had lost their lives on active service with the New Zealand forces during the Second World War, or who had subsequently died of wounds or illness contracted during that conflict. Provision was made for the grant of crosses to the parent(s) as well as the wife or eldest surviving daughter or son. It as subsequently awarded in respect of postwar campaigns: Korea (47), Malaya, South Vietnam (37), and East Timor (3).*
VALUE:

Silver (World War II)	£60–£80
(Later campaigns)	Rare

192. SOUTH AFRICAN MEDAL FOR WAR SERVICE

Date: 1946.
Campaign: Second World War 1939-46.
Branch of Service: South African forces.
Ribbon: Three equal stripes of orange, white and blue, the South African national colours.
Metal: Silver.
Size: 36mm.
Description: (Obverse) South African arms; (reverse) a wreath of protea flowers enclosing the dates 1939 and 1945. Inscribed in English and Afrikaans: SOUTH AFRICA FOR WAR SERVICES on the left and SUID AFRIKA VIR OORLOGDIENSTE on the right.
Clasps: None.
Comments: *Men and women who served for at least two years in any official voluntary organisation in South Africa or overseas qualified for this medal so long as the service was both voluntary and unpaid. Those who already had the South African War Service Medal were ineligible.*
VALUE:

Silver (17,500)	£30–40	*Miniature*	£14

193. SOUTHERN RHODESIA WAR SERVICE MEDAL

Date: 1946.
Campaign: Second World War 1939-45.
Branch of Service: Southern Rhodesian forces.
Ribbon: Dark green with black and red stripes at each edge.
Metal: Cupro-nickel.
Size: 36mm.
Description: (Obverse) King George VI; (reverse) the Rhodesian national arms. FOR SERVICE IN SOUTHERN RHODESIA round the top and the dates 1939-1945 at the foot.
Clasps: None.
Comments: *This very scarce medal was awarded only to those who served in Southern Rhodesia during the period of the War but who were ineligible for one of the campaign stars or war medals.*
VALUE:

Cupro-nickel (1700)	£160–175	*Miniature*	£16

194. NEWFOUNDLAND VOLUNTEER WAR SERVICE MEDAL

Date: 1981.
Campaign: Second World War 1939-45.
Branch of Service: Newfoundland forces.
Ribbon: Deep claret with edges of red, white and blue.
Metal: Bronze.
Size: 37mm.
Description: (Obverse) the royal cypher of George VI surmounted by a crown topped by a caribou, the Newfoundland national emblem; (reverse) Britannia on a scallop shell background guarded by two lions.
Clasps:
Comments: *While the Second World War was being fought, Newfoundland was still a separate British colony which did not enter the Canadian Confederation till 1947. Consequently Newfoundland servicemen did not qualify for the Canadian Volunteer Service medal, and this deficiency was not remedied until July 1981 when the Newfoundland provincial government instituted this medal. Those who had served with the Canadian forces, on the other hand, and already held the Canadian medal, were not eligible for this award. The medal could be claimed by next-of-kin of those who died in or since the war.*

VALUE: Bronze (7,500) £350–450   *Miniature:*   £10–15

195. KOREA MEDAL

Date: July 1951.
Campaign: Korean War 1950-53.
Branch of Service: British and Commonwealth forces.
Ribbon: Yellow, with two blue stripes .
Metal: Cupro-nickel or silver.
Size: 36mm.
Description: (Obverse) Right-facing bust of Queen Elizabeth II by Mary Gillick; there are two obverse types, with or without BR: OMN; (reverse) Hercules wrestling with the Hydra, KOREA in the exergue.
Clasps: None.
Comments: *Awarded to all British and Commonwealth forces who took part in the Korean War between July 1950 and July 27, 1953. British medals were issued in cupro-nickel impressed in small capitals, medals to Australian and New Zealand forces were impressed in large capitals and the Canadian version was struck in silver and has CANADA below the Queen's bust. Particularly prized are medals issued to the 'Glorious Gloucesters' who played a gallant part in the battle of the Imjin River.*

VALUE:		*Miniature*
British, first obverse	£70–90	£7
British, second obverse	£100–150	£7
To Gloucester Regiment	£300–400	
Australian or New Zealand naming	£70–90	
Canadian, silver (27,000)	£60–70	£9

196. SOUTH AFRICAN MEDAL FOR KOREA

Date: 1953.
Campaign: Korea 1950-53.
Branch of Service: South African forces.
Ribbon: Sky blue central band flanked by dark blue stripes and edges of orange.
Metal: Silver.
Size: 38mm.
Description: (Obverse) maps of South Africa and Korea with an arrow linking them and the words VRYWILLIGERS and VOLUNTEERS in the field. (Reverse) the then South African arms surmounted by the crowned EIIR.
Clasps: None.
Comments: *Awarded to the 800 personnel in the contingent sent to Korea by the Union of South Africa. Suspension is by a ring and claw.*

VALUE:

Silver (800)	£280–300	*Miniature*	£25
Pilot's issue	£1000–1500		

197. UNITED NATIONS KOREA MEDAL

Date: December 1950.
Campaign: Korea 1950-53.
Branch of Service: All UN forces.
Ribbon: Seventeen narrow stripes alternating pale blue and white.
Metal: Bronze.
Size: 35mm.
Description: (Obverse) the wreathed globe emblem of the UN; (reverse) inscribed FOR SERVICE IN DEFENCE OF THE PRINCIPLES OF THE CHARTER OF THE UNITED NATIONS.
Clasps: Korea.
Comments: *National variants were produced, but the British type was granted to all personnel of the British and Commonwealth forces who had served at least one full day in Korea or in support units in Japan. Moreover, as those who served in Korea after the armistice in July 1953 were also entitled to the UN medal it is sometimes found in groups without the corresponding British medal. The award was extended to cover the period up to July 27, 1954, the first anniversary of the Panmunjom Truce. Issues to South African personnel were named on the rim.*

VALUE: £20–25 *Miniature* £5

If you know of a British or Commonwealth medal that is not included in the MEDAL YEARBOOK we would be delighted to hear from you.

Or if you can supply us with a photograph of any of the medals not illustrated in this publication we would be pleased to include it next year.

If you can help, please contact the Managing Editor, John Mussell, telephone 01404 46972 or at the address on page 1. Thank you!

198. GENERAL SERVICE MEDAL 1962

Date: 1964.
Campaign: Minor campaigns and operations since 1962.
Branch of Service: British forces.
Ribbon: Deep purple edged with green.
Metal: Silver.
Size: 36mm.
Description: (Obverse) a crowned bust of Queen Elizabeth II; (reverse) an oak wreath enclosing a crown and the words FOR CAMPAIGN SERVICE. It has a beaded and curved suspension above which are mounted campaign clasps.
Clasps: 13 to date (see below); the maximum clasps awarded so far seems to be six.
Comments: *This medal was instituted for award to personnel of all services, and thus did away with the need for separate Army and Navy general service medals. Awards range from a mere 70 for South Vietnam to over 130,000 for service in Northern Ireland.*

VALUE:

		Miniature
Borneo	£35–40	£8–10
Radfan	£50–65	£8–10
South Arabia	£35–45	£8–10
Malay Peninsula	£35–45	£8–10
South Vietnam	Rare	£8–10
Northern Ireland	£40–50	£8–10
Dhofar	£120–140	£8–10
Lebanon	£400–450	£8–10
Mine Clearance	£650–800	£8–10
Gulf	£150–200	£8–10
Kuwait	£300–400	£8–10
N. Iraq & S. Turkey	£300–400	£8–10
Air Operations Iraq	£200–300	£10–12
2 clasps	£40–60	£12–16
3 clasps	£80–120	£14–18
4 clasps	From £140	£16–20

198A. OPERATIONAL SERVICE MEDAL

Date: 1999.
Campaign: Operations after 1 January 2000.
Branch of Service: All branches of the armed forces.
Ribbon: Basic colours with a varying number of thin stripes for each operation.
Metal: Silver.
Size: 36mm.
Description: Not yet available.
Clasps: None.
Comments: *To be awarded for minor campaigns for which a separate medal is not issued, and operations for which the award of a UN or NATO medal is not merited. It replaces the General Service Medal 1962, except for Northern Ireland and Air Operations Iraq.*

VALUE: —

199. UNITED NATIONS EMERGENCY FORCE MEDAL

Date: 1957.
Campaign: Israel and Egypt 1956–57.
Branch of Service: All UN forces.
Ribbon: Sand-coloured with a central light blue stripe and narrow dark blue and green stripes towards each edge.
Metal: Bronze.
Size: 35mm.
Description: (Obverse) the UN wreathed globe emblem with UNEF at the top; (reverse) inscribed IN THE SERVICE OF PEACE. Ring suspension.
Clasps: None.
Comments: *Awarded to all personnel who served with the UN peace-keeping forces on the border between Israel and Egypt following the Sinai Campaign of 1956. These medals were awarded to troops from Brazil, Canada, Colombia, Denmark, Finland, Indonesia, Norway, Sweden and Yugoslavia.*

VALUE:

Bronze	£20–25	*Miniature*	£6

200. VIETNAM MEDAL

Date: July 1968.
Campaign: Vietnam 1964-72.
Branch of Service: Australian and New Zealand forces.
Ribbon: A broad central band of bright yellow surmounted by three thin red stripes (the Vietnamese national colours) and bordered by broader red stripes, with dark and light blue stripes at the edges, representing the three services.
Metal: Silver.
Size: 36mm.
Description: (Obverse) the crowned bust of Queen Elizabeth II; (reverse) a nude male figure pushing apart two spheres representing different ideologies.
Clasps: None.
Comments: *Awarded to personnel who served in Vietnam a minimum of one day on land or 28 days at sea after 28 May 1964. The medal was impressed in large capitals (Australian) or small capitals (New Zealand).*

VALUE:

Australian recipient (18,000)	**£150–170**
New Zealand recipient (3,312)	**£170–200**
Miniature	**£10–12**

200A. VIETNAM LOGISTIC AND SUPPORT MEDAL

Instituted: 1993.
Campaign: Vietnam 1964–68.
Branch of Service: Australian forces.
Ribbon: A broad central band of yellow with three narrow red stripes superimposed. On the left are stripes of red and dark blue and on the right stripes of dark brown and light blue.
Metal: Nickel-silver.
Size: 36mm.
Description: (Obverse) crowned effigy of Queen Elizabeth and titles; (reverse) as MY200 above but with a cartouche containing a ram's head (Royal Australian Mint's mark) near the man's right foot. The suspension bar also differs from MY200 with graduated straight sides.
Clasps: None.
Comments: *Awarded to personnel who served in the Vietnam War but who did not qualify for the Vietnam Medal. It is estimated that about 20,000 individuals are eligible for this award. Recipients include Qantas air crew who took troop flights to Saigon, and civilian entertainers.*
VALUE:

Australian recipient (5121)	£150–300
Miniature	£10–12

201. SOUTH VIETNAM CAMPAIGN MEDAL

Date: 1964.
Campaign: Vietnam 1964–72.
Branch of Service: Allied forces in Vietnam.
Ribbon: White with two broad green stripes towards the centre and narrow green edges.
Metal: Bronze.
Size: Height 42mm; max. width 36mm.
Description: A six-pointed star, with gold rays in the angles. The gilt enamelled centre shows a map of Vietnam engulfed in flames; (reverse) a Vietnamese inscription in the centre.
Clasps: 1960 (bronze, cupro-nickel or silver gilt), 1965 (silver gilt).
Comments: *Awarded by the government of South Vietnam to Australian and New Zealand forces who served at least six months in Vietnam. The original issue, of Vietnamese manufacture, was relatively crude and issued unnamed. Subsequently medals were produced in Australia and these are not only of a better quality but bear the name of the recipient. A third version, made in the USA, has the suspension ring a fixed part of the medal.*
VALUE:

Unnamed	£10–15
Named	£20–30
Miniature	£6–10

202. RHODESIA MEDAL

Date: 1980.
Campaign: Rhodesia 1979–80.
Branch of Service: British and Rhodesian forces.
Ribbon: Sky blue, with a narrow band of red, white and dark blue in the centre.
Metal: Rhodium-plated cupro-nickel.
Size: 36mm.
Description: (Obverse) the crowned bust of Queen Elizabeth II; (reverse) a sable antelope with the name of the medal and the year of issue.
Clasps: None.
Comments: *This medal was awarded to personnel serving in Rhodesia for fourteen days between 1 December 1979 and 20 March 1980, pending the elections and the emergence of the independent republic of Zimbabwe. Medals were issued unnamed or named in impressed capitals. Examples with the word COPY in raised capitals immediately below the suspension fitment are believed to have been issued as replacements for lost medals, although examples with "R" for replacement are also known to exist.*
VALUE:

Cupro-nickel (2500)	£300–350	*Miniature*	£9

203. SOUTH ATLANTIC MEDAL

Date: 1982.
Campaign: Falkland Islands and South Georgia 1982.
Branch of Service: British forces.
Ribbon: Watered silk blue, white, green, white and blue.
Metal: Cupro-nickel.
Size: 36mm.
Description: (Obverse) crowned profile of Queen Elizabeth II; (reverse) laurel wreath below the arms of the Falkland Islands with SOUTH ATLANTIC MEDAL inscribed round the top.
Clasps: None, but a rosette denoting service in the combat zone.
Comments: *Awarded to all personnel who took part in operations in the South Atlantic for the liberation of South Georgia and the Falkland Islands following the Argentinian invasion. To qualify, the recipient had to have at least one full day's service in the Falklands or South Georgia, or 30 days in the operational zone including Ascension Island. Those who qualified under the first condition were additionally awarded a large rosette for wear on the ribbon.*

VALUE:

Army (7000)	£180–250
Royal Navy (13,000)	£170–200
Royal Marines (3700)	£240–280
Royal Fleet Auxiliary (2000)	£120–150
RAF (2000)	£140–160
Merchant Navy and civilians (2000)	£130–150
Miniature	
with rosette	£9
without rosette	£6

203A. SOVIET 40th ANNIVERSARY MEDAL

Date: 1985.
Campaign: Second World War.
Branch of Service: British and Canadian forces who served mainly in RN or MN ships on Arctic convoys.
Ribbon: One half red, the other orange with three black stripes, edged with pale blue. Worn in the Russian style.
Metal: Bronze.
Size: 32mm.
Description: (Obverse) Group of servicemen and women in front of a five-pointed star flanked by oak leaves and the dates 1945–1985 above; (reverse) 40th anniversary of the Victory in the Great Patriotic War 1941–1945, in Russian.
Clasps: None.
Comments: *In 1994 Her Majesty the Queen approved the wearing of this medal awarded by the Soviet Government to selected ex-Servicemen, bearing in mind the changed circumstances in Russia since the award was first issued.*

VALUE:	British striking	£16–20
	Russian striking	£16–20
	Miniature (unofficial)	£9

204. GULF MEDAL

Date: 1992.

Campaign: Kuwait and Saudi Arabia 1990-91.

Branch of Service: British forces.

Ribbon: Sand-coloured broad central band flanked by narrow stripes of dark blue, red and light blue (left) or light blue, red and dark blue (right) representing the sands of the desert and the three armed services.

Metal: Cupro-nickel.

Size: 36mm.

Description: (Obverse) crowned profile of Queen Elizabeth II; (reverse) an eagle and automatic rifle superimposed on an anchor, symbolising the three armed services. The dates of the Gulf War appear at the foot.

Clasps: 2 Aug 1990, 16 Jan–28 Feb 1991.

Comments: *Awarded to personnel who had thirty days continuous service in the Middle East (including Cyprus) between 2 August 1990 and 7 March 1991, or seven days between 16 January 1991 and 28 February 1991, or service with the Kuwait Liaison Team on 2 August 1990, the date of the Iraqi invasion. Two clasps were sanctioned and awarded to personnel who qualified for active service with the Liaison Team or in the operations to liberate Kuwait. A rosette is worn on the ribbon alone to denote the campaign clasps. Naming is in impressed capitals. More than 45,000 medals were awarded. See also the Kuwait and Iraq-Turkey clasps awarded to the General Service Medal 1962. About 1,500 civilians, including members of British Aerospace working at Dahran, also received the medal with the clasp 16 Jan to 28 Feb 1991.*

VALUE:

No clasp	£80–100
16 Jan to 28 Feb 1991	
Regiments/RN/RAF	£160–200
Corps and Artillery	£120–140
Civilians	£100–120
2 Aug 1990	£1200–1600
Miniature	£10

204A. HUMANITARIAN PEACEKEEPING MEDAL

Date: 1999.

Campaign: Humanitarian or peacekeeping operations.

Branch of Service: Military and civilian personnel.

Ribbon: Details not yet available.

Metal: Details not yet available.

Size: Details not yet available.

Description: Details not yet available.

Clasps: Details not yet available.

Comment: *To be issued to military and civilian personnel engaged in operations of a humanitarian or peacekeeping character which do not warrant the issue of an Operational Service Medal and which do not attract the award of a UN medal.*

205. SAUDI ARABIAN MEDAL FOR THE LIBERATION OF KUWAIT

Date: 1991.

Campaign: Gulf War 1991.

Branch of Service: British and Allied forces.

Ribbon: Green with edges of red, black and white (the Saudi national colours).

Metal: White metal.

Size: approx. 45mm across

Description: The white metal medal has a star of fifteen long and fifteen short round-tipped rays, surmounted by a bronze circle bearing a crowned and enwreathed globe on which appears a map of Arabia. Above the circle is a palm tree with crossed scimitars, the state emblem of Saudi Arabia. A scroll inscribed in Arabic and English LIBERATION OF KUWAIT appears round the foot of the circle.

Clasps: None.

Comments: *Awarded by the government of Saudi Arabia to all Allied personnel who took part in the campaign for the liberation of Kuwait, although only a few of the 45,000 British servicemen were subsequently given permission by the Foreign and Commonwealth Office to wear it. The contract for production was shared between Spink and a Swiss company, but subsequently a flatter version, more practicable for wear with other medals, was manufactured in the United States.*

VALUE: £20   *Miniature* £12

205A. MULTINATIONAL FORCE AND OBSERVERS MEDAL

Date: March 1982.

Campaign: Sinai Peninsula.

Ribbon: 36mm with 10mm central white stripe, flanked by 3mm dark green stripes and 10mm orange stripes on the outside.

Metal: Bronze.

Size: 30mm.

Description: (Obverse) a dove clutching an olive branch surrounded by the inscription MULTINATIONAL FORCE & OBSERVERS; (reverse) UNITED IN SERVICE FOR PEACE in five lines.

Comments: *Awarded to personnel of the Multinational Force and Observers (MFO) created in 1979 to monitor the peace agreement between Egypt and Israel. Eligibility for the medal was originally 90 days continuous service in the force, but this was raised to 170 days in March 1985. Subsequent awards for each completed six-month tour is indicated by a silver numeral affixed to the ribbon. It was originally awarded personally by the MFO's first commander, the Norwegian General Fredrik Bull-Hansen. The Force has 3,000 personnel drawn from the armed services of Australia, Canada, Colombia, Fiji, France, Italy, the Netherlands, New Zealand, UK, USA and Uruguay.*

VALUE: £25–30   *Miniature* £7

206. KUWAITI LIBERATION MEDALS

4th grade

Date: 1991.

Campaign: Liberation of Kuwait 1991.

Branch of Service: Allied forces.

Ribbon: Equal stripes of green, white and red (the Kuwaiti national colours) with a black quadrilateral at the upper edge.

Metal: Various.

Size: Various.

Description: The circular medals have different decorative treatments of the Kuwaiti state emblem on the obverse, enshrined in a five-petalled flower (Second Grade), a five-pointed star with radiate background (Third Grade) and a plain medallic treatment (Fourth Grade). All grades, however, have a straight bar suspender of different designs.

Clasps: None.

Comments: *This medal was issued in five grades and awarded according to the rank of the recipient. The Excellent Grade was only conferred on the most senior Allied commanders, the First Grade went to brigadiers and major-generals, the Second Grade to officers of field rank (colonels and majors), the Third Grade to junior officers (captains, lieutenants and equivalent ranks in the other services), and the Fourth Grade to all other ranks. HM Government has decreed that British personnel may accept their medals as a keepsake but permission to wear them in uniform has so far been refused. The Canadian Government has followed the same policy, but the personnel of other Allied nations are permitted to wear their medals.*

VALUE:		*Miniature*
2nd grade	—	
3rd grade	—	
4th grade	£10–15	£12 (silver)

206A. NATO MEDAL

Instituted: December 20, 1994.

Campaigns: Any theatre or area of operations in the service of the North Atlantic Treaty Organization.

Branch of Service: NATO military and service personnel.

Ribbon: NATO blue with a narrow white stripe towards each edge (Former Yugoslavia) or blue with a white central stripe and white edges (Kosovo).

Metal: Bronze

Size: 36mm

Description: (Obverse) the NATO star emblem set in a wreath of olive leaves; (reverse) the title NORTH ATLANTIC TREATY ORGANIZATION and the words IN SERVICE OF PEACE AND FREEDOM in English and French.

Clasps: Former Yugoslavia, Kosovo.

Comments: *The NATO medal was first instituted to reward personnel who took part in the Alliance operations in the former Yugoslavia. Any person serving under NATO command or operational control is eligible for the award. UK Service personnel cannot qualify for the NATO Medal and the UNPROFOR Medal (no. 207) in respect of the same period of service. The qualifying period for the medal is to be designated by the Secretary-General, however, for the operations in the former Yugoslavia the period has been set as 30 days continuous or accumulated service within the theatre of operations inside the former Yugoslavia and the Adriatic, or 90 days within the area of operations but outside the territory of the former Yugoslavia. The medal takes precedence equal to the General Service Medal in order of date of award. Numerals are worn on the ribbon to denote multiple tours.*

VALUE: £20 *Miniature* £8

206B. OMANI 25th NATIONAL DAY MEDAL

Date: November 18, 1995.
Branch of Service: British personnel seconded to the service of the Sultan of Oman.
Ribbon:
Metal:
Size:
Description:
Comments: *This medal was instituted to celebrate the 25th anniversary of the National Day of Oman (November 18). In December 1998 Her Majesty the Queen granted permission for members of the British armed forces to wear this medal.*

VALUE: —

206C. EUROPEAN COMMUNITY MONITORING MISSION MEDAL

Date: 1995.
Campaigns: Former Yugoslavia.
Branch of Service: EC Community Peacekeeping.
Ribbon: Navy with stripes of white and red and thin yellow.
Metal: Silver.
Size: 36mm.
Description: (Obverse) Outline map of Yugoslavia surmounted by the words EC MONITOR MISSION surrounded by a ring of stars; (reverse) a dove of peace.
Comments: *Awarded or 21 days service between July 27, 1991 and June 30, 1993, in and around the former Yugoslavia.*

VALUE: —

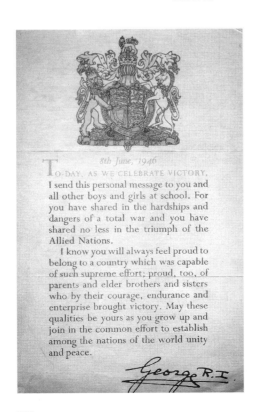

8th June, 1946

TO-DAY, AS WE CELEBRATE VICTORY,
I send this personal message to you and all other boys and girls at school. For you have shared in the hardships and dangers of a total war and you have shared no less in the triumph of the Allied Nations.

I know you will always feel proud to belong to a country which was capable of such supreme effort; proud, too, of parents and elder brothers and sisters who by their courage, endurance and enterprise brought victory. May these qualities be yours as you grow up and join in the common effort to establish among the nations of the world unity and peace.

George R.I

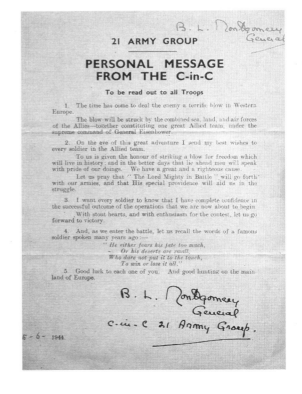

21 ARMY GROUP

PERSONAL MESSAGE FROM THE C-in-C

To be read out to all Troops

1. The time has come to deal the enemy a terrific blow in Western Europe.

The blow will be struck by the combined sea, land, and air forces of the Allies—together constituting one great Allied team, under the supreme command of General Eisenhower.

2. On the eve of this great adventure I send my best wishes to every soldier in the Allied team.

To us is given the honour of striking a blow for freedom which will live in history; and in the better days that lie ahead men will speak with pride of our doings. We have a great and a righteous cause.

Let us pray that "The Lord Mighty in Battle" will go forth with our armies, and that His special providence will aid us in the struggle.

3. I want every soldier to know that I have complete confidence in the successful outcome of the operations that we are now about to begin.

With stout hearts, and with enthusiasm for the contest, let us go forward to victory.

4. And, as we enter the battle, let us recall the words of a famous soldier spoken many years ago:—

"He either fears his fate too much,
Or his deserts are small,
Who dare not put it to the touch,
To win or lose it all."

5. Good luck to each one of you. And good hunting on the mainland of Europe.

B. L. Montgomery
General
C-in-C 21 Army Group.

6 - 6 - 1944

207. UNITED NATIONS MEDAL

Date: 1951.

Campaigns: Various supervisory or observation roles since 1948.

Branch of Service: UN forces.

Ribbons: Various (see below).

Metal: Bronze.

Size: 35mm.

Description: (Obverse) the wreathed globe emblem surmounted by the letters UN; (reverse) plain, inscribed "In the service of peace".

Clasps: CONGO, UNGOMAP, OSGAP, UNSMIH, MINUGUA, UNCRO, ONUMOZ, UNSOM.

Comments: *Apart from the UN Korea and UNEF medals, there have been numerous awards to personnel who served in one or other of the UN peace-keeping actions around the world since the end of the Second World War. The all-purpose medal has been awarded with various distinctive ribbons for service in many of the world's trouble spots. Two versions of the medal exist: globe flat (European) and globe raised (US version). Issues to South African Personnel are named.*

UNTSO United Nations Truce Supervision Organization (Israel, Egypt, Syria since 1948).
Blue ribbon with two narrow white stripes towards the edges.

UNOGIL United Nations Observation Group in Lebanon (1958).
Same ribbon as UNTSO.

ONUC Organisation des Nations Unies au Congo (1960–64).
Originally the same ribbon as UNTSO with clasp CONGO, but a green ribbon, with white and blue edges was substituted in 1963.

UNTEA United Nations Temporary Exacutive Authority (Netherlands New Guinea, 1962).
Blue ribbon with a white central stripe bordered green.

UNMOGIP United Nations Military Observer Group in India and Pakistan since 1949.
Dark green ribbon shading to light green with white and blue edges.

UNIPOM United Nations India Pakistan Observation Mission (1965–66).
Ribbon as UNMOGIP.

UNYOM United Nations Yemen Observation Mission (1963–64).
Ribbon with brown centre, yellow stripes and light blue edges.

UNFICYP United Nations Force in Cyprus (1964–).
Pale blue ribbon with central white stripe bordered in dark blue.

UNEF 2 United Nations Emergency Force 2 patrolling Israeli-Egyptian cease-fire (1973–).
Pale blue ribbon with sand centre and two dark blue stripes.

UNDOF United Nations Disengagement Observer Force, Golan Heights (1974–).
Ribbon of red, white, black and pale blue.

UNIFIL United Nations Interim Force in Lebanon (1978–).
Pale blue ribbon with green centre bordered white and red.

UNGOMAP United Nations Good Offices in Afghanistan and Pakistan.
A bronze bar inscribed UNGOMAP was issued but as the mission was made up from observers from three other missions it can only be found on these ribbons: UNTSO, UNIFIL, UNDOF.

UNIIMOG United Nations Iran-Iraq Monitoring Observation Group.
Pale blue with red, white and green edges.

UNAVEM United Nations Angola Verification Missions: I (1989–91), II (1991–95), III (1995–).
Pale blue ribbon with yellow edges separated by narrow stripes of red, white and black (same for all three).

ONUCA Observadores de las Naciones Unidas en Centro America (Nicaragua and Guatemala).
Pale blue ribbon with dark blue edges and nine thin central green or white stripes.

UNTAG United Nations Transitional Assistance Group (Namibia, 1990).
Sand ribbon with pale blue edges and thin central stripes of blue, green, red, sand and deep blue.

ONUSAL Observadores de las Naciones Unidas en El Salvador.
Pale blue ribbon with a white central stripe bordered dark blue.

UNIKOM United Nations Iraq Kuwait Observation Mission.
Sand ribbon with a narrow central stripe of pale blue.

MINURSO Mission des Nations Unies pour la Referendum dans le Sahara Occidental (UN Mission for the Referendum in Western Sahara).
Ribbon has a broad sandy centre flanked by stripes of UN blue.

UNAMIC United Nations Advanced Mission in Cambodia (Oct. 1991–March 1992).
Pale blue ribbon with central white stripe bordered with dark blue, yellow and red stripes.

UNTAC United Nations Transitional Authority in Cambodia (March 1992–Sept. 1993).
Green ribbon with central white stripe edged with red, pale blue and dark blue.

UNOSOM   United Nations Operations in Somalia (I: 1992–93 and II: 1993–95).
Pale yellow ribbon with central blue stripe edged with green.
UNMIH   United Nations Mission in Haiti
Pale blue ribbon with dark blue and red central stripes edged with white.
UNIMOZ   United Nations Operations in Mozambique (1992–).
Pale blue ribbon edged with white and green stripes.
UNPROFOR   United Nations Protection Force (1992–) operating in the former Yugoslavia, especially Bosnia.
Blue ribbon with central red stripe edged in white and green or brown edges.
UNOMIL   United Nations Observer Mission in Liberia (1993–).
Pale blue ribbon flanked with white stripes with dark blue or red edges.
UNOMUR   United Nations Observer Mission in Uganda/Rwanda (1993–).
Pale blue central stripe edged by white and flanked by equal stripes of black, orange and red.
UNOMIG   United Nations Observer Mission in Georgia (1993–).
Pale blue central stripe flanked by equal stripes of white, green and dark blue.
UNAMIR   United Nations Assistance Mission in Rwanda (1993–).
Pale blue central stripe edged with white and flanked by equal stripes of black, green and red.
UNHQ   General service at UN headquarters, New York.
Plain ribbon of pale blue, the UN colour.
UNPREDEP   United Nations Preventative Deployment in Yugoslavia.
Blue ribbon with central red stripe bearing four yellow lines and flanked by white edging.
UNMOP   United Nations Mission of Observers in Pravlaka.
Dark blue ribbon with central yellow stripe edged with white, and two pale blue stripes.
UNTAES   United Nations Transitional Authority in Eastern Slavonia.
Pale blue ribbon with yellow, red edged with white, and green stripes.
UNMOT   United Nations Peacekeeping Force in Tadjikistan.
Blue ribbon with central green stripe flanked by white stripes.
UNMIBH   United Nations Mission in Bosnia Herzegovina.
Blue ribbon with white central stripe, edged with one green and one red stripe.
UNMOGUA   United Nations Military Observers in Guatemala.
Purple with central blue stripe and two white stripes each with central green line.
UNSMIH   United Nations Support Mission in Haiti (July 1996 –).
Same ribbon as UNMIH above, but with clasp UNSMIH.
UNCRO   United Nations Confidence Restoration Operation in Croatia (1995–96).
Same ribbon as UNPROFOR above, but with clasp UNCRO.
MINUGUA   Mision de las Naciones Unidas en Guatemala.
Same ribbon as UNMOGUA but clasp with initials in Spanish.
ONUMOZ   Operation des Nations Unies pour le referendum dans Mozambique.
Same ribbon as UNIMOZ above. Clasp with French initials.
UNSSM   United Nations Special Service Medal.
Awarded to personal serving at least 90 consecutive days under UN control in operations for which no other UN award is authorised. Blue ribbon with white edges.
OSGAP   Office of the Secretary General for Afghanistan and Pakistan.
Silver clasp worn by Canadian personnel on the ribbons of UNTSO, UNDOF or UNIFIL.
UNOMSIL United Nations Observer Mission in Sierra Leone.
Awarded for 90 days service. White ribbon with blue edges and the Sierra Leone colours (light blue flanked by green stripes) in the centre.
UNPSG United Nations Police Support Group Medal.
A support group of 180 police monitors created in January 1998 initially to supervise the Croatian police in the return of displaced persons. 90 days qualifying service. White ribbon with a broad blue central stripe and narrow dark grey (left) and bright yellow (right) stripes towards the edges.
MINURCA United Nations Verification Mission in the Central African Republic.
Mission instituted April 15, 1998 to monitor the restoration of peace following the Bangui agreement. 90 days qualifying service. Ribbon has a broad blue central stripe flanked by yellow, green, red, white and dark blue stripes on either side.
UNSCOM United Nations Special Service Medal
The UN Special Service Medal with UNSCOM clasp is awarded to personnel with a minimum of 90 days consecutive service or 180 days in all, with UNSCOM in Iraq. Ribbon is UN blue with a white stripe at each edge.
UNMIK United Nations Mission in Kosovo
Pale blue ribbon with wide central dark blue stripe edged with white.
UNAMET United Nations Mission in East Timor
Pale blue ribbon with wide central white stripe edged with yellow and claret.
MONUC United Nations Mission in Kosovo
Pale blue ribbon with wide central dark blue stripe edged with yellow.

VALUE:

Any current issue medal regardless of ribbon	£10–15
Original striking for Cyprus	£25–30
Miniature	£6–8

THE KIWI
SCORPIONS

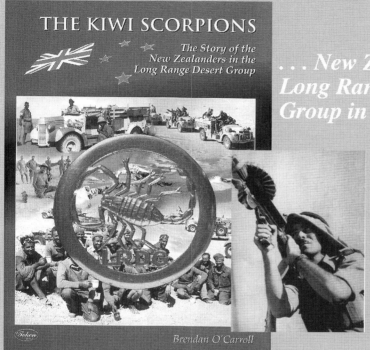

THE KIWI SCORPIONS
The Story of the New Zealanders in the Long Range Desert Group

... New Zealanders in the Long Range Desert Group in World War II

£24.95 *(plus £3.50p&p)*

Brendan O'Carroll

A profusely illustrated, hardbound A4 publication featuring the deeds and actions of New Zealanders of the Long Range Desert Group of World War II. With information that cannot be found anywhere else and illustrations never before published, this extensive publication deserves a place on the bookshelf of any serious military historian. The men, the weapons, the vehicles and the uniforms are all fully described together with the battles and the conditions under which these brave men fought.

ORDER YOUR COPY OF "KIWI SCORPIONS"

Simply write, fax or email your order to the address and numbers below. Remittance of £24.95 (plus £3.50 p&p) payable by cheque, credit card or dollar cheque secures your copy. Strictly limited print run.

TOKEN PUBLISHING LTD
ORCHARD HOUSE, DUCHY ROAD, HEATHPARK, HONITON, DEVON EX14 1YD
TEL: 01404 44166   FAX: 01404 44788   e-mail: sales@tokenpublishing.com

Long and Meritorious Service Medals

A large, varied but until recently relatively neglected category comprises the medals awarded for long service and good conduct or meritorious service. Their common denominator is that the grant of such awards is made in respect of a minimum number of years of unblemished service—"undetected crime" is how it is often described in the armed forces. As their title implies, long service and good conduct medals combine the elements of lengthy service with no transgressions of the rules and regulations. Meritorious service, on the other hand, implies rather more. Apart from a brief period (1916-28) when awards were made for single acts of gallantry, MSMs have generally been granted to warrant officers and senior NCOs as a rather superior form of long service medal.

Long service and good conduct medals do not appear to excite the same interest among collectors as campaign medals. Perhaps this may be accounted for by their image of stolid devotion to duty rather than the romantic connotations of a medal with an unusual clasp awarded for service in some remote and all but forgotten outpost of the Empire. Nevertheless their importance should not be overlooked. Especially in regard to groups consisting primarily of the Second World War medals, they serve a useful purpose in establishing the provenance of the group, on account of the fact that they are invariably named to the recipient.

Service medals include not only such well known types as the Army LSGC (known affectionately as "the mark of the beast" on account of its high incidence on the chests of sergeant-majors), but also awards to the Territorial and Reserve forces, the auxiliary forces, the nursing services, and organisations such as the Royal Observer Corps and the Cadet Force, the Police, the Red Cross and St John's Ambulance Brigade. The Special Constabulary and Fire Brigades also have their own medals bestowed according to length of service and distinguished conduct. These medals may lack the glamour of naval and military awards but in recent years they have become increasingly fashionable with collectors and will certainly repay further study in their own right.

As many of these medals have been in use for eighty years or more with a standard reverse, variation usually lies in the obverse, changed for each successive sovereign. In addition, considerable variety has been imparted by the use of crowned or uncrowned profiles and busts, and changes in titles.

The following is a summary of the principal obverse types which may be encountered, referred to in the text by their type letters in brackets:

Queen Victoria (A) Young Head by William Wyon 1838–60

Queen Victoria (B) Veiled Head by Leonard C. Wyon 1860–87

Queen Victoria (C) Jubilee Head by Sir Joseph E. Boehm 1887–93

Queen Victoria (D) Old Head by Sir Thomas Brock 1893–1901

Edward VII (A) Bareheaded bust in Field Marshal's uniform

Edward VII (B) Bareheaded bust in Admiral's uniform

Edward VII (C) Coinage profile by George W. de Saulles

George V (A) Bareheaded bust in Field Marshal's uniform

George V (B) Bareheaded bust in Admiral's uniform

George V (C) Crowned bust in Coronation robes

George V (D) Crowned bust in Delhi Durbar robes

George V (E) Coinage profile by Bertram Mackennal 1931–36

George VI (A) Crowned bust in Coronation robes

George VI (B) Crowned profile IND: IMP 1937–48

George VI (C) Crowned profile FID: DEF 1949–52

George VI (D) Coinage profile IND: IMP 1937–48

George VI (E) Coinage profile FID: DEF 1949–52

Elizabeth II (A) Tudor crown 1953–80

Elizabeth II (B) St Edward crown 1980–

Elizabeth II (C) Coinage bust BR: OMN 1953–54

Elizabeth II (D) Coinage bust without BR: OMN 1955–

PRINCIPAL OBVERSE TYPES:

Queen Victoria (A) Young Head

Queen Victoria (B) Veiled Head

Queen Victoria (C) Jubilee Head

Queen Victoria (D) Old Head

Edward VII (A) Bareheaded bust in Field Marshal's uniform

Edward VII (B) Bareheaded bust in Admiral's uniform

George V (A) Bareheaded bust in Field Marshal's uniform

George V (B) Bareheaded bust in Admiral's uniform

George V (C) Crowned bust in Coronation robes

George V (E) Coinage profile by Bertram Mackennal

George VI (B) Crowned profile with IND: IMP in legend 1937–48

George VI (C) Crowned profile with FID: DEF 1949–52

George VI (D) Coinage profile with IND: IMP 1937–48

George VI (E) Coinage profile with FID: DEF 1949–52

Elizabeth II (A) Tudor crown 1953–80

Elizabeth II (B) St Edward crown 1980–

Elizabeth II (C) Coinage bust with BR: OMN 1953–54

Elizabeth II (D) Coinage bust without BR: OMN.

208. ROYAL NAVAL MERITORIOUS SERVICE MEDAL

Instituted: 14 January 1919, by Order in Council.
Branch of Service: Royal Navy.
Ribbon: Crimson edged in white, with a central white stripe.
Metal: Silver
Size: 36mm.
Description: (Obverse) effigy of the reigning monarch; (reverse) imperial crown surmounting a wreath containing the words FOR MERITORIOUS SERVICE. The medal was named in large seriffed capitals round the rim.
Comments: *Awarded without annuity or pension to petty officers and ratings of the Royal Navy. Originally it was awarded either for specific acts of gallantry not in the presence of the enemy or for arduous and specially meritorious service afloat or ashore in action with the enemy. Bars were granted for second awards. It was superseded in 1928 by the British Empire Medal for Gallantry or Meritorious Service, but re-instated on 1 December 1977. In this guise it has been awarded to senior petty officers of the Royal Navy, warrant officers and senior NCOs of the Royal Marines, and equivalent ranks in the WRNS and QARNNS, who have at least 27 years service and are already holders of the LSGC medal and three good conduct badges. The medal is not awarded automatically when these criteria are satisfied, as no more than 59 medals may be awarded annually. The revived medal is identical to the Army MSM and can only be distinguished by the naming giving rank and name of ship.*

VALUE:		*Miniature*
George V (B)	Rare	—
George V (B) (1020)	£250–300	£15–20
Elizabeth II (D)	£250–300	£10–12

209. ROYAL MARINES MERITORIOUS SERVICE MEDAL

Instituted: 15 January 1849, by Order in Council.
Branch of Service: Royal Marines.
Ribbon: Plain dark blue.
Metal: Silver.
Size: 36mm.
Description: (Obverse) effigy of the monarch; (reverse) a crowned laurel wreath enclosing the words FOR MERITORIOUS SERVICE.
Comments: *Annuities not exceeding £20 a year might be granted in addition to the medal for distinguished service. Sergeants with a minimum of 24 years service (the last fourteen as a sergeant), 'with an irreproachable and meritorious character' were considered eligible for the award which was extended to discharged sergeants in 1872 when the service qualification was reduced to 21 years. The award of the MSM for gallantry was discontinued in 1874 when the Conspicuous Gallantry Medal was reconstituted. Only six MSMs for gallantry were ever awarded. The medal was identical with the Army MSM, distinguished solely by its ribbon and the naming to the recipient. Under the royal warrants of 1916-19 Marine NCOs became eligible for immediate awards of the MSM for arduous or specially meritorious service. The medals in this case were worn with crimson ribbons with three white stripes and had the obverse showing the King in the uniform of an Admiral or a Field Marshal, depending on whether the award was for services afloat, or with the naval brigades on the Western Front. The use of this medal ceased in 1928 when the BEM for Gallantry was instituted. The Royal Marines MSM was revived in 1977 solely as a long service award and is the same as the naval MSM already noted, differing only in the details of the recipient.*

VALUE: £300–350   *Miniature*   £40–50

210. ARMY MERITORIOUS SERVICE MEDAL

Instituted: 19 December 1845.
Branch of Service: Army.
Ribbon: Plain crimson (till 1916), white edges added (1916-17), three white stripes (since August 1917).
Metal: Silver.
Size: 36mm.
Description: (Obverse) effigy of the monarch; (reverse) a crowned laurel wreath inscribed FOR MERITORIOUS SERVICE.
Comments: *A sum of £2000 a year was set aside for distribution to recipients in the form of annuities not exceeding £20, paid for life to NCOs of the rank of sergeant and above for distinguished or meritorious service. The number of medals awarded was thus limited by the amount of money available in the annuity fund, so that medals and annuities were only granted on the death of previous recipients or when the fund was increased. Until November 1902 holders were not allowed to wear the LSGC as well as the MSM, but thereafter both medals could be worn, the LSGC taking precedence. In 1979, however, the order of precedence was reversed. Until 1951 the MSM could only be awarded when an annuity became available, but since then it has often been awarded without the annuity, the latter becoming payable as funds permit. Since 1956 recipients must have at least 27 years service to become eligible. What was, in effect, a second type of MSM was introduced in October 1916 when immediate awards for exceptionally valuable and meritorious service were introduced. In January 1917 this was extended to include individual acts of gallantry not in the presence of the enemy. No annuities were paid with the immediate awards which terminated in 1928 with the institution of the Gallantry BEM. Bars for subsequent acts of gallantry or life-saving were introduced in 1916, seven being awarded up to 1928. The standard crown and wreath reverse was used but in addition to the wide range of obverse types swivelling suspension was used until 1926, and immediate and non-immediate awards may be distinguished by the presence or absence respectively of the recipient's regimental number. Recent awards of the Elizabethan second bust medals have reverted to swivelling suspension.*

VALUE:		Miniature
Victoria (A) 1847 on edge (110)	£300–500	—
Victoria (A) 1848 below bust (10)	£1500–1850	—
Victoria (A) (990)	£250–350	£30
Edward VII (725)	£150–200	£25
George V (A) swivel (1050)	£100–120	£10–18
George V (A) non-swivel (400)	£100–120	£10–18
George V (A) Immediate awards 1916–28 (26,211+7 bars):		
For Gallantry (366+1 bar)	£200–250	—
Meritorious services (25,845+6 bars)	£80–120	—
George V (E) (550)	£150–200	£10–18
George VI (D) (1090)	£100–150	£10–18
George VI (E) (5600)	£100–150	£10–18
George VI (B) (55)	£800–1000	£10–18
Elizabeth II (C) (125)	£160–180	£10–18
Elizabeth II (D) (2750)	£120–150	£10–18

211. ROYAL AIR FORCE MERITORIOUS SERVICE MEDAL

Instituted: June 1918
Branch of Service: Royal Air Force.
Ribbon: Half crimson, half light blue, with white stripes at the centre and edges.
Metal: Silver.
Size: 36mm.
Description: (Obverse) effigy of the monarch; (reverse) a crowned laurel wreath enclosing the words FOR MERITORIOUS SERVICE. Originally medals were named in large seriffed capitals and were issued in respect of the First World War and service in Russia (1918-20), but later medals were impressed in thin block capitals. The RAF version had a swivelling suspension, unlike its military counterpart.
Comments: *Awarded for valuable services in the field, as opposed to actual flying service. This medal was replaced by the BEM in 1928, but revived in December 1977 under the same conditions as the military MSM. No more than 70 medals are awarded annually. The current issue is similar to the naval and military MSMs, differing only in the naming which includes RAF after the service number.*

VALUE:		*Miniature*
George V (E) (854)	£250–300	£10–15
Elizabeth II (D)	£250–300	£10–15

212. COLONIAL MERITORIOUS SERVICE MEDALS

Instituted: 31 May 1895.
Branch of Service: Colonial forces.
Ribbon: According to issuing territory (see below).
Metal: Silver.
Size: 36mm.
Description: (Obverse) as British counterparts; (reverse) as British type, but with the name of the dominion or colony round the top.
Comments: *Awarded for service in the British dominions, colonies and protectorates.*

Canada: Ribbon as for British Army MSM. CANADA on reverse till 1936; imperial version used from then until 1958. No medals with the Victorian obverse were awarded, but specimens exist.
Cape of Good Hope: Crimson ribbon with central orange stripe. Only one or two Edward VII medals issued.
Natal: Crimson ribbon with a central yellow stripe. Exceptionally, it was awarded to volunteers in the Natal Militia. Fifteen Edward VII medals awarded.
Commonwealth of Australia: Crimson ribbon with two dark green central stripes. Issued between 1903 and 1975.
New South Wales: Crimson ribbon with a dark blue central stripe. Issued till 1903.
Queensland: Crimson ribbon with light blue central stripe. Issued till 1903.
South Australia: Plain crimson ribbon. Issued till 1903.
Tasmania: Crimson ribbon with a pink central stripe. Issued till 1903.
New Zealand: Crimson ribbon with a light green central stripe. Issued since 1898.

VALUE Rare *Miniature* £30–40

213. INDIAN ARMY MERITORIOUS SERVICE MEDAL 1848

Instituted: 20 May 1848, by General Order of the Indian government.
Branch of Service: Forces of the Honourable East India Company and later the Indian armed services.
Ribbon: Plain crimson.
Metal: Silver.
Size: 36mm.
Description: (Obverse) the Wyon profile of Queen Victoria; (reverse) the arms and motto of the Honourable East India Company.
Comments: *Awarded with an annuity up to £20 to European sergeants, serving or discharged, for meritorious service. It was discontinued in 1873.*

VALUE: £250–350   *Miniature*   £100–150

214. INDIAN ARMY MERITORIOUS SERVICE MEDAL 1888

Instituted: 1888.
Branch of Service: Indian Army.
Ribbon: Plain crimson (till 1917); three white stripes added (1917).
Metal: Silver.
Size: 36mm.
Description: (Obverse) the sovereign's effigy; (reverse) a central wreath enclosing the word INDIA surrounded by the legend FOR MERITORIOUS SERVICE with a continuous border of lotus flowers and leaves round the circumference.
Comments: *For award to Indian warrant officers and senior NCOs (havildars, dafadars and equivalent band ranks). Eighteen years of exceptionally meritorious service was the minimum requirement, subject to the availability of funds in the annuity. At first only one medal was set aside for each regiment and thereafter awards were only made on the death, promotion or reduction of existing recipients. On promotion the medal was retained but the annuity ceased. It became obsolete in 1947.*

VALUE:		*Miniature*
Victoria (B)	£80–100	£65
Edward VII (A)	£60–80	£50
George V (D)	£30–40	£45
George V (C)	£30–50	£45
George VI (B)	£30–40	£25

215. AFRICAN POLICE MEDAL FOR MERITORIOUS SERVICE

Instituted: 14 July 1915.
Branch of Service Non-European NCOs and men of the colonial police forces in East and West Africa.
Ribbon: Sand-coloured with red edges.
Metal: Silver.
Size: 36mm.
Description: (Obverse) effigy of the sovereign; (reverse) a crown surmounted by a lion passant gardant within a palm wreath and having the legend FOR MERITORIOUS SERVICE IN THE POLICE and AFRICA at the foot.
Comments: *Awarded for both individual acts of gallantry and distinguished, meritorious or long service. In respect of the lastnamed, a minimum of 15 years exemplary service was required. It was superseded by the Colonial Police Medal in 1938.*

VALUE:		Miniature
George V (A) IND: IMP 1915-31	£300–400	£20–35
George V (A) INDIAE IMP 1931-7	£250–350	£20–35
George VI (B) 1938	Rare	

216. UNION OF SOUTH AFRICA MERITORIOUS SERVICE MEDAL

Instituted: 24 October 1914, by Government gazette.
Branch of Service: Service personnel of South Africa, Southern Rhodesia and Swaziland.
Ribbon: Crimson with blue edges and a central white, blue and white band.
Metal: Silver.
Size: 36mm.
Description: As British military MSM.
Comments: *A total of 46 gallantry and 300 meritorious service awards were made up to 1952 when the medal was discontinued. Of these only two were awarded to South Africans in the RNVR.*

VALUE: Rare

216A. ACCUMULATED CAMPAIGN SERVICE MEDAL

Instituted: January 1994.
Branch of Service: All branches of the armed services.
Ribbon: Purple and green with a gold stripe.
Metal: Silver.
Size: 36mm.
Description: (Obverse) crowned effigy of Queen Elizabeth; (reverse) the inscription FOR ACCUMULATED CAMPAIGN SERVICE set within a four-part ribbon surrounded by a branch of oak leaves with laurel and olive leaves woven through the motto ribbon.
Comments: *Awarded to holders of the General Service Medal 1962 on completion of 36 months accumulated campaign service since August 14, 1969. Further periods of 36 months accumulated campaign service will be denoted by a clasp, indicated as a silver rosette when the ribbon alone is worn.*

VALUE: £125–150   *Miniature* £8

217. ROYAL HOUSEHOLD FAITHFUL SERVICE MEDALS

1st type obv.

Instituted: 1872 by Queen Victoria.
Branch of Service: Royal Household.
Ribbon: Originally Royal Stuart tartan; later, a different ribbon for each monarch: dark blue and red diagonal stripes descending from left to right (George V), the same but descending from right to left (George VI) or dark blue with three red stripes (Elizabeth II).
Metal: Silver.
Size: 27mm (Victoria); 29mm (later awards).
Description: (Obverse) the sovereign's effigy; (reverse) the personal details of the recipient engraved on it. The Victorian medal has a very elaborate suspension ornamented with the crowned royal monogram, with a laurel bar brooch fitting at the top. This medal was not originally intended to be worn with a ribbon, although it had a strip of Royal Stuart tartan behind it. The same medal, but struck in 22 carat gold, was presented to John Brown, the Queen's personal servant. The concept was revived by George V, a silver medal of more conventional appearance being struck with the text FOR LONG AND FAITHFUL SERVICE on the reverse. Thirty, forty and fifty year service bars were also awarded.
Comments: *Intended as a reward to servants of the Royal Household for long and faithful service of at least 25 years. A further 10 years merited a bar. Different ribbons were used for each monarch, corresponding to the crowned cypher joining the medal to the suspension bar on either side of which the recipient's years of service were inscribed. Only two medals have been recorded with the profile of Edward VIII (1936).*

1st type rev.

VALUE:		Miniature
Victoria	From £600	£100–150
George V (E)	£250–300	£30–40
Edward VIII	£1000–£1500	—
George VI (D)	£280–325	£30–40
Elizabeth II (C)	£300–350	£30–40

2nd type obv. (George V).

2nd type rev.

218. ROYAL NAVAL LONG SERVICE AND GOOD CONDUCT MEDAL

1st type obv.

1st type rev.

2nd type rev. wide suspender

Instituted: 24 August 1831, by Order in Council.
Branch of Service: Royal Navy.
Ribbon: Plain dark blue (1831); dark blue with white edges (1848).
Metal: Silver.
Size: 34mm (1831); 36mm (1848).
Description: First type: (Obverse) an anchor surmounted by a crown and enclosed in an oak wreath; (reverse) the recipient's details. Plain ring for suspension.

Second type, adopted in 1848: (Obverse) the sovereign's effigy; (reverse) a three-masted man-of-war surrounded by a rope tied at the foot with a reef knot and having the legend FOR LONG SERVICE AND GOOD CONDUCT round the circumference. This medal originally had a wide suspender bar 38mm, but a narrow suspender was substituted in 1874. Normally the obverse was undated, but about 100 medals were issued in 1849-50 with the obverse of the Naval GSM, with the date 1848 below the Queen's bust. Between 1875 and 1877 a number of medals had the years of service added to the recipient's details, either engraved or impressed on the edge—these medals (about 60 known) are now sought after by collectors. Engraved naming was used from 1875 to 1877, but from then until 1901 impressed naming was adopted. Later medals used the various obverse effigies noted below.

Comments: *Originally awarded for 21 years exemplary conduct, but the period was reduced to 10 years in 1874, then later increased to 15 years. Bars for additional periods of 15 years were instituted by George V. In March 1981 commissioned officers of the naval services became eligible after 15 years service, provided at least 12 years were served in the ranks.*

VALUE:

		Miniature
Anchor 1831-47 (644)	£450–500	—
Victoria (A) wide suspender (3572)	£180–225	—
1848 type (100)	£1000–1200	—
Victoria (A) narrow suspender (4400)	£50–85	£30–40
Year on edge variety (c. 40)	£180–200	
impressed naming (18,200)	£55–75	
Year on edge variety (c. 20)	£180–200	
Edward VII (B)	£35–45	—
George V (B) 1910-20 swivel	£30–40	£5–10
1920–30 non-swivelling bar	£30–40	£5–10
George V (E) 1931-36	£30–50	£5–10
George VI (D) 1937-48	£30–50	£5–10
George VI (E) 1949-52	£30–50	£5–10
Elizabeth II (C) 1953-54	£30–45	£5–10
Elizabeth II (D) 1954-	£30–45	£5–10

2nd type rev. narrow suspender

2nd type obv. George V

219. ROYAL NAVAL RESERVE DECORATION

Instituted: 1908.
Branch of Service: Royal Naval Reserve.
Ribbon: Plain green ribbon, white edges being added from 1941 onwards.
Metal: Silver and silver-gilt.
Size: Height 54mm; max. width 33mm.
Description: A skeletal badge with the royal cypher in silver surrounded by an oval cable and reef knot in silver-gilt, surmounted by a crown and suspension ring.
Comments: *Granted for 15 years commissioned service (sub-lieutenant and above) in the Royal Naval Reserve, active service in wartime counting double. Bars are awarded for additional periods of 15 years. Recipients were entitled to the letters RD after their name, altered to VRD in the 1950s. This decoration was replaced by the VRSM (No. 242A) in 2000.*

VALUE:		Miniature
Edward VII	£120–140	£12–15
George V	£100–120	£10–12
George VI (GRI)	£120–140	£10–12
George VI (GVIR)	£120–140	£10–12
Elizabeth II	£130–150	£10–12

220. ROYAL NAVAL RESERVE LONG SERVICE AND GOOD CONDUCT MEDAL

Instituted: 1908.
Branch of Service: Royal Naval Reserve.
Ribbon: Plain green, white edges and a central white stripe being added in 1941. On the amalgamation of the RNR and RNVR in 1958 the ribbon was changed to five equal stripes of blue, white, green, white and blue.
Metal: Silver.
Size: 36mm.
Description: (Obverse) effigy of the monarch; (reverse) a battleship with the motto DIUTERNE FIDELIS (faithful for ever) at the foot.
Comments: *Awarded to petty officers and ratings of the RNR for 15 years service, war service counting double, with bars for additional 15 year periods. This medal was replaced by the VRSM (No. 242A) in 2000.*

VALUE:		Miniature
Edward VII (B)	£25–30	£15–25
George V (B)	£25–30	£10–15
George V (E)	£25–30	£10–15
George VI (D)	£25–30	£10–15
George VI (E)	£25–30	£10–15
Elizabeth II (C)	£40–50	£10–15
Elizabeth II (D)	£30–40	£10–15

221. ROYAL NAVAL VOLUNTEER RESERVE DECORATION

Instituted: 1908.
Branch of Service: Royal Naval Volunteer Reserve.
Ribbon: 38mm originally plain dark green; dark blue with a central green stripe flanked by narrow red stripes (since 1919).
Metal: Silver and silver-gilt.
Size: Height 54mm; max. width 33mm.
Description: Similar to RNR decoration.
Comments: *Awarded to commissioned officers of the RNVR. The qualifying period was 20 years, service in the ranks counting half and war service counting double. In 1966 the decoration was replaced by the RD following the merger of the RNR and RNVR.*

VALUE:

		Miniature
Edward VII	£120–140	£15–20
George V	£100–120	£10–12
George VI GRI	£120–140	£10–12
George VI GVIR	£120–140	£10–12
Elizabeth II	£130–150	£10–12

222. ROYAL NAVAL VOLUNTEER RESERVE LONG SERVICE AND GOOD CONDUCT MEDAL

Instituted: 1908.
Branch of Service: Royal Naval Volunteer Reserve.
Ribbon: Originally plain green, but subsequently a broad central green bar edged in red with blue stripes at the ends was adopted.
Metal: Silver.
Size: 36mm.
Description: Identical to the RNR medal, but distinguished by the ribbon and the naming which includes the letters RNVR, RCNVR (Canada), RSANVR (South Africa), etc.
Comments: *Awarded to petty officers and ratings for 12 years service with the necessary training, character assessed as "very good" or better throughout the period. War service counted double. The award was extended to the Colonial Navies during the Second World War.*

VALUE:

		Miniature
Edward VII (B)	Rare	£15–25
George V (B)	£35–45	£10–15
George V (E)	£45–55	£10–15
George VI (D)	£35–45	£10–15
George VI (E)	£35–45	£10–15
Elizabeth II (D)	£55–75	£10–15

223. ROYAL FLEET RESERVE LONG SERVICE AND GOOD CONDUCT MEDAL

Instituted: 1919.
Branch of Service: Royal Fleet Reserve.
Ribbon: Blue bordered with thin red stripes and white edges.
Metal: Silver.
Size: 36mm.
Description: Similar to the RNR LSGC but with ring suspension instead of a bar suspender.
Comments: *Awarded for 15 years service in the Fleet Reserve.*

VALUE:		*Miniature*
George V (B)	£25–35	£12–15
George V (E)	£25–35	£8–10
George VI (D)	£25–35	£8–10
George VI (E)	£25–35	£8–10
Elizabeth II (C)	£40–50	£8–10
Elizabeth II (D)	£30–40	£8–10

224. ROYAL NAVAL AUXILIARY SICK BERTH RESERVE LONG SERVICE AND GOOD CONDUCT MEDAL

Instituted: 1919.
Branch of Service: Royal Naval Auxiliary Sick Berth Reserve.
Ribbon: Plain green but later green with a white central stripe and white edges.
Metal: Silver.
Size: 36mm.
Description: Identical to the RNR equivalent, but the letters RNASBR appear after the recipient's name.
Comments: *Arguably the longest title of any British medal, it continued until the RNASBR was disbanded in 1949. The Auxiliary Sick Berth Reserve was created in 1903, members being recruited from the St John Ambulance Brigade. About 780 medals were granted prior to the Second World War and a further 715 between 1939 and 1949.*

VALUE:		*Miniature*
George V (B)	£70–90	£10–15
George V (E)	£80–100	£10–15
George VI (D)	£70–90	£10–15

225. ROYAL NAVAL WIRELESS AUXILIARY RESERVE LONG SERVICE AND GOOD CONDUCT MEDAL

Instituted: 1939.
Branch of Service: Royal Naval Wireless Auxiliary Reserve.
Ribbon: Broad green stripe with narrow red stripes on either side and blue edges.
Metal: Silver.
Size: 36mm.
Description: Identical to the RNR equivalent, but the letters RNWAR after the recipient's name. The last of the service medals with a battleship reverse.
Comments: *Issued till 1957 when the RNWAR was disbanded. It was awarded for 12 years service, only about 200 having been issued.*

VALUE:		*Miniature*
George VI (D)	£140–160	£10–15
Elizabeth II (C)	£140–160	£10–15

226. ROYAL NAVAL AUXILIARY SERVICE LONG SERVICE MEDAL

Instituted: July 1965.
Branch of Service: Royal Naval Auxiliary Service (RNXS), formerly the Royal Naval Minewatching Service.
Ribbon: Dark blue with a narrow green central stripe and broad white bars at the edges bisected by thin dark green stripes.
Metal: Cupro-nickel.
Size: 36mm.
Description: (Obverse) the Queen's effigy; (reverse) a fouled anchor in an oak wreath surmounted by a naval crown.
Comments: *Awarded for 12 years service. Interestingly this medal was the last to be issued with a pure silk ribbon.*

VALUE: Elizabeth II (D)   £120–160   *Miniature*   £8–10

227. ROCKET APPARATUS VOLUNTEER LONG SERVICE MEDAL

Instituted: 1911 by the Board of Trade.
Branch of Service: Rocket Life Saving Apparatus Volunteers,
Ribbon: Watered blue silk with broad scarlet edges.
Metal: Silver.
Size: 36mm.
Description: (Obverse) the effigy of the reigning monarch with the date 1911 below the truncation. (Reverse) exists in four types. The first refers to the Board of Trade but when that department handed over responsibility to the Ministry of Transport in 1942 the wording was amended to read ROCKET APPARATUS VOLUNTEER MEDAL round the circumference. In 1953 the inscription was changed to COAST LIFE SAVING CORPS and then in 1968 to COASTGUARD AUXILIARY SERVICE.
Comments: *Awarded for 20 years service with the Rocket Life Saving Apparatus Volunteers. The RLSAV became the Coast Life Saving Corps in 1953 and the Coastguard Auxiliary Service in 1968, these titles being reflected in the wording on the reverse.*

VALUE:

George V (E)	£50–60
George VI (D) BoT	£60–65
George VI (D) Rocket Apparatus	£60–65
Elizabeth II (E) Coast Life Saving	£100–120
Elizabeth II (E) Coastguard Auxiliary	£100–120

Auctions speak louder than words.
Call Nimrod Dix or Pierce Noonan today
and find out how you can achieve top prices
for all your orders, decorations and medals.

DNW
DIX • NOONAN • WEBB
AUCTIONEERS AND VALUERS

1 Old Bond Street
London W1S 4PB
Tel 020 7499 5022
Fax 020 7499 5023
E-mail: auctions@dnw.co.uk

www.dnw.co.uk

229. ARMY LONG SERVICE AND GOOD CONDUCT MEDAL

1st type obv. Trophy of Arms with badge of Hanover.

2nd type obv. with badge of Hanover omitted and swivel suspender.

Instituted: 1830.

Branch of Service: Army.

Ribbon: Plain crimson was used till 1917 when white stripes were added to the edges. Dominion and colonial medals formerly had crimson ribbons with a narrow central stripe in dark green (Australia), light blue (NSW and Queensland), pink (Tasmania), orange (S. Africa), white (Canada), light green (NZ), broad white (Victoria), scarlet and light blue (Papua NG).

Metal: Silver.

Size: 36mm.

Description: Over the long period in which this medal has been in use it has undergone a number of changes. Until 1901 the obverse bore a trophy of arms with the royal arms in an oval shield in the centre while the reverse bore the inscription FOR LONG SERVICE AND GOOD CONDUCT. The first issue had the royal arms with the badge of Hanover on the obverse and small suspension ring with a plain crimson ribbon. A large ring was substituted in 1831. On the accession of Queen Victoria in 1837 the Hanoverian emblem was dropped from the arms. In 1855 a swivelling scroll suspension was substituted and in 1874 small lettering replaced the original large lettering on the reverse. From 1901, however, the effigy of the reigning sovereign was placed on the obverse although the reverse remained the same. In 1920 the swivelling scroll suspension gave way to a fixed suspender. In 1930 the title of the medal was changed to the Long Service and Good Conduct (Military) Medal; at the same time the design was modified. A fixed suspension bar was added, bearing the words REGULAR ARMY or the name of a dominion (India, Canada, Australia, New Zealand or South Africa). This replaced the Permanent Forces of the Empire LSGC Medal (see below).

Comments: *Originally awarded to soldiers of exemplary conduct for 21 years service in the infantry or 24 years in the cavalry, but in 1870 the qualifying period was reduced to 18 years. During the Second World War commissioned officers were permitted to acquire this medal so long as they had completed at least 12 of their 18 years service in the ranks. Canada discontinued the LSGC medal in 1950 when the Canadian Forces Decoration was instituted, while South Africa replaced it with the John Chard Medal later the same year. From 1930 onwards the lettering of the reverse inscription was in tall, thin letters. In 1940 bars for further periods of service were authorised. The LSGC is invariably named to the recipient. The William IV and early Victorian issues (to 1854) were impressed in the style of the Waterloo Medal and also bore the date of discharge and award. The 1855 issue was not dated, while lettering was impressed in the style of the Military General Service Medal. Later Victorian issues, however, were engraved in various styles, while medals from 1901 onwards are impressed in small capitals of various types. Medals to Europeans in the Indian Army are engraved in cursive script. Recent research by Irvin Mortensen, however, reveals that some medals after 1850 were issued unnamed, and this also accounts for various unofficial styles of naming found on later medals*

1st type rev. large letters

2nd type rev. small letters with swivel suspender

3rd type obv. (George V).

229. ARMY LONG SERVICE & GOOD CONDUCT MEDAL *continued*

Modified design with fixed suspender obv. and (below) rev.

VALUE:		Miniature
William IV small ring 1830–31	£420–450	—
William IV large ring 1831–37	£380–420	—
Victoria without Hanoverian arms 1837–55	£120–150	—
Victoria swivelling scroll suspension 1855–74	£80–100	—
Victoria small reverse lettering 1874–1901	£65–95	£25–30
Edward VII (A) 1902–10	£40–50	£25–30
George V (A) 1911–20	£30–40	£6–10
George V (A) fixed suspender 1920–30	£30–40	£6–10
George V (C) 1930–36	£30–40	£6–10
Commonwealth bar	From £75	£10–20
George VI (D) 1937–48	£25–40	£6–10
Commonwealth bar	From £75	£10–20
George VI (E) 1949–52	£25–40	£6–10
Elizabeth II (C) 1953–54	£45–50	£6–10
Elizabeth II (D) 1954–	£45–50	£6–10
Commonwealth bar	From £100	£12–15

230. ULSTER DEFENCE REGIMENT MEDAL FOR LONG SERVICE AND GOOD CONDUCT

Instituted: 1982.
Branch of Service: Ulster Defence Regiment.
Ribbon: Similar to the Military LSGC medal but with a central green stripe in addition.
Metal: Silver.
Size: 36mm.
Description: (Obverse) the imperial crowned bust of Queen Elizabeth II; (reverse) similar to the Military LSGC medal. Fitted with a fixed suspension bar inscribed UDR.
Comments: *Granted to personnel for 15 years exemplary service after 1 April 1970, with bars for additional 15-year periods. It is also awarded to officers provided that at least 12 of their 15 years service was in the ranks.*

VALUE:

Elizabeth II (B)	£80–100		*Miniature*	£8–10

231. VOLUNTEER OFFICER'S DECORATION

Instituted: 25 July 1892.
Branch of Service: Volunteer Force.
Ribbon: Plain green.
Metal: Silver and silver-gilt.
Size: Height 42mm; max. width 35mm.
Description: An oval skeletal badge in silver and silver-gilt, with the royal cypher and crown in the centre, within a wreath of oak leaves. It is suspended by a plain ring with a laurel bar brooch fitted to the top of the ribbon. Although issued unnamed, many examples were subsequently engraved or impressed privately. Two versions of the Victorian decoration were produced, differing in the monogram—VR for United Kingdom recipients and VRI for recipients in the dominions and colonies.
Comments: *The basic qualification was 20 years commissioned service in the Volunteer Force, a precursor of the Territorial Army, non-commissioned service counting half. By Royal Warrant of 24 May 1894 the decoration was extended to comparable forces overseas, the qualifying period for service in India being reduced to 18 years. The colonial VD was superseded in 1899 by the Colonial Auxiliary Forces Officers Decoration and the Indian Volunteer Forces Officers Decoration. In the United Kingdom it was superseded by the Territorial Decoration, on the formation of the TF in 1908. A total of 4,710 decorations were awarded. Awards in Bermuda continued until 1930.*

VALUE:

		Miniature
Victoria VR	£70–80	£10–20
Victoria VRI	£250–300	£25–35
Edward VII	£70–80	£15–25
George V	£75–85	£25–40

232. VOLUNTEER FORCE LONG SERVICE AND GOOD CONDUCT MEDAL

Instituted: 1894.
Branch of Service: Volunteer Force.
Ribbon: Plain green, but members of the Honourable Artillery Company were granted a distinctive ribbon in 1906, half scarlet, half dark blue with yellow edges—King Edward's racing colours.
Metal: Silver.
Size: 36mm.
Description: (Obverse) effigy of the reigning monarch; (reverse) a laurel wreath on which is superimposed ribbons inscribed FOR LONG SERVICE IN THE VOLUNTEER FORCE.
Comments: *This medal was awarded for 20 years service in the ranks. Officers could also receive the medal, being eligible on account of their non-commissioned service. Many officers then gained sufficient commission service to be awarded either the Volunteer Decoration or (from 1908) the Territorial Decoration. The medal was extended to Colonial Forces in June 1896, the titles of the monarch being appropriately expanded for this version. This medal was superseded by the Territorial Force Efficiency Medal in 1908, although it continued to be awarded until 1930 in Bermuda, India, Isle of Man (Isle of Man Vols.) and the 7th Volunteer Battalion of the King's (Liverpool) Regiment.*

VALUE:

		Miniature
Victoria Regina (C) (UK)	£45–50	
Unnamed	£25	£20–25
Victoria Regina et Imperatrix (C) (overseas)	£55–85	£20–25
Edwardus Rex (A)	£45–50	£15–25
Edwardus Rex et Imperator (A) (colonial)	£45–55	£15–25
Edwardus Kaisar-i-Hind (A) (India)	£60–80	£15–25
George V (A) (India)	£30–50	£15–20
George V (A) (Isle of Man)	£120–150	£15–20

233. TERRITORIAL DECORATION

Instituted: 29 September 1908.
Branch of Service: Territorial Force, later Territorial Army.
Ribbon: 38mm plain dark green with a central yellow stripe.
Metal: Silver and silver-gilt.
Size: Height 46mm; max. width 35mm.
Description: A skeletal badge with the crowned monogram of the sovereign surrounded by an oval oak wreath, fitted with a ring for suspension.
Comments: *Awarded for 20 years commissioned service, service in the ranks counting half and war service double. It was superseded by the Efficiency Decoration in 1930. A total of 4,783 decorations were awarded.*

VALUE:		*Miniature*
Edward VII (585)	£75–85	£15–20
George V (4,198)	£75–85	£10–12

234. TERRITORIAL FORCE EFFICIENCY MEDAL

Instituted: 1908.
Branch of Service: Territorial Force.
Ribbon: 32mm plain dark green with a central yellow stripe.
Metal: Silver.
Size: Height 38mm; max. width 31mm.
Description: An oval medal fitted with claw and ring suspension. (Obverse) the sovereign's effigy; (reverse) inscribed with the name of the medal in four lines.
Comments: *Granted for a minimum of 12 years service in the Territorial Force. It was superseded in 1921 by the Territorial Efficiency Medal when the service was renamed.*

VALUE:		*Miniature*
Edward VII (A) (10,812)	£65–80	£15–20
George V (A) (37,726)	£30–40	£15–20
George V first clasps (362)	£40–50	

235. TERRITORIAL EFFICIENCY MEDAL

Instituted: 1921.
Branch of Service: Territorial Army.
Ribbon: 32mm plain dark green with yellow edges.
Metal: Silver.
Size: Height 38mm; max. width 31mm.
Description: As above, but with the name amended and inscribed in three lines.
Comments: *Introduced following the elevation of the Territorial Force to become the Territorial Army. It was superseded by the Efficiency Medal in 1930.*

VALUE:			
George V (A)	£25–35	*Miniature*	£10–15

236. EFFICIENCY DECORATION

Instituted: 17 October 1930.
Branch of Service: Territorial Army (UK), the Indian Volunteer Forces and the Colonial Auxiliary Forces.
Ribbon: 38mm plain dark green with a central yellow stripe.
Metal: Silver and silver-gilt.
Size: Height 54mm; max. width 37mm.
Description: An oval skeletal badge in silver and silver-gilt with the crowned monogram in an oak wreath, the ring for suspension being fitted to the top of the crown. It differs also from the previous decorations in having a suspender bar denoting the area of service: Territorial (UK), India, Canada, Fiji or other overseas country being inscribed as appropriate, but the previous ribbon was retained.
Comments: *Recipients in Britain were allowed to continue using the letters TD after their names, but in the Commonwealth the letters ED were used instead. The 20-year qualification was reduced to 12 years in 1949, bars for each additional 6 years being added. In 1969 the British bar was changed to T & AVR, on the establishment of the Territorial and Army Volunteer Reserve, the ribbon being then altered to half green, half blue, with a central yellow stripe. In 1982 the title of Territorial Army was resumed, so the inscription on the bar reverted to TERRITORIAL but the blue, yellow and green ribbon was retained. This decoration was superseded by the VRSM (No. 242A) in 2000.*

VALUE:

	Territorial	T&AVR	Commonwealth
George V	£70–80	—	£80–100
George VI (GRI)	£70–80	—	£80–100
George VI (GVIR)	£70–80	—	—
Elizabeth II	£75–85	£100–120	—

Miniature £8–20

237. EFFICIENCY MEDAL

Instituted: 17 October 1930.
Branch of Service: Territorial Army (UK), Indian Volunteer Forces and Colonial Auxiliary Forces.
Ribbon: 32mm green with yellow edges. Members of the HAC wear the medal with the scarlet and blue ribbon edged in yellow.
Metal: Silver.
Size: Height 39mm; max. width 32mm.

237. EFFICIENCY MEDAL *continued*

Description: An oval silver medal. (Obverse) the monarch's effigy; (reverse) inscribed FOR EFFICIENT SERVICE. In place of the simple ring suspension, however, there was now a fixed suspender bar decorated with a pair of palm leaves surmounted by a scroll inscribed TERRITORIAL or MILITIA (for UK volunteer forces), while overseas forces had the name of the country.

Comments: *This medal consolidated the awards to other ranks throughout the volunteer forces of Britain and the Commonwealth. The basic qualification was 12 years service, but war service and peacetime service in West Africa counted double. The Militia bar was granted to certain categories of the Supplementary Reserve until the formation of the Army Emergency Reserve in 1951. In 1969 the bar inscribed T & AVR was introduced, along with a ribbon half blue, half green, with yellow edges. The bar TERRITORIAL was resumed in 1982 but the ribbon remained the same. For the distinctive medal awarded in the Union of South Africa see number 254. Instead of the second obverse of Queen Elizabeth II, Canada adopted a type showing the Queen wearing the Imperial Crown. This medal was superseded by the VRSM (No. 242A) in 2000.*

VALUE:	Territorial	Militia	T&AVR	Commonwealth
George V (C)	£25–35	£40–50	—	£50–65*
George VI (A)	£25–35	£40–50	—	£80–90*
George VI (C)	£25–35	£40–50	—	£60–75*
Elizabeth II (A)	£45–50	—	—	*
Elizabeth II (B)	£45–50	—	£60–80	*

Miniature from £15

*These prices are for the commoner Commonwealth types. However, some are extremely rare as can be seen in the table below where the issue numbers are indicated in brackets.

George V (C)	*George VI (A)*	*George VI (C)*	*Elizabeth II (A)*	*Elizabeth II (B)*
—	—	—	Antigua (3)	—
Australia	Australia	Australia	Australia	Australia
Barbados	Barbados	Barbados	Barbados	Barbados
Bermuda	Bermuda	Bermuda	Bermuda	Bermuda
British Guiana (15)	British Guiana	British Guiana	British Guiana	—
British Honduras (1)	British Honduras (23)	British Honduras (3)	British Honduras (13)	—
—	Burma (111)	—	—	—
Canada	Canada	Canada	Canada (Rare)	Canada (Rare)
Ceylon	Ceylon	Ceylon	Ceylon (69)	—
—	Dominica (130)	—	—	—
Falkland Islands (29)	Falkland Islands (29)	—	Falkland Islands	Falkland Islands
Fiji (29)	Fiji (35)	Fiji (9)	Fiji (7)	Fiji (33)
—	—	Gibraltar (15)	Gibraltar	Gibraltar
—	Gold Coast (275)	Gold Coast (35)	—	—
—	Grenada (1)	—	—	—
—	Guernsey (3)	Guernsey (4)	Guernsey (3)	Guernsey (35)
Hong Kong (21)	Hong Kong (50)	Hong Kong (224)	Hong Kong (145)	Hong Kong (268)
India	India	—	—	—
Jamaica	Jamaica	Jamaica	Jamaica	—
—	Jersey (40)	Jersey (7)	—	Jersey (1)

237. EFFICIENCY MEDAL *continued*

George V (C)	George VI (A)	George VI (C)	Elizabeth II (A)	Elizabeth II (B)
—	Kenya (1)	Kenya (159)	Kenya (36)	—
—	Leeward Islands (49)	Leeward Islands (14)	Leeward Islands (2)	—
—	Malaya	Malaya	Malaya (54)	—
—	Malta (320)	Malta (84)	Malta (7)	Malta (36)
—	—	—	Mauritius (71)	—
—	—	—	—	Montserrat (6)
New Zealand (71)	New Zealand (34)	New Zealand	New Zealand	New Zealand
Nigeria (1)	—	Nigeria (7)	Nigeria (3)	—
—	—	—	Rhodesia/Nyasaland (7)	—
—	—	—	St Christopher Nevis (13)	—
—	St Lucia (2)	—	—	—
—	St Vincent (1)	—	—	—
S. Rhodesia (17)	S. Rhodesia (230)	S. Rhodesia (24)	S. Rhodesia (6)	—
—	Trinidad/Tobago (228)	Trinidad/Tobago (46)	Trinidad/Tobago (5)	—

238. ARMY EMERGENCY RESERVE DECORATION

Instituted: 17 November 1952.
Branch of Service Army Emergency Reserve.
Ribbon: 38mm dark blue with a central yellow stripe.
Metal: Silver and silver-gilt.
Size: Height 55mm; max. width 37mm.
Description: An oval skeletal badge, with the monarch's cypher surmounted by a crown in an oak wreath. Suspension is by a ring through the top of the crown and it is worn with a brooch bar inscribed ARMY EMERGENCY RESERVE.
Comments: *Awarded for 12 years commissioned service. Officers commissioned in the Army Supplementary Reserve or Army Emergency Reserve of Offices between 8 August 1942 and 15 May 1948 who transferred to the Regular Army Reserve of Officers after 10 years service were also eligible. War service counts double and previous service in the ranks counts half. The ERD was abolished in 1967 on the formation of the Territorial and Army Volunteer Reserve.*

VALUE:

Elizabeth II	£110–130	*Miniature*	£10–14

239. ARMY EMERGENCY RESERVE EFFICIENCY MEDAL

Instituted: 1 September 1953.
Branch of Service: Army Emergency Reserve.
Ribbon: 32mm dark blue with three central yellow stripes.
Metal: Silver.
Size: Height 39mm; max. width 31mm.
Description: This oval medal is similar to the Efficiency Medal previously noted, but has a scroll bar inscribed ARMY EMERGENCY RESERVE.
Comments: *Awarded for 12 years service in the ranks or for service in the Supplementary Reserve between 1924 and 1948 prior to transferring to the Army Emergency Reserve. War service counted double. It was abolished in 1967, following the formation of the Territorial and Army Volunteer Reserve.*

VALUE:

Elizabeth II	£140–160	*Miniature*	£10–12

240. IMPERIAL YEOMANRY LONG SERVICE AND GOOD CONDUCT MEDAL

Instituted: December 1904, by Army Order number 211.
Branch of Service: Imperial Yeomanry.
Ribbon: 32mm plain yellow.
Metal: Silver.
Size: Height 38mm; max. width 31mm.
Description: Upright oval. (Obverse) the sovereign's effigy; (reverse) inscribed IMPERIAL YEOMANRY round the top and the usual long service and good conduct inscription in four lines across the middle.
Comments: *Awarded to NCOs and troopers of the Imperial Yeomanry for 10 years exemplary service. It became obsolete in 1908 when the Territorial Force was created. Nevertheless 48 medals were awarded in 1909, one in 1910, one in 1914 and one in 1917. All medals were issued with the bust of King Edward VII on the obverse.*

VALUE:

Edward VII (A) (1674)	£200–240	*Miniature*	£50–60

241. MILITIA LONG SERVICE AND GOOD CONDUCT MEDAL

Instituted: December 1904, by Army Order number 211.
Branch of Service: Militia.
Ribbon: 32mm plain light blue.
Metal: Silver.
Size: Height 38mm; max. width 31mm.
Description: An upright oval medal. (Obverse) the effigy of the monarch; (reverse) similar to the preceding but inscribed MILITIA at the top of the reverse.
Comments: *Qualifying service was 18 years and 15 annual camps. It was superseded by the Efficiency Medal with the Militia bar in 1930.*

VALUE: | | | *Miniature* |
|---|---|---|
| Edward VII (A) (1446) | £180–220 | £50–60 |
| George V (C) (141) | £190–240 | £50–60 |

242. SPECIAL RESERVE LONG SERVICE AND GOOD CONDUCT MEDAL

Instituted: June 1908, by Army Order.
Branch of Service: Special Reserve.
Ribbon: Dark blue with a central light blue stripe.
Metal: Silver.
Size: Height 38mm; max. width 31mm.
Description: As the foregoing but inscribed SPECIAL RESERVE round the top of the reverse.
Comments: *Awarded to NCOs and men of the Special Reserve who completed 15 years service and attended 15 camps. A total of 1078 medals were awarded between 1908 and 1936, with solitary awards in 1947 and 1953.*

VALUE: | | | *Miniature* |
|---|---|---|
| Edward VII (A) | £185–225 | £50–60 |
| George V (C) | £175–220 | £50–60 |

242A. VOLUNTEER RESERVES SERVICE MEDAL

Instituted: 1999.
Branch of Service: Volunteer reserves of all three armed services.
Ribbon: Dark green with three narrow central stripes of dark blue, scarlet and light blue, separated from the green by two narrow bands of gold.
Metal: Silver.
Size: Height 38mm; width 32mm.
Description: An oval medal. (Obverse)the sovereign's effigy; (reverse) inscribed FOR SERVICE IN THE VOLUNTEER RESERVES above a spray of aok.
Comments: *Awarded to all ranks of the volunteer reserves who complete ten years of continuous service. Bars for additional five-year periods of efficient service are also awarded. This medal replaces the Royal Naval Reserve Decoration, the Royal Naval Reserve Long Service and Good Conduct Medal, the Efficiency Decoration, the Efficiency Medal and the Air Efficiency Award. It carries no rights to the use of post-nominal letters.*

VALUE: — *Miniature:* £10

243. INDIAN ARMY LONG SERVICE AND GOOD CONDUCT MEDAL FOR EUROPEANS 1848

Instituted: 20 May 1848, by General Order of the Indian government.
Branch of Service: Indian Army.
Ribbon: Plain crimson.
Metal: Silver.
Size: 36mm.
Description: (Obverse) a trophy of arms, not unlike its British counterpart, but a shield bearing the arms of the Honourable East India Company was placed in the centre. (Reverse) engraved with the recipient's name and service details. In 1859 some 100 medals were sent to India by mistake, with the Wyon profile of Queen Victoria on the obverse and a reverse inscribed FOR LONG SERVICE AND GOOD CONDUCT within an oak wreath with a crown at the top and a fouled anchor at the foot.
Comments: *Awarded to European NCOs and other ranks of the Indian Army on discharge after 21 years meritorious service. It was discontinued in 1873 after which the standard Army LSGC medal was granted.*

VALUE:

		Miniature
HEIC arms	£275–365	£100–150
Victoria (A) (100)	£350–465	£80–100

HEIC arms type.

Victoria type.

244. INDIAN ARMY LONG SERVICE AND GOOD CONDUCT MEDAL (INDIAN)

Instituted: 1888.
Branch of Service: Indian Army.
Ribbon: Originally plain crimson but white edges were added in 1917.
Metal: Silver.
Size: 36mm.
Description: (Obverse) the sovereign's effigy; (reverse) the word INDIA set within a palm wreath surrounded by a border of lotus flowers and leaves. The inscription FOR LONG SERVICE AND GOOD CONDUCT appears between the wreath and the lotus flowers.
Comments: *Awarded to native Indian NCOs and other ranks for 20 years meritorious service. The medal became obsolete in 1947 when India achieved independence.*

VALUE:		*Miniature*
Victoria (B) Kaisar-i-Hind	£70–90	£40–50
Edward VII (A) Kaisar-i-Hind	£40–50	£40–50
George V (D) Kaisar-i-Hind	£20–30	£25–30
George V (C) Rex Et Indiae Imp	£30–40	£25–30
George VI (B)	£20–30	£15-20

245. INDIAN VOLUNTEER FORCES OFFICERS' DECORATION

Instituted: May 1899, but not issued until 1903.
Branch of Service: Indian Volunteer Forces.
Ribbon: Plain green.
Metal: Silver and silver-gilt.
Size: Height 65mm; max. width 35mm.
Description: An oval skeletal badge with the royal monogram within an oval band inscribed INDIAN VOLUNTEER FORCES surmounted by a crown fitted with a suspension bar and an elaborate silver brooch.
Comments: *Awarded for 18 years commissioned service, with any service in the ranks counting half. It was superseded by the Efficiency Decoration with* India *bar in 1930, although the first awards were not gazetted until 1933. A total of 1,170 decorations were awarded, the last in 1934.*

VALUE:		*Miniature*
Edward VII	£150–200	£20–25
George V	£150–200	£15–20

246. COLONIAL AUXILIARY FORCES OFFICERS' DECORATION

Instituted: 18 May 1899.
Branch of Service: Colonial Auxiliary Forces.
Ribbon: Plain green.
Metal: Silver and silver-gilt.
Size: Height 66mm; max. width 35mm.
Description: Similar to the previous decoration, with an oval band inscribed COLONIAL AUXILIARY FORCES.
Comments: *Awarded to officers of auxiliary forces everywhere except in India, service in West Africa counting double. Although issued unnamed, it was usually impressed or engraved privately. Examples to officers in the smaller colonies command a considerable premium. It became obsolete in 1930.*

VALUE:

		Miniature
Victoria	£220–240	£20–30
Edward VII	£180–200	£15–25
George V	£140–160	£12–18

247. COLONIAL AUXILIARY FORCES LONG SERVICE MEDAL

Instituted: 18 May 1899.
Branch of Service: Colonial Auxiliary Forces.
Ribbon: Plain green.
Metal: Silver.
Size: 36mm.
Description: (Obverse) the effigy of the reigning monarch; (reverse) an elaborate rococo frame surmounted by a crown and enclosing the five-line text FOR LONG SERVICE IN THE COLONIAL AUXILIARY FORCES.
Comments: *Awarded for 20 years service in the ranks, West African service counting double. It was superseded in 1930 by the Efficiency Medal with the appropriate colonial or dominion bar.*

VALUE:

		Miniature
Victoria (D)	£90–100	£25–35
Edward VII (A)	£80–90	£20–25
George V (A)	£70–80	£12–15

If you know of a British or Commonwealth medal that is not included in the MEDAL YEARBOOK we would be delighted to hear from you.

Or if you can supply us with a photograph of any of the medals not illustrated in this publication we would be pleased to include it next year.

If you can help, please contact the Managing Editor, John Mussell, telephone 01404 46972 or at the address on page 1. Thank you!

---

248. COLONIAL LONG SERVICE AND GOOD CONDUCT MEDALS

Instituted: May 1895.
Branch of Service: Indian and Colonial forces.
Ribbon: Crimson with a central stripe denoting the country of service (see no. 212).
Metal: Silver.
Size: 36mm.
Description: Similar to its British counterpart except that the name of the country appeared on the reverse.
Comments: *Awarded to warrant officers, NCOs and other ranks for distinguished conduct in the field, meritorious service and long service and good conduct. Medals of the individual Australian colonies were superseded in 1902 by those inscribed COMMONWEALTH OF AUSTRALIA. The Colonial LSGC medal was replaced in 1909 by the Permanent Forces of the Empire Beyond the Seas LSGC award.*

VALUE: Rare   *Miniature*   £35–50

249. PERMANENT FORCES OF THE EMPIRE BEYOND THE SEAS LONG SERVICE AND GOOD CONDUCT MEDAL

Instituted: 1909.
Branch of Service: Colonial and Dominion forces.
Ribbon: Maroon bearing a broad white central stripe with a narrow black stripe at its centre.
Metal: Silver.
Size: 36mm.
Description: (Obverse) the effigy of the reigning sovereign; (reverse) the legend PERMANENT FORCES OF THE EMPIRE BEYOND THE SEAS round the circumference, with FOR LONG SERVICE AND GOOD CONDUCT in four lines across the centre.
Comments: *This award replaced the various colonial LSGC medals, being itself superseded in 1930 by the LSGC (Military) Medal with appropriate dominion or colonial bar. It was awarded for 18 years exemplary service.*

VALUE:		*Miniature*
Edward VII (A)	£200–300	£50–60
George V (C)	£80–100	£40–50

250. ROYAL WEST AFRICA FRONTIER FORCE LONG SERVICE & GOOD CONDUCT MEDAL

Instituted: September 1903.
Branch of Service: Royal West Africa Frontier Force.
Ribbon: Crimson with a relatively broad green central stripe.
Metal: Silver.
Size: 36mm.
Description: (Obverse) the effigy of the reigning monarch. Two reverse types were used, the word ROYAL being added to the regimental title in June 1928.
Comments: *Awarded to native NCOs and other ranks for 18 years exemplary service.*

VALUE: Rare   *Miniature*   £25–30

251. KING'S AFRICAN RIFLES LONG SERVICE AND GOOD CONDUCT MEDAL

Instituted: March 1907.
Branch of Service: King's African Rifles.
Ribbon: Crimson with a broad green central stripe.
Metal: Silver.
Size: 36mm.
Description: Very similar to the foregoing, apart from the regimental name round the top of the reverse.
Comments: *Awarded to native NCOs and other ranks for 18 years exemplary service.*

VALUE:			*Miniature*
	George V	Rare	£25–80
	George VI (B)	£220–250	£15–25

252. TRANS-JORDAN FRONTIER FORCE LONG SERVICE AND GOOD CONDUCT MEDAL

Instituted: 20 May 1938.
Branch of Service: Trans-Jordan Frontier Force.
Ribbon: Crimson with a green central stripe.
Metal: Silver.
Size: 36mm.
Description: Similar to the previous medals, with the name of the Force round the circumference.
Comments: *This rare silver medal was awarded for 16 years service in the ranks of the Trans-Jordan Frontier Force. Service in the Palestine Gendarmerie or Arab Legion counted, so long as the recipient transferred to the Frontier Force without a break in service. Only 112 medals were awarded before it was abolished in 1948.*

VALUE: Rare

253. SOUTH AFRICA PERMANENT FORCE LONG SERVICE AND GOOD CONDUCT MEDAL

Instituted: 29 December 1939.
Branch of Service: South African forces.
Ribbon:
Metal: Silver.
Size: 36mm.
Description: (Obverse) Crowned effigy of King George VI; (reverse) FOR LONG SERVICE AND GOOD CONDUCT in four lines across the upper half and VIR LANGDURIGE DIENS EN GOEIE GEDRAG in four lines across the lower half. It also differs from its British counterpart in having a bilingual suspension bar.
Comments: *Awarded to NCOs and other ranks with a minimum of 18 years service.*

VALUE:			*Miniature*
George VI (B)	£120–140		£10–15
George VI (C)	£150–170		£10–15

254. EFFICIENCY MEDAL (SOUTH AFRICA)

Instituted: December 1939.
Branch of Service: Coast Garrison and Active Citizen Forces of South Africa.
Ribbon: 32mm plain dark green with yellow edges.
Metal: Silver.
Size: Height 38mm; max. width 30mm.
Description: An oval silver medal rather similar to the Efficiency Medal (number 237) but having a scroll bar inscribed UNION OF SOUTH AFRICA with its Afrikaans equivalent below. The reverse likewise bears a bilingual inscription.
Comments: *Awarded for 12 years non-commissioned service in the Coast Garrison and Active Citizen Forces. A bar, bearing in the centre a crown, was awarded for every six years of additional service. It was replaced in 1952 by the John Chard Medal.*

VALUE: £55–65   *Miniature*   £10–20

254A. ROYAL HONG KONG REGIMENT DISBANDMENT MEDAL

Instituted: 1995.
Branch of Service: Royal Hong Kong Regiment (Volunteers).
Ribbon: Half red and half blue with a central yellow stripe.
Metal: Cupro-nickel.
Size: 38mm.
Description: (Obverse) Regimental badge with dates 1854 and 1995 either side and ROYAL HONG KONG REGIMENT THE VOLUNTEERS around. (Reverse) Coat of Arms of Hong Kong with DISBANDMENT MEDAL 3rdSEPTEMBER 1995 (date of disbandment) around.
Comment: *Available to those serving with the Regiment as the end of the Crown Colony became imminent. Recipients, however, had to purchase their medals.*

VALUE: —   *Miniature*   —

255. CANADIAN FORCES DECORATION

Instituted: 15 December 1949.
Branch of Service: Canadian Forces.
Ribbon: 38mm orange-red divided into four equal parts by three thin white stripes.
Metal: Silver-gilt (George VI) or gilded tombac brass (Elizabeth II).
Size: Height 35mm; max. width 37mm.
Description: A decagonal (ten-sided) medal. The George VI issue has a suspension bar inscribed CANADA and the recipient's details engraved on the reverse, whereas the Elizabethan issue has no bar, the recipient's details being impressed on the rim. The reverse has a naval crown at the top, three maple leaves across the middle and an eagle in flight across the foot. In the George VI version the royal cypher is superimposed on the maple leaves.
Comments: *Awarded to both officers and men of the Canadian regular and reserve forces for 12 years exemplary service, with a bar for each additional 10 years.*

VALUE:			*Miniature*
George VI (E)		£50–60	£10–20
Elizabeth II (D)		£30–40	£10–20

256. VICTORIA VOLUNTEER LONG AND EFFICIENT SERVICE MEDAL

Instituted: 26 January 1881 but not given royal sanction until 21 April 1882.
Branch of Service: Volunteer Forces, Victoria.
Ribbon: White, with broad crimson bars at the sides.
Metal: Silver.
Size: 39mm.
Description: (Obverse) the crowned badge of Victoria with LOCAL FORCES VICTORIA round the circumference; (reverse) inscribed FOR LONG AND EFFICIENT SERVICE. Two types of obverse exist, differing in the motto surrounding the colonial emblem. The first version has AUT PACE AUT BELLO (both in peace and war) while the second version is inscribed PRO DEO ET PATRIA (for God and country).
Comments: *Awarded to officers and men of the Volunteers in the colony of Victoria for 15 years service. Awards to officers ended in 1894 with the introduction of the Volunteer Officers Decoration. This medal was replaced by the Commonwealth of Australia LSGC medal in 1902.*

1st type obv.

VALUE: Rare

2nd type obv.

257. NEW ZEALAND LONG AND EFFICIENT SERVICE MEDAL

Instituted: 1 January 1887.
Branch of Service: Volunteer and Permanent Militia Forces of New Zealand.
Ribbon: Originally plain crimson, but two white central stripes were added in 1917.
Metal: Silver.
Size: 36mm.
Description: (Obverse) an imperial crown on a cushion with crossed sword and sceptre and NZ below, within a wreath of oak-leaves (left) and wattle (right) and having four five-pointed stars, representing the constellation Southern Cross, spaced in the field; (reverse) inscribed FOR LONG AND EFFICIENT SERVICE. Plain ring suspension.
Comments: *Awarded for 16 years continuous or 20 years non-continuous service in the Volunteer and Permanent Militia Forces of New Zealand. It became obsolete in 1931 following the introduction of the LSGC (Military) medal with bar for New Zealand.*

VALUE: 1887-1931   £75–100   *Miniature*   £10–15

258. NEW ZEALAND VOLUNTEER SERVICE MEDAL

Instituted: 1902.
Branch of Service: Volunteer Forces, New Zealand.
Ribbon: Plain drab khaki.
Metal: Silver.
Size: 36mm
Description: (Obverse) a right-facing profile of King Edward VII with NEW ZEALAND VOLUNTEER round the top and 12 YEARS SERVICE MEDAL round the foot; (reverse) a kiwi surrounded by a wreath. Plain ring suspension.
Comments: *This rare silver medal (obsolete by 1912) was awarded for 12 years service. Two reverse dies were used. In type I (1902–04) the kiwi's beak almost touches the ground, whereas in Type II (1905–12) there is a space between the tip of the beak and the ground. Only about 100 of Type I were produced, but 636 of Type II.*

VALUE: Type I   £250–350   *Miniature*   £80–100
             Type II   £180–220

259. NEW ZEALAND TERRITORIAL SERVICE MEDAL

Instituted: 1912.
Branch of Service: Territorial Force, New Zealand.
Ribbon: Originally as above, but replaced in 1917 by a ribbon of dark khaki edged with crimson.
Metal: Silver.
Size: 36mm.
Description: (Obverse) left-facing bust of King George V in field marshal's uniform; (reverse) similar to the above.
Comments: *It replaced the foregoing but became obsolete itself in 1931 when the Efficiency Medal with New Zealand bar was adopted.*

VALUE:
        George V   £75–100   *Miniature*   £10–15

261. ULSTER DEFENCE REGIMENT MEDAL

Instituted: 1982.
Branch of Service: Ulster Defence Regiment.
Ribbon: Dark green with a yellow central stripe edged in red.
Metal: Silver.
Size: 36mm.
Description: (Obverse) crowned head of Elizabeth II (B); (reverse) crowned harp and inscription ULSTER DEFENCE REGIMENT with a suspender of laurel leaves surmounted by a scroll bar bearing the regiment's initials.
Comments: *Awarded to part-time officers and men of the Ulster Defence Regiment with 12 years continuous service since 1 April 1970. A bar for each additional six-year period is awarded. Officers are permitted to add the letters UD after their names. This medal is to be superseded by the Northern Ireland Home Service Medal.*

VALUE:

Elizabeth II (B)	£150–200	*Miniature*	£6–8

261A. ULSTER DEFENCE REGIMENT MEDALLION

Instituted: 1987.
Branch of Service: Relatives of the Ulster Defence Regiment.
Ribbon: Dark green with a central yellow stripe, flanked by two narrow red stripes.
Metal: Silver.
Size: 36mm.
Description: Uniface medal showing a crowned Irish harp flanked by sprays of shamrocks. Ring suspension. Ribbons of awards to widows and other female relatives mounted as a bow with a brooch fitment.
Comments: *Designed by Colour Sergeant Win Clark and struck by Spink & Son, it was commissioned by the Regiment for presentation to the families of UDR personnel killed during the conflict in Northern Ireland as a token of appreciation.*

VALUE: —

262. CADET FORCES MEDAL

Instituted: February 1950.
Branch of Service: Cadet Forces.
Ribbon: A broad green central band bordered by thin red stripes flanked by a dark blue stripe (left) and light blue stripe (right, with yellow edges).
Metal: Cupro-nickel.
Size: 36mm.
Description: (Obverse) the effigy of the reigning monarch; (reverse) a hand holding aloft the torch of learning. Medals are named to recipients on the rim, in impressed capitals (Army and Navy) or engraved lettering (RAF).
Comments: *Awarded to commissioned officers and adult NCOs for 12 years service in the Cadet Forces. A bar is awarded for each additional 8 years.*

VALUE:

		Miniature
George VI (C)	£60–70	£8–12
Elizabeth II (A, BRITT: OMN)	£60–80	£8–12
Elizabeth II (A, DEI GRATIA)	£60–70	£8–12

263. ROYAL OBSERVER CORPS MEDAL

Instituted: 31 January 1950 but not awarded until 1953.
Branch of Service: Royal Observer Corps.
Ribbon: Pale blue with a broad central silver-grey stripe edged in dark blue.
Metal: Cupro-nickel.
Size: 36mm.
Description: (Obverse) effigy of the reigning monarch; (reverse) an artist's impression of a coast-watcher of Elizabethan times, holding a torch aloft alongside a signal fire, with other signal fires on hilltops in the background. The medal hangs from a suspender of two wings. An obverse die with the effigy of George VI was engraved, but no medals were struck from it.
Comments: *Awarded to part-time officers and observers who have completed 12 years satisfactory service and full-time members for 24 years service. A bar is awarded for each additional 12-year period. Home Office scientific officers and other non Royal Observer Corps members of the United Kingdom Warning and Monitoring Organisation were eligible for the Civil Defence Medal (no. 264) until being stood down on September 30, 1991. This entailed serving for 15 years alongside ROC members who received their own medal for 12 years' service.*

VALUE:		*Miniature*
Elizabeth II (C)	£70–80	£8–12
Elizabeth II (D)	£70–80	£8–12

264. CIVIL DEFENCE LONG SERVICE MEDAL

Instituted: March 1961.
Branch of Service: Civil Defence and other auxiliary forces.
Ribbon: Blue bearing three narrow stripes of yellow, red and green.
Metal: Cupro-nickel.
Size: 36mm.
Description: (Obverse) the effigy of the reigning monarch; (reverse) two types. Both featured three shields flanked by sprigs of acorns and oak leaves. The upper shield in both cases is inscribed CD but the initials on the lower shields differ, according to the organisations in Britain and Northern Ireland respectively—AFS and NHSR (British) or AERS and HSR (Northern Ireland).
Comments: *Issued unnamed to those who had completed 15 years service in a wide range of Civil Defence organisations. It was extended to Civil Defence personnel in Gibraltar, Hong Kong and Malta in 1965. The medal became obsolescent in the UK after the Civil Defence Corps and Auxiliary Fire Service were disbanded in 1968, but members of the CD Corps in the Isle of Man and Channel Islands are still eligible.*

VALUE:		*Miniature*
British version	£20–25	£8–12
Northern Ireland version	£80–95	—

British rev.

Northern Ireland rev.

264A. AMBULANCE SERVICE (EMERGENCY DUTIES) LONG SERVICE AND GOOD CONDUCT MEDAL

Instituted: 5 July 1996.

Branch of Service: Ambulance services in England and Wales, Scotland, Northern Ireland, the Isle of Man and the Channel Islands.

Ribbon: Green with, on either side, a white stripe on which is superimposed a narrow green stripe.

Metal: Cupro-nickel.

Size: 36mm.

Description: (Obverse) crowned effigy of the reigning monarch, ELIZABETH II DEI GRATIA REGINA F.D.; (reverse) FOR EXEMPLARY SERVICE round the top, with either the emblem of the Ambulance Services of Scotland or the remainder of the United Kingdom in the centre below. Fitted with a ring for suspension.

Comments: *Both full- and part-time members of Ambulance Services are eligible provided they are employed on emergency duties. Service prior to 1974 in ambulance services maintained by local authorities counts. For paramedics and technicians the qualifying service is 20 years. For ambulance officers and other management grades, at least seven of their 20 years' service must have been spent on emergency duties.*

VALUE: UK version £20–30 *Miniature* £35–40
Scottish version £30–40

264B. ASSOCIATION OF CHIEF AMBULANCE OFFICERS SERVICE MEDAL

Instituted: —.

Branch of Service: Members of the Ambulance Service.

Ribbon: Dark green with twin central red stripe edged with yellow.

Metal: Bronze.

Size: 36mm.

Description: (Obverse) symbol of the Association (caduceus on a wheel) surrounded by ASSOCIATION OF CHIEF AMBULANCE OFFICERS; (reverse) FOR SERVICE surrounded by a laurel wreath.

Comments: *Issued by members of the Association to ambulencemen who have performed exemplary service.*

VALUE: £30–40 Miniature —

265. WOMEN'S VOLUNTARY SERVICE LONG SERVICE MEDAL

Instituted: 1961.

Branch of Service: Women's Royal Voluntary Service.

Ribbon: Dark green with twin white stripes towards the end and broad red edges.

Metal: Cupro-nickel.

Size: 36mm.

Description: (Obverse) the interlocking initials WVS in an ivy wreath (although the WVS acquired the Royal title in 1966 only one obverse has so far been used); (reverse) three flowers, inscribed SERVICE BEYOND SELF round the circumference.

Comments: *Issued unnamed and awarded for 15 years service. Bars for additional 15 year periods are awarded. Although the majority of the 35,000 (approx.) medals have been awarded to women there has also been a substantial number of male recipients.*

VALUE: £10–15 *Miniature* £15–20

266. VOLUNTARY MEDICAL SERVICE MEDAL

Instituted: 1932.

Branch of Service: British Red Cross Society and the St Andrew's Ambulance Corps (Scotland).

Ribbon: Red with yellow and white stripes.

Metal: Originally struck in silver but since the 1960s it has been produced in cupro-nickel.

Size: 36mm.

Description: (Obverse) the veiled bust of a female holding an oil lamp, symbolic of Florence Nightingale; (reverse) the crosses of Geneva and St Andrew, with the inscription FOR LONG AND EFFICIENT SERVICE.

Comments: *Awarded for 15 years service, with a bar for each additional period of five years. The service bars are embellished with a Geneva cross or saltire (St Andrew) cross, whichever is the more appropriate.*

VALUE:	Silver	£15–20
	Cupro-nickel	£10–15
	Miniature	£8–10

267. SERVICE MEDAL OF THE ORDER OF ST JOHN

Instituted: 1898.

Branch of Service: The Most Venerable Order of the Hospital of St John of Jerusalem.

Ribbon: Three black and two white stripes of equal width.

Metal: Silver (1898-1947), silvered base metal (1947-60), silvered cupro-nickel (1960-66) and rhodium-plated cupro-nickel (since 1966).

Size: 38mm.

Description: (Obverse) an unusual veiled bust of Queen Victoria with her name and abbreviated Latin titles round the circumference. A new obverse was adopted in 1960 with a slightly reduced effigy of Queen Victoria and less ornate lettering. (Reverse) the royal arms within a garter surrounded by four circles containing the imperial crown, the Prince of Wales's feathers and the armorial bearings of the Order and of HRH the Duke of Clarence and Avondale, the first Sub-Prior of the Order. Between the circles are sprigs of St John's Wort. Round the circumference is the Latin inscription MAGNUS PRIORATUS ORDINIS HOSPITALIS SANCTI JOHANNIS JERUSALEM IN ANGLIA in Old English lettering.

Comments: *Originally awarded for 15 years service to the Order in the United Kingdom (12 in the Dominions and 10 in the Colonies) but the qualifying period has now been reduced to 12 years service, except that overseas service outside South Africa, New Zealand, Canada and Australia remains 10 years. A silver bar was introduced in 1911 for additional periods of five years. From then until 1924 the bar was inscribed 5 YEARS SERVICE but then a design showing a Maltese cross flanked by sprays of St John's Wort was substituted. Bars for 20 years service were subsequently instituted in silver-gilt. Suspension by a ring was changed in 1913 to a straight bar suspender. Although awarded for long service this medal should not be solely referred to as a long service award as it can also be awarded for conspicuous service—when so awarded it was distinguished by the addition of a silver palm leaf on the ribbon. The silver palm was discontinued in 1949, after only three years. It is believed to be the only medal still issued bearing the bust of Queen Victoria (the effigy was first sculptured by HRH Princess Louise, daughter of Queen Victoria).*

Ribbon embellishments:

5-year cross

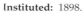

Palm leaf for conspicuous service

Voluntary Aid Detachment

Military Hospital Reserve

Ribbon bars:

5-year bar (second type)

VAD (or MHR)

Illustrations by M. Thomas, courtesy of Roy Gould

VALUE:		*Miniature*
Silver, ring suspension	£15–20	£15–20
Silver, straight bar suspension	£12–16	£12–15
Base metal, first obverse	£8–12	£6–10
Base metal, second obverse	£8–12	£6–10

268. ROYAL AIR FORCE LONG SERVICE AND GOOD CONDUCT MEDAL

Instituted: 1 July 1919.
Branch of Service: Royal Air Force.
Ribbon: Dark blue and maroon with white edges.
Metal: Silver/silver-plated.
Size: 36mm.
Description: (Obverse) the effigy of the reigning monarch; (reverse) the RAF eagle and crown insignia.
Comments: *Awarded to NCOs and other ranks of the RAF for 18 years exemplary service, reduced in 1977 to 15 years. Provision for bars for further periods of service was made from 1944 onwards. Before 1945 conduct below the required standard was permitted to count if the airman had displayed higher exemplary conduct against the enemy, gallantry or some special service in times of emergency. From 1944 prior service in the Navy and Army up to a maximum of four years could be counted. In 1947 officers became eligible for the medal provided they had had at least 12 years service in the ranks. Recipients' details are inscribed on the rim. The later issues are of silver-plated base metal.*

VALUE: | | | *Miniature* |
|---|---|---|
| George V (E) | £70–90 | £15–20 |
| George VI (D) | £30–40 | £10–15 |
| George VI (E) | £40–45 | £10–15 |
| Elizabeth II (C) | £40–45 | £8–10 |
| Elizabeth II (D) | £40–45 | £8–10 |

269. ROYAL AIR FORCE LEVIES LONG SERVICE AND GOOD CONDUCT MEDAL

Instituted: 1948.
Branch of Service: RAF Levies, Iraq.
Ribbon: As the preceding.
Metal: Silver.
Size: 36mm.
Description: Similar to the previous type but was fitted with a clasp inscribed ROYAL AIR FORCE LEVIES IRAQ.
Comments: *Awarded to the locally commissioned officers and men of the RAF Levies in Iraq, for 18 years service (the last 12 to be of an exemplary nature). The Iraq Levies were raised in 1919 and became the responsibility of the RAF in 1922, maintaining law and order by means of light aircraft and armoured cars. The force was disbanded in 1955 when the RAF withdrew from Iraq. Only about 300 medals were issued.*

VALUE: | | |
|---|---|
| George VI (E) | £800–1000 |
| Elizabeth II (C) | £900–1100 |
| Elizabeth II (D) | £900–1100 |

270. AIR EFFICIENCY AWARD

Instituted: September 1942
Branch of Service: Royal Air Force.
Ribbon: Green with two light blue stripes towards the centre.
Metal: Silver.
Size: Height 38mm; max. width 32mm.
Description: An oval medal with a suspender in the form of an eagle with wings outspread. (Obverse) the effigy of the reigning monarch; (reverse) inscribed AIR EFFICIENCY AWARD in three lines.
Comments: *Granted for 10 years efficient service in the Auxiliary and Volunteer Air Forces of the United Kingdom and Commonwealth. A bar was awarded for a further ten-year period. Officers are permitted to add the letters AE after their name. This award was replaced in 2000 by the VRSM (No. 242A).*

VALUE:

George VI (D)	£70–90
George VI (E)	£70–90
Elizabeth II (C)	£80–90
Elizabeth II (D)	£70–90
Miniature (all)	£8–12

271. POLICE LONG SERVICE AND GOOD CONDUCT MEDAL

Instituted: 14 June 1951.
Branch of Service: Police Forces.
Ribbon: Dark blue with twin white stripes towards each end.
Metal: Cupro-nickel
Size: 36mm.
Description: (Obverse) the effigy of the reigning monarch; (reverse) a standing female allegorical figure of Justice, with scales in one hand and a wreath in the other. Named on the rim.
Comments: *awarded for 22 years full-time service in any UK constabulary. By a Royal Warrant of 1 May 1956 it was extended to police forces in Australia, Papua New Guinea and Nauru. The Australian award was replaced in 1976 by the National Medal.*

VALUE:		*Miniature*
George VI (C)	£30–35	£5–8
Elizabeth II (A)	£40–50	£5–8
Elizabeth II (D)	£30–35	£5–8

272. SPECIAL CONSTABULARY LONG SERVICE MEDAL

Instituted: 30 August 1919.
Branch of Service: Special Constabulary.
Ribbon: A broad red stripe in the centre flanked by black and white stripes.
Metal: Bronze.
Size: 36mm.
Description: (Obverse) the effigy of the reigning monarch; (reverse) a partial laurel wreath with a six-line text inscribed FOR FAITHFUL SERVICE IN THE SPECIAL CONSTABULARY. A second reverse was introduced in 1956 for 15 years service in the Ulster Special Constabulary, the text being modified to permit the inclusion of the word ULSTER. A third type was introduced in 1982 for 15 years service in the RUC Reserve and is thus inscribed.
Comments: *Awarded to all ranks in the Special Constabulary for 9 years unpaid service, with more than 50 duties per annum. War service with at least 50 duties counted triple. A clasp inscribed THE GREAT WAR 1914-18 was awarded to those who qualified for the medal during that conflict. Clasps inscribed LONG SERVICE, with the date, were awarded for additional ten-year periods.*

VALUE:

		Miniature
George V (C)	£8–10	£3–5
George V (E)	£8–10	£3–5
George VI (D)	£8–10	£3–5
George VI (E)	£50–75	£4–8
Elizabeth II (C)	£20–30	£4–8
Elizabeth II (D)	£20–30	£4–8
Elizabeth II (D) Ulster	£100–120	£8–12
Elizabeth II (D) RUC Reserve	£120–140	£8–12

273. ROYAL ULSTER CONSTABULARY SERVICE MEDAL

Instituted: 1982.
Branch of Service: RUC and its Reserve.
Ribbon: Green, with narrow central stripes of red, black and dark blue.
Metal: Cupro-nickel.
Size: 36mm.
Description: (Obverse) the effigy of Queen Elizabeth II; (reverse) the crowned harp insignia of the RUC with the words FOR SERVICE round the foot.
Comments: *Awarded for 18 months continuous service since 1 January 1971, but the award was made immediate on the recipient also being awarded a gallantry decoration or a Queen's commendation.*

VALUE:

Elizabeth II (D)	£80–100	*Miniature*	£10–15

274. COLONIAL POLICE LONG SERVICE MEDAL

Instituted: 1934.
Branch of Service: Colonial police forces.
Ribbon: Green centre bordered with white and broad blue bars towards the edges.
Metal: Silver.
Size: 36mm.
Description: (Obverse) the effigy of the reigning monarch; (reverse) a police truncheon superimposed on a laurel wreath.
Comments: *Originally awarded to junior officers who had completed 18 years exemplary service but latterly awarded to officers of all ranks who have the required service qualification. A bar is awarded on completing 25 years service and a second bar after 30 years. These are represented on the ribbon bar in working dress by silver rosettes. The number (where applicable), rank and name as well as (for George VI and later issues) the relevant force in which the recipient is serving at the time of the award is engraved on the rim, often locally and therefore in a variety of styles.*

VALUE:		*Miniature*
George V (C)	£80–100	£12–18
George VI (B)	£45–55	£10–15
George VI (C)	£45–55	£10–15
Elizabeth II (A)	£45–55	£10–15
Elizabeth II (B)	£45–55	£10–15

275. COLONIAL SPECIAL CONSTABULARY LONG SERVICE MEDAL

Instituted: 1957.
Branch of Service: Colonial Special Constabulary.
Ribbon: Two thin white stripes on a broad green centre, with broad blue edges.
Metal: Silver.
Size: 36mm.
Description: (Obverse) the effigy of the reigning monarch; (reverse) the crowned royal cypher above the words FOR FAITHFUL SERVICE in a laurel wreath.
Comments: *Awarded for nine years unpaid or 15 years paid service in a colonial special constabulary. A bar is awarded for further ten-year periods.*

VALUE:			
Elizabeth II (A)	£180–220	*Miniature*	£15–20

www.speedbid.com

YOUR OWN MEDAL AUCTION

276. ROYAL CANADIAN MOUNTED POLICE LONG SERVICE MEDAL

Instituted: 14 January 1933, by Order in Council.
Branch of Service: Royal Canadian Mounted Police.
Ribbon: Dark blue with two gold stripes towards the edges.
Metal: Silver.
Size: 36mm.
Description: (Obverse) the effigy of the reigning monarch; (reverse) the RCMP insignia with the legend FOR LONG SERVICE AND GOOD CONDUCT.
Comments: *Awarded to all ranks of the RCMP who had served 20 years. Bronze, silver or gold bars were awarded for 25, 30 or 35 years further service. A French language version of the later issue also exists.*

VALUE:		*Miniature*
George V (C)	£500–600	£15–25
George V (E)	£500–600	£15–25
George VI (B)	£450–500	£8–10
George VI (C)	£450–500	£5–10
Elizabeth II (A)	£250–300	£5–10
Elizabeth II (French)	£500–600	£5–10

277. CEYLON POLICE LONG SERVICE AND GOOD CONDUCT MEDAL (I)

Instituted: 1925.
Branch of Service: Ceylon Police.
Ribbon: Very similar to that of the Special Constabulary Long Service Medal.
Metal: Silver.
Size: 36mm.
Description: (Obverse) coinage profile of King George V by Sir Bertram Mackennal; (reverse) an elephant surmounted by a crown. Ring suspension.
Comments: *Awarded for 15 years active service. It was superseded in 1934 by the Colonial Police Long Service Medal.*

VALUE:		
George V (E)	£300–350	*Miniature* —

278. CEYLON POLICE LONG SERVICE AND GOOD CONDUCT MEDAL (II)

Instituted: 1950.
Branch of Service: Ceylon Police.
Ribbon: Dark blue edged with khaki, white and pale blue.
Metal: Cupro-nickel.
Size: 36mm.
Description: (Obverse) the effigy of the reigning monarch; (reverse) similar to the foregoing, but without the crown above the elephant, to permit the longer inscription CEYLON POLICE SERVICE. Straight bar suspender.
Comments: *Awarded for 18 years exemplary service. Bars for 25 and 30 years service were also awarded. It became obsolete when Ceylon (now Sri Lanka) became a republic in 1972.*

VALUE:		*Miniature*
George VI (C)	£280–320	£15–20
Elizabeth II (A)	£250–300	£10–15

279. CYPRUS MILITARY POLICE LONG SERVICE & GOOD CONDUCT MEDAL

Instituted: October 1929.
Branch of Service: Cyprus Military Police.
Ribbon: Yellow, dark green and yellow in equal bands.
Metal: Silver.
Size: 36mm.
Description: (Obverse) King George V; (reverse) the title of the police round the circumference and the words LONG AND GOOD SERVICE in four lines across the middle.
Comments: *Awarded to those who had three good conduct badges, plus six years exemplary service since the award of the third badge, no more than four entries in the defaulters' book and a minimum of 15 years service. Officers who had been promoted from the ranks were also eligible. No more than 7 officers and 54 other ranks were awarded this medal during its brief life before it was superseded in 1934 by the Colonial Police Long Service Medal.*

VALUE: George V   Rare

279A. ROYAL FALKLAND ISLANDS POLICE JUBILEE MEDAL

Date: 1996
Branch of Service: Royal Falkland Islands Police
Ribbon: Blue with a central white stripe edged in black and a thin red central stripe.
Metal: Silver.
Size: 36mm.
Description: (Obverse) Elizabeth II (A); (reverse) arms of the colony; ROYAL FALKLAND ISLANDS POLICE round top and double dated 1846-1996 round foot. Fitted with ring suspension and a brooch clasp at the top of the ribbon.
Comments: *Awarded to all officers serving in the Royal Falkland Islands Police on 15 October 1996. Only 27 medals were awarded.*

VALUE: £1000–1500

280. HONG KONG POLICE MEDAL FOR MERIT

Instituted: May 3, 1862.
Branch of Service: Hong Kong Police.
Ribbon: Various, according to class (see below).
Metal: Gold, silver or bronze.
Size: 36mm.
Description: (Obverse) the effigy of the reigning monarch; (reverse) inscribed in three lines HONG KONG POLICE FORCE FOR MERIT within a laurel wreath and beaded circle. Examples have been recorded with the effigy of Queen Victoria as on the Abyssinian and New Zealand Medals (123–124), and King George V types C and E.
Comment: *Exceptionally awarded in five different classes according to the length and type of service. The 1st Class medal was struck in gold and worn with a maroon (VC) ribbon, the 2nd Class in silver with a plain yellow ribbon, the 3rd Class in bronze with a central black stripe on the yellow ribbon, the 4th Class in bronze with two central black stripes in the yellow ribbon, and the 5th Class (confined to the Police Reserve) in bronze had a green ribbon with two black central stripes. The 4th Class was engraved on the reverse above the wreath. These medals were superseded in April 1937 by the Hong Kong Police Silver Medal, only four of which was awarded before it was replaced by the Colonial Police Medal for Meritorious Service 1938.*

VALUE:	1st class	2nd class	3rd class	4th class
Victoria	—	£450–500	£400–450	£250–300
Edward VII	Rare	£450–500	£350–450	£250–300
George V (B)	Rare	£400–450	£300–350	£225–275
George V (C)	Rare	£$00–450	£300–350	£225–275

280A. HONG KONG DISTRICT WATCH FORCE MERIT MEDAL

Instituted: 1868.
Branch of Service: District Watch Force.
Ribbon: Very dark green with a central deep red stripe.
Metal: Silver.
Size: 31mm with a prominent rim.
Description: (Obverse) four Chinese characters "Great Britain Hong Kong" above a watchman's lamp, superimposed on a cutlass and police baton, with the Chinese characters for "District Watch Force" and "Medal" at the sides; (reverse) DISTRICT WATCHMEN'S FORCE FOR MERIT within a laurel wreath.
Comment: *While the Hong Kong Police was principally a mixed force of Europeans and Indians, operated in the business and higher class residential areas, and was paid for out of the colony's revenues, the District Watch Force was a purely Chinese organisation, raised by prominent citizens of the colony to patrol and police the Chinese parts of the city. Its members had statutory powers, were uniformed and were trained and functioned in the style of the old parish constables, rather than in the gendarmerie style of the Hong Kong Police which was colonial in nature and imposed on society rather than integrated with it. The District Watch Force ceased to function at the time of the Japanese invasion in 1941 and was not revived on liberation.*

VALUE: £500

280B. ROYAL HONG KONG POLICE COMMEMORATION MEDAL

Instituted: 1996.
Branch of Service: Royal Hong Kong Police.
Ribbon: Black, magenta and old gold (colours of the turban worn by the original Punjabi constables).
Metal: Silver.
Size: 38mm.
Description: (Obverse) the RHKP crest; (reverse) crossed tipstaves inside a laurel wreath with the dates 1844 and 1997.
Comment: *The medal, approved by Commissioner Eddie Hui Kion, is available on purchase (HK$1,000, about £80) to those who served in the Hong Kong Police (1844–1969) and the Royal Hong Kong Police (1969–97). Made by Spink & Son and cased. Apparently only about 2,000 of the 40,000 eligible have purchased the medal owing to the cost. Purchasers' details are engraved in bold upright capitals in a variety of formats. The medal, worn on the right breast, has the same status as the Royal Hong Kong Regiment Disbandment Medal (254A).*

VALUE: £100   *Miniature*   £30

280C. ROYAL HONG KONG AUXILIARY POLICE COMMEMORATION MEDAL

Instituted: 1996.
Branch of Service: Royal Hong Kong Auxiliary Police.
Ribbon: Black, magenta and old gold (colours of the turban worn by the original Punjabi constables).
Metal: Silver.
Size: 38mm.
Description: Similar to the above, but inscribed ROYAL HONG KONG AUXILIARY POLICE FORCE.
Comment: *Similar to the above this medal is available for purchase. Some 5,000 auxiliary policemen and women being eligible for the award.*

VALUE: £120   *Miniature*   £30

281. HONG KONG ROYAL NAVAL DOCKYARD POLICE LONG SERVICE MEDAL

Instituted: 1920.
Branch of Service: Hong Kong Royal Naval Dockyard Police.
Ribbon: Yellow with two royal blue stripes towards the centre.
Metal: Gilt bronze or silver.
Size: 31mm.
Description: (Obverse) the effigy of the reigning monarch; (reverse) the title of the Police within a laurel wreath. Swivel ring suspension.
Comments: *Awarded for 15 years service. Although the Dockyard closed in 1961 men who transferred to other police divisions continued to be awarded the medal up to 1973. About 280 medals in all were issued.*

VALUE:		Miniature
George V (E)	£200–250	—
George VI (C)	£160–180	—
George VI (D)	£200–250	—
Elizabeth II (C)	£200–250	—

281A. HONG KONG DISCIPLINED SERVICES MEDAL

Instituted: 1986.
Branch of Service: Hong Kong Customs & Excise and Immigration Service.
Ribbon: Green bordered by vertical stripes of dark blue with a strip of sky blue at each edge.
Metal: Silver.
Size: 36mm.
Description: (Obverse) crowned effigy of Queen Elizabeth II (B); (reverse) armorial bearings of Hong Kong, with the inscription "For Long Service and Good Conduct".
Clasps: Awarded after 25 and 30 years, denoted by silver rosettes on ribband in working dress.
Comments: *Awarded after 18 years continuous service. Engraved with name and rank on rim. Some 1,739 medals were awarded between 1987 and the return of Hong Kong to China on June 30, 1997. This appears to have been the only medal awarded to Customs officers.*

VALUE:	Customs	Immigration
Medal	£100–£150	£250–£300
1st clasp	£250–£300	£500–£700
2nd clasp	£400–£500	Unique

282. MALTA POLICE LONG SERVICE AND GOOD CONDUCT MEDAL

Instituted: 1921.
Branch of Service: Malta Police.
Ribbon: Dark blue with a narrow central silver stripe.
Metal: Silver.
Size: 36mm.
Description: (Obverse) the effigy of King George V; (reverse) an eight-pointed Maltese cross in a laurel wreath with the title of the service and FOR LONG SERVICE AND GOOD CONDUCT round the circumference.
Comments: *Awarded to sergeants and constables with 18 years exemplary service. Officers who had had 18 years in the ranks were also eligible for the award. It was superseded by the Colonial Police Long Service Medal in 1934. No more than 99 medals were awarded.*

VALUE:		Miniature
George V (E)	£300–350	£50–75
George V (C)	£350–400	£50–75

282A. MAURITIUS POLICE LONG SERVICE AND GOOD CONDUCT MEDAL: I

Instituted: —.
Branch of Service: Mauritius Police.
Ribbon: Three types: (a) 36mm half black, half white; (b) 33mm white with a broad royal blue central stripe; (c) blue with two narrow white stripes towards the edges.
Metal: Bronze.
Size: Oval, 40x33mm or 39x31mm.
Description: (Obverse) crown surmounting crossed tipstaves with the motto PAX NOBISCUM (Peace be with us) and the legend POLICE DEPARTMENT round the top and MAURITIUS at the foot; (reverse) palm fronds enclosing a theee-line inscription FOR GOOD CONDUCT. Fitted with a ring for suspension. Medals with 33mm ribbon fitted at top with a pin brooch by Hunt & Roskill.
Comment: *It is believed that the different ribbons indicated different periods of service, but confirmation is sought. It is presumed that this medal was superseded by no. 282B.*

VALUE: £100–150   *Miniature*   £10–15

282B. MAURITIUS POLICE LONG SERVICE AND GOOD CONDUCT MEDAL: II

Instituted: —.
Branch of Service: Mauritius Police
Ribbon: Green centre flanked by white stripes and broad blue stripes towards the edges.
Metal: Silver.
Size: 36mm.
Description: (Obverse) the effigy of Queen Elizabeth II; (reverse) police truncheon on a laurel wreath.
Comments: *This medal is identical to the Colonial Police Long Service Medal (no. 274) except that the inscription substituted the name MAURITIUS for COLONIAL. It has been recorded in a medal group of 1976 and may have been introduced in or about 1968 when Mauritius attained independence.*

VALUE: £75–85

283. NEW ZEALAND POLICE MEDAL

Instituted: 1886.
Branch of Service: New Zealand Police.
Ribbon: Originally plain crimson but in 1917 it was changed to a pattern very similar to that of the Permanent Forces of the Empire Beyond the Seas LSGC medal.
Metal: Silver.
Size: 36mm.
Description: The original obverse was very similar to that of the NZ Long and Efficient Service Medal, with the crown, crossed sword and sceptre motif within a wreath of oak and fern leaves. Two types of suspension for this medal are known: the normal type has a bar suspender but a very rare variant has a ring suspender. By Royal Warrant of 8 September 1976 an obverse portraying Queen Elizabeth was introduced. The reverse was plain with the words FOR LONG SERVICE AND GOOD CONDUCT across the field.
Comments: *Awarded for 14 years service. Bars for further eight-year periods were added in 1959, reduced to seven years in 1963, the total length of service being indicated on the bar. A new medal, introduced in 1994 but retaining the original name, will be found in the New Zealand section (no. NZ16).*

VALUE:		*Miniature*
Regalia obverse, bar suspension	£100–120	£10–15
Regalia obverse, ring suspension	Rare	—
Elizabeth II	£90–110	£10–15

283A. SEYCHELLES POLICE LONG SERVICE AND GOOD CONDUCT MEDAL

Instituted: —.
Branch of Service: Seychelles Police.
Ribbon: Crimson.
Metal: Bronze.
Size: Oval, 40x33mm.
Description: (Obverse) crown surmounting crossed tipstaves with legend POLICE DEPARTMENT round the top and SEYCHELLES at the foot; (reverse) palm fronds enclosing a three-line inscription FOR GOOD CONDUCT. Fitted with a ring for suspension.
Comments: *Like the Mauritius Police Medal (282A) it is presumed that this medal became obsolete on the introduction of the Colonial Police Long Service Medal in 1934. Details of qualifying terms of service and other regulations are sought.*

VALUE: £100–150   *Miniature*   —

284. SOUTH AFRICA POLICE GOOD SERVICE MEDAL

Instituted: 1923.
Branch of Service: South Africa Police.
Ribbon: Broad black centre, flanked by white stripes and green borders.
Metal: Silver.
Size: 36mm.
Description: (Obverse) South African coat of arms; (reverse) bilingual inscriptions separated by a horizontal line. Three versions of the medal have been recorded. In the first version inscriptions were in English and Dutch, the latter reading POLITIE DIENST with VOOR TROUWE DIENST (for faithful service) on the reverse. In the second, introduced in 1932, Afrikaans replaced Dutch and read POLISIE DIENS and VIR GETROUE DIENS respectively. In the third version, current from 1951 to 1963, the Afrikaans was modified to read POLISIEDIENS and VIR TROUE DIENS respectively.
Comments: *Awarded to other ranks for 18 years exemplary service or for service of a gallant or particularly distinguished character. In the latter instance a bar inscribed MERIT-VERDIENSTE was awarded. The medal was replaced by the South African Medal for Faithful Service.*

VALUE:		
	1st type	£20–30
	2nd type	£15–25
	3rd type	£15–25
	Miniature	£10–12

285. SOUTH AFRICAN RAILWAYS AND HARBOUR POLICE LONG SERVICE AND GOOD CONDUCT MEDAL

Instituted: 1934.
Branch of Service: South African Railways and Harbour Police.
Ribbon: Similar to the Police Good Service Medal but with the colours reversed—a green central stripe flanked by white stripes and blue edges.
Metal: Silver.
Size: 36mm.
Description: (Obverse) the Union arms with S.A.R. & H. POLICE at the top and S.A.S.- EN HAWE POLISIE round the foot, but this was changed in 1953 to S.A.S. POLISIE at the top and S.A.R. POLICE at the foot. (Reverse) six line bilingual inscription.
Comments: *Awarded for 18 years unblemished service. Immediate awards for gallant or especially meritorious service earned a bar inscribed MERIT - VERDIENSTE (later with the words transposed). The medal was superseded in 1960 by the Railways Police Good Service Medal.*

VALUE: 1st type   £30–40   2nd type   £20–30

286. FIRE BRIGADE LONG SERVICE MEDAL

Instituted: 1 June 1954.
Branch of Service: Fire Services.
Ribbon: Red with narrow yellow stripes towards the end and yellow borders.
Metal: Cupro-nickel.
Size: 36mm.
Description: (Obverse) the Queen's effigy; (reverse) two firemen manning a hose. Ring suspension.
Comments: *Awarded to all ranks of local authority fire brigades, whether full- or part-time for 20 years exemplary service.*

VALUE:
Elizabeth II   £35–40   *Miniature*   £6–10

286A. ASSOCIATION OF PROFESSIONAL FIRE BRIGADE OFFICERS LONG SERVICE MEDAL

Branch of Service: Association of Professional Fire Brigade Officers.
Ribbon: A red central stripe flanked by narrow white stripes and broad black edges (silver medal) or grey edges (bronze medal).
Metal: Silver or bronze.
Size: 38mm.
Description: (Obverse) allegorical female figure carrying a palm frond and bestowing a laurel crown on a kneeling fireman; an early fire appliance in the background; blank exergue; (reverse) an oak wreath enclosing a four-line inscription ASSOCIATION OF PROFESSIONAL FIRE BRIGADE OFFICERS FOR LONG SERVICE. Fitted with a swivelling bar suspension.
Comments: *The medal in silver was awarded to professional fire brigade officers for a minimum of 20 years full time service and in bronze for lesser periods. Engraved on the rim with the rank and name of the officer, together with the year of the award.*

VALUE: —

286B. BRITISH FIRE SERVICES ASSOCIATION MEDAL

Instituted: 1949.
Branch of Service: British Fire Services Association.
Ribbon: 33mm with a central silver-grey stripe flanked by black and white stripes and a broad red edge.
Metal: Bronze.
Size: 38mm.
Description: (Obverse) identical to 286A; (reverse) badge of the Association: a wreathed flag within a circle inscribed FOR LONG SERVICE & EFFICIENCY, surmounted by a fireman's helmet and surrounded by ladders and hoses. THE BRITISH FIRE SERVICES ASSOCIATION round the circumference. The medal has an ornamental scrolled suspender with a bar inscribed BFSA. The recipient's name and service number are engraved on the rim.
Comments: *The British Fire Services Association was formed in 1949 by the amalgamation of the National Fire Brigades Association and the Professional Fire Brigades Association. This medal thus superseded 286A.*

VALUE: —

287. COLONIAL FIRE BRIGADE LONG SERVICE MEDAL

Instituted: 1934.
Branch of Service: Colonial Fire Services.
Ribbon: Blue with twin green central stripes separated and bordered by thin white stripes.
Metal: Silver.
Size: 36mm.
Description: (Obverse) the effigy of the reigning monarch; (reverse) a fireman's helmet and axe. Ring suspension.
Comments: *Awarded to junior officers for 18 years full-time exemplary service. Bars are awarded for further periods of service.*

VALUE:		*Miniature*
George V (E)	£300–350	£15–20
George VI (D)	£250–300	£10–15
George VI (E)	£250–300	£10–15
Elizabeth II (C)	£250–300	£10–15
Elizabeth II (D)	£250–300	£10–15

288. CEYLON FIRE BRIGADE LONG SERVICE & GOOD CONDUCT MEDAL

Instituted: 1950.
Branch of Service: Ceylon Fire Service.
Ribbon: Similar to the Police Medal, but with a thin central white stripe through the dark blue band.
Metal: Silver.
Size: 36mm.
Description: As the Police Medal, but with a reverse inscribed CEYLON FIRE SERVICES.

VALUE:		*Miniature*
George VI	£300–400	—
Elizabeth II	£300–400	—

289. COLONIAL PRISON SERVICE LONG SERVICE MEDAL

Instituted: October 1955.
Branch of Service: Colonial Prison Services.
Ribbon: Green with dark blue edges and a thin silver stripe in the centre.
Metal: Silver.
Size: 36mm.
Description: (Obverse) Queen Elizabeth II; (reverse) a phoenix rising from the flames and striving towards the sun.
Comments: *Awarded to ranks of Assistant Superintendent and below for 18 years exemplary service. Bars are awarded for further periods of 25 or 30 years service.*

VALUE:			
Elizabeth II	£225–250	*Miniature*	£8–12

290. SOUTH AFRICAN PRISON SERVICE FAITHFUL SERVICE MEDAL

Instituted: September 1922.
Branch of Service: South African Prison Service.
Ribbon: Broad green centre flanked by white stripes and blue edges.
Metal: Silver.
Size: 36mm.
Description: (Obverse) arms of the Union of South Africa, of identical design to no. 284 except with GEVANGENIS DIENST round the top and PRISONS SERVICE round the foot. (Reverse) inscribed FOR FAITHFUL SERVICE across the upper half and in Dutch VOOR TROUWE DIENST across the lower half.
Comments: *Awarded to prison officers with 18 years exemplary service. Immediate awards for gallantry or exceptionally meritorious service received the Merit bar. In 1959 this medal was superseded by a version inscribed in Afrikaans.*

VALUE: £30–40   *Miniature*   —

291. SOUTH AFRICA PRISONS DEPARTMENT FAITHFUL SERVICE MEDAL

Instituted: 1959.
Branch of Service: South African Prisons Department.
Ribbon: Broad blue centre flanked by white stripes and green edges.
Metal: Silver.
Size: 36mm.
Description: (Obverse) arms of the Union of South Africa, of identical design to no. 284 except with DEPARTEMENT VAN GEVANGENISSE round the top and PRISONS DEPARTMENT round the foot. (Reverse) VIR TROUE DIENS across the upper half and FOR FAITHFUL SERVICE across the lower half.
Comments: *The conditions of the award were similar to the previous medal, the main difference being the change of title and the substitution of Afrikaans inscriptions for Dutch. This medal was superseded by the Prisons Department Faithful Service Medal of the Republic of South Africa, instituted in 1965.*

VALUE: £30–40   *Miniature*   —

A GUIDE TO POLICE MEDALS OF THE WORLD
By Roger Campion
Author of *The Call of Duty*

This exciting new publication from TOKEN PUBLISHING LTD, provides an indepth guide to the most commonly found medals awarded by the Police forces of the World to their men and women.

For many years the author, an ex-policeman, has been dedicated to researching these medals and the result is a profusely illustrated, accurate guide to this fascinating area of medal collecting

£19.95 *(plus £3.00 p&p)*

Publication Date December 2001

To order your copy call: 01404 44166
E-mail your order to: orders @tokenpublishing.com
Or visit our website @ www.tokenpublishing.com

View our extensive range of quality books on www.tokenpublishing.com

TOKEN PUBLISHING LTD, ORCHARD HOUSE, DUCHY ROAD, HEATHPARK, HONITON, EX14 1YD

Coronation and Jubilee Medals

The first official royal medal was that cast by Henry Basse in 1547 for the accession of the young King Edward VI. It is known cast in gold or silver and is a curious example of bad design and poor workmanship for such an august occasion. No coronation medals were produced in honour of either Mary or Elizabeth I, but under James VI and I there was a small silver medal struck at the Royal Mint to mark the king's accession in 1603. These early medals celebrated the accession of the new sovereign, rather than the act of crowning itself.

To mark the coronation of James I, however, a small silver medalet was struck for distribution among the people who attended the ceremony, and this may be regarded as the forerunner of the modern series. This bore a Latin title signifying that James was Caesar Augustus of Britain and Heir to the Caesars. Thereafter medals in gold, silver or base metals were regularly struck in connection with the coronations of British monarchs. These were purely commemorative and not intended for wear, so they lack rings or bars for suspension.

By the early 19th century medals were being struck by many medallists for sale as souvenirs to the general public. At least fifteen different medals greeted the coronation of William IV in 1830 and more than twice that number appeared seven years later for the coronation of Queen Victoria. That paled into insignificance compared with the number produced for the coronation of Edward VII in 1902. On that occasion numerous civic authorities, organizations, industrial concerns and business firms issued medals in celebration—well over a hundred different medals and medalets were produced.

Sir George Frampton designed two silver medals, and one of these was mounted with a suspender and a blue ribbon with a thin white stripe and scarlet edges. This medal was distributed to notable personages attending the ceremony and established the precedent for subsequent coronation medals which came to be regarded as an award in recognition of services rendered in connection with the coronation, from the Earl Marshal of England to the private soldiers taking part in the ceremonial parades. In more recent times the coronation medal has even been given to people who were not present at the ceremony but who performed notable public service in the coronation year.

Many other royal events have been commemorated by medals over the centuries. Royal weddings and the birth of the heir to the throne were regularly celebrated in this manner. Important anniversaries in long reigns have been the subject of numerous commemorative medals. The Golden Jubilee of George III in 1809-10, for example, resulted in over 30 different medals. Five times that number greeted the Golden Jubilee of Queen Victoria in 1887, but among them was an official medal intended for wear by those on whom it was conferred.

Even this, however, was not the first of the royal medals intended to be worn. This honour goes to a very large medal celebrating the proclamation of Victoria as Empress of India in 1877. Although fitted with a suspender bar and worn from a ribbon round the neck, it was not permitted for officers and men to wear this medal while in uniform. Later medals, however, were permitted to be worn when in uniform, but after other orders, decorations and campaign medals.

In the following listing (291A–291N) are the official Coronation Medals of James I, 1603, to Victoria, 1838. All were originally non-wearing, i.e. without suspension or ribbon, although some were later pierced or fitted with suspension for wearing. **Values are for silver medals only.**

291A. JAMES I CORONATION MEDAL

Date: 1603.
Metal: Silver.
Size: 28mm.
Description: (Obverse) Bust of King James I facing right. Legend: IAC: I: BRIT: CAE: AVG: HAE CAESArum cae D.D. (Reverse) Lion rampant facing left. Legend: ECCE PHA(R)OS POPVLIQ(VE) SALVS (Behold a lighthouse and safety of the people)

VALUE:
Silver: £320–450

291B. CHARLES I CORONATION MEDAL

Date: 1626.
Metal: Gold, silver.
Size: 28mm.
Designer: Nicholas Briot.
Description: Bust of Charles I facing right. Legend: CAROLVS. I. DG. MAG. BRITAN. FRAN. ET. HIB. REX. (Reverse) An arm issuing from a cloud and holding a sword. Legend: DONEC. PAX. REDDITA. TERRIS. (As long as Peace returns to the lands).

VALUE: Silver: £300–400

291C. CHARLES I CORONATION MEDAL

Date: 1633 (Scottish Coronation)
Metal: Gold, silver.
Size: 28mm.
Designer: Nicholas Briot.
Mintage: Gold (3), silver (Unknown)
Description: Bust of Charles I facing left. Legend: CAROLVS DG SCOTIAE. ANGLIAE. FR. ET. HIB. REX. (Reverse) A rose bush surmounted by a thistle. Legend: HINC. NOSTRAE. CREVERE. ROSAE (From this our roses abound). Exergue: CORON. 18 JVNII 1633

VALUE: Silver: £280–350

291D. CHARLES II CORONATION MEDAL

Date: 1651 (Scottish Coronation).
Metal: Gold, silver.
Size: 31mm.
Designer: Sir James Balfour.
Description: Bust of Charles II facing right. Legend: CAROLVS.2. D.G. SCO. ANG. FRA. ET. HI. REX. FI. DE. cor. i. ia. scon. 1651. (Reverse) Lion rampant facing left, holding a thistle. Legend: NEMO. ME. IMPVNE. LACESSET (No one touches me with impunity).

VALUE: Silver: £300–400

291E. CHARLES II CORONATION MEDAL

Date: 1661 (English Coronation).
Metal: Gold, silver.
Size: 30mm.
Designer: Thomas Simon.
Description: Bust of Charles II facing right. Legend:
  CAROLVS .II.DG ANG. SCO. FR. ET. HI REX.
  (Reverse) Charles II, wearing royal robe, seated on
  throne facing left, holding sceptre. Angel hovering
  over him placing crown on his head. Legend:
  EVERSO. MISSVS. SVCCVRRERE. SECLO. XXIII APR.
  1661 (the times having been turned upside down, he
  has been sent to succour us)

VALUE: Silver: £120–220

291F. JAMES II CORONATION MEDAL

Date: 1685.
Metal: Gold, silver, copper (?)
Size: 34mm.
Designer: John Roettier.
Mintage: Gold (200), silver (800), copper
  (Unknown).
Description: Bust of James II facing right, laureate.
  Legend: JACOBVS. II. D.G. ANG. SCO. FR. ET.
  HI. REX. (Reverse) Hand holding the crown
  above a laurel branch resting on a pillow.
  Legend: A. MILITARI. AD. REGIAM. (from
  soldiering to the palace). Exergue:
  INAVGVRAT. 23. AP. 1685.

VALUE: Silver: £250–350

291G. WILLIAM AND MARY CORONATION MEDAL

Date: 1689.
Metal: Gold, silver, lead.
Size: 34mm.
Designer: John Roettier.
Mintage: Gold (515), silver (1,200), lead
  (Unknown).
Description: Conjoint busts of William and Mary
  facing right. Legend: GVLIELMVS. ET. MARIA.
  REX. ET. REGINA. (Reverse) Two-horse vehicle
  lower left, Jove in cloud above right. Legend:
  NE TOTVS ABSVMATVR. (let not the whole be
  consumed). Exergue: INAVGVRAT. II. AP.
  1689.

VALUE: Silver: £180–280

291H. ANNE CORONATION MEDAL

Date: 1702.
Metal: Gold, silver, base metal.
Size: 34mm.
Designer: John Croker.
Mintage: Gold (858), silver (1,200), base metal (Unknown).
Description: Bust of Queen Anne facing left. Legend: ANNA. D:G: MAG: BR. FR. ET. HIB: REGINA. (Reverse) Pallas Athene, left, with shield and lightning bolts, attacking recumbent monster, right. Legend: VICEM GERIT. ILLA. TONANTIS. Exergue: INAVGVRAT. XXIII. AP. MDCCII. (As, making sounds, she conducts herself).

VALUE: Silver: £130–200

291I. GEORGE I CORONATION MEDAL

Date: 1714.
Metal: Gold, silver, base metal.
Size: 34mm.
Designer: John Croker
Mintage: Gold (330), silver (1,200), base metal (Unknown).
Description: Bust of George I facing right. Legend: GEORGIVS. DG. MAG. BR. FR. ET. HIB. REX. (Reverse) Seated King, left, being crowned by Britannia standing right. Exergue: INAVGVRAT. XX. OCT. MDCCXIIII.

VALUE: Silver: £140–200

291J. GEORGE II CORONATION MEDAL

Date: 1727.
Metal: Gold, silver, base metal.
Size: 34mm.
Designer: John Croker
Mintage: Gold (238), silver (800), base metal (Unknown)
Description: Bust of George II facing left. Legend: GEORGIVS. II. D.G. MAG. BR. FR. ET. HIB. REX. (Reverse) King seated on throne, left being crowned by Britannia, standing right. Legend: VOLENTES. PER. POVLOS (through the will of the people) Exergue: CORON. XI. OCTOB. MDCCXXVII.

VALUE: Silver: £140–220

291K. GEORGE III CORONATION MEDAL

Date: 1761.
Metal: Gold, silver, bronze
Size: 34mm.
Designer: Lorenz Natter.
Mintage: Gold (858), silver (800), bronze
(unknown)
Description: Bust of George III facing right.
Legend: GEORGIVS. III. D.G. M. BRI. FRA. ET.
HIB. REX. F.D. (Reverse) Britannia standing
left, crowning King seated right. Legend:
PATRIAE. OVANTI. (Crowned as the country
rejoices). Exergue: CORONAT. XXII. SEPT.
CI ƆIƆ CCLXI

VALUE: Silver: £250–350

291L. GEORGE IV CORONATION MEDAL

Date: 1821.
Metal: Gold, silver, bronze
Size: 35mm.
Designer: Benedetto Pistrucci.
Mintage: Gold (1,060), silver (800), bronze
(unknown, over 1,525)
Description: Bust of George IV, laureate, facing
left. Legend: GEORGIVS IIII D.G.
BRITANNIARUM REX F.D. (Reverse) Three
standing ladies, left, facing seated King, right.
Behind King stands angel holding crown
above his head. Legend: PROPRIO JAM JURE
ANIMO PATERNO (already by special right,
inaugurated in the spirit of his father).
Exergue: INAUGURATUS DIE JULII. XIX
ANNO. MDCCXXI.
Comments: *A slightly smaller and thinner version of
this medal was struck and pierced for suspension
from a plain maroon ribbon. These medals are
invariably named to members of the
Buckinghamshire Yeomanry Cavalry Hussars who
took part in lining the route of the procession. This
is believed to be the first coronation medal designed
to be worn.*

VALUE: Gold £90–150
Silver £100–120
Bronze £80–100

291M. WILLIAM IV CORONATION MEDAL

Date: 1831.
Metal: Gold, silver, bronze
Size: 34mm.
Designer: William Wyon
Mintage: Gold (1,000), silver (2,000), bronze
(1,133)
Description: Head of William IV facing right.
Legend: WILLIAM THE FOURTH CROWNED
SEP: 8 1831 (Reverse) Head of Queen Adelaide
facing right. Legend: ADELAIDE. QUEEN
CONSORT. CROWNED SEP: 8 1831.

VALUE: Silver: £100–160

291N. VICTORIA CORONATION MEDAL

Date: 1838.
Metal: Gold, silver, bronze.
Size: 36mm.
Designer: Benedetto Pistrucci.
Mintage: Gold (1,369), silver (2,209), bronze (1,871)
Description: Head of Queen Victoria facing left. Legend: VICTORIA D.G. BRITANNIARUM REGINA F.D. (Reverse) Three ladies symbolic of England, Scotland and Ireland, standing left, presenting crown to Queen, seated on a dais, right. A lion lies behind her chair. Legend: ERIMUS TIBI NOBILE REGNUM (We shall be a noble Kingdom to you). Exergue: INAUGURATA DIE JUNII XXVIII MDCCCXXXVIII.

VALUE:　　　Gold　£600–800
　　　　　　Silver　£90–120
　　　　　　Bronze £70–90

292. EMPRESS OF INDIA MEDAL

Date: 1877.
Ribbon: 42mm crimson edged in gold.
Metal: Gold or silver.
Size: 58mm.
Description: (Obverse) a left-facing bust of Queen Victoria wearing a veil and a coronet, her name and the date of her elevation being inscribed round the circumference. (Reverse) a broad zigzag border enclosing the words EMPRESS OF INDIA and its equivalent in Urdu and Hindi across the field.
Comments: *Issued to celebrate the proclamation of Victoria as Empress of India on 1 January 1877. It was awarded in gold to Indian princes and high-ranking British officials. Indian civilians and selected officers and men of the various British and Indian regiments serving in India at the time were awarded the silver medal. It was issued unnamed but many examples were subsequently engraved or impressed privately.*

VALUE:		*Miniature*
Gold	£2000–2500	£250–350
Silver	£285–375	£100–150

292A. VISIT OF THE PRINCE OF WALES TO INDIA MEDAL 1875

Date: 1875–76.
Ribbon: 38mm plain white.
Metal: Gold, silver or white metal with a silver crown.
Size: Oval 48mmx77mm.
Description: (Obverse) left-facing effigy of the Prince of Wales (later King Edward VII) surrounded by a laurel wreath and surmounted by a crown fitted to a suspension ring; (reverse) Prince of Wales's emblem surrounded by the chain of the GCSI.
Comments: *A large oval medal was struck to commemorate the state visit of HRH the Prince of Wales to India. Some 48 medals were struck in gold, 165 in silver and an unknown number in white metal. The gold medals are impressed on the rim with a small numeral, and engraved with the recipient's name in block capitals. The medals were numbered and named in strict order of precedence. The silver medal has a frosted relief on a mirror table, serially numbered on the edge but not named. 13 small silver badges were also presented. In addition a small silver medalet was issued with an obverse similar to the reverse of the large medal but with the initials A and E either side and a reverse inscribed HRH ALBERT EDWARD PRINCE OF WALES 1875–76.*

VALUE:

Gold (48)	£7000–8000
Silver (165)	£1000–1500
White metal	£200–250
Silver badge (13)	Rare
Silver medalet	—

293. JUBILEE MEDAL 1887

Date: 1887.
Ribbon: Broad central blue band with wide white stripes at the edges.
Metal: Gold, silver or bronze.
Size: 30mm.
Description: (Obverse) the bust of Queen Victoria by Sir Joseph Edgar Boehm; (reverse) an elaborate wreath in which are entwined the heraldic flowers of the United Kingdom. This encloses an eight-line inscription surmounted by a crown: IN COMMEMORATION OF THE 50th YEAR OF THE REIGN OF QUEEN VICTORIA 21 JUNE 1887. The reverse was designed by Clemens Emptmayer.

Comments: *Struck to celebrate the 50th anniversary of Victoria's accession to the throne. The medal in gold was given to members of the Royal Family and their personal guests. The silver medal was given to members of the Royal Household, government ministers, senior officials, distinguished foreign visitors, naval and military officers involved in the Jubilee parade on 21 June 1887 and the captains of vessels taking part in the great Naval Review at Spithead. The bronze medal was given to selected NCOs and men who took part in the parade or the Spithead Review. All medals were issued unnamed with a ring for suspension. When the Diamond Jubilee was celebrated ten years later holders of the 1887 medal were given a clasp in the form of a cable entwined around the date 1897 and surmounted by an imperial crown. Twin loops at the ends enabled the clasp to be sewn on to the ribbon.*

VALUE:

	without clasp	with clasp	*Miniature*
Gold	£1100–1300	Rare	£25–30
Silver	£75–85	£110–120	£15–20 (add £30 for clasp)
Bronze	£65–75	£100–110	£15–20 (add £30 for clasp)

294. JUBILEE (POLICE) MEDAL 1887

Date: 1887.
Ribbon: Plain dark blue.
Metal: Bronze.
Size: 36mm.
Description: (Obverse) the veiled profile of Queen Victoria; (reverse) a wreath surmounted by a crown and enclosing the inscription: JUBILEE OF HER MAJESTY QUEEN VICTORIA. The year appears at the foot and the name of the force round the top.
Comments: *Issued to all ranks of the Metropolitan and City of London Police involved in the parades and celebrations on 21 June 1887. Medals are believed to have been issued with the inscription POLICE AMBULANCE round the top but confirmation of this is required. Clasps for 1897 were likewise issued ten years later.*

VALUE:

	without clasp	with clasp	*Miniature*
Metropolitan Police (1400)	£20–25	£25–35	£15–20
City of London Police (900)	£40–50	£30–40	£15–20
			(add £5 for clasp)

295. JUBILEE MEDAL 1897

Date: 1897.
Ribbon: Dark blue with two broad white bands and dark blue edges.
Metal: Gold, silver or bronze.
Size: 30mm.
Description: This medal is very similar to the 1887 issue, differing solely in the date and anniversary on the reverse. Around 980 medals were awarded to army officers.

VALUE:

		Miniature
Gold (73)	£850–1000	—
Silver (3040)	£75–80	£12–15
Bronze (890)	£75–80	£12–15

296. JUBILEE MEDAL (MAYORS AND PROVOSTS) 1897

Date: 1897.
Ribbon: White with two broad dark blue bands and white edges.
Metal: Gold or silver.
Size: Height 48mm; max. width 40mm.
Description: A diamond-shaped medal with ring suspension, reminiscent of the *Klippe* coinage of central Europe. Both sides had circular centres with trefoil ornaments occupying the angles. (Obverse) the Wyon profile of the young Victoria at the time of her accession; (reverse) Sir Thomas Brock's Old Head veiled bust of the Queen.
Comments: *The gold version was presented to Lord Mayors and Lord Provosts while the silver medal was granted to Mayors and Provosts. Small silver medals of more conventional circular format were produced with these motifs and sold as souvenirs of the occasion.*

VALUE:

		Miniature
Gold (14)	Rare	£180–200
Silver (512)	£250–300	£80–120

297. JUBILEE (POLICE) MEDAL 1897

Date: 1897.
Ribbon: Plain dark blue.
Metal: Bronze.
Size: 36mm.
Description: Very similar to the 1887 issue with the dates suitably amended and the name of the service round the top of the reverse.
Comments: *Separate issues were made in respect of the Police Ambulance service, St John Ambulance Brigade and the Metropolitan Fire Brigade. Holders of the previous medal merely received the 1897 clasp.*

VALUE:		*Miniature*
Metropolitan Police (7500)	£16–20	£15–20
City of London Police (535)	£40–50	£15–20
Police Ambulance (210)	£180–200	£30–35
St John Ambulance Brigade (910)	£60–70	£20–25
Metropolitan Fire Brigade (950)	£60–70	£50–70

298. CEYLON DIAMOND JUBILEE MEDAL 1897

Date: 1897.
Ribbon: Plain red.
Metal: Gold or silver.
Size: 35mm.
Description: (Obverse) the Boehm bust of Queen Victoria with the dates 1837-1897 at the foot. (Reverse) an elephant and a stupa (dome-shaped Buddhist shrine), with two lines of concentric inscriptions: TO COMMEMORATE SIXTY YEARS OF HER MAJESTY'S REIGN and, unusually, THE RT. HON. SIR J. WEST RIDGEWAY K.C.B., K.C.M.G., GOVERNOR. A crown above the rim was fixed to a ring for suspension.
Comments: *Awarded to local dignitaries and leading officials in the Ceylon government.*

VALUE:		*Miniature*
Gold	Rare	£300–350
Silver	£200–250	£100–120

299. HONG KONG DIAMOND JUBILEE MEDAL

Date: 1897.
Ribbon: Three equal bands of dark blue, maroon and dark blue.
Metal Silver, possibly also bronze.
Size: 36mm.
Description: (Obverse) the Boehm bust of Queen Victoria with the date 1897 at the foot; (reverse) a seascape with a British three-masted sailing ship and a Chinese junk in the background and two figures shaking hands in the foreground. The name of the colony appears at the top, while two concentric inscriptions read SIR WILLIAM ROBINSON G.C.M.G. GOVERNOR and TO COMMEMORATE SIXTY YEARS OF HER MAJESTY'S REIGN 1837-1897.
Comments: *Very little is known for certainty about this medal, on account of the fact that the colonial records were destroyed during the Japanese occupation.*

VALUE:	
Silver	£300–400
Bronze	£180–230

299A. LAGOS DIAMOND JUBILEE MEDAL

Date: 1897.
Ribbon: Dark blue with two broad white stripes towards the edges.
Metal Silver.
Size: 34mm.
Description: (Obverse) the veiled crowned profile of Queen Victoria (similar to the Egypt Medal 1882, No. 131) inscribed VICTORIA QUEEN AND EMPRESS with a Tudor rose at the foot; (reverse) QUEEN'S DIAMOND JUBILEE LAGOS round the circumference, with JUNE 22ND 1897 in the centre.
Comments: *Issued to civil and military personnel associated with the Diamond Jubilee celebrations in the crown colony of Lagos (1886–1906 when it was incorporated in the colony and protectorate of Southern Nigeria).*

VALUE: Rare

300. VISIT TO IRELAND MEDAL 1900

Date: 1900.
Ribbon: Plain dark blue.
Metal: Bronze.
Size: 36mm.
Description: (Obverse) a half-length version of the Boehm bust of Queen Victoria; (reverse) the female allegorical figure of Hibernia looking out over Kingstown (Dun Laoghaire) harbour in which the Royal Yacht can be seen (far left). Unusually, the medal was mounted with a suspension bar decorated with shamrocks.
Comments: *The medal designed by G. W. de Saulles commemorated Queen Victoria's visit to Ireland in 1900. It was awarded to officers of the Royal Irish Constabulary and Dublin Metropolitan Police who were involved in security and policing the various events connected with the visit. The medal was worn with the same ribbon as the Jubilee Police medals.*

VALUE:
　　　Bronze (2285)　　£60–70　　*Miniature*　　£35–40

300A. VISIT TO THE COLONIES MEDAL 1901

Date: 1901.
Ribbon: Unknown.
Metal: Silver.
Size: Oval 20 x 24mm.
Description: (Obverse) a crowned anchor with the royal garter and rose emblem inset; (reverse) inscribed T.R.H. DUKE & DUCHESS OF CORNWALL & YORK—BRITISH COLONIES 1901 H.M.S. OPHIR.
Comments: *This small medalet was issued to commemorate the visit of the Duke and Duchess of Cornwall and York to the British Colonies aboard HMS Ophir in 1901.*

VALUE: —

301. CORONATION MEDAL 1902

Date: 1902.
Ribbon: Dark blue with a central red stripe and white edges.
Metal: Silver or bronze.
Size: Height 42mm; max. width 30mm.
Description: (Obverse) the left-facing conjoined busts of King Edward VII and Queen Alexandra, both crowned and wearing coronation robes. (Reverse) the crowned royal cypher above the date of the actual ceremony. The medal has an elaborate raised rim decorated with a wreath culminating in a crown through which the ring for suspension was looped.
Comments: *This medal, designed by Emil Fuchs and struck by Messrs. Elkington & Co., celebrated the coronation of King Edward VII on 9 August 1902. It was presented in silver to members of the Royal Family, foreign dignitaries, high officials of the government, senior officials and service officers involved in the celebrations. Selected NCOs and other ranks of the Army and Navy taking part in the parades were awarded the medal in bronze. Both versions were issued unnamed.*

VALUE:			*Miniature*
Silver (3493)	£60–65		£10–12
Bronze (6054)	£40–50		£10–12

302. CORONATION MEDAL (MAYORS AND PROVOSTS) 1902

Date: 1902.
Ribbon: Dark blue with a narrow white central stripe and crimson borders.
Metal: Silver.
Size: 32mm.
Description: (Obverse) conjoined right-facing busts of the King and Queen; (reverse) the crowned cypher and date. It differed from the ordinary medal by having flat, broad borders decorated with the heraldic flowers of the United Kingdom culminating at the top in a simple suspension ring.
Comments: *The medal was designed by Emil Fuchs and struck by Messrs. Elkington & Co.*

VALUE:
Silver	£120–130	*Miniature*	£40–60

303. CORONATION (POLICE) MEDAL 1902

Date: 1902.
Ribbon: Red, with a narrow dark blue central stripe.
Metal: Silver or bronze.
Size: 36mm.
Description: (Obverse) the left-facing bust of King Edward VII; (reverse) a crown above a nosegay of heraldic flowers with the words CORONATION OF HIS MAJESTY KING EDWARD VII 1902 in the upper field. The name or initials of the service appeared round the top, LCC MFB signifying London County Council Metropolitan Fire Brigade.
Comments: *Issued to all ranks of the police and associated services involved in the coronation celebrations, and awarded in silver or bronze to officers and other ranks respectively. Thje medal was designed by G. W. de Saulles.*

VALUE:	Silver	*Miniature*	Bronze	*Miniature*
Metropolitan Police	£250–300 (51)	£15–20	£12–15 (16,700)	£15–20
City of London Police	£500–600 (5)	£15–20	£40–45 (1060)	£15–20
LCC MFB	£350–400 (9)	£30–35	£40–50 (1000)	£35–50
St John Ambulance Brigade	—	£15–20	£40–50 (912)	£15–20
Police Ambulance Service	—	£30–35	£200–220 (204)	£35–50

304. CEYLON CORONATION MEDAL 1902

Date: 1902.
Ribbon: Plain blue.
Metal: Gold.
Size: 35mm.
Description: (Obverse) a crowned left-facing bust of King Edward VII; (reverse) the elephant and stupa motif previously used. The concentric inscription on the reverse now tactfully omitted any reference to the governor: IN COMMEMORATION OF THE CORONATION OF H.M. KING EDWARD VII 1902. The medal was fitted with a ring for suspension.
Comments: *Like its predecessor, this rare medal was struck for presentation to local dignitaries and government officials.*

VALUE:
    Gold   Rare   *Miniature*   —

305. HONG KONG CORONATION MEDAL 1902

Date: 1902.
Ribbon: None officially designated.
Metal: Silver and Bronze.
Size: 36mm.
Description: (Obverse) conjoined right-facing busts of King Edward VII and Queen Alexandra with their names round the circumference; (reverse) the maritime motif of the Diamond Jubilee medal with new inscriptions in two concentric curves: SIR HENRY A. BLAKE G.C.M.G. GOVERNOR (inner) and TO COMMEMORATE THE CORONATION OF THEIR MAJESTIES THE KING & QUEEN (outer). Fitted with a suspension ring.
Comments: *Issued to all British and Indian officers and other ranks serving in the colony as well as local police. Some 6,000 medals were produced by Edmonds & Son, London, and issued in cases.*

VALUE:
    Bronze   £45–65
    Silver   £140–180

305A. NATAL CORONATION MEDAL 1902

Date: 1902.
Ribbon: Dark blue with a central claret stripe.
Metal: Silver.
Size: 29mm and 51mm.
Description: (Obverse) a right-facing crowned bust of King Edward VII with the inscription TO COMMEMORATE THE CORONATION OF KING EDWARD VII: (reverse) Royal coat of arms above two running wildebeests, inscribed (round top) EDWARDUS DEI GRATIA BRITANNIAR REX F:D and (round bottom) COLONY OF NATAL 26 JUNE 1902. Ring suspension.
Comments: *Issued unnamed to native chiefs. The larger medal was issued without suspension.*

VALUE: 29mm   £100–150
               51mm   £300–400

306. DELHI DURBAR MEDAL 1903

Date: 1903.
Ribbon: Pale blue with three dark blue stripes.
Metal: Gold or silver.
Size: 38.5mm.
Description: (Obverse) a right-facing crowned bust of the King Emperor with DELHI DARBAR 1903 on the right side; (reverse) a three-line inscription in Farsi across the field, which translates as "By grace of the Lord of the Realm, Edward, King, Emperor of India, 1901", with an elaborate border of roses, thistles, shamrocks and Indian flowers. Ring suspension.
Comments: *Struck to celebrate the Durbar of the King Emperor at Delhi on 1 January 1903. It was awarded in gold to the rulers of the Indian princely states and in silver to lesser dignitaries, government officials, and officers and other ranks of the armed services actually involved in the celebrations.*

VALUE:

		Miniature
Gold (140)	£800–1000	—
Silver (2567)	£85–110	£15–20

307. VISIT TO SCOTLAND MEDAL 1903

Date: 1903.
Ribbon: Plain red.
Metal: Bronze.
Size: 36mm.
Description: Very similar to the Police Coronation medal but the year was changed to 1903 and the inscription SCOTTISH POLICE appeared round the top of the reverse. The medal was named to the recipient on the rim. An ornate clasp decorated with a thistle was worn above the suspension bar.
Comments: *This medal was designed by G. W. de Saulles and struck to commemorate Their Majesties' post-coronation tour of Scotland in May 1903. It was awarded to the police and troops involved in parades and escort duties, as well as the ancillary services such as the Fire Brigade and the St Andrew's Ambulance Association.*

VALUE:

Bronze (2957)	£55–60	*Miniature*	£30–40

308. VISIT TO IRELAND MEDAL 1903

Date: 1903.
Ribbon: Pale blue.
Metal: Bronze.
Size: 36mm.
Description: (Obverse) bust of King Edward VII; (reverse) as 1900 medal with the date altered at the foot. The suspension brooch is ornamented with shamrocks.
Comments: *This medal was designed by G. W. de Saulles and struck to mark the King's visit to Ireland in July 1903. It was awarded on the same terms as the Visit to Ireland Medal 1900.*

VALUE:

Bronze (7757)	£60–70	*Miniature*	£35–45

308A. VISIT OF THE PRINCE AND PRINCESS OF WALES TO INDIA

Instituted: 1905–06

Ribbon: Neck ribbon 55mm wide, maroon with wide blue stripes towards each edge.

Metal: Frosted silver.

Size: 46mm.

Description: (Obverse) conjoined busts of the Prince and Princess of Wales (later King George V and Queen Mary), facing right. ELKINGTON (manufacturers) inscribed below busts. (Reverse) badge of the Prince of Wales surrounded by the chain of the GCSI, with legend T.R.H. THE PRINCE & PRINCESS OF WALES VISIT TO INDIA 1905–6.

Comments: *Only 72 medals were struck, 70 of which were bestowed on British and Indian officials.*

VALUE: £300–400   *Miniature:*   £25–30

308B. GEORGE PRINCE OF WALES MEDAL

Instituted: 1905-06.

Ribbon: 15mm, red, white and blue in equal parts.

Metal: Silver or gold.

Size: Oval 20 x 24mm.

Description: (Obverse) the Prince of Wales's plumes surrounded by the Garter and the chain and badge of the GCSI, flanked in the field by the letters G and M; (reverse) inscription T.R.H. GEORGE PRINCE OF WALES & VICTORIA MARY PRINCESS OF WALES with INDIA 1905-6 in the upper centre.

Comments: *The 26 gold medals were given by Their Royal Highnesses to their personal staff, while a total of 1,625 silver medals were presented to all hands aboard HMS* Renown *and* Terrible *and the Royal Yacht* Osborne.

VALUE:

Gold (26)	£800–1000
Silver (1625)	£80–120

309. CORONATION MEDAL 1911

Date: 1911.

Ribbon: Dark blue with two thin red stripes in the centre.

Metal: Silver.

Size: 32mm.

Description: (Obverse) conjoined left-facing busts of King George V and Queen Mary in their coronation robes within a floral wreath; (reverse) the crowned royal cypher above the date of the coronation itself. Plain ring suspension.

Comments: *Designed by Sir Bertram McKennal, MVO, ARA, these medals were issued unnamed but may sometimes be found with unofficial engraving. Those who were also entitled to the Delhi Darbar Medal received a crowned clasp inscribed DELHI if they had previously been awarded the coronation medal. This was the first occasion that the medal might be awarded to those not actually present at the ceremony itself.*

VALUE: *Miniature:*

Silver (15,901)	£30–35	£5–10
Clasp Delhi (134)	£80–100	£55–30

310. CORONATION (POLICE) MEDAL 1911

Date: 1911.
Ribbon: Red with three narrow blue stripes.
Metal: Silver.
Size: 32mm.
Description: (Obverse) a crowned left-facing bust of King George V; (reverse) an imperial crown with an ornate surround. The inscription CORONATION 1911 appears at the foot and the name of the service at the top. Ring suspension.
Comments: *By now the number of police and ancillary services had grown considerably, as witness the various reverse types which may be encountered in this medal. The medal was designed by Sir Bertram McKennal, MVO, ARA,*

VALUE: *Miniature*

Metropolitan Police (19,783)	£10–15	£12–15
City of London Police (1400)	£40–50	£12–15
County and Borough Police (2565)	£65–75	£15–20
Police Ambulance Service*	£280–320	£30–35
London Fire Brigade (1374)	£40–50	£25–30
Royal Irish Constabulary (585)	£70–80	£30–50
Scottish Police (280)	£90–100	£30–50
St John Ambulance Brigade*	£40–50	£12–15
St Andrew's Ambulance Corps*	£120–150	£40–50
Royal Parks (109)	£240–280	£40–50

* A total of 2623 medals was awarded to these three services, the Police Ambulance medal being the scarcest and St John Ambulance medal the commonest.

311. VISIT TO IRELAND MEDAL 1911

Date: 1911.
Ribbon: Dark green with thin red stripes towards either end.
Metal: Silver.
Size: 36mm.
Description: Very similar to the foregoing, distinguished only by the reverse which is inscribed CORONATION 1911 round the top, with the actual date of the visit round the foot.
Comments: *This medal was designed by Sir Bertram McKennal, MVO, ARA and was granted to prominent civic dignitaries and members of the Irish police forces involved in the royal visit to Ireland which took place on 7-12 July 1911.*

VALUE:
    Silver (2477)   £50–75   *Miniature*   £25–30

311A. EAST INDIAN RAILWAY COMPANY ROYAL VISIT TO INDIA MEDAL 1911

Date: 1911.
Ribbon: Dark blue with a central maroon stripe flanked by narrow gold stripes.
Metal: Gilded bronze.
Size: 32mm.
Description: (Obverse) the arms of the East Indian Railway Company surrounded by the inscription EAST INDIAN RAILWAY COMPANY with a winged wheel at the foot; (reverse) a ten-line inscription FOR SERVICES RENDERED DURING THE RAILWAY JOURNEYS OF THEIR MAJESTIES THE KING EMPEROR AND QUEEN EMPRESS IN INDIA 1911.
Comments: *Very little is known about this rare medal, but it is believed to have been awarded to members of the Honour Guard of the East Indian Railway Volunteer Rifle Corps and employees of the company present during the tour of India undertaken in 1911 by King George V and Queen Mary. It is believed that no more than 30 medals were issued.*

VALUE: £100–£120

312. DELHI DURBAR MEDAL 1911

Date: 1911.
Ribbon: Dark blue with two narrow red stripes in the middle.
Metal: Gold or silver.
Size: 38.5mm.
Description: (Obverse) the conjoined crowned busts of King George V and Queen Mary in a floral wreath; (reverse) an elaborate Farsi text which translates as "The Durbar of George V, Emperor of India, Master of the British Lands".
Comments: *This medal marked the Delhi Durbar held in the King Emperor's honour in December 1911. Most of the gold medals went to the Indian princely rulers and top government officials, 10,000 of the 30,000 silver medals were awarded to officers and other ranks of the British and Indian Armies for exemplary service, without their necessarily being present at the Durbar itself.*

VALUE:		*Miniature*
Gold (200)	£800–850	—
Silver (30,000)	£35–45	£6–10

312A. VISIT OF KING GEORGE V AND QUEEN MARY TO INDIA 1911–12

Date: 1911–12.
Ribbon: None.
Metal: Silver.
Size: Oval 20 x 24mm.
Description: (Obverse): GRI entwined initials as a monogram above the dates 1911–12; (reverse) MRI monogram and dates, suspended from a bar by a simple ring and scroll suspender.

VALUE: £40–60

312B. VISIT OF THE PRINCE OF WALES TO INDIA 1921–22

Date: 1921–22.
Ribbon: Neck ribbon 55mm maroon with broad blue stripes towards each edge.
Metal: Frosted silver.
Size: 50mm.
Description: (Obverse) bust of Prince of Wales facing left with inscription EDWARD PRINCE OF WALES INDIA 1921–1922; (reverse) badge of the Prince of Wales surrounded by the chain of the GCSI. Fitted with a plain suspension ring.
Comments: *Only 84 medals were awarded in connection with the visit of HRH the Prince of Wales (later King Edward VIII and Duke of Windsor) to India in the course of his world tour aboard HMS Renown.*

VALUE: £500–650   *Miniature*   £40–60

312C. WELCOME HOME MEDAL FOR THE PRINCE OF WALES

Date: 1922.
Ribbon: Green with red central stripe.
Metal: Bronze.
Size: 35mm.
Description: Oval.
Comments: *Struck by F. Bowcher to mark the return of the Prince of Wales to England after his world tour.*

VALUE: £50–65

312D. VISIT OF THE PRINCE OF WALES TO BOMBAY MEDAL 1921

Date: 1921.
Ribbon: Not known.
Metal: Bronze.
Size: Oval 38mm x 30mm.
Description: An oval medal. (Obverse) bust of the Prince of Wales facing right, with the inscription EDWARD PRINCE OF WALES and surmounted by the Prince of Wales's feathes and motto ICH DIEN; (reverse) VISIT OF HIS ROYAL HIGHNESS BOMBAY NOVEMBER 1921 in six lines.
Comment: *Presented to the leading military and civil dignitaries present during the visit of the Prince of Wales. The number issues is not known but is believed to be very small.*

VALUE: £60–£80

313. JUBILEE MEDAL 1935

Date: 1935.
Ribbon: Red with two dark blue and one white stripes at the edges.
Metal: Silver.
Size: 32mm.
Description: (Obverse) left-facing conjoined half-length busts of King George V and Queen Mary in crowns and robes of state; (reverse) a crowned GRI monogram flanked by the dates of the accession and the jubilee.
Comments: *This medal, designed by Sir William Goscombe John, RA, was issued to celebrate the Silver Jubilee of King George V and widely distributed to the great and good throughout the Empire.*

VALUE:
   Silver (85,234)   £20–25   *Miniature*   £6–10

313A. ISLE OF MAN SILVER JUBILEE MEDAL 1935

Date: 1935.
Ribbon: Three equal stripes of red, white and blue. However some medals had their ribbons substituted with black to mark the death of the King in 1936.
Metal: Silver.
Size: 32mm.
Description: (Obverse) conjoined busts of King George V and Queen Mary in an inner circle surrounded by the legend KING GEORGE V & QUEEN MARY REIGNED 25 YEARS; (reverse) Triskelion emblem with the legend IN COMMEMORATION OF THE SILVER JUBILEE 1935. Suspended from a brooch bar of seven overlapping panels. The centre panel has the royal cypher GvR while the outer panels have two leaves in each.
Comments: *This medal is an unofficial issue struck to celebrate the Silver Jubilee. It is included here as it was apparently presented to civic dignitaries and officials in the island.*

VALUE: £100–120

314. CORONATION MEDAL 1937

Date: 1937.
Ribbon: Blue edged with one red and two white stripes.
Metal: Silver.
Size: 32mm.
Description: (Obverse) conjoined busts of King George VI and Queen Elizabeth in their robes of state without any inscription. The stark simplicity of this motif was matched by a reverse showing the crowned GRI over the inscription CROWNED 12 MAY 1937, with the names of the King and Queen in block capitals round the circumference.
Comments: *Issued to celebrate the coronation of King George VI on 12 May 1937.*

VALUE:
    Silver (90,000)   £20–25   *Miniature*   £6–10

315. CORONATION MEDAL 1953

Date: 1953.
Ribbon: Dark red with two narrow blue stripes in the centre and narrow white edges.
Metal: Silver.
Size: 32mm.
Description: (Obverse) a right-facing bust of Queen Elizabeth II in a Tudor crown and robes of state, the field being otherwise plain. (Reverse) a similar crown over the royal monogram EIIR with the legend QUEEN ELIZABETH II CROWNED 2ND JUNE 1953 round the circumference. Ring suspension.
Comments: *This medal celebrated the coronation of Queen Elizabeth II on 2 June 1953. News that Edmund Hillary and Sherpa Tenzing had successfully attained the summit of Everest reached London on the morning of the Coronation. Subsequently the members of the Hunt Expedition were invited to Buckingham Palace on 16 July 1953 where, on Her Majesty's own initiative, they were presented with coronation medals engraved MOUNT EVEREST EXPEDITION on the rim, following the precedent of the Mwele medals of 1895–96.*

VALUE:
		Miniature
Silver (129,000)	£25–30	£5–10
Mount Everest Expedition (37)	£600	

315A. ROYAL VISIT TO NEW ZEALAND MEDAL 1953-54

Date: 1953.
Ribbon: Dark blue.
Metal: Copper-coloured alloy.
Size: 38mm.
Description: (Obverse) right-facing crowned bust of Queen Elizabeth II wearing Tudor crown; (reverse) the crowned New Zealand coat of arms surrounded by sprays of flowers and the inscription ELIZABETH II ROYAL VISIT 1953–54. The copper-coloured medal is hung by a ring from a scalloped suspender as illustrated.
Comment: *Issued to all New Zealand school-children in 1953, accompanied by a folder telling the story of the Royal Family, with pictures of the Cornonation regalia, royal palaces and descriptions. The medals themselves are fairly common, but those with the accompanying folder are very rare.*

VALUE: £2–3

316. JUBILEE MEDAL 1977

Date: 1977.
Ribbon: White with thin red stripes at the edges, a broad blue stripe in the centre and a thin red stripe down the middle of it.
Metal: Silver.
Size: 32mm.
Description: (Obverse) Right-facing profile of Queen Elizabeth II wearing the St Edward's crown—the first time this design was employed; (reverse) a crown and wreath enclosing the words THE 25TH YEAR OF THE REIGN OF QUEEN ELIZABETH II 6 FEBRUARY 1977. A distinctive reverse was used in Canada, showing the dates of the reign flanking the royal monogram round the foot, CANADA round the top and a large stylised maple leaf in the centre.
Comments: *The 25th anniversary of the Queen's accession was marked by the release of this unnamed medal.*

VALUE:		*Miniature*
General issue (30,000)	£130–150	£6–10
Canadian issue (30,000)	£70–90	£6–10

316A. QUEEN ALEXANDRA'S CHILDREN'S BANQUET MEDAL 1914

Date: 28 December 1914.
Ribbon: White, with red stripes at each edge.
Metal: Bronze.
Size: 38mm.
Description: (Obverse) bust of Queen Alexandra facing right with the inscription A GIFT FROM QUEEN ALEXANDRA; (reverse) central inscription FEAR GOD, HONOUR THE KING surrounded by the legend GUILDHALL BANQUET TO OUR SOLDIERS' & SAILORS' CHILDREN 28th DEC. 1914. The suspension is ornate and has the arms of the City of London superimposed.
Comments: *This medal, designed and manufactured by Elkington, was issued unnamed to 1,300 children and a small number of Chelsea pensioners who attended a banquet at the Guildhall on 28 December 1914. The children, between the ages of eight and thirteen, were the sons and daughters of men in the Fleet or on the Western Front. One child was chosen from each family by Sir James Gildea of the Soldiers' and Sailors' Families' Association. Relatively few medals appear to have survived.*

VALUE: £50–£70

WE ARE LOOKING FOR NEW MEMBERS

THE LIFE SAVING AWARDS
RESEARCH SOCIETY

THREE JOURNALS ISSUED PER YEAR

CURRENT SUBSCRIPTIONS

UNITED KINGDOM – £10.00 ($15.00)
OVERSEAS – £12.00 ($20.00)

APPLY TO:

THE MEMBERSHIP SECRETARY

"LITTLE SADLERS"
10 UPPER EDGEBOROUGH ROAD,
GUILDFORD, SURREY GU1 2BG
UNITED KINGDOM

Medals for Saving Life

Until the establishment of the government's own gallantry awards for the saving of life (the Sea Gallantry Medal (Foreign Services), instituted in 1841 and the Sea Gallantry Medal of 1854 and the Albert Medal of 1866), it was left entirely to private individuals and organizations to reward those who risked their own lives to save the lives of others. Although the medals granted from the late eighteenth century onwards are unofficial, they are of considerable human interest and are now very much sought after, preferably with the citations, diplomas, printed testimonials and other collateral material. The most commonly found of these medals are listed in broadly chronological order of their institution. However, listed below is the very wide range of Institutions and other bodies who have issued or continue to give awards for life saving, as currently known to the Life Saving Awards Research Society. The Society would be very pleased to hear from readers of this Yearbook of any that are not on the list. Many of the following awards are as yet incompletely researched, and it is our intention to include many of these in this section when the research has been completed by the Life Saving Awards Research Society.

LIFE SAVING SOCIETY / FUNDS

Royal Humane Society
Bolton & District Humane Society
Bristol Humane Society
Carnegie Hero Fund Trust
Fleetwood Humane Society
Glasgow Humane Society
Grimsby Humane Society
The Hundred of Salford Humane Society
Jersey Humane Society
Liverpool Shipwreck & Humane Society
Norfolk Humane Society
Northants Humane Society
Port of Plymouth Humane Society
The Royal National Lifeboat Institution
The (Royal) Society for the Protection of Life from Fire
The Royal Life Saving Society (Mountbatten Medal)
Shipwrecked Fishermen & Mariners Royal Benevolent Society
Suffolk Humane Society
Tayleur Fund
Tynemouth Trust

NEWSPAPERS/MAGAZINES

The Quiver Medal
Answers Medal
Associated Newspapers Medal
Daily Herald (Order of Industrial Heroism)
Daily Sketch Medal
Fleet (For Merit) Medal
Golden Penny Medal
Pluck Medal
Post Office Magazine (St. Martin's Medal)
Ally Sloper's Medal
To-Day (Gallantry Fund) Medal

MUNICIPAL AUTHORITIES

Birmingham Fire Medal
Dundee Corporation Medal for Bravery
Folkestone Bravery Medal
The Corporation of Glasgow Bravery Medal
Liverpool Corporation Medal for Bravery
Metropolitan/LCC/London Fire Brigade Bravery Medal
Plymouth City Police Bravery Medal
Southend-on-Sea Pier Department Life Saving Medal
The Strathclyde Bravery Medal

The Golden Penny Award and the Liverpool Corporation Medal for Bravery

YOUTH ORGANISATIONS

The Boys Brigade
The Girl Guides Association
The Scouts Association

ANIMAL SOCIETIES

Dumb Friends League
National Canine Defence League
Peoples Dispensary for Sick Animals
Royal Society for the Prevention of Cruelty to
    Animals

COMMERCIAL ORGANISATIONS

Castle Mail Steam Packet Co.
Imperial Chemical Industries
Lever Brothers
Lloyds
Silk Cut Awards

NON-COMMERCIAL ORGANISATIONS

Imperial Merchant Services Guild
Mercantile Marine Service Association
St. Andrews Ambulance Association Bravery Medal
Order of St. John of Jerusalem Life Saving Medal
Shipping Federation

SPECIFIC RESCUES

Indian Chief Medal (Ramsgate Medal)
CQD Medal
SS Drummond Castle
SS Lusitania (Wanderer)
Osip Medal
HMS Niger Meda (Deal)
Henry Vernon Crew Fund Medal

COLLIERY DISASTERS

Little Hulton 1866
Hamstead Colliery 1908
Hartley Colliery 1862
Hulton Coliery 1910
Sacriston Colliery 1903

OTHER DISASTERS

Glasgow Plague Medal 1900
Maidstone Typhoid Medal 1897
Moray Floods Medal 1829

RAILWAYS

London, Midland & Scottish Railway
London & North Eastern Railway
London Passenger Transport Board
Midland Railway
Southern Railway

PRIVATE AWARDS

Too numerous to mention—but each a tale of heroism in
its own right!

Maidstone Typhoid Medal 1897.

To-day (Gallantry Fund) Medal.

Ally Sloper's Medal.

*Illustrated are just some of the
medals that are currently being
researched by the Life Saving
Awards Research Society and
which it is hoped will feature in
forthcoming issues of the
MEDAL YEARBOOK.*

317. ROYAL HUMANE SOCIETY MEDALS

Date: 1774.

Ribbon: None (1774-1869); plain navy blue (1869); thin central yellow stripe and white edges added (silver medal, 1921).

Metal: Gold, silver or bronze.

Size: 51mm (1774-1869); 38mm (1869-).

Description: (Obverse) a cherub, nude but for a flowing cloak, blowing on a burnt-out torch explained by the Latin legend LATEAT SCINTILLVLA FORSAN (perhaps a tiny spark may be concealed). A three-line Latin text across the exergue reads SOC. LOND. IN RESUSCITAT INTERMORTUORUM INSTIT. with the date in roman numerals. (Reverse) an oak wreath containing the engraved details of the recipient and the date of the life-saving act. Round the circumference is a Latin motto HOC PRETIVM CIVE SERVATO TVLIT (He has obtained this reward for saving the life of a citizen). When the rescue attempt was unsuccessful, however, the medal was granted without this inscription. Later medals of similar design were struck also in bronze.

Comments: *The society was formed in 1774 for the specific purpose of diffusing knowledge about the techniques of resuscitation and saving life from drowning. From the society's inception large medals were struck in gold or silver. Monetary rewards, medals, clasps and testimonials were granted to those who saved life, or attempted to save life from drowning, but later the society's remit was broadened to include "all cases of exceptional bravery in rescuing or attempting to rescue persons from asphyxia in mines, wells, blasting furnaces or in sewers where foul air may endanger life".*

Although not intended for wear, the large medals were often pierced or fitted with a ring or bar for suspension from a ribbon. The details of the recipient and the act were engraved on the reverse.

In 1869 permission was given for the medals to be worn. As a result the diameter was reduced to 38mm and a scroll suspension was fitted for wear with a navy blue ribbon. At the same time the Latin text of the "unsuccessful" and "successful" medals was altered to read VIT. PERIC. EXPOS. D.D. SOC REG. HVM. (the Royal Humane Society presented this gift, his life having been exposed to danger) and VIT. OB. SERV. D.D. SOC, REG. HVM. (the Royal Humane Society presented this gift for saving life) respectively. Details of the recipient and the act were engraved on the rim. In 1921 the ribbon of the silver medal was changed to navy blue with a central yellow stripe and white edges, but the plain navy blue ribbon was retained for the bronze medal. Scrolled clasps with the initials R.H.S. were awarded for subsequent acts of lifesaving.

In 1873 the Stanhope Gold Medal, in memory of Captain C.S.S. Stanhope, RN, was instituted for award to the person performing the bravest act of life-saving during the year. The first Stanhope medals were similar to the society's small silver medal, differing only in the addition of a clasp inscribed STANHOPE MEDAL and the year, but since 1937 the Stanhope Medal has been identical to the other medals, differing solely in the metal. In 1921, however, the ribbon for the Stanhope Gold Medal was changed to one of navy blue with yellow and black edges.

VALUE:	Gold	Silver	Bronze
Large successful	—	£220–300	£80–130
Large unsuccessful	—	£250–350	£100–150
Small successful	—	£150–250	£60–100
Small unsuccessful	—	£180–280	£75–130
Stanhope Gold Medal	£1750–2200	—	—
Miniature	£250–300	£20–25	£15–20

317A. GLASGOW HUMANE SOCIETY MEDAL

Instituted: 1780.
Ribbon:
Metal: Gold or silver.
Size: 42mm.
Description: (Obverse) a naturalistic treatment of the elements of the Glasgow civic arms: the tree that never grew, the bird that never flew, the fish that never swam and the bell than never rang, with edge inscription GLASGOW HUMANE SOCIETY INSTITUTED 1780; (reverse) PRESENTED BY THE GLASGOW HUMANE SOCIETY TO above a horizontal tablet engraved with the name of the recipient; below: FOR INTREPIDITY OF COURAGE AND SUCCESS IN SAVING THE LIFE OF A FELLOW CITIZEN.
Comments: *Awarded mainly for saving people from drowning in the Clyde and Kelvin rivers, but also for rescues in the Firth of Clyde.*

VALUE:

Gold:	Rare	
Silver:	£500–700	

318. HUNDRED OF SALFORD HUMANE SOCIETY MEDALS

Date: 1824.
Ribbon: Plain dark blue.
Metal: Gold, silver or bronze.
Size: 32mm (circular type); height 49mm; max. width 41mm (cruciform type).
Description: Circular silver or bronze medals were awarded from 1824 onwards, with the recipient's name and details engraved on the reverse, and featuring a cherub kindling a spark similar to the Royal Humane Society's medal, on the obverse. Around the time of the society's centenary in 1889, however, a more elaborate type of medal was devised, with the circular medal superimposed on a cross of distinctive shape, so that the society's name could be inscribed on the arms. The recipient's details are again found on the reverse.
Comments: *This society was formed in 1789 to serve the needs of the Salford and Manchester area. After a few years it was dissolved, but was revived again in 1824. These awards ceased in 1922.*

VALUE:

	Gold	Silver	Bronze	Miniature
Circular medal	Rare	£150–180	£100–130	—
Cruciform medal	—	£90–120	—	—

If you know of a British Life Saving medal that is not included in the MEDAL YEARBOOK we would be delighted to hear from you.

Or if you can supply us with a photograph of any of the medals not illustrated in this publication we would be pleased to include it next year.

If you can help, please contact the Managing Editor, John Mussell, telephone 01404 46972 or at the address on page 1. Thank you!

319. ROYAL NATIONAL LIFEBOAT INSTITUTION MEDAL

Date: 1825.
Ribbon: Plain blue.
Metal: Gold, silver or bronze.
Size: 36mm.
Description: The first medals bore the effigy of George IV on the obverse and it was not until 1862 that this was replaced by a garlanded profile of Victoria by Leonard C. Wyon. Medals portraying Edward VII and George V were introduced in 1902 and 1911 respectively, but when permission to portray George VI was refused in 1937 the RNLI adopted a profile of its founder, Sir William Hillary, instead. All but the Edwardian medals have a reverse showing a drowning seaman being rescued by three men in a boat with the motto LET NOT THE DEEP SWALLOW ME UP. The Edwardian medals have the seated figure of Hope adjusting the lifejacket on a lifeboatman. The twin-dolphin suspension (first fitted in the 1850s) has a plain blue ribbon, and clasps inscribed SECOND SERVICE, THIRD SERVICE and so on are awarded for subsequent acts of gallantry.
Comments: *The RNLI was founded, as the Royal National Institution for the Preservation of Life from Shipwreck, on 4 March 1824 and began awarding medals the following year to "persons whose humane and intrepid exertions in saving life from shipwreck on our coasts are deemed sufficiently conspicuous to merit honourable distinction". Its title changed to the Royal National Lifeboat Institution in 1854.*

VALUE:	Gold	Silver	Bronze
George IV	£1200–1500	£250–300	—
Victoria	£1200–1500	£250–300	—
Edward VII	£1800–2200	£800–1000	—
George V	£1500–2000	£400–500	£300–400
Hillary	£2000–2500	£500–600	£300–400

319A. ROYAL NATIONAL LIFEBOAT INSTITUTION CROSS

Date: 7 May 1901.
Ribbon: Blue watered silk.
Metal: Gold, or silver with enamels.
Size:
Description: A wavy cross in dark blue enamel, with the initials RNLI in the angles interlaced with a rope, surmounted by a Royal Crown fitted with a ring for suspension. First Class (gold) and Second Class (silver).
Comments: *The original decoration, designed by Charles Dibdin, the RNLI Secretary, was instituted as a reward for Branch Honorary Secretaries and Ladies Auxiliaries for long and devoted service. 36 awards were made initially, followed by 18 other awards in 1902–9. Thereafter a new decoration, awarded to men and women in two classes, was proposed. Designed by Mr Burke of the College of Heralds and manufactured by Garrards in 1912. Objections raised by King George V led to the cross being discontinued on May 14, 1914, by which time only ten gold awards had been made and no silver awards, the latter known only as a sample in the RNLI archives. No record of the design of the 1901–09 award has been preserved.*

VALUE: —

320. MEDALS OF THE SOCIETY FOR THE PROTECTION OF LIFE FROM FIRE

Date: 1836.
Ribbon: Plain scarlet.
Metal: Silver or bronze.
Size: 52mm (I and II), 45mm (III), 42mm (IV &V) and 40mm (VI).
Description: The first medal (type I) had a radiate eye in garter on the obverse and a reverse giving the recipient's details in an oak-leaf wreath. They were fitted with a ring suspender. The Society was granted the Royal title in 1843 and a new medal (type II) was adopted the following year, with the word ROYAL added and the date at the foot of the obverse changed to 1844. In the early 1850s type III was introduced, with an obverse of a man carrying a woman away from a fire. This and type IV (1892) were struck in silver or bronze. As royal patronage ended with the death of Queen Victoria, a new medal (type V) was required in 1902 without the Royal title. Types IV and V show a man rescuing a woman and two children from a fire. The reverse of this medal has the words DUTY AND HONOR within a wreath, the recipient's details being placed on the rim. Type VI , awarded from 1984, is a bronze medal without suspension with the recipient's details engraved on the reverse.

VALUE:			Silver	Bronze
I	Eye and garter (1836)		£500–600	—
II	Eye and garter (1844)		£500–600	—
III	Man and woman (1850s)		£220–300	Rare
IV	Man, woman and children (1892)		£350–450	Rare
V	As type IV but "Royal" removed (1902)		£200–250	£150–200
VI	As type IV but details on rev.		—	Rare
Miniature (type IV)			£60–80	—

321. LLOYD'S MEDAL FOR SAVING LIFE AT SEA

Date: 1836.
Ribbon: Blue, striped white, red and white in the centre.
Metal: Gold, silver or bronze.
Size: 73mm or 36mm.
Description: Both large and small medals had similar motifs. (Obverse) the rescue of Ulysses by Leucothoe; (reverse) an ornate wreath.
Comments: *The first medals, introduced in 1836, had a diameter of 73mm and were not intended for wear, but in 1896 the diameter was reduced to 36mm and a ring fitted for suspension with a ribbon.*

VALUE:			*Miniature*
	Large silver	£450–550	—
	Large bronze	£250–350	—
	Small silver	£250–350	£60–80
	Small bronze	£200–250	£40–50

322. LIVERPOOL SHIPWRECK AND HUMANE SOCIETY'S MARINE MEDALS

Date: 1839.
Ribbon: Plain dark blue.
Metal: Gold, silver or bronze.
Size: 54mm (type I), 45mm x 36mm (oval, type II) or 38mm (type III).
Description: (Obverse) a man on a spar of wreckage, taking an inert child from its drowning mother, with the stark legend LORD SAVE US, WE PERISH. This motif was retained for smaller, oval medals (type II) introduced around 1867 with the name of the Society round the edge, and a simple wreath reverse. The suspender was mounted with the Liver Bird emblem. A smaller circular version (type III) was adopted in 1874/75 and fitted with a scroll suspender. In this type the Liver Bird appeared in a wreath on the reverse. Bars engraved with the details were awarded for subsequent acts of life-saving. In addition to the general Marine medals there were distinctive awards in connection with specific marine rescues and funded separately. These had the type III obverse, but the reverse was inscribed CAMP & VILLAVERDE or BRAMLEY-MOORE. A glazed silver medal inscribed IN MEMORIAM was granted to the next of kin of those who lost their lives while attempting to save the lives of others.
Comments: *The Society was formed in 1839 to administer funds raised to help and reward those who distinguished themselves in saving life as a result of a hurricane which swept the Irish Sea in January of that year. The first medals were struck in 1844 and presented for rescues dating back to November 1839. They were large (54mm) in diameter, without suspension.*

VALUE:

	Gold	Silver	Bronze
Large (54mm) 1844	Rare	£250–350	—
Oval 1867	—	£400–450	—
Small (38mm) 1874/5	£1200–1500	£60–150	£60–120
Camp & Villaverde	—	£450–600	£400–450
Bramley-Moore	—	£450–600	£400–450
In Memoriam	—	£600–700	—
Miniature **(type III)**	—	£90–100	—

323. SHIPWRECKED FISHERMEN AND MARINERS ROYAL BENEVOLENT SOCIETY MEDAL

Date: 1851.
Ribbon: Navy blue.
Metal: Gold or silver.
Size: 36mm.
Description: (Obverse) the Society's arms; (reverse) inscribed PRESENTED FOR HEROIC EXERTIONS IN SAVING LIFE FROM DROWNING with a quotation from Job 29: 13 at the foot. The circumference is inscribed ENGLAND EXPECTS EVERY MAN WILL DO HIS DUTY, a quotation from Lord Nelson's signal to the fleet at Trafalgar, 1805. The first medals had a straight suspender but by 1857 a double dolphin suspender had been adopted (five variations of this suspender can be identified). Details of the recipient's name and the date of the rescue are engraved on the edge.
Comments: *The Society was founded in 1839 to raise funds for shipwrecked fishermen and mariners and the families of those lost at sea.*

VALUE		Gold	Silver
	Straight suspender	Rare	£180–250
	Dolphin suspender	Rare	£180–250
	Miniature	—	£90–100

324. TAYLEUR FUND MEDAL

Date: 1854.
Ribbon: Dark blue.
Metal: Gold or silver.
Size: 45mm.
Description: (Obverse) a sinking ship with the legend TAYLEUR FUND FOR THE SUCCOUR OF SHIPWRECKED STRANGERS; (reverse) details of the award engraved.
Comments: *In January 1854 the emigrant ship* Tayleur *foundered in Bantry Bay, Ireland. A fund was started for the relief of the survivors and the surplus used to issue silver life-saving medals. The first awards were made in 1861. Medals are known to have been awarded for eight separate rescues, the last in 1875. In December 1913 the residue of the Tayleur Fund was transferred to the RNLI and the issue of medals terminated.*

VALUE:

Gold (2)	Rare
Silver (37)	£350–550

325. HARTLEY COLLIERY MEDAL

Date: 1862.
Ribbon: None.
Metal: Gold or silver.
Size: 53mm
Description: (Obverse) an angel with mine rescuers and disaster victims. Details of the award were engraved on the reverse.
Comments: *Some 204 miners perished in the disaster which overtook the Hartley Colliery, Northumberland on 10 January 1862. This medal was awarded to those involved in the rescue operations.*

VALUE:

Gold (1)	Rare
Silver (37)	£250–350

325A. MERCANTILE MARINE SERVICE ASSOCIATION MEDAL

Date: 1872.
Ribbon: Blue.
Metal: Gold (2) and silver (74).
Size: 38mm.
Description: The obverse has a border with the legend "MERCANTILE MARINE SERVICE ASSOCIATION". In the centre are two seated figures of Neptune and Britannia. Neptune has a shield decorated with an anchor; Britannia a shield decorated with a sailing ship. Between the two figures are Cornucopias, Mercury's staff and a Liver bird. Beneath the two figures are the words "INCORPOR-ATED BY SPECIAL ACT OF PARLIAMENT", and the maker's name Elkington & Co. Liverpool. The reverse bears a wreath containing the engraved details of the incident and the recipient's name.
Comments: *The medal was instituted by the MMSA in 1875 but the first awards were made retrospectively for rescues in 1872. The award was generally given to the Master and senior officers of ships engaged in life saving actions, but towards the end of its issuance some of the recipients were not officers. The last known award was made in 1906.*

VALUE:

Gold	Silver
—	£350–450

326. LIFE SAVING MEDAL OF THE ORDER OF ST JOHN

Date: 1874.
Ribbon: Black, embroidered with the eight-point cross in white (1874), black watered silk (1888), white inner and red outer stripes added, separated by a black line(1950) which was subsequently removed in 1954.
Metal: Gold, silver or bronze.
Size: 36mm.
Description: The first medals had a plain eight-pointed cross of the Order on the obverse with the legend AWARDED BY THE ORDER OF ST JOHN OF JERUSALEM IN ENGLAND. A second type of medal was adopted in 1888 and showed two tiny lions and two tiny unicorns in the interstices of the cross, the reverse shows sprigs of St John's wort and the legend FOR SERVICE IN THE CAUSE OF HUMANITY. Clasps for further awards were instituted in 1892.
Comments: *Instituted on 15 December 1874 and awarded for gallantry in saving life, these medals were originally granted in bronze or silver, but gold medals were also struck from 1907.*

VALUE:

	Gold	Silver	Bronze
1st type 1874	—	£600–800	£400–500
2nd type 1888	Rare	£600–800	£400–500
Miniature	—	£40–50	£30–40

327. LIVERPOOL SHIPWRECK AND HUMANE SOCIETY'S FIRE MEDAL

Date: 1883.
Ribbon: Plain scarlet.
Metal: Gold, silver or bronze.
Size: 38mm.
Description: (Obverse) a fireman descending the stairs of a burning house carrying three children to their kneeling mother, her arms outstretched to receive them. (Reverse) the wreathed Liver Bird previously noted for the third type of Marine medal. The medal is fitted with a scroll suspender. Clasps engraved with the details are awarded for subsequent acts.
Comments: *The first recipient was William Oversly in November 1883, for rescuing a child from a burning house. The first woman recipient was Miss Julia Keogh (12 February 1895) who saved two children in a house fire.*

VALUE:

	Gold	Silver	Bronze
Fire medal	Rare	£250–300	£150–180
Miniature	—	£40–50	£40–50

328. LLOYD'S MEDALS FOR MERITORIOUS SERVICE

Date: 1893.
Ribbon: Red with blue stripes towards the edges (1893); blue with broad white stripes towards the edges (since 1900).
Metal: Silver or bronze.
Size: 36mm x 38mm (star), 39mm x 29mm (oval), 36mm (circular).
Description: The original medal was a nine-pointed rayed star in bronze with the arms of Lloyd's on the obverse, suspended by a ring from a red ribbon with blue stripes towards the edge. A silver oval medal was introduced in 1900 with Lloyd's arms on the obverse and details of the recipient engraved on the reverse. This medal was fitted with a twin dolphin suspender and a blue ribbon with broad white stripes towards the edge. A third type, introduced in 1913, was a circular medal, struck in silver or bronze, with Lloyd's shield on the obverse. The fourth type, still current, was introduced in 1936 and has the full arms, with crest, motto and supporters, on the obverse. The ribbon is suspended by a ring.
Comments: *These medals have been awarded to officers and men for extraordinary services in the preservation of vessels and cargoes from peril.*

VALUE:

	Silver	Bronze
Star 1893	—	£100–120
Oval 1900	£400–450	—
Circular 1913	£320–350	£280–320
Circular 1936	—	—
Miniature (circular)	£60–80	—

329. LIVERPOOL SHIPWRECK AND HUMANE SOCIETY'S GENERAL MEDAL

Date: 1894.
Ribbon: Five equal stripes, three red and two white.
Metal: Gold, silver or bronze.
Size: 38mm.
Description: (Obverse) a cross pattee with a wreathed crown at the centre and the legend FOR BRAVERY IN SAVING LIFE with the date 1894 at the foot; (reverse) the wreathed Liver Bird of the Marine medal, type III. Fitted with an ornate bar suspender. Bars for subsequent awards are granted.
Comments: *The first award was made on 9 June 1894 to Constables Twizell and Dean who were both injured whilst stopping runaway horses.*

VALUE:

	Gold	Silver	Bronze
General medal	Rare	£200–250	£150–200
Miniature	—	£80–100	—

329A. QUIVER MEDAL

Date: c.1897.
Ribbon: Dark blue, with a broad diagonal white stripe.
Metal: Silver (29) or bronze (29).
Size: 38mm.
Description: A thick medal weighing two ounces. (Obverse) a naked figure holding a rescued child, with the winged skeletal figure of Death hovering over a stormy sea in the background; (reverse) a laureated tablet bearing the name of the recipient and the date of the act. The circumference is inscribed round the top: FOR HEROIC CONDUCT IN THE SAVING OF LIFE and THE QUIVER MEDAL round the foot. The very elaborate suspension ring is in the form of a laurel wreath and is fitted to the suspender bar by means of a scroll inscribed THE QUIVER MEDAL. Brooch mounting at top of ribbon.
Comments: *The popular Victorian magazine* Quiver *took a keen interest in promoting safety at sea and organised a Lifeboat Fund which provided not only a number of lifeboats named* Quiver *but also this gallantry award. At least 58 silver and bronze medals were awarded of which four were presented to the survivors of the Margate surf boat disaster on December 2, 1897. A specially struck medal (odf a different design) was awarded by* Quiver *to Captain Inch of "Volturne" fame.*

VALUE: £200–250

330. DRUMMOND CASTLE MEDAL

Date: 1896.
Ribbon: Plain crimson.
Metal: Silver.
Size: 38mm.
Description: (Obverse) the veiled profile of Queen Victoria; (reverse) a wreath enclosing the name of the ship and the date of its sinking with the legend FROM QUEEN VICTORIA A TOKEN OF GRATITUDE. Fitted with a scrolled suspender.
Comments: *Presented on behalf of Queen Victoria by officials from the British Embassy in Paris to inhabitants of Brest, Ushant and Molene for their generosity and humanity in rescuing and succouring the survivors of the SS* Drummond Castle *which struck a reef off Ushant on 16 June 1896. Of the 143 passengers and 104 crew, all but three perished. 282 medals were struck and 271 of these were awarded to those who helped save the living and assisted in the recovery and burial of the victims.*

VALUE:

    Silver (282)   £200–250   *Miniature*   —

331. CARNEGIE HERO FUND MEDAL

Date: 1908.
Ribbon: None.
Metal: Bronze.
Size: 90mm.
Description: (Obverse) an angel and a nude male figure surrounded by an inscription "HE SERVES GOD BEST WHO MOST NOBLY SERVES HUMANITY"; (reverse) two wreaths surrounding a central tablet inscribed "FOR HEROIC ENDEAVOUR TO SAVE HUMAN LIFE 19…" surrounding a further inscription "PRESENTED BY THE TRUSTEES OF THE CARNEGIE HERO FUND". Details of the recipient are engraved on the rim.
Comments: *The Carnegie Hero Fund Trust was established in Scotland by Andrew Carnegie in 1908. The first medallion was awarded posthumously on 26 November 1909 to Thomas Wright for a life saving act on 23 September 1908. To date 173 medallions have been awarded.*

VALUE:
    Bronze   £500–700

332. C.Q.D. MEDAL

Date: 1909.
Ribbon: Plain dark blue.
Metal: Silver.
Size: 45mm.
Description: (Obverse) the SS Republic with the initials C.Q.D. at the top; (reverse) the words FOR GALLANTRY across the middle, with a very verbose inscription round the circumference and continued in eight lines across the field. Ring suspension. Issued unnamed, but examples are known with the recipient's name and ship privately engraved.
Comments: *This medal takes its curious name from the CQD signal (Come Quick Danger) sent out by the Italian steamer* Florida *when it collided in thick fog with the White Star liner* Republic *on 21 January 1909. The liner* Baltic *responded to the call. The* Republic *was the more severely damaged vessel, but all of her passengers and crew were transferred, first to the* Florida *and then to the* Baltic, *before she sank. The saloon passengers of the* Baltic *and* Republic *subscribed to a fund to provide medals to the crews of all three ships in saving more than 1700 lives.*

VALUE:
    Silver   £200–250

333. RSPCA MARGARET WHEATLEY CROSS

Date: 1936.
Ribbon: 32mm blue with a white stripe towards each edge.
Metal: Bronze.
Size: 33mm square.
Description: Cross pattee with a central circular cross with rounded ends superimposed. R.S.P.C.A. across the top arm of the outer cross and INSTD. 1936 across the lower arm. THE MARGARET WHEATLEY CROSS inscribed in four lines across the centre. (Reverse) central circle inscribed FOR BRAVING DEATH ON BEHALF OF ANIMALS, above and below a raised horizontal panel engraved with the details of the award. Fixed ring for suspension.
Comments: *The RSPCA's highest award, it was named in memory of 16 year-old Margaret Wheatley who was killed by a train at Grange-over-Sands on June 4, 1936 while saving her dog who had got trapped on the railway line. She was posthumously awarded the RSPCA's Silver Medal and was also the first recipient of the cross named in her honour. To date, a total of 70 crosses have been awarded, at least 32 of them posthumously.*

VALUE: Rare

333A. RSPCA LIFE-SAVING MEDAL

Date: 1909.
Ribbon: Blue with three white stripes in the centre, the central stripe being narrower than the others (silver); blue with a central white stripe flanked by narrow red and white stripes (bronze).
Metal: Silver or bronze.
Size: 36mm.
Description: (Obverse) a seated female figure surrounded by a cow, sheep, cat, dog, goat and horse; (reverse) plain, with an inscription. The recipient's name usually appears on the rim. Both medals have a brooch bar inscribed FOR HUMANITY.
Comments: *Instituted in 1909 by the Royal Society for the Prevention of Cruelty to Animals, this medal is awarded in silver or bronze for acts of gallantry in saving the lives of animals.*

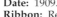

VALUE:			*Miniature*
Silver	£100–130		£20–25
Bronze	£80–100	£15–20	

334. SCOUT ASSOCIATION GALLANTRY MEDAL

Date: 1909.
Ribbon: Red (bronze), blue (silver) or half red, half blue (gilt).
Metal: Bronze, silver and gilt.
Size: 33mm.
Description: A cross pattée with the Scout fleur-de-lis emblem at the centre with the motto "BE PREPARED" and the words "FOR GALLANTRY" or "FOR SAVING LIFE". The name and details of the recipient are engraved on the plain reverse. Suspension is by a ring or straight bar. A plain bar is awarded for additional acts of gallantry.
Comments: *The Scout movement began informally in 1907 and the Boy Scouts Association was founded a year later. Gallantry awards were instituted in 1908 and 1909. The bronze cross is the highest award of the Association for gallantry, granted for special heroism or action in the favce of extraordinary risk. The silver cross is awarded for gallantry in circumstances of considerable risk. The gilt cross is awarded for gallantry in circumstances of moderate risk. A bar may be awarded to the holder of any gallantry award for further acts of gallantry in circumstances of similar risk.*

VALUE:	Bronze	£350–450
	Silver	£300–400
	Gilt	£200–300

334A. BOYS' BRIGADE CROSS FOR HEROISM

Date: September 1902.
Ribbon: Originally royal blue with two equal white stripes, but changed to plain royal blue in 1941.
Metal: Bronze.
Description: A cross pattee formed of four V-shaped finials linked to a circular disc inscribed the BOYS' BRIGADE CROSS FOR HEROISM and enclosing the emblem of the Boys' Brigade. The cross has a suspension ring and a plain brooch bar at the top of ribbon. There are two types, with or without a Geneva cross behind the anchor in the emblem (added in 1926 when the Boys' Life Brigade amalgamated with the Boys' Brigade).
Comments: *First awarded in 1904, the cross was awarded only 194 times up to the end of 1985, including five posthumous awards. Simon Herriott, aged 8, became the youngest holder in 1980.*

VALUE:	First type (without central cross)	Rare
	Second type (with central cross)	£500

334B. BOYS' LIFE BRIGADE MEDAL

Date:
Ribbon: Red.
Metal: Bronze.
Description: (Obverse) A Geneva cross within a crowned circle and a radiate background, the circle inscribed TO SAVE LIFE; a scroll round the foot inscribed THE BOYS LIFE BRIGADE; (reverse) personal details of the recipient. Fitted with a plain suspension ring. The brooch bar is the form of a scroll with a laurel wreath superimposed on the middle and a clasp bearing the date of the award.
Comments: *The Boys' Life Brigade amalgamated with the Boys' Brigade in 1926 and the award of this life-saving medal was then abolished.*

VALUE: Rare

335. CARPATHIA AND TITANIC MEDAL

Date: 1912.
Ribbon: Maroon.
Metal: Gold, silver or bronze.
Size: Height 40mm; max. width 35mm.
Description: The ornately shaped medal, in the best Art Nouveau style, has the suspension ring threaded through the head of Neptune whose long beard flows into two dolphins terminating in a fouled anchor and ship's spars. (Obverse) the Carpathia steaming between icebergs; (reverse) a twelve-line inscription, with the name of the manufacturer at the foot. It was worn from a straight bar suspender.
Comments: *This medal recalls one of the greatest tragedies at sea, when the White Star liner* Titanic *struck an iceberg on her maiden voyage and sank with the loss of 1490 lives. The 711 survivors were picked up by the* Carpathia *whose officers and men were subsequently awarded this medal in gold, silver or bronze according to the rank of the recipient.*

VALUE:	Gold (14)	£7000–10,000
	Silver (110)	£3000–6000
	Bronze (180)	£2500–4000

336. CORPORATION OF GLASGOW BRAVERY MEDAL

Date: 1924
Ribbon: Green with red edges.
Metal: Gold, silver or bronze.
Size: 38mm (type I) or 33mm (type II).
Description: Type I: (obverse) Fame blowing a trumpet and holding a laurel wreath in front of a circular scrolled cartouche inscribed FOR BRAVERY; (reverse) plain, engraved with the name and details of the recipient. Type II: (obverse) wreath enclosing the words "FOR BRAVERY"; (reverse) Arms of the Corporation of Glasgow and details of the recipient. Fitted with a ring suspension and an ornate thistle brooch inscribed GALLANTRY in a scroll.
Comments: *Following the reorganisation of local government in Scotland in 1975, the award ceased and was replaced by the Strathclyde Regional Council Medal for Bravery.*

VALUE:	Type I	Type II
Gold	£250–300	£250–300
Silver	£180–230	£180–230
Bronze	£100–150	—

337. LLOYD'S MEDAL FOR SERVICES TO LLOYDS

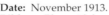

Date: November 1913.
Ribbon: Blue with broad white stripes towards the edge.
Metal: Silver.
Size: 36mm.
Description: (Obverse) Neptune in a chariot drawn by four horses; (reverse) an oak-leaf wreath enclosing a scroll inscribed FOR SERVICES TO LLOYD'S. Fitted with ring suspension.
Comments: *Instituted by Lloyd's Committee, this medal was intended to reward services of a general nature.*

VALUE:		Miniature
Gold (14)	£1500–2000	—
Silver (10)	£800–1000	£65–70

338. LLOYD'S MEDAL FOR BRAVERY AT SEA

Date: 1940.
Ribbon: White with broad blue stripes at the sides.
Metal: Silver.
Size: 36mm.
Description: (Obverse) a seated nude male figure holding a laurel wreath, extending his hand towards a ship on the horizon; (reverse) a trident surmounted by a scroll inscribed BRAVERY, enclosed in a wreath of oak leaves. It has a ring suspender.
Comments: *Instituted by Lloyd's Committee, it was awarded to officers and men of the Merchant Navy and fishing fleets for exceptional bravery at sea in time of war. A total of 523 medals was awarded up to December 1947 when it was discontinued.*

VALUE:			
Silver	£500–700	*Miniature*	£65–75

339. LIVERPOOL SHIPWRECK AND HUMANE SOCIETY'S SWIMMING MEDAL

Date: 1885
Ribbon: Five equal bars, three blue and two white.
Metal: Silver or bronze.
Size: Height 44mm; max. width 30mm.
Description: This extremely ornate medal has a twin dolphin suspender and a free form. (Obverse) a wreath surmounted by crossed oars and a trident, with a lifebelt at the centre enclosing the Liver Bird emblem on a shield; (reverse) plain, engraved with the recipient's name and details.
Comments: *Not granted for life-saving as such, but for proficiency in swimming and life-saving techniques.*

VALUE:

Silver	£40–60
Bronze	£30–50

340. BINNEY MEMORIAL MEDAL

Date: 1947.
Ribbon: None.
Metal: Bronze.
Size: 48mm.
Description: (Obverse) a bust of Captain R.D. Binney, CBE, RN; (reverse) inscription FOR COURAGE IN SUPPORT OF LAW AND ORDER and AWARDED TO above the recipient's name on a raised tablet.
Comments: *Instituted in memory of Captain Ralph Douglas Binney who was killed on 8 December 1944 in the City of London while attempting to apprehend two armed robbers single-handedly. It is awarded annually to the British citizen who displays the greatest courage in support of law and order within the areas under the jurisdiction of the Metropolitan Police and the City of London Police. The medal is not intended for wear. See MEDAL NEWS, August 1998 for a detailed article on the medal by Victor Knight.*

VALUE: Bronze   £400–600

340A. ORDER OF INDUSTRIAL HEROISM

Date: 1923.
Ribbon: Bright watered red.
Metal: Bronze.
Size: 28mm.
Description: (Obverse) a modern interpretation of St Christopher carrying Christ (by Eric Gill); (reverse) inscription ORDER OF INDUSTRIAL HEROISM around the perimeter and in the upper half AWARDED BY THE DAILY HERALD above the recipient's name and date of award.
Comments: *Created by the* Daily Herald *and first issued in 1923. It was given as a reward to the "workers" who demonstrated bravery in the workplace and was initially only to be awarded to members of a Trade Union. However, there are numerous examples of the awards being given to non Union members and the definition of "workplace" was wide. The award was intimately associated with the* Daily Herald *throughout the lifetime of the newspaper and when it ceased publication in 1963 the award was discontinued. The medal was always awarded with a certificate and a monetary award. 440 were awarded.*

VALUE: Bronze   £400–600

340B. TYNEMOUTH MEDAL

Date: 1895.
Ribbon: Dark blue.
Metal: Gold or silver.
Size: Silver 51mm (gold smaller).
Description: **Silver:** (obverse) a scene viewed from the north of King Edward's Bay at Tynemouth, with Pen Bal Crag surmounted by a lighthouse. In the left foreground is a ship, sinking by the stern and a lifeboat putting off into stormy seas to the rescue. Around the top is the inscription PALAM QUI MERUIT and around the bottom TYNEMOUTH MEDAL; (reverse) recipient's engraved name surrounded by a laurel wreath. The medal is suspended by a scroll suspender with an ornate bar. **Gold:.** The obverse is similar to the silver medal but has no motto and there are numerous changes to the scene. The reverse carries the motto on a large lifebuoy within which are the details of the recipient.
Comments: *The Tynemouth Medal Trust was formed in response to a request from Mr E. B. Convers, a New York lawyer, who had witnessed a rescue in the Tynemouth area. He was so impressed that he had a medal designed and produced and sent 100 silver medals to the Trustees to be awarded for acts of heroism to Tynesiders worldwide, or for acts of heroism in the Tyne and the surrounding area. A variant to the silver medal exists in which the reverse of the medal is inverted in relation to the suspender—this is known as the Tynemouth Extension Medal.*

VALUE:	Silver (approx. 100) £250–350	Gold	Rare

340C. HUMANE SOCIETY OF NEW ZEALAND MEDALS

Date: 1898.
Ribbon: Scarlet edged with broad beige stripes on which was embroidered gold fern leaves (1898–1914) or 32mm plain royal blue (from, 1915).
Metal: Gold, silver and bronze versions.
Size:
Description: Originally an eight-pointed cross with ball points, with a circular medallion at the centre showing two figures surrounded by an inscription ROYAL HUMANE SOCIETY at the top and NEW ZEALAND round the foot, the cross mounted on an oak wreath surmounted by a Royal Crown fitted with a plain ring for suspension. The reverse was engraved with the recipient's name, date and details of the award. The second type consists of a circular medal with (obverse) an allegorical life-saving scene, name of the Society round the top and FOR LIFE SAVING in two lines in the field; (reverse) a laurel wreath with the recipient's name and details engraved in the centre. Early versions of this medal had a scrolled swivel suspension bar but later versions had a plain suspension bar. The top of the ribbon is fitted with a plain brooch.
Comments: *Presented by the Governor General as Patron of the Royal Humane Society of New Zealand. Only one or two awards are made each year. The medal is worn on the right breast. Until 1913 the Society also awarded a special gold medal, known as the Stead Medal, for acts of outstanding bravery. It was similar to the gold medal but had a suspension bar inscribed STEAD MEDAL. It was revived in 1963 for award to unsuccessful nominees for the Stanhope Gold Medal.*

VALUE:	Gold	Silver	Bronze
Type I	£1,500 (6)	£1,000 (73)	£600 (89)
Type II	£1,200 (10)	£600 (82)	£400 (449)
Stead Gold Medal	Rare		

340D. THE DALE AWARD

Instituted: November 1940.

Ribbon: White with broad blue and narrow black stripes towards the edges.

Metal: Silver.

Size: 33mm.

Description: (Obverse) a central medallion enamelled in white bearing the spires of Coventry Cathedral, surrounded by an inscription: THE DALE AWARD/COVENTRY.NOV.14.1940; (reverse) a laurel wreath enclosing a ten-line inscription across the middle: AWARDED BY THE COVENTRY HOSPITAL FUND FOR DEVOTION TO HOSPITAL & AMBULANCE DUTY DURING THE COVENTRY AIR RAID NOVEMBER 14th 1940. The rim bears the Birmingham assay marks and maker's mark of Thomas Fattorini. The medal was not named.

Comments: *This medal is know to have been awarded to a St John's Ambulance driver but nothing further is known and details of the Dale Award and a list of recipients are sought.*

VALUE: —

340E. LONDON PASSENGER TRANSPORT BOARD MEDAL FOR BRAVERY

Instituted: 1940.

Ribbon: Red with green central stripe and four narrow white stripes on either side.

Metal: Cupro-nickel.

Size: 38mm.

Description: (Obverse) a naked man kneeling and turning a large wheel; (reverse) the words LONDON TRANSPORT above a sprig of laurel, with a space for the recipient's name and a three-line inscription across the foot: FOR BRAVERY AND DEVOTION TO DUTY. Plain suspension bar and an ornamental brooch fitment at the top of the ribbon.

Comments: *This medal was instituted by Lord Ashfield, Chairman of the LPTB, to reward "special deeds of bravery" undertaken by LTPB staff during the Blitz. Only nine medals were awarded (all presented on February 21, 1941) before the medal was discontinued, after some government pressure, to encourage nominations for the official civilian bravery awards of the George Cross and George Medal. A few unnamed specimens are known, possibly reaching the market from the stock of John Pinches when they ceased business.*

VALUE:

Named	Rare
Unnamed	£150

340F. LONDON, MIDLAND AND SCOTTISH RAILWAY MEDAL

Date: 1940.
Ribbon: Dark blue.
Metal: Silver.
Size: 38mm.
Description: (Obverse) Three different steam locomotive smoke stacks with a radiant sun in the right background with the inscription LONDON, MIDLAND AND SCOTTISH RAILWAY round the circumference; (reverse) a locomotive driving wheel on which is superimposed at the left a sprig of laurel, with the inscription FOR COURAGE or FOR MERIT round the top of the circumference. The date 1940 appears in the exergue. Fitted with a plain ring for suspension.
Comments: *Instituted by the Chairman of the LMS Company for acts of gallantry or meritorious service, hence the two different reverse types. The Chairman, Lord Stamp, was killed in an air raid in 1941 and it is believed that many of the records relating to this medal perished with him. Although the exact number of awards is not known, it is believed that about 20 awards were made.*

VALUE:

For courage	Rare
For merit	Rare

340G. SOUTHERN RAILWAY MERITORIOUS SERVICE MEDAL

Date: 1940.
Ribbon: Green with railway track and sleepers in gold.
Metal: Silver gilt.
Size: 38mm.
Description: (Obverse) a cross formy with SR in a circle at the centre, superimposed on a laurel wreath surrounded by a locomotive driving wheel; (reverse) FOR MERIT in seriffed capitals over a space for the recipient's name and SOUTHERN RAILWAY across the foot. The ornamental suspension bar is in the form of a vehicle spring. This medal was designed by Kruger Gray and struck at the Royal Mint.
Comments: *Instituted by the Directors of the Company for award to those employees who had been honoured by the King. 18 medals were awarded at a ceremony on August 16, 1940, and a further six medals were subsequently awarded.*

VALUE: Rare

340H. LONDON AND NORTH EASTERN RAILWAY GALLANTRY MEDAL

Date: 1941.
Ribbon: Dark blue with a central white stripe flanked by narrow white stripes.
Metal: Silver with a matt finish.
Size: 38mm.
Description: (Obverse) a shield containing the arms of the company, superimposed on a laurel wreath surrounded by the inscription LONDON AND NORTH EASTERN RAILWAY on a raised band; (reverse) a scroll for the recipient's name superimposed on a laurel wreath with the rising sun in the background. The raised band is inscribed FOR COURAGE AND RESOURCE. Fitted with a plain suspension bar and an ornamental brooch bar at the top of the ribbon.
Comments: *Awarded "for outstanding acts of gallantry and resource which are not connected with enemy action, but which are of such a standard as would warrant recommendations for Government recognition had the acts been connected with enemy action". As some of the medals were awarded for actions resulting from enemy air raids the phrase "not connected with enemy action" was very liberally interpreted. A total of 22 medals were awarded, the last in 1947.*

VALUE: Rare

340I. SHROPSHIRE SOCIETY LIFE SAVING MEDAL

Date: —
Ribbon: 30mm with two equal stripes of blue and yellow.
Metal: Silver.
Size: 50mm.
Description: (Obverse) a left-facing profile of Captain Matthew Webb whose name appears round the top, with the inscription BORN IN SHROPSHIRE 1848—SWAM THE CHANNEL 1875 round the foot. Fitted with a plain ring for suspension and a brooch bar at the top of the ribbon.
Comment: *Struck by John Pinches and presented by the Shropshire Society in London for outstanding acts of bravery in Shropshire. It is not known how many were awarded. An example of this medal, awarded in 1923, fetched £520 at Glendining's sale on March 28, 2001 against an estimate of £150–£200.*

VALUE: £500–700

340J. NEWFOUNDLAND SILVER STAR FOR BRAVERY

Date: 1897.
Ribbon: Two equal stripes of dark blue and crimson.
Metal: Silver.
Size: 36mm max.
Description: A six-pointed radiate star with ball ornaments in the interstices, surmounted by a circular medallion showing a ship in distress and having the inscription FOR BRAVERY AT SEA in a collar. Fitted with a plain ring for suspension.
Comment: *Originally instigated by the Governor of Newfoundland, Sir Terence O'Brien, in 1893, as a bravery award. A total of 27 were made. In 1897 three were awarded to those who assisted in putting out a fire on the SS Aurora which, loaded with dynamite, was docked in St John's Harbour, Newfoundland. These three were altered to have the name of SS Aurora added to the legend.*

VALUE: £750–1000

Miscellaneous Medals

Under this heading are grouped a very disparate range of medals whose only common denominator is that they do not fit conveniently into one or other of the preceding categories. They are not without considerable interest, the polar medals in particular having a very keen following and a buoyant market.

341. KING'S AND QUEEN'S MESSENGER BADGE

Date: 1722.
Ribbon: Garter blue.
Metal: Silver gilt.
Size: Earliest issues variable according to monarch and jeweller; since George V—45mm x 34mm.
Description: (Issues since George V) an upright oval fitted with a plain suspension ring and having a greyhound suspended by a ring from the foot of the rim. (Obverse) the Garter inscribed HONI SOIT QUI MAL Y PENSE enclosing the royal cypher; (reverse) plain, engraved with an official number of issue and, on occasion, the name of the messenger.
Comments: *Messengers can be traced back to 1199, but prior to George I badges were not issued. Few of the earlier badges can be found due to a hand in and melt down order instituted by George III in 1762. During the reign of Victoria a number of different shapes and sizes were used for the badges, due to a misunderstanding whereby individual messengers obtained their insignia from different jewellers instead of the Jewel Office. Since 1870 Garrards have been responsible for the design, submission and production of Messengers badges. From 1876 to 1951 the Foreign Office, as Controllers of the Corps of Messengers, purchased and held all badges for issue to those appointed as messengers. Since 1951 messengers, on satisfactorily completing a period of probation, are given a registered number and letter of permission to purchase their badges through the Crown Jewellers.*

VALUE:		
	George III	£1500–2000
	George IV	£1200–1500
	William IV	£1200–1500
	Victoria	£1000–1500
	Edward VII	£600–800
	George V	£500–700
	George VI	£500–700
	Elizabeth II	£600–800

342. ARCTIC MEDAL

Instituted: 30 January 1857.
Ribbon: 38mm plain white.
Metal: Silver.
Size: Height 46mm; max. width 32mm.
Description: An octagonal medal with a beaded rim, surmounted by a nine-pointed star (representing the Pole Star) through which the suspension ring is fitted. (Obverse) an unusual profile of Queen Victoria, her hair in a loose chignon secured with a ribbon. (Reverse) a three-masted sailing vessel amid icebergs with a sledge party in the foreground and the dates 1818-1855 in the exergue. The medal was issued unnamed, but is often found privately engraved.
Comments: *Awarded retrospectively to all officers and men engaged in expeditions to the polar regions from 1818 to 1855, including those involved in the on-going search for the ill-fated Franklin Expedition of 1845-8. Thus the medal was granted to civilians, scientists, personnel of the French and US Navies and employees of the Hudson's Bay Company who took part in a number of abortive search parties for Sir John Franklin and his crew. Some 1106 medals, out of 1486 in all, were awarded to officers and ratings of the Royal Navy.*

VALUE:
    Silver   £300–375   *Miniature* £150–200

343. ARCTIC MEDAL

Instituted: 28 November 1876.
Ribbon: 32mm plain white.
Metal: Silver.
Size: 36mm
Description: A circular medal with a raised beaded rim and a straight bar suspender. (Obverse) a veiled bust of Queen Victoria wearing a small crown, dated 1876 at the foot; (reverse) a three-masted ship icebound.

Comments: *Granted to officers and men of HM ships* Alert *and* Discovery *who served in the Arctic Expedition between 17 July 1875 and 2 November 1876. The medal was later extended to include the crew of the private yacht* Pandora *commanded by Allen Young which cruised in polar waters between 25 June and 19 October 1875 and from 3 June to 2 November 1876. Medals were impressed with the name and rank of the recipient. Only 170 medals were awarded.*

VALUE:
    Silver £900–1250 *Miniature* £200–250

344. POLAR MEDAL

Instituted: 1904.

Ribbon: 32mm plain white.

Metal: Silver or bronze.

Size: 33mm octagonal.

Description: (Obverse) the effigy of the reigning sovereign; (reverse) a view of the Royal Research Ship *Discovery* with a man-handling sledge party in the foreground.

Comments: *Originally issued in silver to officers and in bronze to petty officers and ratings, but the bronze medals were discontinued in 1939 and since then only silver medals have been awarded. On Scott's first expedition (1902–04) bronze medals were also awarded officers, including Evans of the Broke. Apart from the 1904 issue of bronze medals, all Polar Medals have been fitted with a clasp giving details of the service for which they were awarded. However, those receiving the bronze medal for the first time (21) in 1917 also had no clasp, the date being on the rim. Those already having a bronze medal (3) received a 1917 dated clasp. The 1904 bronze issue included four dated 1902–03, 23 dated 1902–04 and 33 1903–04. Only three women have received the Polar Medal: Lady Virginia Fiennes, and one other the NZ scientist Mary Bradshaw. Medals are named to the recipient, engraved on the earlier and most recent issues and impressed in small capitals on the earlier Elizabethan issues. Clasps for subsequent expeditions are awarded. Altogether some 880 silver and 245 bronze medals for the Antarctic and 73 silver medals for the Arctic have been awarded to date. Of these almost 670 have been awarded in the present reign alone. 8 medals have been awarded for service in both the Arctic and Antarctic and 3 for Antarctic and Arctic (differentiating where first service took place). No bronze medals were issued for Arctic service.*

VALUE:	Silver	Miniature (no clasp)	Bronze	Miniature (no clasp)
Edward VII	from £1,250	£50–80	from £1,000	£30–50
George V (B)	from £1,000	£40–60	from £750	£30–50
George V (C)	—	£40–60	from £750	£30–50
George V (E)	from £1,000	£40–60	—	£30–50
George VI	from £800	£25–40	from £750	£20–30
Elizabeth II	from £800	£30–25	—	£20–30

345. KING EDWARD VII MEDAL FOR SCIENCE, ART AND MUSIC

Instituted: 1904

Ribbon: 35mm scarlet with a broad central band of dark blue and thin white stripes towards the edges.

Metal: Silver.

Size: 32mm.

Description: The raised rim consisted of a laurel wreath and has a ring for suspension. (Obverse) the conjoined busts of King Edward VII and Queen Alexandra; (reverse) the Three Graces engaged in various cultural pursuits.

Comments: *This short-lived medal was discontinued only two years later. It was awarded in recognition of distinguished services in the arts, sciences and music.*

VALUE:	
Silver	£700–800

346. ORDER OF THE LEAGUE OF MERCY

Date: 1900.
Ribbon: 38mm watered white silk with a central broad stripe of dark blue.
Metal: Silver.
Size: Height 51mm; max. width 39mm.
Description: An enamelled red cross surmounted by the Prince of Wales's plumes enfiladed by a coronet, with a central medallion depicting a group of figures representing Charity, set within a laurel wreath.
Comments: *Appointments to the Order were sanctioned and approved by the sovereign on the recommendation of the Grand President of the League of Mercy as a reward for distinguished personal service to the League in assisting the support of hospitals. Ladies and gentlemen who rendered such aid for at least five years were eligible for the award. In 1917 King George V instituted a bar to be awarded to those who gave continuing service over a period of many years after receiving the Order itself. The Order was last awarded in 1946, the League itself ceasing to exist in 1947.*

VALUE:

Badge of the Order	£30–50	*Miniature*	£20–25

347. INDIAN TITLE BADGE

Instituted: 12 December 1911.
Ribbon: Light blue edged with dark blue (1st class); red edged with dark red (2nd class); or dark blue edged with light blue (3rd class).
Metal: Silver or silver-gilt.
Size: Height 58mm; max. width 45mm.
Description: A radiate star topped by an imperial crown with a curved laurel wreath below the crown and cutting across the top of a central medallion surrounded by a collar inscribed with the appropriate title. The medallion bears the left-facing crowned profile of King George V or the right-facing crowned bust of King George VI. (Reverse) plain, but engraved with the name of the recipient.
Comments: *Introduced by King George V on the occasion of the Delhi Durbar of 1911 and awarded in three classes to civilians and Viceroy's commissioned officers of the Indian Army for faithful service or acts of public welfare. Recipients proceeded from the lowest grade to higher grades, each accompanied by a distinctive title. Each grade was issued in Hindu and Muslim versions, differing in title: Diwan Bahadur (Muslim) or Sardar Bahadur (Hindu), Khan Bahadur (Muslim) or Rai or Rao Bahadur (Hindu) and Khan Sahib (Muslim) or Rai or Rao Sahib (Hindu), in descending order of grade. These title badges took precedence after all British and Indian orders and decorations, and before campaign medals.*

VALUE:

Diwan Bahadur	£60–70
Sardar Bahadur	£60–70
Khan Bahadur	£50–60
Rao Bahadur	£50–60
Khan Sahib	£45–60
Rao Sahib	£45–60
Miniature	£30–35

348. BADGES OF HONOUR (AFRICAN COUNTRIES)

Instituted: 1922.
Ribbon: Plain yellow, 38mm (neck) or 32mm (breast).
Metal: Bronze.
Size: 65mm x 48mm (neck); 45mm x 33mm (breast).
Description: Oval badges with a raised rim of laurel leaves terminating at the top in an imperial crown flanked by two lions. (Obverse) a crowned effigy of the reigning monarch; (reverse) the crowned cypher of the monarch or some emblem symbolic of the particular country with the country name in the exergue.
Comments: *The badge accompanied a certificate of honour awarded to chiefs and other persons of non-European descent who had rendered loyal and valuable service to the government of the territory. T he original award was a neck badge suspended by a ribbon, but from 1954 onwards recipients were given the option of taking the award as a neck or breast badge. These awards were quite distinct from the decorations known as the Native Chiefs Medals (see number 70). They were first awarded to Ugandans but later extended to other 14 British territories in East and West Africa as well as the three High Commisson territories in Southern Africa. They are believed to have fallen into abeyance in the early 1980s.*

VALUE:

George V	Rare
George VI	Rare
Elizabeth II (neck)	Rare
Elizabeth II (breast)	Rare

348A. BADGES OF HONOUR (NON-AFRICAN COUNTRIES)

Instituted: 1926.
Ribbon: 38mm watered silk mustard yellow.
Metal: Silver gilt.
Size: 41mm (George VI) or 32 mm (Elizabeth II).
Description: Circular with a raised rim of laurel leaves bearing a ring for suspension. (Obverse) crowned effigy of the reigning monarch; (reverse) the emblem of the country with the name round the foot.
Comments: *These medals accompanied certificates of honour awarded to indigenous persons who had rendered valuable service to the colony or protectorate. These awards appear to have been in abeyance since the early 1980s. Exceptionally, the New Hebrides badge was awarded to three British officers (Colonel (now General Sir Charles) Guthrie, Lieutenant-Colonel C. H. C. Howgill and HRH the Duke of Gloucester) in connection with the "Coconut War" in July 1980, instead of a campaign medal. The reverse types show the badges of 28 colonies or protectorate.*

VALUE:

		Miniatures:	
George V	Rare	Bermuda & New Hebridies	Rare
George VI	Rare		
Elizabeth II	Rare		

349. NAVAL ENGINEER'S GOOD CONDUCT MEDAL

Instituted: 1842.
Ribbon: Originally plain dark blue but later broad blue with whiteedges.
Metal: Silver.
Size: 35mm.
Description: (Obverse) a two-masted paddle steamer with a trident in the exergue; (reverse) a circular cable cartouche enclosing a crowned fouled anchor and the legend FOR ABILITY AND GOOD CONDUCT. Between the cable and the rim the details of the recipient were engraved round the circumference. Considering the rarity of the award, it is even more remarkable that the medals have several unique features. Shaw's medal, for example, had oak leaves in the exergue, flanking the trident, but this feature was omitted from later medals. Medals have been recorded with a straight bar suspender, a steel clip and ring suspender or fixed ring suspension with one or two intermediate rings.
Comments: *This medal was abolished five years after it was instituted, only seven medals being awarded in that period: to William Shaw (1842), William Dunkin (1842), William Johnstone (1843), John Langley (1843), J.P. Rundle (1845), George Roberts (1845) and Samuel B. Meredith (1846). Restrikes were produced in 1875 and at a later date. The original medals have a grooved rim, the 1875 restrikes a diagonal grained rim and the later restrikes a plain, flat rim.*
VALUE:

Original	Rare
1875 restrike	£120–140
Later restrike	£80–100

350. INDIAN RECRUITING BADGE (GEORGE V)

Instituted: 1917.
Ribbon: Plain dark green.
Metal: Bronze.
Size: Height 45mm; max. width 48mm.
Description: A five-pointed star with ball finials, surmounted by a wreathed gilt medallion bearing a left-facing crowned bust of King George V, inscribed FOR RECRUITING WORK DURING THE WAR.
Comments: *Awarded to Indian officers and NCOs engaged in recruitment of troops. It could only be worn in uniform when attending durbars or state functions, but at any time in plain clothes.*

VALUE: George V   £50–60   *Miniature*   £30–40

351. INDIAN RECRUITING BADGE (GEORGE VI)

Instituted: 1940.
Ribbon: Emerald green divided into three sections interspersed by narrow stripes of red (left) and yellow (right).
Metal: Silver and bronze.
Size: Height 42mm; max. width 39mm.
Description: A multi-rayed silver breast badge surmounted by an imperial crown with a suspension ring fitted through the top of the crown. In the centre is superimposed a bronze medallion bearing the left-facing crowned profile of King George VI, within a collar inscribed FOR RECRUITING.
Comments: *Awarded to selected civilian and military pensioners, full-time members of the Indian Recruiting Organisation, fathers and mothers having at least three children in the armed services, and wives having a husband and at least two children serving in the defence forces.*

VALUE: George VI   £40–50   *Miniature*   £25–40

352. NAVAL GOOD SHOOTING MEDAL

Instituted: August 1902.

Ribbon: Dark blue with a red central stripe edged in white.

Metal: Silver.

Size: 36mm.

Description: (Obverse) the effigy of the reigning monarch; (reverse) a nude figure of Neptune holding five thunderbolts in each hand. In the background can be seen the bows of a trireme and the heads of three horses, with a trident in the field. The Latin motto VICTORIA CURAM AMAT (Victory loves care) appears round the circumference. Fitted with a straight suspension bar. The recipient's name, number, rank, ship and calibre of gun are impressed round the rim.

Comments: *Instituted to promote excellent gunnery performances in the annual Fleet Competitions, it was first awarded in 1903 but was discontinued in 1914. Subsequent success was marked by the issue of a clasp bearing the name of the ship and the date. A total of 974 medals and 62 bars were awarded. 53 men received one bar, three men got two bars and only one achieved three bars.*

VALUE:

		Miniature
Edward VII	£180–200	£50–60 (in silver)
George V	£200–220	£30–35 "

353. ARMY BEST SHOT MEDAL

Instituted: 30 April 1869.

Ribbon: Watered crimson with black, white and black stripes at the edges.

Metal: Silver.

Size: 36mm.

Description: (Obverse) the veiled diademmed profile of Queen Victoria; (reverse) Victory bestowing a laurel crown on a naked warrior armed with a quiver of arrows and a bow and holding a target, impaled with arrows, in his other hand. Fitted with a straight suspension bar.

Comments: *This medal, sometimes referred to as the Queen's Medal, was awarded annually to the champion in the Army marksmanship contests held at Bisley. It was originally struck in bronze, but was upgraded to silver in 1872. The award ceased in 1882, but was revived in 1923 and thereafter known as the King's Medal. The original reverse was retained, with the appropriate effigy of the reigning sovereign on the obverse. Since 1953 it has been known as the Queen's Medal again. In the post-1923 medals a bar bears the year of the award, with additional year clasps for subsequent awards. Until 1934 a single medal was awarded each year, but in 1935 two medals were granted, for the champion shots of the Regular and Territorial Armies respectively. Subsequently additional medals have been sanctioned for award to the military forces of India, Canada, Australia, New Zealand, Ceylon, Rhodesia, the British South Africa Police, the Union of South Africa, Pakistan, Jamaica and Ghana.*

VALUE:

		Miniature
Victoria bronze	Rare	—
Victoria silver	Rare	—
George V	£700–800	£30–40
George VI	£700–800	£30–40
Elizabeth II	£700–800	£10–15

354. QUEEN'S MEDAL FOR CHAMPION SHOTS OF THE ROYAL NAVY AND ROYAL MARINES

Instituted: 12 June 1953.
Ribbon: Dark blue with a red central stripe bordered white.
Metal: Silver.
Size: 36mm.
Description: (Obverse) the effigy of Queen Elizabeth II; (reverse) Neptune (as on the Naval Good Shooting Medal).
Comments: *Instituted as the naval counterpart of the Army best shot medal.*

VALUE:

Elizabeth II	£700–800	Miniature	£10–15

355. QUEEN'S MEDAL FOR CHAMPION SHOTS OF THE ROYAL AIR FORCE

Instituted: 12 June 1953.
Ribbon: Broad crimson centre flanked by dark blue stripes bisected by thin light blue stripes.
Metal: Silver.
Size: 36mm.
Description: (Obverse) the effigy of Queen Elizabeth II; (reverse) Hermes kneeling on a flying hawk and holding the caduceus in one hand and a javelin in the other. The recipient's details are engraved on the rim and the medal is fitted with a straight bar suspender.
Comments: *Competed for at the annual RAF Small Arms Meeting at Bisley.*

VALUE:

Elizabeth II	—	Miniature	£10–15

356. QUEEN'S MEDAL FOR CHAMPION SHOTS OF THE NEW ZEALAND NAVAL FORCES

Instituted: 9 July 1958.
Ribbon: Crimson centre bordered with white and broad dark blue stripes at the edges.
Metal: Silver.
Size: 36mm.
Description: (Obverse) the effigy of Queen Elizabeth II; (reverse) similar to that of the Naval Good Shooting Medal of 1903-14. Fitted with a clasp bearing the year of the award and a straight suspension bar.
Comments: *Awards were made retrospective to 1 January 1955. This medal is awarded for marksmanship in an annual contest of the New Zealand Naval Forces. Additional clasps are granted for further success.*

VALUE:

Elizabeth II	Rare	Miniature	—

357. UNION OF SOUTH AFRICA COMMEMORATION MEDAL

Instituted: 1910.
Ribbon: 38mm orange-yellow with a broad central dark blue stripe.
Metal: Silver.
Size: 36mm.
Description: (Obverse) the uncrowned effigy of King George V; (reverse) Mercury as God of Commerce and Prosperity, bending over an anvil, forging the links of a chain symbolic of the uniting of the four colonies (Cape Colony, Natal, Orange Free State and the Transvaal), with the date 1910 in the exergue and the legend TO COMMEMORATE THE UNION OF SOUTH AFRICA.
Comments: *This was the first medal struck in the reign of George V and resulted from the South Africa Act of 1909. This Act proclaimed the unification on 31 May 1910, of the self-governing four colonies into a legislative Union, becoming provinces of the Union of South Africa. This medal, the reverse of which was designed by Sir Bertram MacKennal, and the obverse by Mr Sydney Marsh, was struck to mark the opening of the first Parliament of the Union by HRH the Duke of Connaught. Awarded to those who took part in the inauguration of the Parliament. Additionally it was also awarded to certain officers and men of HMS* Balmoral Castle, *a Union Castle liner specially commissioned as a man-of-war to convey HRH the Duke of Connaught as the King's representative to South Africa for the celebrations. A total of 551 medals were struck by the Royal Mint, and were issued unnamed, although privately named medals are in existence.*

VALUE: Named £250–300   Unnamed £200–240   *Miniature* £20–30

358. DEKORATIE VOOR TROUWE DIENST

Instituted: 1920.
Ribbon: A broad dark blue central stripe flanked on one side by a gold bar with a thin red stripe superimposed towards the edge, and on the other side by a yellow bar with a thin white stripe towards the edge. Transvaal recipients wore the ribbon with the red to the centre of the chest; Orange Free State recipients wore the ribbon with the white stripe to the centre of the chest.
Metal: Silver.
Size: 36mm.
Description: (Obverse) the arms of the Transvaal; (reverse) the arms of the Orange Free State. Fitted with a fixed suspender. Recipients wore the medal with the appropriate state arms showing.
Comments: *This medal which is correctly named the Dekoratie Voor Trouwe Dienst was awarded by the Union of South Africa to officers of the two former Boer republics for distinguished service during the Second Boer War of 1899-1902.*

The other side is similar to no. 359 illustrated below.

VALUE: Silver (591)   £100–150

359. ANGLO-BOERE OORLOG (WAR) MEDAL

Instituted: 1920.
Ribbon: Broad green and yellow stripes with three narrow stripes of red, white and dark blue in the centre. Transvaal recipients wore the ribbon with the green to the centre of the chest, while Orange Free State recipients wore it with the yellow towards the centre.
Metal: Silver.
Size: 36mm.
Description: Both sides inscribed ANGLO-BOER OORLOG round the top, with the dates 1899-1902 round the foot. Medallions set in a border of a square and quatrefoil show the arms of the Orange Free State on one side and the Transvaal on the other. The medal was worn with the side showing the arms of the appropriate state uppermost. Fitted with a straight bar swivelling suspender.
Comments: *Correctly named the Anglo-Boer Oorlog Medal, this was awarded by the Union government to officers and men of the former Boer republics for loyal service in the war against the British.*

The other side is similar to no. 358 illustrated above.

VALUE: Silver   £70–90   *Miniature*   £15–20

360. COMMONWEALTH INDEPENDENCE MEDALS

Pakistan Independence Medal.

Since the partition of the Indian sub-continent in 1947 and the emergence of the Dominions of India and Pakistan, it has been customary for medals to be issued to mark the attainment of independence. As these medals are invariably awarded to British service personnel taking part in the independence ceremonies, they are appended here, in chronological order of institution, the date of the actual award, where later, being given in parentheses. These medals invariably have symbolic motifs with the date of independence inscribed. The distinctive ribbons are noted alongside. All are 32mm wide unless otherwise stated.

India 1947 (1948) three equal stripes of orange, white and green
Pakistan 1947 (1950) dark green with a central thin white stripe
Nigeria 1960 (1964) three equal stripes of green, white and green
Sierra Leone 1961 three equal stripes of green, white and blue
Jamaica 1962 black centre flanked by yellow stripes and green edges
Uganda 1962 (1963) six stripes of black, yellow, red, black, yellow and red
Malawi 1964 three equal stripes of black, red and green
Guyana 1966 36mm red centre flanked by yellow stripes and broad green edges. The green and yellow separated (left) by a thin black stripe and (right) by a thin pale blue stripe
Fiji 1970 Grey-blue with bars half red, half white, towards each end
Papua New Guinea 1975 Red bordered by thin stripes of yellow and white, with black edges
Solomon Islands 1978 five equal stripes of blue, yellow, white, yellow and green
Gilbert Islands (Kiribati) 1980 half red, half black, separated by a thin white stripe, and edged in yellow
Ellice Islands (Tuvalu) 1980 equal stripes of red, white and red edged yellow. the white stripe bisected by a thin blue stripe
Zimbabwe 1980 Silver or bronze 38mm black centre flanked by red and yellow stripes with edges of green or blue
Vanuatu 1980 (1981) 25mm four equal stripes of red, black, yellow and dark brown
St Christopher, Nevis and Anguilla 1983 bars of green (left) and red (right) with a black central bar having two thin white stripes, flanked by yellow stripes

VALUE: From £20   *Miniature*   £10–20

361. MALTA GEORGE CROSS FIFTIETH ANNIVERSARY COMMEMORATIVE MEDAL

Instituted: 1992.
Ribbon: Dark blue with central stripes of white and red (the Maltese national colours).
Metal: Cupro-nickel.
Size: 36mm.
Description: (Obverse) the crowned arms of the island, which include the George Cross in the upper left corner, with the date 1992 at the foot. (Reverse) a replica of the George Cross with the eight-pointed Maltese Cross at the top and the date 1942 at the foot, with a legend BHALA SHIEDA TA'EROIZMU U DEDIKAZZJONI on one side and TO BEAR WITNESS TO HEROISM AND DEVOTION on the other. Suspension is by a fixed bar decorated with laurels, attached to a ring.
Comments: *Sanctioned by the government of Malta to celebrate the fiftieth anniversary of the award of the George Cross by King George VI to the island for its heroic resistance to prolonged Axis attack during the Second World War. The medal has been awarded to surviving veterans who served in Malta in the armed forces and auxiliary services between 10 June 1940 and 8 September 1943. Permission for British citizens to wear this medal was subsequently granted by the Queen. As a number of veterans applied for the medal after the cut-off date of 15 April 1994, the Maltese Government sanctioned a second striking—these medals carry the word COPY below the right arm of the George Cross.*
VALUE:

Cupro-nickel	£80–100	*Miniature*	£8–10
Restrike	£60–70		

362. SHANGHAI VOLUNTEER CORPS MEDAL

Date: 1854
Ribbon:
Metal: Silver.
Size: 38mm
Description:
Comment: *Awarded to the officers and men of the Shanghai Volunteers who took part in the battle of Soo Chow Creek (also known as the battle of Muddy Flats) which took place in April 28, 1854. Examples are of the greatest rarity and the last one to appear at auction was sold in 1991. Further details are sought.*

VALUE: £800–850

363. SHANGHAI JUBILEE MEDAL

Instituted: 1893.
Ribbon: Watered silk half bright red, half white or red with 4mm central white stripe.
Metal: Silver or bronze.
Size: 36mm.
Description: (Obverse) triple-shield arms of the municipality surrounded by a band with thistles, shamrocks and roses round the foot and NOVEMBER 17 1843 round the top. (Reverse) a scrolled shield with the words SHANGHAI JUBILEE and NOVEMBER 17 1843 and inscribed diagonally across the centre with the recipient's name in block capitals. The shield is flanked by Chinese dragons and above is a steamship and the sun setting on the horizon. The rim is engraved 'Presented by the Shanghai Municipality'. Issued with a small suspension ring, but often replaced by a straight bar. This medal has also been recorded with an ornamental silver brooch bearing the dates 1843–1893 on the second type of ribbon.
Comments: *The British settlement in Shanghai was founded in 1843 and formed the nucleus of the International Settlement established in 1854 under the control of an autonomous Municipal Council. In effect the International Settlement functioned as an autonomous City State administered by a Municipal Committee formed from those nations comprising the Settlement. This was abolished when Shanghai was overrun by Imperial Japanese troops in 1941.*

VALUE:	Silver (625)	£250–300
	Bronze (100)	£250–300

364. SHANGHAI FIRE BRIGADE LONG SERVICE MEDAL

Instituted: Before 1904.
Ribbon: Black with broad crimson borders.
Metal: Silver.
Size: 31mm.
Description: (Obverse) an armorial device featuring a Chinese dragon standing on a symbolic high-rise building on which is displayed a flame on a pole crossed by a hook and ladder, with MIH-HO-LOONG SHANGHAI round the top and the motto "Say the word and down comes your house" round the foot; (reverse) blank. It seems strange that no Chinese characters appear on the medal. Ring and double claw suspension, with a broad silver brooch bar at the top of the ribbon.
Comment: *Awarded for a minimum of twelve years regular service with the Municipal Fire Brigade. The award was presumably in abeyance following the Japanese invasion in 1937 and the wholesale destruction of the international commercial metropolis.*

VALUE: £300

365. SHANGHAI VOLUNTEER FIRE BRIGADE LONG SERVICE MEDAL

Instituted: 1904.
Ribbon: Red with white edges.
Metal: Gold, silver or bronze.
Size: 36mm.
Description: (Obverse) the arms and motto of the Municipality surrounded by a collar inscribed SHANGHAI VOLUNTEER FIRE BRIGADE ESTABLISHED 1866. (Reverse) a pair of crossed axes surmounted by a fireman's helmet under which is a horizontal tablet on which are engraved the recipient's dates of service. Round the circumference is inscribed FOR LONG SERVICE (top) and WE FIGHT THE FLAMES (foot) with quatrefoil ornaments separating the two inscriptions. Fitted with a swivelling scroll suspender.
Comments: *The medal in silver was awarded to members of the Volunteer Fire Brigade for five years service, for eight years service a clasp was added to the ribbon and for 12 years service the medal was awarded in gold. Bronze medals exist but are believed to have been specimens only.*

VALUE: Silver   £450–500

366. SHANGHAI VOLUNTEER CORPS LONG SERVICE MEDAL

Instituted: 1921.
Ribbon: Equal bands of red, white and blue, the red bisected by a thin green stripe, the white by black and the blue by yellow.
Metal: Silver.
Size: 36mm.
Description: (Obverse) an eight-pointed radiate star bearing a scroll at the top inscribed 4th APRIL 1854. The arms of the Municipality superimposed on the star and surrounded by a collar inscribed SHANGHAI VOLUNTEER CORPS. Round the foot of the medal is a band inscribed FOR LONG SERVICE. (Reverse) plain, engraved with the name of the recipient and his period of service.
Comments: *The Volunteer Corps was raised in 1853 to protect the British and other foreign settlements. The date on the scroll alludes to the Corps' first engagement, the Battle of Muddy Flat. The Corps was cosmopolitan in structure, although the British element predominated. It was disbanded in September 1942, nine months after the Japanese overran the International Settlement. Awarded for 12 years good service, the last medal was awarded in 1941.*

VALUE: Silver   £250–300   *Miniature*   £25–40

367. SHANGHAI MUNICIPAL POLICE DISTINGUISHED CONDUCT MEDAL

Instituted: 1924.
Ribbon: Red with a central blue stripe (1st class); red with a blue stripe at each edge (2nd class).
Metal: Silver or bronze.
Size: 36mm.
Description: (Obverse) arms of the Municipality and the inscription SHANGHAI MUNICIPAL POLICE; (reverse) the words FOR DISTINGUISHED CONDUCT. The recipient's name and rank was engraved round the rim.
Comments: *Awarded to officers and men of the Municipal Police in two classes, distinguished solely by their ribbons and the metal used (silver or bronze). A sliding clasp was fitted to the ribbon to denote a second award; this featured the Municipal crest and was engraved on the reverse with the details of the award. Only six awards were ever made, including two to Europeans.*

VALUE:		
	Silver	£800–900
	Bronze	£650–750

368. SHANGHAI MUNICIPAL POLICE LONG SERVICE MEDAL

Instituted: 1925.
Ribbon: Brown with a central yellow band edged in white.
Metal: Silver.
Size: 36mm.
Description: (Obverse) arms of the Municipality within a collar inscribed SHANGHAI MUNICIPAL POLICE; (reverse) plain apart from the inscription FOR LONG SERVICE in two lines across the centre. The recipient's name and rank were engraved round the rim in upper and lower case lettering. Awards to Indians were named in cursive script with the Hindi equivalent alongside. Fitted with a swivelling scroll suspender.
Comments: *Awarded for 12 years good service in the Shanghai Municipal Police, an international force composed largely of Sikhs, Chinese and White Russians as well as British ex-soldiers and policemen. Dated clasps for further five year periods of service were awarded. The medal was abolished in 1942.*

VALUE:			Miniature
	Silver	£280–300	£45–50
	With clasp	£350–400	£50–60

369. SHANGHAI MUNICIPAL POLICE (SPECIALS) LONG SERVICE MEDAL

Instituted: 1929.
Ribbon: Dark brown with three white bars, each bisected by a thin yellow stripe.
Metal: Silver.
Size: 36mm.
Description: (Obverse) the arms of the Municipality with the motto OMNIA JUNCTA IN UNO (all joined in one) round the circumference. (Reverse) inscribed SHANGHAI MUNICIPAL POLICE (SPECIALS) FOR LONG SERVICE in six lines. A unique award to A.L. Anderson (1930) was inscribed on the reverse FOR DISTINGUISHED AND VALUABLE SERVICES.
Comments: *Awarded for 12 years active and efficient service in the Special Constabulary. Some 52 medals and 8 clasps for additional service are recorded in the* Shanghai Gazette, *but the actual number awarded was probably greater. The medal was discontinued in 1942.*

VALUE:		
	With clasp	Very rare
	Without clasp	£450–500

370. SHANGHAI MUNICIPAL COUNCIL EMERGENCY MEDAL

Instituted: 1937.
Ribbon: 38mm bright red, having a broad white central stripe bordered black and yellow edges separated from the red by thin black stripes.
Metal: Bronze.
Size: 40mm.
Description: An eight-pointed star with ring suspension. (Obverse) a central medallion superimposed on the radiate star with the triple-shield arms of the Municipality surrounded by a collar inscribed SHANGHAI MUNICIPAL COUNCIL. (Reverse) a laurel wreath enclosing the words FOR SERVICES RENDERED - AUGUST 12 TO NOVEMBER 12 1937.
Comments: *Awarded to members of the Police, Volunteer Corps, Fire Brigade and civilians for services during the emergency of August-November 1937 when fighting between the Chinese and Japanese in and around Shanghai threatened to encroach on the International Settlement. Issued unnamed, but accompanied by a certificate bearing the name and unit of the recipient. Examples have been seen with the recipient's name engraved on the reverse.*
VALUE:

Bronze star	£80–100	*Miniature*	£25–30

371. AUTOMOBILE ASSOCIATION SERVICE CROSS

Date: 1956.
Ribbon: Yellow with three narrow black stripes.
Metal: Silver.
Size: 36mm.
Description: A silver cross flory terminating in scrolls, with the AA emblem surmounted in the centre.
Comments: *Established in commemoration of the Association's Golden Jubilee, the Cross is the highest award to AA patrolmen and other uniformed members of staff for conspicuous acts of bravery involving an imminent risk of personal injury whilst on duty in uniform, or whilst engaged in an action related to duty. To date only 15 crosses have been awarded. A monetary reward accompanies the Cross.*

VALUE: Rare

372. AUTOMOBILE ASSOCIATION SERVICE MEDAL

Date: 1956.
Ribbon: Half yellow, half black.
Metal: Silver.
Size: 36mm.
Description: A circular medal in the form of the AA badge with wings sprouting from the top and flanking a claw and ring suspension. (Obverse) AA superimposed on a wheel, with the inscription AUTOMOBILE ASSOCIATION/SERVICE MEDAL round the circumference; (reverse) details of the award.
Clasp: A silver-gilt and red enamel clasp inscribed 192064 (ie. 20 years good driving, 1964) has been reported.
Comments: *Like the Cross, the Medal of the Association was instituted in commemoration of the Association's Golden Jubilee. The medal is awarded to members of the uniformed staff for courageous or outstanding initiative and devotion to duty. To date, only 60 medals have been awarded, including four in 1997, mainly for life-saving and bravery in accidents. A monetary reward accompanies the Medal. A Service Citation is also awarded for lesser acts, a total of 63 having been bestowed so far.*

VALUE: Rare

373. SUFFRAGETTE MEDAL

Instituted: 1909.
Campaign: Votes for women.
Ribbon: Three equal stripes of purple, silver and green.
Metal: Silver.
Size: 20mm.
Clasps: Prison bars surmounted by a broad arrow, or an enamelled bar in the WSPU colours.
Description: A small silver medal suspended by a ring from a bar with scrolled finials, engraved with the date of the award. A similarly scrolled brooch bar at the top of the ribbon is inscribed FOR VALOUR. The plain medal is engraved HUNGER STRIKE in various styles and hallmarked.
Comments: *This medal was awarded by the Women's Social and Political Union (WSPU) to those militant Suffragettes who were imprisoned for various acts of violence and who went on hunger strike while in prison. At first they were forcibly fed under the most barbaric conditions, as a result of which several died. The government then introduced the Cat and Mouse Act, whereby hunger strikers at the point of death were released, but were then re-arrested and returned to prison when they had recovered sufficiently from their ordeal. Bars were awarded in respect of subsequent periods of imprisonment and hunger strike.*

VALUE: £3500–£4000 (unboxed)
          £5000–£6000 (in personally inscribed case)

374. FLORENCE NIGHTINGALE MEDAL

Date: May 16, 1912.
Ribbon: White with narrow red and broad stripes towards the edges.
Metal: Silver with enamels.
Size:
Description: An upright elliptical medal coming to a point at both ends, with a three-quarter length portrait of Florence Nightingale from the Crimean War period, inscribed MEMORIAM FLORENCE NIGHTINGALE 1820–1910 AD. The reverse bears the recipient's name.
Comments: *Instituted by the International Committee of the Red Cross for award to trained nurses, matrons, nursing organisers or voluntary aids for distinguished or exceptional service. Awards are made every other year on the anniversary of Miss Nightingale's birthday. This medal has been awarded very sparingly.*

VALUE: £500–£750

375. ANZAC COMMEMORATIVE MEDAL

Date: 1967.
Ribbon: None.
Metal: Bronze.
Size: 35mm max.
Description: (Obverse) a medallion surmounted by a Royal Crown with a laurel wreath and the word ANZAC in a scroll below. In the field is the date 1915 above a picture of John Simpson and his donkey saving a wounded soldier at Gallipoli. (Reverse) a map of Australia and New Zealand with the Southern Cross constellation. The reverse of the scroll has New Zealand fern leaves.
Comments: *This medal was instituted jointly by the governments of Australia and New Zealand and awarded to surviving veterans of the Australian and New Zealand Army Corps who served in the Gallipoli campaign. Next-of-kin of servicemen killed in action or who had since died could apply for a half-size lapel badge bearing the obverse design.*

VALUE: £20–30

376. NEW ZEALAND CADET DISTRICT MEDALS

Date: 1902.
Ribbon: Plain khaki or tan with a central pink flanked by dark green stripes.
Metal: Silver.
Size: 32mm.
Description: (Obverse) profile of Edward VII or George V with inscription FOR KING AND COUNTRY: PUBLIC SCHOOL CADETS, N.Z.; (reverse) DEFENCE NOT DEFIANCE round the top, with DISTRICT PRIZE (or CHALLENGE) MEDAL AWARDED TO in three lines, leaving space for the name of the recipient to be engraved below.
Comments: *These medals were instituted folllowing the establishment of the Public School Cadets in 1902 and were awarded in two classes in Challenge competitions or as prizes in the annual examinations.*

VALUE: District Challenge £100
District Prize £90

377. DICKIN MEDAL

Date:
Ribbon:
Metal: Silver.
Size: 36mm.
Description: (Obverse) a laurel wreath enclosing the inscription "For Gallantry" in raised cursive script over the motto WE ALSO SERVE in block capitals; the initials PDSA in a tablet at the top of the wreath; (reverse) the date, name of recipient and details of the award. Fitted with a plain ring for suspension.
Comment: *Awarded by the People's Dispensary for Sick Animals to recognise acts of bravery by birds and animals in wartime, and consequently popularly known as the Animals' VC. It was very rarely awarded, only one medal having been granted since 1949.*

VALUE: £4,000–£5,000

378. NATIONAL CANINE DEFENCE LEAGUE MEDAL

Date:
Ribbon: Red.
Metal: Silver.
Size: 38mm.
Description: (Obverse) standing figure of Victory holding a sword, with her right hand resting on a dog; (reverse) the date, name of recipient and details of the award. Fitted with a plain ring for suspension.
Comment: *Awarded by the National Canine Defence League to recognise acts of bravery by dogs.*

VALUE: £1,000–£1,500

Unofficial medals

Interest has been steadily growing in recent years in unofficial medals, a subject on the fringes of medal collecting. The term is deliberately vague and encompasses a very wide range of medals, medalets and medallions of a commercial, private or local nature. Such a generic term would, for example, include regimental medals awarded for marksmanship or good conduct, often associated with official medal groups of the 19th century. This is a very esoteric group, often consisting of medals which were specially engraved for the occasion and therefore exceedingly difficult to quantify.

On the other hand, many of the earlier medals, now highly regarded as forerunners of the general campaign series, were unofficial in origin, and relied upon the enterprise of public-spirited indviduals and prize agents such as Alexander Davison (nos. 78 and 85) or Matthew Boulton (no. 84), generals such as Elliot (no. 74), Earl St Vincent (no. 80) or Gordon of Khartoum (no. 133) or even private bodies such as the Highland Society (no. 83).

Then there is the large and fascinating group of civic or institutional medals which were presented to volunteers returning from the Boer War of 1899–1902. M.G. Hibbard, in his splendid monograph *Boer War Tribute Medals* (1982), recorded no fewer than 78 such medals, 40 from towns and cities in England, 25 from other parts of the United Kingdom and 13 from Commonwealth countries. Some of these were fitted with ribbons and were obviously intended for wear alongside the official medals of the war; others were 'danglers' intended to be fitted to watch-chains; and others still were not fitted with any form of suspension and were thus in the nature of commemorative medals intended purely as a memento of volunteer service.

So far as can be ascertained, such tribute medals were not produced in previous conflicts, which were predominantly fought by regular troops; and such was the scale of the involvement of volunteers and later conscripts in the First World War that the cost of providing civic medals of this nature would have been prohibitive. Instead, returning soldiers had to be content with some form of paper testimonial, at best. A notable exception was the gold medal presented by the Lord Mayor of London to the members of the anti-aircraft gun crews which shot down the first Zeppelin (listed below).

Apart from that, the Boer War group therefore constitutes a unique, but clearly defined group. They are, however, generally outside the scope of this YEARBOOK, although it should be noted that several medals in this category have long been accepted in the regular canon: the Kimberley Star (no. 154), the Kimberley Medals (no. 155), the Yorkshire Imperial Yeomanry Medal (no. 156) and the Medal for the Defence of Ookiep (no. 157). The reason for their acceptance is quite arbitrary, and just why the Yorkshire Imperial Yeomanry medal should be so highly regarded while others are not seems to rest on the fact that this medal is more commonly met with than the others— which is hardly a valid criterion.

For the sake of completing the record we have endeavoured to introduce a number of unofficial medals, particularly as groups including certain of these medals are coming onto the market and inevitably some purchasers are curious to know their origins.

In addition there are a number of other unofficial medals available to veterans such as the "Battle for Britain" medal with its various clasps but **it is not the intention to make this a definitive guide**, so we have decided to limit this section to those medals that were initially commissioned or supported by the relevant veterans associations and mainly produced in recent years in order to fill the gap left in the official series.

Credit for reviving such medals must go to the Mayor of Dunkirk on whose initiative the medal awarded to survivors of the 1940 evacuation was instituted in 1965. Subsequently distribution of this medal was taken over by the Dunkirk Veterans' Association, applications being strictly limited to those who could prove that they had taken part in that historic event. This practice continued with the commissioning of the Bomber Command Medal by their Association in response to the long-standing grievance of veterans of the Second World War who felt that their contribution to the ultimate victory had been deliberately ignored for political reasons. The success of this medal encouraged the production of similar awards for other categories of servicemen, or for campaigns which many felt should have had a distinctive campaign medal.

It must be stressed that all of these medals are available for purchase only by bona-fide veterans or their proven next of kin with sales also benefiting related charities. The wearing of these medals has always been a contentious issue with veterans choosing to wear them below but never alongside their official decorations.

As many of these medals are still being struck, it has been decided not to give valuations for this section.

U0. CHERRY MEDAL

Date: 1904.
Campaign: China, 1900–4
Branch of Service: Royal Navy.
Ribbon: Cherry red.
Metal: Silver.
Size: 38mm.
Description: (Obverse) a bare cherry tree with five naval officers in the foreground and a large number of other officers, all in frock coats, moving up in single file, with a scroll across the foot inscribed in Latin SUB HOC CERESO MANEMUS (under this cherry tree we remain); (reverse) a fouled anchor flanked by the Golden Fleece and a Chinese Dragon with the legend ARGONAUT CHINA 1900–1904 round the circumference. The medal is fitted with a plain suspension ring.
Comments: *The name of the medal and the colour of ribbon allude to Captain George Henry Cherry RN, commander of HMS* Argonaut *which served on the China Station in 1900-4. The five officers on one side of the tree represent the only ones remaining of the original number when the ship was paid off: Lieutenant Arthur Vernon Ross, Captain T. H. Hawkins RM, Chief Engineer A. W. Turner, Senior Engineer T. W. Cleave and Chaplain T. A. Dexter. The other line represents those officers who left the ship during the commission. The obverse motto contains a spelling error: CERESO instead of CERASO. This medal started off as a joke. Captain Cherry was a terrible martinet and his disgruntled officers felt that they deserved a medal for having to put up with him. It was designed by Miss Ross, sister of the senior watchkeeper, and struck by Gamage's of London. Only 100 medals were struck. Originally it was intended to be given only to the five officers who had stuck it out to the bitter end, but others complained and thus were awarded the medal with a bar indicating each year of service. Many years later, Admiral Cherry was offered one of the medals and graciously received it.*

U1. LORD MAYOR OF LONDON'S GOLD MEDAL FOR THE DESTRUCTION OF ZEPPELIN L15

Date: 1916.
Campaign: First World War.
Branch of Service: Royal Artillery.
Ribbon:
Metal: 9 carat gold.
Size: 29mm.
Description: (Obverse) the arms of Sir Charles Wakefield within a double ring inscribed PRESENTED BY THE LORD MAYOR round the top and COLONEL SIR CHARLES WAKEFIELD round the foot; (reverse) An anti-aircraft gun and two scrolls inscribed WELL HIT and MARCH 31st and number L15. It is engraved near the top with the rank and name of the recipient. It was issued unmounted but various ornamental suspensions loops were later fitted privately.
Comments: *The Lord Mayor of London offered a reward of £500 to the first gun crew to shoot down a Zeppelin. On 3 April 1916 Capt. J. Harris submitted a claim on behalf of the Purfleet gun crew that they were responsible for the bringing down of the airship L15, but it later transpired that gun crews from Abbey Wood, Dartford, Erith, North Woolwich, Plumstead and the Royal Arsenal, among others, were also involved. It was decided to use the prize money in procuring these medals, a total of 353 being awarded.*

U2. DUNKIRK MEDAL

Date: 1960.
Ribbon: Chrome yellow with one thin and one wide red stripe each side with two very thin black lines bisecting both sides.
Metal: Bronze.
Size: 36mm wide.
Description: (Obverse) a shield bearing the arms of Dunkirk (a lion passant above a heraldic dolphin) mounted on an anchor; (reverse) a circle bearing a burning lamp with DUNKERQUE 1940 beneath, surrounded by a laurel wreath and surmounted by crossed swords; the whole mounted on and surrounded by a laurel wreath.
Comments: *This medal was first made available to veterans of the Dunkirk evacuation and later administered by the now disbanded Dunkirk Veterans Association. It was created by the French National Association of Veterans of the Fortified Sector of Flanders and of Dunkirk and awarded in recognition of the sacrifice of 30,000 combatants between 29 May and 3 June 1940.*

U3. BOMBER COMMAND MEDAL

Date: 1985.
Campaign: Second World War.
Branch of Service: RAF Bomber Command.
Ribbon: Midnight blue with a central flame stripe and blue-grey edges.
Metal: Cupro-nickel.
Size: 36mm.
Description: (Obverse) A Tudor crown surmounting a laurel wreath containing the letters RAF, flanked by smaller wreaths containing the brevet letters of the aircrew signifying courage, team spirit and leadership; (reverse) a Lancaster bomber flanked by the dates 1939 and 1945 with inscription A TRIBUTE TO THE AIRCREW OF BOMBER COMMAND round the circumference.
Comments: *Produced at the behest of Air Vice Marshal Donald Bennett following a design competition in MEDAL NEWS. The competition was the brainchild of author Alan Cooper campaigning on behalf of Bomber Command veterans. The first medal was struck by Lady Harris (widow of the wartime commander of Bomber Command).*

U4. NORMANDY CAMPAIGN MEDAL

Date: 1987.
Campaign: Service in the Normandy campaign between June 6 and August 20, 1944.
Branch of Service: All British and Allied forces.
Ribbon: Dark red with deep navy blue stripes towards the edges and light blue edges, symbolising the three services.
Metal: Cupro-nickel.
Size: 36mm.
Description: (Obverse) insignia of the combined services surrounded by 13 stars (representing the USA) and the inscription BLESSENT MON COEUR D'UNE LANGUEUR MONOTONE ("soothe my heart with dull languor"), a quotation from Verlaine broadcast by the BBC at 21.15 on June 5, 1944 to signal the start of the D-Day operations. (Reverse) a tank landing craft with its ramp on the beaches of France symbolised by fleurs-de lis; NORMANDY CAMPAIGN round the top and the date of the campaign inscribed on the ramp. The medal is fitted with a plain suspension bar while the ribbon bears a clasp inscribed NORMANDY between oak leaves.
Comments: *Commissioned by the Normandy Veterans Association whose Welfare and Benevolent Fund benefited from the proceeds of sales.*

U5. ARCTIC CAMPAIGN MEDAL

Date: 1991.
Campaign: Second World War.
Branch of Service: Personnel of the Russian convoys.
Ribbon: 32mm watered weave in equal bands of blue and white representing ice and sea.
Metal: Cupro-nickel.
Size: 36mm.
Description: (Obverse) a liberty ship framed in the cross-hair of a U-boat periscope, with the inscription FOR SERVICE IN THE ARCTIC ZONE 1939-45 round the top; (reverse) four figures representing merchant seaman, Royal Naval, Army and RAF personnel, with the inscription THE ARCTIC CAMPAIGN round the top.
Comments: *This award was proposed by the Russian Convoy Club in conjunction with the North Russia Club, who are the beneficiaries of the project.*

U6. MERCHANT NAVAL SERVICE MEDAL

Date: 1992.
Campaign: Second World War.
Branch of Service: Merchant Navy and DEMS Gunners.
Ribbon: Dark blue with a central narrow white stripe flanked by broader green and red stripes, representing the navigation lights of an approaching ship.
Metal: Cupro-nickel.
Size: 36mm.
Description: (Obverse) a stockless anchor encompassed by its heavy cable, surmounted by the initials MN; (reverse) a capstan surmounted by a naval crown and flanked by grotesque sea monsters, the whole encircled by a rope tied at the foot in a reef knot. The outer circumferance is inscribed FOR MERCHANT NAVAL SERVICE. The medal is fitted to a plain suspension bar by an ornamental scroll.
Comments: *Veterans were eligible for this medal in respect of at least two years' service in the Merchant Navy. The award was inspired by the fact that although service in the mercantile marine was recognised after World War I it was ignored after World War II. King George's Fund for Sailors' benefits from the sale of this medal.*

U7. ALLIED EX-PRISONERS OF WAR MEDAL

Date: 1991.
Campaign: All wars of the 20th century.
Branch of Service: Prisoners of war.
Ribbon: Green with red edges. The centre has a broad black stripe edged in white, having a white strand of barbed wire running down the middle.
Metal: Cupro-nickel.
Size: 36mm.
Description: (Obverse) a young bird trapped by barbed wire, against a globe of the world, with the inscription INTERNATIONAL PRISONERS OF WAR; (reverse) a twisted barb of wire whose four strands divide the inscription INTREPID AGAINST ALL ADVERSITY. Fitted with a plain suspension bar.
Comments: *This award proposed by the National Ex Prisoners of War Association is applicable to any former PoWs whose countries were allies of Britain at the time of their capture irrespective of whether the United Kingdom was itself involved in the conflict.*

U8. RESTORATION OF PEACE MEDAL

Date: 1995.
Campaign: Second World War.
Branch of Service: Armed forces and civilians involved in the war effort.
Ribbon: Rich claret with a central broad gold stripe.
Metal: High-security HS1 gold-coloured alloy.
Size: 36mm.
Description: (Obverse) the letter V enclosing the date 1945, superimposed on a globe with the inscription A TIME FOR PEACE round the circumference; (reverse) a simple wreath enclosing the inscription FOR ALL WHO STRIVED (<u>sic</u>) FOR PEACE. The plain suspension bar is fitted to the medal by a peace dove on both sides.
Comments: *Produced at the behest of the British Red Cross Society to mark the 50th anniversary of the cessation of hostilities in the Second World War.*

U9. SUEZ CANAL ZONE MEDAL

Date: 1995.
Campaign: Suez Canal Zone, 1945-57.
Branch of Service: British and French forces.
Ribbon: Sand-coloured edged with narrow stripes of red, white and blue. A broad central crimson stripe has a light blue stripe down the middle.
Metal: High-security HS1 gold-coloured alloy.
Size: 36mm.
Description: (Obverse) the Sphinx and Pyramid flanked by the dates 1951-54 and 1956-57, representing the two most recent periods of conflict; (reverse) stylised papyrus grass with the words TO MARK SERVICE IN THE CANAL ZONE at left. Fitted with an ornamental suspension bar in the form of Pharaonic wings.
Comments: *The Ex-Services Mental Welfare Society (Combat Stress) is the beneficiary of this project.*

U10. NATIONAL SERVICE MEDAL

Date: 1991.
Campaign: Period of conscription, 1939-60.
Branch of Service: National Service, both military and civilian.
Ribbon: Dark blue with a narrow central gold stripe and narrow white and red stripes at the edges representing the involvement of the Royal British Legion.
Metal: Cupro-nickel.
Size: 36mm.
Description: (Obverse) the seated figure of Britannia supported by a lion, with the inscription NATIONAL SERVICE 1939-1960; (reverse) a wreath enclosing the inscription FOR CROWN AND COUNTRY. Fitted with scrolled suspension.
Comments: *Between January 1939 when the National Service Act was passed, and December 1960 when it was repealed, some 5,300,000 young people were conscripted into the armed services. The medal was proposed by the Royal British Legion and almost 100,000 have been issued to date.*

U11. JORDAN SERVICE MEDAL

Instituted: April 1997.

Branch of Service: British ex-service personnel who served in the Hashemite Kingdom of Jordan between 1948 and 1957 and again during the 1958 emergency, i.e. the 16th Independent Parachute Brigade and attached units.

Ribbon: Golden sand, edged on both sides with four thin stripes of the Jordanian national colours (black, white, green and red).

Metal: Gilt brass.

Size: 36mm.

Description: (Obverse) Effigy of King Hussein; (reverse) inscription in raised lettering: FOR SERVICE IN THE HASHEMITE KINGDOM OF JORDAN, with or without the date 1958 below.

Comments: *This medal was produced on the initiative of G.E. Harris of Haverfordwest with the approval of the late King Hussein. Sales of the medal benefit the SSAFA Forces Help charity. It was manufactured by the Bigbury Mint, Ermington, Devon. To date 1,725 veterans (including two ladies) have applied for the medal (either version), including two of the four female nurses who served in Jordan.*

U12. HONG KONG SERVICE MEDAL

Instituted: 1999.

Branch of Service: All former civil and military personnel who served for a minimum of six months in the Crown Colony of Hong Kong, or their next of kin.

Ribbon: Pale blue with a central yellow stripe.

Metal: Gilt metal.

Size: 36mm.

Description: (Obverse) Bird of Paradise surounded by the words HONG KONG SERVICE MEDAL 1841–1997; (reverse) HONG KONG in Cantonese characters surrounded by a circular wreath. The medal is suspended from a unique suspender depicting two mythical Chinese dragons.

Comments: *SSAFA Forces Help, the ex-servicemen's charity, benefits from the sales of this medal.*

U13. BRITISH FORCES GERMANY MEDAL

Instituted: 1999.

Branch of Service: All British service personnel in Germany, 1945–89.

Ribbon: 32mm NATO blue with central narrow stripes of black, red and gold (the German national colours).

Metal: Rhodium-plated cupro-nickel.

Size: 36mm.

Description: (Obverse) Standing figures of a soldier and airman holding the Union Jack, BRITISH FORCES GERMAY round the top with ARMY 1945–1989 RAF round the foot; (reverse) a laurel wreath incorporating the recipient's name, rank and service number over the years of service. Plain suspension bar. Royal Naval personnel who served in Germany are awarded a clasp to the medal.

Comments: *All men and women who served with the British Forces in Germany from the end of World War II until 1989 are eligible for this medal designed by Martin Duchemin and available from Royal British Legion Industries.*

INTERNATIONAL MEDALLISTS
REPLACEMENT MEDAL SERVICE

DO YOU KNOW ABOUT THE
COMMEMORATIVE MEDALS
AVAILABLE FOR:

- HONG KONG SERVICE
- NATIONAL SERVICE
- MERCHANT NAVAL SERVICE
- SUEZ (CANAL ZONE)
- NORMANDY CAMPAIGN
- ARCTIC CAMPAIGN
- PRISONERS OF WAR
- BOMBER COMMAND W.W.II
- RESTORATION OF PEACE 1945
- MALTA G.C. 50th ANNIV. *

DO YOU KNOW THAT EACH MEDAL
BENEFITS THE RELEVANT CHARITY
OR ASSOCIATION (EXCEPT *)

DO YOU KNOW THAT OVER
£375,000 HAS BEEN DONATED
TO DATE (APRIL 2001) FROM
THE SALE OF THESE MEDALS?

APPLICATION FORMS AND DETAILS
OF THESE AND REPLACEMENT MEDALS
AVAILABLE BY CONTACTING

AWARD PRODUCTIONS LTD. (DEPT MYB)
PO BOX 300, SHREWSBURY, SY5 6WP, UK.
TELEPHONE; 01952 510053 FAX; 01952 510765
E-MAIL; award@crown-lane.co.uk   WEB SITE: www.awardmedals.com

ALSO SEE COMMEMORATIVE MEDALS SECTION OF THE MEDAL YEARBOOK

MEDALLISTS TO THE
ROYAL BRITISH LEGION

Provincial
Police
medals

In addition to the official medals and decorations awarded to police officers (see nos. 271, etc.) there are a number of medals which have been instituted by county or civic constabularies for long and distinguished service. As the ribbons of these awards are sometimes noted on the tunics of policemen we have decided to include these semi-official awards in a separate section. It is our intention, in a future edition of MEDAL YEARBOOK, to extend this treatment to the semi-official awards made by county and regional fire brigades and the Special Constabulary, on the same basis. It is also the intention to include the current market value of all of these medals where possible.

We are indebted to Roger Campion for furnishing us with details of no fewer than 20 provincial police medals, the result of a long time study of this absorbing subject. Should readers know of any other medals we would be grateful for their details for inclusion in forthcoming editions of the MEDAL YEARBOOK.

The medals have been listed here in alphabetical order by place of origin, irrespective of the date of institution. The Metropolitan Police, founded in 1829, and its neighbour, the City of London Police, are conspicuous by their absence from this survey, and it is suspected that both forces must have produced distinctive awards at some time during their long history.

Accordingly, the first distinctive police medal so far recorded is the Liverpool City Police Order of Merit which dates from 1852. Significantly, several other awards were instituted in 1897, the year of Queen Victoria's Diamond Jubilee, a period when the resources of the police forces must have been stretched to the limit in crowd control. This set the ball rolling, and in the ensuing years many constabularies followed suit. The great majority of the older-established awards ceased by the end of 1951, when the Police LS&GC was introduced. These medals therefore survive as tangible mementoes of

the period when distinct constabularies existed at county, city and even borough level. Only one county constabulary—Dunbartonshire—is thought to have awarded a medal to its regular officers to celebrate the coronation of 1902 and this is included for the first time this year, thanks to the knack of Ian Hall in unearthing previously unknown police medals. There may be more out there that we are yet to hear of. If you know of any, please get in touch to ensure that the section is as complete as possible. A few entries are reproduced without pictures and we are keen to put this right, if you can help please let us know.

All the forces in the section are now gone and the medals are one of the few tangible mementoes of the history of policing in the United Kingdom and the days when it was very much a local matter. Most of the medals are attractive in design and feature the city or borough coat of arms, a further reminder of truly local community policing.

Because of the scarcity of these medals on the market it has been decided not to attempt to give valuations for this section.

For more information on the police medals of the world you need:

A GUIDE TO POLICE MEDALS
OF THE WORLD

by Roger Campion

Published December 2001   **Price £19.95**

P1. ABERDEEN CITY CONSTABULARY MEDAL

Instituted: 5 July 1909.
Branch of Service: Aberdeen City Constabulary.
Ribbon: Royal blue.
Metal: Silver.
Size: 39mm.
Description: (Obverse) The Seal of the City of Aberdeen with the legend AWARDED BY THE TOWN COUNCIL OF ABERDEEN around the circumference; (reverse) a laurel wreath with the inscriptions FOR SPECIAL SERVICE and CITY CONSTABULARY with a space between the two for the rank and name of the recipient and the date of the award. The exergue has a motif of a constable's helmet superimposed on a pair of crossed truncheons. The ribbon was attached by a ring suspender.
Comments: *Awarded to officers who distinguished themselves in the execution of their duty. The first award made in 1909 was cast in gold but further awards were of silver. The medal was discontinued in 1936. The Constabulary was founded in 1818 but became a part of Grampian Police on 16 April 1975.*

P2. BIRKENHEAD CONSTABULARY GOOD SERVICE MEDAL

Instituted: 13 September 1897.
Branch of Service: Birkenhead Constabulary.
Ribbon: Red with two stripes of dark blue all equal in width.
Metal: Silver and Bronze.
Size: 39mm.
Description: (Obverse) left-facing conjoined Young Head and Old Head of Queen Victoria surrounded with the inscription VICTORIA DIAMOND JUBILEE 1837–1897; (reverse) the Arms of Birkenhead and town motto contained within an oak and laurel wreath tied at its base all surrounded by the legend FOR GOOD SERVICE and BIRKENHEAD CONSTABULARY. The recipient's name, rank and number were engraved on the rim. A plain straight swivelling suspender was employed.
Comments: *The medal was issued to all members of the constabulary with 20 or more years service to mark the Diamond Jubilee of Queen Victoria. Silver medals (10) were issued to officers and 12 bronze medals to sergeants and constables. The medals were presented in a black box marked in gold lettering with the recipient's rank and number. Although it wasn't formally abolished until 1951 no more medals were ever issued. Founded in 1833, Birkenhead amalgamated with the Cheshire Constabulary in 1967 and became a part of Merseyside Police on 1 April 1974.*

P3. BOLTON COUNTY BOROUGH POLICE LONG SERVICE MEDAL

Instituted: 30 July 1913.
Branch of Service: Bolton County Borough Police.
Ribbon: Blue with two red stripes (5mm) placed 6mm from each end.
Metal: Silver.
Size: 34mm.
Description: (Obverse) the arms of the City of Bolton surrounded by a raised circle with the legend FOR GOOD SERVICE (above) and BOLTON BOROUGH POLICE (below); (reverse) a laurel wreath surrounding a central field containing the inscription PRESENTED BY THE WATCH COMMITTEE and the date of the award in four lines. The medal is suspended from an ornate bar attached by a claw fitting.
Comments: *Initially awarded for 25 years service without default, the period was reduced to 20 years in 1931. Silver slip-on bars were awarded for each additional five years service. The bars were plain and usually inscribed with OVER 25 YEARS or OVER 30 YEARS although unmarked examples exist. The medals were engraved on the lower rim with the recipient's rank, name and date of appointment. Discontinued at the outbreak of World War II and formally abolished in 1951. The Bolton County Borough Police Force was founded in 1839. In 1969 it joined with several others to form the Lancashire Constabulary but became part of the Greater Manchester Police on 1 April 1974.*

P4. BOOTLE BOROUGH CONSTABULARY GOOD CONDUCT MEDAL

Instituted: August 1897.
Branch of Service: Bootle Borough Constabulary.
Ribbon: Five equal stripes of blue, white, blue, white, blue.
Metal: Silver and bronze.
Size: 32mm.
Description: (Obverse) the Old Head of Queen Victoria with the inscription VICTORIA DIAMOND JUBILEE 1837–1897; (reverse) the Coat of Arms of the Borough with BOROUGH OF BOOTLE above. This is surrounded by an outer ring bearing the words AWARDED FOR GOOD CONDUCT 1837–1897. The rank and name of the recipient was engraved on the lower rim. The medal hung from a plain straight suspender and claw fitting.
Comments: *Initially issued by the Watch Committee to commemorate the Diamond Jubilee and retained for award to members of the force for 15 years service without blemish. Bronze medals were awarded to sergeants and constables and silver medals to officers of the rank of inspector and above. Plain bars were awarded for further unblemished service. It was abolished in 1948. The force was founded on 1 July 1887 but ceased to exist in 1967 on amalgamation with the Liverpool City Police to form the Liverpool and Bootle Police. It now forms part of the Merseyside Police.*

P5. BRIGHTON BOROUGH POLICE MERITORIOUS CONDUCT MEDAL

Instituted: 7 February 1902
Branch of Service: Brighton Borough Police.
Ribbon: Royal blue.
Metal: 22ct gold.
Size: 34mm.
Description: (Obverse) Coat of Arms of Brighton Borough within a wreath of laurel; (reverse) engraved with the rank and name of the recipient, the date of the award and brief details of the circumstances. The medal was hung from a gold suspender ring with a plain brooch bar some (but not all) of which were inscribed BOROUGH OF BRIGHTON POLICE MEDAL for fixing to the tunic.
Comments: *Issued to all ranks of the force for especially meritorious service. The first medal was awarded for saving life at the scene of a fire with others granted later for saving lives at sea, the arrest of an armed criminal and destroying a ferocious dog. There is one recorded instance of a bar being awarded for a second act of courage. The bar was ornate with laurel leaves at the top and sides and inscribed with the name of the recipient and date of the award.*

The Brighton Borough Police was founded in 1838 but ceased to exist as a separate force on 31 December 1967 when it amalgamated with the Sussex Constabulary. It was a part of the Sussex Combined Police from 1 April 1943 until 31 March 1947 for the duration of the Second World War.

P6. BRISTOL CITY POLICE LONG SERVICE AND GOOD CONDUCT MEDAL

Instituted: 8 December 1926.
Branch of Service: Bristol City Police.
Ribbon: Dark red with a central green stripe 6.5mm wide.
Metal: Silver.
Size: 36mm.
Description: (Obverse) arms of the City of Bristol surrounded by a band with the legend FOR GOOD SERVICE above and BRISTOL CITY POLICE below; (reverse) a laurel wreath tied with a ribbon with the recipient's name, rank and number inscribed in the centre. It was suspended from a plain straight swivelling bar
Comments: *Rewarded for 17 years service with exemplary conduct. Bars were awarded for each additional five years service. The bars were also made of silver. The medal was discontinued in 1951 on the introduction of the National Police Long Service and Good Conduct Medal. A total of 610 were awarded, made up as follows: 112 without bars, 359 with 1 bar, 105 with 2 bars, 23 with 3 bars, 11 with 4 bars. Bristol City Police was founded in 1836. On 1 April 1974 the force amalgamated with the Somerset and Bath Constabulary and a part of the Gloucestershire Constabulary to form the current Avon and Somerset Constabulary.*

P7. CAMBRIDGE CITY POLICE LONG SERVICE MEDAL

Instituted: 1913.
Branch of Service: Cambridge City Police.
Ribbon: Red with a blue central stripe.
Metal: Silver.
Size: 36mm.
Description: (Obverse) the Coat of Arms of the City of Cambridge with the legend CAMBRIDGE BOROUGH POLICE FOR LONG SERVICE around the circumference; (reverse) a wreath of laurel tied with a ribbon with the rank and name of the recipient and date of the award inscribed in the centre. The medal was attached by a claw to a plain straight swivelling suspender
Comments: *Awarded to members of the force after 25 years service without blemish. It appears to have been a short-lived medal with no record of any award after 1914. The force was founded in 1836 but ceased to exist in 1965 when it was amalgamated with the Cambridgeshire Constabulary to form the Mid-Anglia Police. It was renamed the Cambridgeshire Constabulary on 1 April 1974.*

P8. CARDIFF CITY POLICE AND FIRE BRIGADE MEDAL FOR CONSPICUOUS BRAVERY

Instituted: 11 May 1908.
Branch of Service: Cardiff City Police Force and Fire Brigade.
Ribbon: Yellow with three red chevrons.
Metal: Silver.
Size: 39mm.
Description: (Obverse) the Coat of Arms of the City of Cardiff with the legend FOR CONSPICUOUS BRAVERY below; (reverse) a seven line inscription PRESENTED BY THE CARDIFF WATCH COMMITTEE TO (rank, number and name) FOR CONSPICUOUS BRAVERY. A claw fitting and ornate swivelling scroll suspender were used.
Comments: *The medal carried a non-pensionable allowance of 2/- (10p) a week for life. Plain silver, slip-on clasps were awarded for any subsequent act of bravery. The unusual ribbon displayed a single chevron when worn in undress uniform. The medal was not awarded after 1929. The Cardiff City Police was founded as the Cardiff Borough Police in 1836 and became a part of South Wales Constabulary on 1 April 1969.*

P8A. DUMBARTONSHIRE COUNTY COUNCIL CORONATION MEDAL 1902

Instituted: 1902.
Branch of Service: Dunbartonshire County Constabulary.
Ribbon: Royal blue.
Metal: Silver and bronze.
Size: 34mm.
Description: (Obverse) the crowned and robed bust of King Edward VII facing right with the words EDWARD VII and the date 1902 on the left and KING OF GREAT BRITAIN & IRELAND EMPEROR OF INDIA in nine lines in the right third of the medal; (reverse) the coat of arms of Dunbartonshire with the date JUNE 26 (left) and 1902 (right) in a scroll on each side. The legend DUMBARTONSHIRE COUNTY COUNCIL lies around the upper circumference. It should be noted that subsequently the county name changed its spelling to Dunbartonhire although the county town remains Dumbarton. In a scrolled panel in the lower half of the medal is the inscription PRESENTED TO MEMBERS OF THE DUMBARTONSHIRE CONSTABULARY TO COMMEMORATE THE CORONATION OF HIS MAJESTY KING EDWARD VII in five lines. The medal hangs from a plain ring suspender. Issued unnamed.
Comments: *Awarded at the time of the 1902 coronation to all members of the Constabulary. Silver medals were given to officers of the rank of inspector and above and bronze to sergeants and constables. No more than 100 of both types were issued. The Dunbartonshire Constabulary was formed in 1840 but ceased to exist in 1975 when it became part of Strathclyde Police.*

P9. EXETER CITY POLICE LONG SERVICE AND EFFICIENCY MEDAL

Instituted: May 1928.

Branch of Service: Exeter City Police.

Ribbon: White with two broad (8mm) grass green stripes. A miniature has been seen with the full-size ribbon folded in at each end to leave a green ribbon with a central white stripe all of equal width.

Metal: Silver.

Size: 36mm.

Description: (Obverse) the arms of the City of Exeter with the legend FOR LONG SERVICE AND EFFICIENCY around the circumference; (reverse) hat of maintenance superimposed on two crossed swords of state with the legend CITY OF EXETER POLICE FORCE around the circumference. It was suspended from a straight bar.

Comments: *Awarded for 17 years efficient and zealous service without default. Bars were awarded for each additional five years service at 22, 27 and 32 years. All medals were engraved on the rim with the name of the recipient. About 35 were awarded. Discontinued in June 1939.*

Exeter City Police was founded in 1836 but ceased to exist as a separate force in 1966 on amalgamation with the Devon Constabulary to form the Devon and Exeter Constabulary. It is now a part of the Devon and Cornwall Constabulary.

P10. GRIMSBY COUNTY BOROUGH POLICE GOOD SERVICE MEDAL

Instituted: November 1914.

Branch of Service: Grimsby County Borough Police.

Ribbon: Dark blue with crimson edges and a crimson central line.

Metal: Silver and bronze.

Size: 35mm.

Description: (Obverse) Coat of Arms of the County Borough of Grimsby inside an oak wreath. Around the circumference is the inscription FOR GOOD SERVICE above and COUNTY BOROUGH OF GRIMSBY POLICE below; (reverse) a laurel wreath tied with a ribbon around a central field containing the legend PRESENTED BY THE WATCH COMMITTEE and the date in five lines. The recipient's rank and name are engraved on the lower rim. The medal employed a claw fitting and plain straight swivelling suspender.

Comments: *The medal was given as a reward for 25 years unblemished service. Officers of the rank of inspector or above were awarded silver medals and sergeants and constables bronze. At least one example exists with the date of the award engraved on the lower rim not the reverse. The medal was discontinued in 1941 although serving holders were permitted to wear them until they retired. The force was founded in 1846 and survived until 1969 when it was amalgamated with the Lincolnshire County Constabulary and Lincoln City Police. It became a part of Humberside Police on 1 April 1974.*

P11. LEAMINGTON SPA BOROUGH POLICE CORONATION MEDAL

Instituted: 1902.
Branch of Service: Leamington Spa Borough Police.
Ribbon: Sea blue.
Metal: Silver.
Size: 32mm.
Description: (Obverse) the conjoined crowned heads of King Edward VII and Queen Alexandra inscribed HM EDWARD VII KING to the left and HM ALEXANDRA QUEEN to the right with PROCLAIMED 1901 at the base; (reverse) inscribed with the words PRESENTED BY ALDERMAN WACKRILL JP TO THE LEAMINGTON BOROUGH POLICE FORCE AND FIRE BRIGADE ON THE OCCASION OF THE CORONATION OF HIS MAJESTY EDWARD VII JUNE 26th 1902 in eleven lines. The medal hung from a plain suspender attached by a ring.
Comments: *Awarded to celebrate the coronation in 1902. The Leamington Spa Borough Police was founded in 1835 and amalgamated with the Warwickshire County Constabulary in 1947.*

P12. LINCOLN CITY POLICE GOOD SERVICE MEDAL

Instituted: 17 June 1926.
Branch of Service: Lincoln City Police.
Ribbon: Dark red with a broad green central stripe.
Metal: Silver.
Size: 32mm.
Description: (Obverse) arms of the City of Lincoln surrounded by a laurel wreath and surmounted by a scroll bearing the motto FLOREAT LINDUM with the legend FOR GOOD SERVICE above and LINCOLN CITY POLICE below; (reverse) a wreath of laurel tied at the base with a ribbon usually with the recipient's name, rank and number inscribed centrally. Examples exist with the central field left blank and the recipient's name inscribed on the lower rim. It was suspended from a swivelling straight bar by a claw.
Comments: *Awarded by the City Watch Committee to officers on completion of 20 years service without default. It was abolished in October 1941 although holders still serving were allowed to wear their medals until they retired. The force was founded in 1836 but ceased to exist on 1 April 1967 on amalgamation with the Lincolnshire Police.*

P13. LIVERPOOL CITY POLICE ORDER OF MERIT

Instituted: October 1851.
Branch of Service: Liverpool City Police Force.
Ribbon: Blue with red edges and a red central stripe.
Metal: Silver.
Size: 32mm.
Description: (Obverse) Coat of Arms of the City of Liverpool surrounded with a laurel leaf and with the city motto DEUS NOBIS HAEC OTIA FECIT in a banner above and the date 9th OCT 1851 along the bottom; (reverse) the inscription PRESENTED BY THE WATCH COMMITTEE TO (engraved name) AS A REWARD FOR GOOD CONDUCT in nine lines in the central field with ORDER OF MERIT (above) and LIVERPOOL POLICE FORCE (below) around the circumference on a raised circle. The medal hung from a plain swivelling suspender bar.
Comments: *Awarded to officers with good conduct records for at least five years to commemorate the visit of Queen Victoria to the city on 9 October 1851. Each period of five years was signified by the award of a bar up to a maximum of three. There were 112 recipients at a parade held on 5 August 1852–72 were awarded with one bar, 26 with two bars and 14 with three. The Liverpool City Police was amalgamated with the Bootle Borough Constabulary in 1967 and became part of Merseyside Police in 1974.*

P14. LIVERPOOL CITY POLICE DIAMOND JUBILEE GOOD SERVICE MEDAL

Instituted: 1897.
Branch of Service: Liverpool City Police.
Ribbon: Blue with red edges and a red central stripe.
Metal: Silver and bronze.
Size: 32mm.
Description: (Obverse) the Old Head of Queen Victoria with the words VICTORIA DIAMOND JUBILEE above and the dates 1837–1897 below; (reverse) the Liver Bird on a shield topped with the royal crown surrounded by a wreath of oak and laurel. A scroll above the shield contains the legend DEUS NOBIS HAEC OTIA FECIT. In addition the words FOR GOOD SERVICE and LIVERPOOL CITY POLICE are found around the circumference above and below the shield. With a claw fitting and straight swivelling suspender.
Comments: *Silver medals were awarded to officers of the rank of inspector and above who had 20 years service with unblemished records on 20 June 1897 or were serving officers on 20 June 1887 and had continued to serve for a further 10 years without default. Bronze medals were awarded to sergeants and constables with 20 years approved service.*

P15. LIVERPOOL CITY POLICE GOOD SERVICE MEDAL

Instituted: 1900.
Branch of Service: Liverpool City Police.
Ribbon: Red with a single blue diagonal stripe (silver medal); blue with a single red diagonal stripe (bronze medal). From 1930 both ribbons were changed to a more conventional design: red with a blue central stripe and a white stripe on either side (silver); blue with a central red stripe and a white stripe on either side (bronze).
Metal: Silver and bronze.
Size: 32 mm.
Description: (Obverse) identical to the reverse of the Liverpool City Police Diamond Jubilee issue (P14); (reverse) a wreath of laurel with a central field containing an inscription with the words PRESENTED BY THE WATCH COMMITTEE, sometimes with the date of the award and the recipient's name engraved on the rim, sometimes with all details on the reverse.
Comments: *Inspired by the medal issued to commemorate the Diamond Jubilee of Queen Victoria in 1897 with the same qualifying criteria appilcable. From 1918 onwards the bronze medal was given after 20 years and the silver medal awarded after 25 years service. A bar was awarded for each additional five years service after the award of the silver medal. Service in excess of 30 years was denoted by a bar with the legend SERVICE OVER 30 YEARS. The medals were discontinued in 1951.*

P16. MANCHESTER CITY POLICE BRAVERY MEDAL

Instituted: February 1894.
Branch of Service: Manchester City Police.
Ribbon: Crimson.
Metal: Silver.
Size: 32mm.
Description: (Obverse) The Coat of Arms of the City of Manchester inscribed above with MANCHESTER CITY POLICE and below with FOR BRAVERY; (reverse) a laurel wreath tied at the base with a ribbon surrounding the central area which was available for the rank and name of the recipient together with the date of the award. The medal was fitted to a swivelling suspender of ornate design by means of a claw and attached to the uniform by a buckle pin.
Comments: *Awarded to members of the City Force in recognition of acts of outstanding bravery. Further acts performed could be rewarded by the granting of a bar. 71 medals were awarded and it is thought that four bars were granted. No medals were granted after 1948. The force was founded in 1839 and amalgamated with the Salford City Police in 1968 until 1 April 1974 when it became a part of the Greater Manchester Police.*

P17. NEW WINDSOR BOROUGH POLICE CORONATION MEDAL 1902

Instituted: 1902.
Branch of Service: New Windsor Borough Police.
Ribbon: Red with green stripe at either edge 6.5mm wide.
Metal: Bronze.
Size: 32mm.
Description: (Obverse) The conjoined heads of King Edward VII and Queen Alexandra facing right with the words KING EDWARD and QUEEN ALEXANDRA around. The designer's name is also visible; (reverse) the coat of arms of the Borough of Windsor and WINDSOR BOROUGH in a scroll beneath and a crown above. The word POLICE is shown below the scroll with an encircling band and the inscription TO COMMEMORATE THE CORONATION 1902. With a claw fitting and straight swivelling suspender.
Comments: *Issued to members of the force who took part in the Coronation. The medals were originally issued unnamed although some exist with the name and rank of the recipient engraved on the lower rim. The New Windsor Borough was founded in 1836 but merged with the Berkshire Constabulary in April 1947. It now forms part of the Thames Valley Police.*

P18. NEW WINDSOR BOROUGH POLICE CORONATION MEDAL 1911

Instituted: 1911.
Branch of Service: New Windsor Borough Police.
Ribbon: Red with green stripe at either edge 6.5mm wide.
Metal: Bronze
Size: 32mm.
Description: (Obverse) the conjoined heads of King George V and Queen Mary facing left; (reverse) very similar to the 1902 medal with the coat of arms of the Borough of Windsor but without the crown—all surrounded by a band containing the words TO COMMEMORATE THE CORONATION 1911.
Comments: *Issued to all officers of all ranks who were on duty during the Coronation.*

P19. PLYMOUTH CITY POLICE CONSPICUOUS BRAVERY AND GOOD SERVICE MEDAL

Instituted: 16 April 1930.
Branch of Service: Plymouth City Police.
Ribbon: Dark red with two broad blue stripes and a central blue line.
Metal: Silver.
Size: 36 mm.
Description: (Obverse) arms of the City of Plymouth surrounded by a laurel leaf wreath topped with an imperial crown to which the suspension ring was attached; (reverse) a rectangular panel for the recipient's name and the legend PLYMOUTH CITY CONSTABULARY above and GOOD SERVICE below. Very few medals were inscribed with the recipient's name.
Comments: *Awarded for 17 years service without default or for an act of conspicuous gallantry. Bars were awarded for each additional five years service. Where an officer who had been awarded a medal for service performed an act of gallantry he was awarded a bar inscribed FOR GALLANTRY. Where the award was for gallantry and the officer subsequently fulfilled the conditions relating to an award for good service he was also entitled to a bar. There are no known instances of this occurring and any inscription on the bar is a matter for conjecture. Approximately 200+ medals were awarded. Discontinued in 1951 on the introduction of the National Police Long Service and Good Conduct Medal. Plymouth City Police was founded in 1836 but ceased to exist as a separate force in June 1967 when it was amalgamated with two other forces to form the Devon and Cornwall Constabulary.*

P20. READING BOROUGH POLICE BRAVERY MEDAL

Instituted: 26 April 1904.
Branch of Service: Reading Borough Police.
Ribbon: Royal blue with a central white stripe 4.5 mm wide.
Metal: Bronze.
Size: 39 mm.
Description: (Obverse) The Arms of the Borough of Reading with the legend READING POLICE above and FOR BRAVERY below on a surrounding raised circle; (reverse) left plain for the recipient's details to be engraved. An ornate scrolled swivelling suspender was used.
Comments: *Instituted at the suggestion of the Chief Constable, Captain John Henderson, and awarded to members of the force for acts of special bravery or for saving life. Most recorded awards were made for stopping runaway horses. A bar was awarded for further acts by the same officer (one such award recorded—to Constable 17 Gillings in 1908 and 1909). Gratuities were usually given to the recipient. It was discontinued in 1951. The Reading Borough Police was founded in 1836 but became part of the Thames Valley Police on 1 April 1968.*

P21. REIGATE BOROUGH POLICE GOOD SERVICE MEDAL

Instituted: September 1913.
Branch of Service: Reigate Borough Police.
Ribbon: Medium blue.
Metal: Silver.
Size: 32 mm.
Description: (Obverse) the Coat of Arms of the Borough with the inscription 25 YEARS GOOD SERVICE above and REIGATE BOROUGH POLICE below; (reverse) a wreath of oak leaves with the recipient's rank and name and the date of the award. The medal hung from a plain straight suspender.
Comments: *Awarded to all members of the force for 25 years good service without a blemish on their records. The medal was discontinued in 1943 when the borough force was combined with the Surrey Constabulary and Guildford Borough Police under the wartime defence regulations to form the Surrey Joint Constabulary.*

P22. ROCHDALE COUNTY BOROUGH POLICE BRAVERY MEDAL

Instituted: 15 November 1928.
Branch of Service: Rochdale County Borough Police Force.
Ribbon: Red.
Metal: Silver.
Size: 35 mm.
Description: (Obverse) the Rochdale Coat of Arms and borough motto surrounded by the legend ROCHDALE COUNTY BOROUGH POLICE; (reverse) a three line inscription AWARDED BY THE WATCH COMMITTEE followed by the rank and name of the recipient. Around the circumference were the words FOR EXTREME BRAVERY. It was suspended from a swivelling suspender with a floral design and attached to the uniform by an ornate pin buckle.
Comments: *Awarded to members of the Borough Police Force for acts of outstanding bravery. It was retained after the Police Long Service and Good Conduct Medal was introduced but finally discontinued in 1969 when the Rochdale County Borough Police was amalgamated with others to form the Lancashire Constabulary. It became a part of the Greater Manchester Police on 1 April 1974.*

P23. ROCHDALE COUNTY BOROUGH POLICE LONG SERVICE MEDAL

Instituted: 14 August 1930.
Branch of Service: Rochdale County Borough Police.
Ribbon: Blue with a central red stripe, all of equal width (silver medal) Blue with two bands of red, all of equal width (bronze medal).
Metal: Silver and bronze.
Size: 35 mm.
Description: (Obverse) Coat of Arms of the Borough of Rochdale with the town motto and the legend ROCHDALE COUNTY BOROUGH POLICE around the circumference; (reverse) a six line inscription in the central field AWARDED BY THE WATCH COMMITTEE TO (rank and name). Around the circumference was the legend FOR LONG AND FAITHFUL SERVICE. The medals were suspended to a plain straight swivelling suspender by a claw.
Comments: *The bronze medal was awarded after 20 years service and the silver after 25 years, both requiring a clean record. They were discontinued in 1949.*

P23A. TAYSIDE POLICE MEDAL FOR MERITORIOUS CONDUCT

Instituted: 1996.
Branch of Service: Tayside Police.
Ribbon: Police blue, with two white stripes towards the centre, fitted with a brooch pin for suspension.
Metal: Silver.
Size: 36mm.
Description: (Obverse) a crowned thistle on a dark blue ground with the motto SEMPER VIGILO (always on guard) at the foot, in red, white, green and blue enamels; (reverse) details of the award.
Comments: *Awarded to police officers and members of the public for actions which fall short of national recognition but which are deemed to be above the standard required for a Chief Constable's commendation.*

VALUE: —

P24. WIGAN BOROUGH POLICE GOOD SERVICE MEDAL

Instituted: —
Branch of Service: Wigan Borough Police.
Ribbon: Dark blue with a red central stripe.
Metal: Silver.
Size: 35 mm.
Description: (Obverse) The Coat of Arms of the Borough of Wigan within an outer circle containing the legend FOR GOOD SERVICE (above) and WIGAN BOROUGH POLICE (below); (reverse) a laurel wreath tied at the base with a bow surrounding a central field containing an inscription with the rank and name of the recipient together with the date he joined the force. The medal has an ornamental scroll suspender attached by a swivelling claw fitting. The ribbon is attached by a brooch fitting.
Comments: *The Wigan County Borough Police was founded in 1836 but later amalgamated with the Lancashire County Constabulary and eleven other borough forces to form the Lancashire Constabulary. It became a part of Greater Manchester Police on 1 April 1974.*

Awards of the British Commonwealth

In recent years many countries of the British Commonwealth have created their own individual systems of Honours and Awards. However, some British awards are still recognised within these systems. The medals and awards of these countries instituted prior to their own systems being introduced, are included in the main section of this book. In this section of the YEARBOOK we include the latest honours and awards of AUSTRALIA, NEW ZEALAND and, new for this edition, SOUTH AFRICA, together with their current Orders of Precedence encompassing their own and former British honours and awards. We also include the Orders of Precedence in Canada. It is anticipated that the latest honours and awards for Canada and selected other countries of the former British Commonwealth will be included at a future date. There is now a new website for Australian Honours and Medals, maintained by the Awards and National Symbols branch in Canberra, ACT www.itsanhonour.gov.aus. The site is currently being updated and, apart from listing the Australian honours and awards, will have a search facility to enable researchers to trace medal details of Australians back to 1901, the year of Federation. It will also be possible to search for awards by localities, defined by postcodes. This will be one of the most powerful tools for military historians, medal collectors and family historians.

THE ORDER OF PRECEDENCE IN AUSTRALIA
(including British awards)

Victoria Cross
George Cross
Cross of Valour
Most Noble Order of the Garter
Most Ancient and Most Noble Order of the Thistle
Knight Grand Cross, the Most Honourable Order of the Bath
Order of Merit
Knight, the Order of Australia
Knight Grand Cross, the Most Distinguished Order of St Michael & St George
Knight Grand Cross, the Royal Victorian Order
Knight Grand Cross, the Order of the British Empire
Companion, the Order of Australia
Companion of Honour
Knight Commander, the Most Honourable Order of the Bath

Knight Commander, the Most Distinguished Order of St Michael & St George
Knight Commander, the Royal Victorian Order
Knight Commander, the Order of the British Empire
Knight Bachelor
Officer, the Order of Australia
Companion, the Most Honourable Order of the Bath
Companion, the Most Distinguished Order of St Michael & St George
Commander, the Royal Victorian Order
Commander, the Order of the British Empire
Star of Gallantry
Star of Courage
Distinguished Service Order
Distinguished Service Cross (Australian)
Member, the Order of Australia
Lieutenant, the Royal Victorian Order

Officer, the Order of the British Empire
Companion, the Imperial Service Order
Member, the Royal Victorian Order
Member, the Order of the British Empire
Conspicuous Service Cross
Nursing Service Cross
Royal Red Cross 1st Class
Distinguished Service Cross (British)
Military Cross
Distinguished Flying Cross
Air Force Cross
Royal Red Cross 2nd Class
Medal for Gallantry
Bravery Medal
Distinguished Service Medal (Australian)
Public Service Medal
Australian Police Medal
Australian Fire Service Medal
Member of the Order of Australia
Order of St John
Distinguished Conduct Medal
Conspicuous Gallantry Medal
George Medal
Conspicuous Service Medal
Antarctic Medal
Queen's Police Medal for Gallantry
Queen's Fire Service Medal for Gallantry
Distinguished Service Medal (British)
Military Medal

Distinguished Flying Medal
Air Force Medal
Queen's Gallantry Medal
Royal Victorian Medal
British Empire Medal
Queen's Police Medal for Distinguished Service
Queen's Fire Service Medal for Distinguished Service
Commendation for Gallantry
Commendation for Brave Conduct
Queen's Commendation for Brave Conduct
Commendation for Distinguished Service
War Medals in order of campaign
Australian Active Service Medal
Australian Service Medal
Australian Active Service Medal 1945–75
Australian Service Medal 1945–75
Police Overseas Service Medal
Civilian Service Medal
Polar Medal
Imperial Service Medal
Coronation/Jubilee Medals
Defence Force Service Medal
Reserve Force Decoration
Reserve Force Medal
National Medal
Champion Shots Medal
Long Service Medals
Independence/Anniversary Medals
Approved Foreign Orders, Medals and Decorations
  in order of date of award.

"The Australian and New Zealand troops have indeed
proved themselves worthy sons of the Empire."
GEORGE R.I.

Australian medals

Since 1975 Australia has instituted a number of purely Australian awards. Medals and decorations pertaining to Australia, instituted prior to 1975 will be found in chronological sequence within the main text of this book.

The Australian system was inaugurated on February 14, 1975 when the Order of Australia, four bravery awards and the National Medal were established by Letters Patent. Since then a further 27 medals, decorations, commendations and citations have been introduced, which, including the various grades of the Order of Australia, brings the total to 37. A very detailed and comprehensive account of the Australian awards will be found in *The National Honours & Awards of Australia* by Michael Maton (1995). They are listed below in order of precedence. To date few of these new awards have come onto the market, thus we have not always been able to give an accurate valuation other than to indicate that the award is "Rare".

A1. VICTORIA CROSS FOR AUSTRALIA

Instituted: 1991.
Ribbon: Crimson 38mm wide.
Metal: Bronze.
Size: 35mm at each axis.
Description: A cross pattée with raised edges. (Obverse) a crowned lion standing on the royal crown, with the words FOR VALOUR on a semi-circular scroll below; (reverse) a circle containing the date of the action for which it was awarded. The Cross is suspended by a ring attached to the cross and a V-lug below a straight suspension bar ornamented with laurels.
Comments: *The Victoria Cross for Australia is identical to the British award and is awarded, with the approval of the Queen, by an instrument signed by the Governor-General on the recommendation of the Minister of Defence. Some 96 Australians have won the VC since 1856, the most recent being Warrant Officer Keith Payne for bravery in Vietnam (May 1969). No award of the Australian VC has yet been made.*

VALUE: As no. 24

A2. CROSS OF VALOUR

Instituted: 1975.
Ribbon: Magenta 38mm wide with a blood-red central band of 16mm.
Metal: Gold.
Size: 42mm.
Description: A straight-armed Greek cross with diminishing rays between the arms, ensigned by St Edward's crown and an integral suspension bar inscribed FOR VALOUR. The cross is surmounted by the heraldic shield of Australia topped by the Star of the Federation.
Comments: *Intended to replace the British civilian award of the George Cross. To date, only three CVs have been awarded.*

VALUE: Rare

A3. ORDER OF AUSTRALIA

Instituted: 1975.

Ribbon: Royal blue bearing scattered gold mimosa blossoms of various sizes (General Division); similar, but with gold edges (Military Division)

Neck/shoulder badge

Breast badge

KNIGHTS AND DAMES OF THE ORDER

The insignia consists of a neck badge and breast badge. In the case of a Dame there was the option of a neck badge or a shoulder badge, the latter being identical in every respect save the mounting. The neck badge is worn with a 16mm ribbon, while the shoulder badge of the Dame is worn with a 28mm ribbon. The breast badge is worn on the left side of a coat or outer garment.

Neck Badge: A gold disc 60mm in diameter, jewelled and having at its centre the arms of Australia enamelled in full colour on a blue ground decorated with two branches of mimosa. The whole is ensigned by the St Edward Crown in full colour with a suspension ring at the top.

Breast Badge: The emblem of the Order, 80mm in diameter, in gold, jewelled, and having the arms of Australia at the centre, surmounted by the St Edward Crown.

Comments: *There is also a miniature, 20mm in diameter, worn with the 16mm ribbon, a lapel badge, 10mm in diameter for ordinary civilian wear, and a ladies' badge mounted on a brooch bar. Knights and Dames are entitled to the prefix "Sir" or "Dame" and to use the postnominal letters AK or AD respectively. Between May 24, 1976, when the grade of Knights and Dames was introduced, and March 3, 1986 when these grades were abolished, a total of 11 Knights and two Dames were created, excluding the Queen (Sovereign of the Order) and the Prince of Wales.*

VALUE:		
	Breast badge	Rare
	Neck/shoulder badge	Rare
	Miniature badge	—

Companion's badge.

COMPANION OF THE ORDER

The insignia consists of a gold neck badge (men) or shoulder badge (women) 60mm in diameter, similar to the Knight's badge but having at its centre a circlet of blue enamel edged in gold containing two sprigs of mimosa and inscribed AUSTRALIA at the foot. These badges are worn with a 16mm neck ribbon or 38mm shoulder bow respectively. Miniatures, lapel and brooch badges with jewelled centres identical to those of the Knights or Dames, are also worn. Companions have the postnominal letters AC after their name.

Comments: *Up to 1994 214 Companions had been appointed in the General Division and 17 in the Military Division.*

VALUE:	Neck badge	Rare
	Miniature badge	Rare

Officer's badge.

OFFICER OF THE ORDER

The insignia is a badge similar to that of the Companion but only 55mm in diameter, and in silver-gilt instead of gold. The miniature, lapel badge and brooch badges have a blue enamel centre. Officers have the postnominal letters AO after their name.

Comments: *Up to 1994 1,164 Officers had been appointed, 990 in the General Division and 174 in the Military Division.*

VALUE:	Badge	£800–2000
	Miniature badge	£50–80

Member's badge.

MEMBER OF THE ORDER

The insignia is a badge consisting of the emblem of the Order, 45mm in diameter in silver-gilt but without the enamelled centre, although the miniature, lapel badge and brooch badges have a blue enamel centre. Members have the postnominal letters AM.

Comments: Up to 1994 3,727 Members had been appointed to the Order, 3,064 in the General Division and 663 in the Military Division.

VALUE:	Badge	£450–1000
	Miniature badge	£50–80

For the Medal of the Order of Australia (see no. A15)

A4. STAR OF GALLANTRY

Instituted: 1991.
Ribbon: Deep orange with chevrons of light orange, points upwards.
Metal: Silver-gilt.
Size: 37mm.
Description: A seven-pointed Federation Star ensigned by a St
    Edward crown affixed to a suspension bar inscribed FOR
    GALLANTRY. (Obverse) a smaller Federation Star 22mm across,
    surrounded by stylised flames representing action under fire:
    (reverse) central horizontal panel on a stepped background.
Comments: *Second and subsequent awards are denoted by a silver-gilt
    34mm bar with a replica of the Federation Star at the centre. Recipients
    are entitled to the postnominal letters SG. To date no award has been
    made.*

VALUE: —

A5. STAR OF COURAGE

Instituted: 1975.
Ribbon: Blood-red 32mm with a magenta central band 16mm wide.
Metal: Silver.
Size: 50mm.
Description: A seven-pointed, ribbed star surmounted by the
    heraldic shield of Australia and ensigned by a St Edward Crown
    affixed to a suspension bar inscribed FOR COURAGE.
Comments: *Subsequent awards are denoted by a silver bar bearing a replica
    of the star. Recipients are entitled to the postnominal letters SC. Since
    1976 less than 60 Stars of Courage have been awarded. No awards were
    made in 1979 or 1982 and the most in any on year was 7 (1988 and
    1991). One foreign award has been made, to Flight Lieutenant Holden,
    RNZAF, for his part in rescuing six trapped passengers from a helicopter
    crash in 1981.*

VALUE: £5000–12,000

A6. DISTINGUISHED SERVICE CROSS

Instituted: 1991.
Ribbon: Ochre-red flanked by silver-blue bands.
Metal: Nickel-silver.
Size: 41mm.
Description: (Obverse) a modified Maltese cross with a seven-
    pointed Federation Star at the centre and flames in the interstices.
    It is ensigned with a St Edward Crown affixed to a plain
    suspension bar. (Reverse) plain but for a horizontal panel giving
    details of the award.
Comments: *Nickel-silver bars are granted for subsequent awards and have
    a Federation Star at the centre. Recipients are entitled to the postnominal
    letters DSC. So far only two awards have been made (November 1993) to
    senior Army officers commanding Australian forces assisting the UN
    peace-keeping operations in Somalia.*

VALUE: Rare

A7. CONSPICUOUS SERVICE CROSS

Instituted: 1989.
Ribbon: 32mm wide, with alternate diagonal stripes of bush green and sandy gold 6mm wide.
Metal: Nickel-silver.
Size: 38mm.
Description: A modified Maltese cross with fluted rays between the arms. (Obverse) the constellation of the Southern Cross within laurel leaves, ensigned with a St Edward's Crown affixed to a plain suspension bar. (Reverse) a horizontal panel for details of the award.
Comments: *Instituted to award all ranks of the armed services for outstanding service and devotion to duty in non-warlike situations. Since its inception only 129 crosses have been awarded (29 to the Navy, 39 to the RAAF and 61 to the Army). Recipients are entitled to the postnominal letters CSC.*

VALUE: £500–1000

A8. NURSING SERVICE CROSS

Instituted: 1991.
Branch of Service: Members of the Nursing Services of the Army, RAN and RAAF.
Ribbon: 32mm red flanked by broad white stripes.
Metal: Silver.
Size: 43mm.
Description: A stepped cross with straight arms, with a red enamelled plain cross at the centre and ensigned with the St Edward Crown affixed to a plain suspension bar. (Reverse) a horizontal panel superimposed on a pattern of fluted rays.
Comments: *Awarded for outstanding devotion and competency in the performance of nursing duties in support of the armed forces. Recipients are entitled to the postnominal letters NSC. To date, only four crosses have been awarded, two each to members of the RAAF and Army Nursing Services.*

VALUE: Rare

A9. MEDAL FOR GALLANTRY

Instituted: 1991.
Ribbon: 32mm light orange with chevrons of deep orange, points upwards.
Metal: Silver-gilt.
Size: 38mm.
Description: (Obverse) Federation Star surrounded by flames and surmounted by a St Edward Crown affixed to a suspension bar inscribed FOR GALLANTRY; (reverse) horizontal panel on a background of fluted rays.
Comments: *Awarded to all ranks of the armed services for acts of gallantry in action in hazardous circumstances. To date 13 medals have been awarded.*

VALUE: Rare

A10. BRAVERY MEDAL

Instituted: 1975.
Ribbon: 32mm with 15 alternating stripes of blood-red and magenta.
Metal: Bronze.
Size: 38mm.
Description: (Obverse) heraldic shield and Federation Star on a circular zigzag border; (reverse) zigzag pattern.
Comments: *Awarded to civilians and members of the armed services in non-warlike conditions for acts of bravery in hazardous circumstances. Recipients are entitled to the postnominal letters BN. Some 307 medals have been awarded since 1976.*

VALUE: £500–2000

A11. DISTINGUISHED SERVICE MEDAL

Instituted: 1991.
Ribbon: 32mm silver-blue with three stripes of ochre-red.
Metal: Nickel-silver.
Size: 38mm.
Description: (Obverse) Federation Star with flames in the angles; (reverse) horizontal panel on a ground of fluted rays.
Comments: *Awarded to all ranks of the armed services for distinguished leadership in action. Recipients are entitled to the postnominal letters DSM. To date 21 awards of the DSM have been made, the first in November 1993 to Corporal Thomas Aitken as a section commander in Somalia during Operation Solace.*

VALUE: **Rare**

A12. PUBLIC SERVICE MEDAL

Instituted: 1989.
Ribbon: 32mm with 12 alternating stripes of green and gold of varying widths, the widest green on the left and widest gold on the right.
Metal: Nickel-silver.
Size: 38mm.
Description: (Obverse) an inner circle showing four planetary gears spaced equidistant from a central sun gear, surrounded by the inscription PUBLIC SERVICE. An outer circle shows 36 upright human figures representing a wide range of professions and activities. (Reverse) a wreath of mimosa surrounding the text FOR OUTSTANDING SERVICE.
Comments: *Awarded for outstanding public services at Commonwealth, State or Local Government levels. The number of medals allocated to each state is limited annually to 33 (commonwealth), 22 (New South Wales), 17 (Victoria), 11 (Queensland), 6 each (Western and Southern Australia), 3 (Tasmania) and 2 (Northern Territory). Awards may be made to Norfolk Island once every three years. Recipients are entitled to the postnominal letters PSM.*

VALUE: £100–200   *Miniature*   £10–15

A13. AUSTRALIAN POLICE MEDAL

Instituted: 1986.
Ribbon: 32mm white with a central broad dark blue stripes.
Metal: Nickel-silver.
Size: 38mm.
Description: (Obverse) effigy of Queen Elizabeth within a Federation
   Star, with an outer pattern of fluted rays; (reverse) wreath of
   golden wattle enclosing the inscriptions AUSTRALIAN POLICE
   MEDAL and FOR DISTINGUISHED SERVICE.
Comments: *Awarded for distinguished service among members of the
   Australian Federal Police and the forces of the states and territories.
   Awards are limited annually to no more than one per thousand members
   (or proportionately) in each force, plus one additional medal for the whole
   of Australia. Recipients are entitled to the postnominal letters APM.*

VALUE: £250–400   *Miniature*   £10–15

A14. AUSTRALIAN FIRE SERVICE MEDAL

Instituted: 1988.
Ribbon: 32mm central gold band bearing an irregular pattern of red
   flames and flanked by green stripes.
Metal: Cupro-nickel.
Size: 38mm.
Description: (Obverse) effigy of Queen Elizabeth superimposed on a
   Federation Star composed of flames; (reverse) inscriptions
   AUSTRALIA FIRE SERVICE MEDAL and FOR DISTINGUISHED
   SERVICE on a background of flames.
Comments: *Awarded for distinguished service among members of the fire
   services on the basis of one annually for every 1,000 full-time and one for
   every 25,000 part-time or volunteer firemen. Recipients are entitled to the
   postnominal letters AFSM.*

VALUE: £250–400   *Miniature*   £10–15

A15. MEDAL OF THE ORDER OF AUSTRALIA

Instituted: 1976.
Ribbon: Royal blue 32mm, with gold mimosa decoration (General
   Division), or edged with gold (Military Division).
Metal: Silver-gilt.
Size: 40mm.
Description: (Obverse) emblem of the Order of Australia surmounted
   by St Edward crown affixed to a plain suspension bar.
Comments: *The medal of the Order is awarded for meritorious service.
   Holders of the medal are entitled to the postnominals OAM.*

VALUE: £250–350   *Miniature*   £20–25

A16. CONSPICUOUS SERVICE MEDAL

Instituted: 1989.
Ribbon: 32mm wide with alternating diagonal stripes of bush green and sandy gold 3mm wide.
Metal: Nickel-silver.
Size: 38mm.
Description: (Obverse) the Southern Cross encircled by laurel leaves; (reverse) a horizontal panel on a ground of fluted rays.
Comments: *Awarded to all ranks of the armed forces for meritorious achievement in non-warlike situations. Recipients are entitled to the postnominal CSM.*

VALUE: £200–350   *Miniature*   £10–15

A17. ANTARCTIC MEDAL

Instituted: 1987.
Ribbon: 32mm snow-white moire with 3mm edges in three shades of blue merging with the white.
Metal: Nickel-silver.
Size: 38mm.
Description: An octagonal medal surmounted by an ice crystal device affixed to a plain suspension bar. (Obverse) a global map of the Southern Hemisphere showing Australia and Antarctica, and the legend FOR OUTSTANDING SERVICE IN THE ANTARCTIC; (reverse) a polar explorer outside Sir Douglas Mawson's hut, leaning into a blizzard and wielding an ice-axe.
Comments: *Awarded to persons who have given outstanding service in connection with Australian Antarctic expeditions. Recipients must have a minimum of 12 months service in Antarctica. Clasps are inscribed with the year of service or with TO 1992 for persons who have served in Antarctica over several years. A total of 50 medals were awarded between 1987 and 1994, 1987 being the commonest date.*

VALUE: £350–500   *Miniature*   £30–35

A18. COMMENDATION FOR GALLANTRY

Instituted: 1991.
Ribbon: Plain orange 32mm wide and 90mm long.
Metal: Silver-gilt.
Size: 22mm.
Description: The insignia consists of a row of flames tapering towards the ends, with a seven-pointed Federation Star superimposed.
Comments: *Instituted for civilian acts of gallantry considered to be of lesser magnitude than those for which the star or medal would be awarded. To date three awards have been made.*

VALUE: Rare

A19. COMMENDATION FOR BRAVE CONDUCT

Instituted: 1975.
Ribbon: Blood-red 32mm wide and 90mm long.
Metal: Silver-gilt.
Size: 30mm.
Description: A sprig of mimosa, mounted diagonally near the foot of the ribbon.
Comments: *Intended to reward acts of bravery worthy of recognition but less than those for which the CV, SC or BM would be considered appropriate. Some 474 commendations were awarded between 1975 and 1994.*

VALUE: £150–500   *Miniature*   £5–10

A20. COMMENDATION FOR DISTINGUISHED SERVICE

Instituted: 1991.
Ribbon: Ochre-red 32mm wide and 90mm long.
Metal: Nickel-silver.
Size: 22mm.
Description: A central Federation Star mounted on a row of flames tapering towards the end.
Comments: *Awarded for distinguished performance of duties. To date 33 awards have been made, including six to the RAN (Gulf War) and six to the Army (Somalia).*

VALUE: **Rare**

A21. AUSTRALIAN ACTIVE SERVICE MEDAL

Instituted: 1991.
Ribbon: 32mm with a central red stripe, flanked by stripes of silver-green, light-green, gold, dark green and brown.
Metal: Nickel-silver.
Size: 38mm.
Description: (Obverse) a seven pointed Federation Star within a laurel wreath; (reverse) FOR ACTIVE SERVICE within a laurel wreath.
Clasps: Balkans, Cambodia, East Timor, Kuwait, Somalia, Vietnam 1975,
Comments: *Awarded for active service in various conflicts, denoted in each case by a campaign clasp. The Kuwait clasp recognised service in the Gulf theatre of operations between January 17, 1991 and February 28, 1991. Service before and after those dates was awarded by the Australian Service Medal with the appropriate clasp. The Somalia clasp was awarded for active service between January 10, 1993 and May 21, 1993 during Operation Solace. The Cambodia clasp was awarded for active service with UNTAC between October 1991 to October 1993. In August 1998 the Governor General altered the regulations and the Vietnam 1975 and Cambodia clasps are now awarded to the AASM. Holders of the Australian Service Medal (No. A22) will now receive the AASM.*

VALUE:

	RAN	RAAF	Army
Kuwait	£250–300 (937)	£300–450 (126)	£400–500 (41)
Somalia	£400–500 (20)	—	£250–350 (1016)
Miniature	£10–12		

A22. AUSTRALIAN SERVICE MEDAL

Instituted: 1991.
Ribbon: 32mm with a central brown stripe flanked by stripes of dark green, light green, gold and silver-green.
Metal: Nickel-silver.
Size: 38mm.
Description: (Obverse) a modified heraldic shield on a background of the lines of longitude, surmounted by a St Edward crown affixed to a plain suspension bar; (reverse) clusters of mimosa blossom, surrounding a Federation Star inscribed FOR SERVICE.
Clasps: Balkans, Bougainville, Cambodia, East Timor, Ethiopia/Eritrea, Guatemala, Gulf, Iran-Iraq, Kashmir, Korea, Kuwait, Middle East, Mozambique, Namibia, Peshawar, Rwanda, SE Asia, Sierra Leone, Sinai, Solomon Is., Somalia, Special Ops, West Sahara, Uganda.
Comments: *For service with multinational peacekeeping forces. In many cases, the appropriate UN medal was also awarded. Some 2,363 medals and clasps have been issued to the RAN, 632 to the RAAF and 2,618 to the Army.*

VALUE: £200–500   *Miniature*   £15–20

A23. POLICE OVERSEAS SERVICE MEDAL

Instituted: 1992.
Ribbon: 32mm with a chequerboard pattern of black and white squares.
Metal: Nickel-silver.
Size: 38mm.
Description: (Obverse) globe surmounted by a branch of wattle, the whole enclosed in a chequerboard pattern and surmounted by a St Edward crown affixed to a plain suspension bar.
Clasp: Cyprus, Cambodia (20), Somalia (2), Mozambique (20), Haiti (30), Bouganville (22) and East Timor (300+) denoted by a globe emblem on the ribbon bar. Several officers have received two or three clasps and at least five officers have five clasps.
Comments: *Awarded to members of Australian police forces serving as members of peace-keeping missions under the auspices of the United Nations. Consequently recipients also receive the appropriate UN medals.*

VALUE: £200–500   *Miniature*   £25–30

A24. DEFENCE FORCE SERVICE MEDAL

Instituted: 1982.
Ribbon: 32mm azure blue with two gold stripes.
Metal: Cupro-nickel.
Size: 38mm.
Description: A circular chamfered medal bearing a Federation Star on which appears the insignia of the three defence forces. The medal is ensigned by the St Edward Crown affixed to a plain suspension bar. (Reverse) inscription FOR EFFICIENT SERVICE IN THE PERMANENT FORCES.
Clasp: Awarded for further periods of five years service.
Comments: *The medal is granted for 15 years service in the Defence Force, of which 12 years must have been as a member of the permanent Force.*

VALUE: £75–100   *Miniature*   £10–12

A25. RESERVE FORCE DECORATION

Instituted: 1982.
Ribbon: 32mm azure blue with a broad central band of gold.
Metal: Cupro-nickel.
Size: Oval 44mm high and 36mm wide.
Description: (Obverse) the joint services emblem on a radiate ground within a wreath of wattle; (reverse) inscribed FOR EFFICIENT SERVICE IN THE RESERVE FORCES.
Clasps: bar with the Royal Cypher flanked by sprigs of wattle.
Comments: *Awarded for a minimum of 15 years service as an officers in the Reserve Forces. Clasps for additional service of five years are granted.*

VALUE: £200–250

A26. RESERVE FORCE MEDAL

Instituted: 1982.
Ribbon: 32mm azure blue with narrow gold edges.
Metal: Cupro-nickel.
Size: Oval 44mm high and 36mm wide.
Description: (Obverse) insignia of the joint services on a rayed background; (reverse) inscription FOR EFFICIENT SERVICE IN THE RESERVE FORCES.
Comments: *Awarded to non-commissioned officers and other ranks of the reserve forces on completion of 15 years service. Clasps for further five-year periods of service have the Royal Cypher flanked by sprigs of wattle*

VALUE: £175–250

A26A. DEFENCE LONG SERVICE MEDAL

Instituted: 1998.
Ribbon: 32mm with central 10mm panel of seven narrow alternating stripes of azure blue and gold flanked by 7mm broad azure stripes and 4mm gold edges.
Metal: Nickel-silver.
Size: 38mm.
Description: A circular medal ensigned with the St Edward Crown attached to the suspension bar. (Obverse) the Australian Defence Force emblem surrounded by two sprays of wattle leaves and blossom; (reverse) a central horizontal panel surrounded by the inscription FOR SERVICE IN THE AUSTRALIAN DEFENCE FORCE.
Clasps: Bar with the Royal Cypher flanked by sprigs of wattle.
Comments: *This medal supersedes the Defence Force Service Medal, the Reserve Force Decoration and Reserve Force Medal. It is awarded on completion of 15 years service, clasps being awarded for further periods of service.*

VALUE: —

A27. NATIONAL MEDAL

Instituted: 1975.
Ribbon: 32mm with 15 alternating gold and blue stripes.
Metal: Bronze.
Size: 38mm.
Description: (Obverse) arms of the Commonwealth of Australia on a ground of mimosa blossom within a recessed circle. Incuse inscription round the edge: THE NATIONAL MEDAL FOR SERVICE. (Reverse) plain.
Comments: *Awarded to members of the various uniformed services for long service and good conduct, being a minimum of 15 years in one service or an aggregate of 15 years in two or more services. An amendment by Letters Patent in 1987 extended the award of this medal to the prison services. Bars for further periods of 10 years service are available.*

VALUE: £75–100 *Miniature* £8–12

A28. CHAMPION SHOTS MEDAL

Instituted: 1988.
Ribbon: 32mm central dark blue stripe flanked by red and light blue stripes.
Metal: Antiqued brass.
Size: 38mm.
Description: (Obverse) a wreathed vertical panel with the Southern Cross and two crossed rifles; (reverse) plain.
Comments: *Only three medals are awarded annually, to the respective champion shots of the RAN, RAAF and Army. Of the seven RAAF awards, Sgt Philip MacPherson has won the medal three times (1991–3) and Sgt Brett Graeme Hartman has won it four times (1988–90 and 1994).*

VALUE: Rare *Miniature* £10–12

A29. CIVILIAN SERVICE MEDAL, 1939–1945

Instituted: 1994.
Ribbon: 32mm ochre-red central stripe flanked by narrow white stripes and broad stripes of opal green towards the edges.
Metal: Bronze.
Size: 38mm.
Description: (Obverse) the Southern Cross superimposed on a globe surrounded by mimosa blossoms; (reverse) horizontal panel for the recipient's name, with 1939 above and 1945 below.
Comments: *Awarded to civilians who had assisted Australia's war effort in a wide variety of organisations and who served under quasi-military conditions for at least 180 days. The medal may be awarded posthumously and presented to the next-of-kin. It is estimated that up to 70,000 people are eligible for this medal.*

VALUE: £100–150 *Miniature* £8–10

A30. AUSTRALIAN ACTIVE SERVICE MEDAL, 1945–1975

Instituted: 1995.
Ribbon: 32mm central thin red stripe flanked by narrow yellow stripes and broad stripes of pale blue, black and purple towards the edge.
Metal: Nickel-silver.
Size: 38mm.
Description: (Obverse) the seven-pointed Federation star surrounded by the legend THE AUSTRALIAN ACTIVE SERVICE MEDAL 1945–1975; (reverse) a wreath of mimosa sourrounding a plaque for the recipient's details.
Clasp: Korea, Malaya, Malaysia, Thailand, Thai-Malay, Vietnam.
Comments: *This medal fills a gap between the Australian Service Medal (no. 190) and the current Australian Service Medal which was instituted in 1975. It is awarded to all ranks of the armed forces for warlike service in theatres of operation between the end of the Second World War and February 13, 1975. The medal is worn immediately after any Second World War awards and before any other campaign awards.*

VALUE: £150–250   *Miniature*   £10–12

A31. AUSTRALIAN SERVICE MEDAL, 1945–1975

Instituted: 1995.
Ribbon: 32mm central thin yellow stripe flanked by narrow green stripes flanked by grey with wide navy blue stripe at left and pale blue at right.
Metal: Nickel-silver.
Size: 38mm.
Description: (Obverse) the arms of the Commonwealth of Australia surrounded by the legend THE AUSTRALIAN SERVICE MEDAL 1945–1975; (reverse) seven-pointed Federation star with space for recipient's details, surrounded by mimosa leaves.
Clasps: Berlin, FESR, Germany, Indonesia, Japan, Kashmir, Korea, Middle East, PNG, SE Asia, Special Ops, SW Pacific, Thailand, W New Guinea.
Comments: *This medal fills a gap between the Australian Service Medal (no. 190) and the current Australian Service Medal which was instituted in 1975. It is awarded to all ranks of the Australian Defence Force for non-warlike service in theatres of operation between the end of the Second World War and February 13, 1975. It is estimated that about 65,000 people are eligible for this medal. The medal is worn after campaign awards and before long service and foreign awards.*

VALUE: £100–300   *Miniature*   £12–15

A32. UNIT CITATION FOR GALLANTRY

Instituted: 1991.
Ribbon: Green encased in a silver-gilt rectagular frame with flame decoration. A seven-pointed Federation Star in silver-gilt in worn in the centre.
Comments: *This system was borrowed from the USA, many Australian formations and units receiving American unit citations during the Vietnam War. So far, however, no Unit Citations for Gallantry have been awarded. The citation is worn by all members of the unit receiving the citation for extraordinary gallantry in action, and appears on the right breast (Army and RAAF) or below the medal ribbons on the left breast (RAN). So far no Unit Citations for Gallantry have been awarded.*

VALUE: —

A33. MERITORIOUS UNIT CITATION

Instituted: 1991.
Ribbon: Gold encased in a rhodium-plated silver frame with flame decoration. A rhodium-plated silver Federation Star is mounted in the centre.
Comments: *Awarded to members of a unit for sustained outstanding service in warlike operations. So far only three Meritorious Unit Citations have been issued, all to units of the RAN for service in the Gulf War, 1990–91.*

VALUE: Rare

A34. AUSTRALIAN MERCHANT NAVY SERVICE CROSS

Instituted: 1998.
Branch of Service: Australian Merchant Navy.
Ribbon: Blue with narrow white central stripe and white edges.
Metal: Silver.
Size: 36mm.
Description: A cross fourchée on which is superimposed a small circular medallion bearing the insignia of the Australian Merchant Navy. Fitted with bar suspender.
Clasp: A gold laurel spray.
Comments: *This semi-officialmedal was created in 1998 to mark United Nations Year of the Ocean, September 24 being designated by the UN International Maritime Organisation as Day of the Merchant Mariner. The cross is awarded to officers for 15 years bona fide service on Articles of Agreement. Clasps are awarded for each additional 15 years service.*

VALUE: —

A35. AUSTRALIAN MERCHANT NAVY MERITORIOUS MEDAL

Instituted: 1998.
Branch of Service: Australian Merchant Navy.
Ribbon: Watered silk white with broad blue edges and central stripe.
Metal: Silver.
Size: 38mm.
Description: (Obverse) the crowned insignia of the Merchant Navy; (reverse) AUSTRALIAN MERCHANT NAVY MERITORIOUS MEDAL. Fitted with an ornamental bar suspender.
Comments: *This semi-official medal is awarded for an exceptional contribution to the Merchant Navy over a long period of time, but may also be awarded for an individual act of bravery by a seafarer.*

VALUE: —

A36. AUSTRALIAN MERCHANT NAVY COMMENDATION

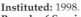

Instituted: 1998.
Branch of Service: Australian Merchant Navy.
Ribbon: Watered silk with a dark blue centre, white stripes and light blue edges.
Metal: Silver.
Size: 36mm.
Description: A laurel wreath joined at the top by a merchant navy crown attached to a ring for suspension.
Comments: *This semi-official medal is awarded for an ongoing or individual contribution by a person in one of the many fields of maritime endeavour including education, research and development, maritime business, industrial relations and professional achievement.*

VALUE: —

A37. GALLIPOLI MEDAL

Instituted: 25 April 1990.
Branch of Service: ANZAC veterans of the Gallipoli campaign.
Ribbon: Central broad deep blue stripe, flanked by narrow crimson stripes and broad edges of yellow and light blue respectively.
Metal: Bronze.
Size: 36mm.
Description: A small circular medal superimposed on an eight-pointed star with ring suspension. (Obverse) a Tudor crown surrounded by the inscription GALLIPOLI 1914-15.
Comments: *This medal was originally approved by King George V but was never issued at the time. In April 1990 it was presented unofficially to the 200 surviving Gallipoli veterans to mark the 75th anniversary of the ill-fated landings on the Turkish coast, although we understand that it is still available via commercial sources.*

VALUE: £60–80

A38. ARMISTICE REMEMBRANCE MEDAL

Instituted: 2000.
Branch of Service: Surviving veterans of the First World War.
Ribbon: Red with a black central stripe and narrow black edges.
Metal: Silver.
Size: 36mm.
Description: (Obverse) a 'Digger' in the uniform of the First World War with the legend 80TH ANNIVERSARY ARMISTICE REMEMBRANCE MEDAL; (reverse) the words LEST WE FORGET in three lines within a wreath of ferns surmounted by a seven-pointed star. Fitted with a suspension bar with a Tudor crown on both sides.
Comments: *Awarded to all veterans of the First World War who were still alive on 11 November 1998, the 80th anniversary of the Armistice.*

VALUE: —

A39. NEW SOUTH WALES CORRECTIVE SERVICE BRAVERY MEDAL

Instituted: 1989.
Ribbon: Dark blue with a broad crimson central stripe.
Metal: Silver-gilt.
Description: A cross pattée with radiations in the angles and surmounted by a St. Edward's crown fitted to a ring for suspension. (Obverse) the arms of New South Wales within a circular band inscribed CORRECTIVE SERVICE N.S.W., with a scroll at the foot inscribed FOR BRAVERY; (reverse) plain.
Comments: *Awarded to prison officers for bravery.*

VALUE: —

A40. NEW SOUTH WALES CORRECTIVE SERVICE EXEMPLARY CONDUCT CROSS

Instituted: 1989.
Ribbon: Navy blue with a broad gold central stripe.
Metal: Silver.
Descrpiton: A seven-pointed star surmounted by a large St. Edward's crown fitted to a suspension ring. (Obverse) the arms of New South Wales within a circular band inscribed CORRECTIVE SERVICE N.S.W., with a scroll at the foot inscribed EXEMPLARY CONDUCT; (reverse) plain.
Comments: *Awarded to prison officers for exemplary conduct.*

VALUE: —

A41. NEW SOUTH WALES CORRECTIVE SERVICE MERITORIOUS SERVICE MEDAL

Instituted: 1989.
Ribbon: Red with a broad central gold stripe.
Metal: Bronze.
Size: 36mm.
Description: An elongated circle fitted with a suspension bar. (Obverse) the arms of New South Wales, with N.S.W. CORRECTIVE SERVICE at the top and LONG SERVICE at the foot; (reverse) FOR TWENTY YEARS SERVICE in four lines within a wreath.
Comments: *Awarded for 20 years service in the New South Wales prison service. Originally a bronze clasp for 30 years service was added after a further ten years, but this was replaced on 14 May 1999 by a bronze clasp for 25 years and silver clasps for 30, 35 and 40 years service.*

VALUE: —

A42. NEW SOUTH WALES CORRECTIVE SERVICE LONG SERVICE MEDAL

Instituted: 1989.
Ribbon: Navy blue with two silver stripes.
Metal: Bronze.
Size: 36mm.
Description: A circular medal fitted with a plain suspension bar. (Obverse) the crowned emblem of the Corrective Service with a wreath at the foot; (reverse) a laurel branch round the left side, with the words FOR FIFTEEN YEARS SERVICE in four lines on the right.
Comments: *Awarded for 15 years service in the New South Wales prison service.*

VALUE: —

A43. COMMISSIONER'S VALOUR AWARD

Instituted: 1987.
Ribbon: Light blue with narrow white stripes towards the edges and dark blue edges.
Metal: Silver.
Description: A cross pattée with a crowned and enamelled centrepiece bearing the insignia of the New South Wales Police Service within a wreath, inscribed FOR BRAVERY.
Comments: *Awarded to police officers where an act of conspicuous merit involving exceptional bravery is in evidence. It is very sparingly awarded, although eight awards were made in both 1993 and 1994.*

VALUE: —

A44. COMMISSIONER'S COMMENDATION FOR COURAGE

Instituted: 1970.
Ribbon: Light blue with a narrow central white stripe and narrow white edges.
Description: The insignia of the New South Wales Police Service affixed directly to the ribbon.
Comments: *Awarded to police officers where the risk to life has been less apparent, but where sufficient courage has been shown under hazardous circumstances to warrant the award. There is no restriction on the number of awards and about 90 are made annually.*

VALUE: —

A45. COMMISSIONER'S COMMENDATION FOR SERVICE

Instituted: 1970.
Ribbon: Light blue with narrow white edges.
Description: The insignia of the New South Wales Police Service affixed directly to the ribbon.
Comments: *Awarded to police officers for outstanding service. About ten commendations are awarded annually.*

VALUE: —

A46. COMMISSIONER'S UNIT CITATION

Instituted: 1994.
Description: A silver bar in the form of a wreath containing a light blue insert.
Comments: *Awaded to units, patrols, groups, squads and commands where outstanding service involving bravery or actions of obvious merit have been evident. The emblem is worn by each member of the unit, while the unit receives a framed citation for display. About five citations are awarded annually.*

VALUE: —

A47. QUEENSLAND PRISON SERVICE SUPERINDENDENT'S LONG SERVICE MEDAL

Instituted: Before 1988.
Ribbon: Dark blue with three narrow silver stripes.
Description: An eight-pointed Maltese cross superimposed on a wreath surmounted by a St. Edward's crown attached to a ring for suspension from a rectangular bar inscribed MERITORIOUS SERVICE. The top of the ribbon has a similar brooch bar with the recipient's details engraved on the reverse. The centre of the cross has the arms of Queensland.

VALUE: —

A48. QUEENSLAND PRISON SERVICE OFFICERS LONG SERVICE MEDAL

Instituted: Before 1988.
Ribbon: Silver with two narrow dark blue stripes.
Description: A circular medal fitted with a loop for suspension via a ring attached to an ornamental rectangular bar. The brooch bar at the top of the ribbon bears the recipient's personal details on the reverse. (Obverse) the crowned and wreathed insignia of the Queensland Prison Service with the inscription LONG AND MERITORIOUS SERVICE round the foot.

VALUE: —

A49. QUEENSLAND POLICE VALOUR AWARD

Instituted: 1993.
Ribbon: Maroon, light blue and dark blue in equal widths.
Metal: Silver.
Description: A Maltese cross superimposed on a wreath, with an enamelled centrepiece featuring the St. Edward's crown within a wreath and surrounded by the inscription QUEENSLAND POLICE VALOUR AWARD.
Comments: *This decoration is apparently similar to the Queensland Police Award which was discontinued in the 1930s.*

VALUE: —

A49. HUMANITARIAN OVERSEAS SERVICE MEDAL

Instituted: 16 April 1999.
Ribbon: Green with a central gold stripe.
Metal: Nickel-silver.
Size: 38mm.
Description: A circular medal (obverse) a stylised eucalyptus tree surrounded by a ring of gum nuts; (reverse) a ring of gum nuts with the recipients details engraved in the centre.
Clasps: Somalia, Vietnam, Great Lakes, Cambodia, Balkans, East Timor, South Sudan.
Comments: *This medal is intended to be awarded to civilians who have provided outstanding humanitarian service overseas (although service personnel may be considered for the award in exceptional circumstances) and is believed to be the first medal of its kind. As most government employees will be eligible for the Australian Service medals, it is anticipated that this medal will be awarded to non-government employees or volunteers and as there is no time limit to the award it can be awarded retrospectively.*

VALUE: —

A50. AUSTRALIAN CADET FORCES SERVICE MEDAL

Instituted: December 1999.
Ribbon: Stripes of blue and gold with three outer stripes of navy, red and light blue.
Metal:
Description: (Obverse) the emblem of the Australian Cadet Force ensigned with St Edward's Crown; (reverse) the Commonwealth Star overlayed by a bar engraved with the recipient's name.
Comment: *Awarded to officers and instructors of cadets, for efficient long service of 15 years, with a additional clasp for each additional five years.*

VALUE: —

A51. EMERGENCY SERVICE MEDAL

Instituted: 1999.
Ribbon: Orange and white chequered pattern edged in blue.
Metal: Silver and bronze coloured metals.
Description: (Obverse) a triangular device containing a seven-pointed Commonwealth Star surrounded by 24 dots representing emergency services operating around the clock.
Comment: *Awarded for outstanding duty be members of the emergency services, including state organisations and voluntary emergency services, and to persons who render distinguished service relating to emergency management, training or education Only one award is made to any one person. Holders are entitled to the postnominal letters ESM.*

VALUE: —

A52. AMBULANCE SERVICE MEDAL

Instituted: 1999.
Ribbon: Chevrons of white, red and silver.
Metal: Silver and bronze.
Description: A circular medal featuring a Maltese cross, with the seven-pointed Commonwealth Star at the centre, surrounded by 24 dots symbolising a 24 hour service.
Comment: *Awarded for distinguished service by members of the civilian ambulance services. Only one award is made to any individual, entitled to the post-nominal letters ASM.*
VALUE: —

A53. AUSTRALIAN SPORTS MEDAL

Instituted: 2000.
Ribbon: Sand-coloured with four narrow black stripes towards the right side, of varying widths.
Metal: Silver.
Description: (Obverse) a stylised view of the Sydney Olympic Stadium with the Southern Cross constellation above; (reverse) the Olympic Stadium and inscription 'To commemorate Australian sporting achievement' and the date 2000.
Comments: *This medal was only awarded during the year of the Sydney Olympic Games and was intended to reward Australian sporting achievement. Both current and former sports men and women have been honoured, as well as coaches, sports scientists, officials, team managers and even those who maintain playing fields and sporting facilities.*

VALUE: —

www.tokenpublishing.com

for all your collecting needs

EUGENE G. URSUAL

MILITARY ANTIQUARIAN, INC.
Over 25 years in business

SPECIALISING IN:
**MEDALS, ORDERS,
DECORATIONS,
MINIATURE MEDALS,
MILITARY ANTIQUITIES**

Want lists solicited
All transactions unconditionally guaranteed

Subscriptions:
**CANADIAN RESIDENTS: $12.84 per year
ONTARIO RESIDENTS: $13.80 per year
U.S.A. $15.00 per year, OVERSEAS: $20.00 per year (£9.00)**

We publish ten lists per year

North American Representative for Dix Noonan Webb

**P.O. BOX 788, KEMPTVILLE, ONTARIO
CANADA K0G 1J0**
Telephone: 1–613–258–5999   Fax: 1–613–258–9118

Check our website at www.medalsofwar.com
E-Mail us at egu@magma.ca

Canadian medals

Apart from such British campaign awards as the Louisburg Medal of 1758 (71) and the Canada General Service Medal (125) awarded to those who helped to put down the Fenian Raids of 1866 and 1870 and the Red River rebellion of the latter year, distinctive medals relating to military service in Canada date from 1902 when Canadian versions of the Meritorious Service Medal (212) and Colonial Long Service and Good Conduct Medal (248) were instituted. Subsequently there were also Canadian versions of the Permanent Forces of the Empire Beyond the Seas Long Service and Good Conduct Medal (249) and the military Long Service and Good Conduct Medal (229). Similarly, both the Efficiency Decoration (236) and the Efficiency Medal (237) were issued with suspension bars denoting service in Canada. Distinctive versions of certain British medals, such as the Defence Medal (185) and the Korea Medal (195), struck in silver instead of base metal, will also be found in the appropriate sections of this volume.

Several awards which were purely Canadian in character will also be found in earlier sections of this book, as they were authorised or instituted by the imperial government. Thus the Canadian Forces Decoration (255), instituted in 1949 to recognise service during World War II, comes under this category, as do the Canadian Volunteer Service Medal of 1943 (188) and the various types of Canadian Memorial Cross (188A) awarded to the relatives of service personnel who gave their lives in both world wars. Also included are awards by Newfoundland which did not enter the Confederation of Canada until 1947. For this reason Newfoundland servicemen were not eligible for the Canadian Volunteer Service Medal, and it was not until 1981 that this deficiency was remedied by the institution of a separate Newfoundland Volunteer War Service Medal (194).

The move towards purely Canadian medals, however, began to develop in the inter-war period, but the earliest awards were confined to the Royal Canadian Mounted Police and include a number of medals which were authorised by the various provinces. In 1967 Canada celebrated the centenary of confederation and the opportunity was then taken to institute the Order of Canada, with its associated Medal of Courage, as well as the Centennial Medal. Five years later, Canada inaugurated a full range of honours and awards and over the intervening years this has been extended considerably.

As this section of the YEARBOOK is completely new we have been unable to source illustrations for every medal although it is hoped to increase this in future editions. As we have little experience of the Canadian market it has been decided not to include prices at this stage.

THE ORDER OF PRECEDENCE IN CANADA

Victoria Cross
Cross of Valour
Companion of the Order of Canada
Commander of the Order of Military Merit
Commander of the Royal Victorian Order
Officer of the Order of Canada
Officer of the Order of Military Merit
Lieutenant of the Royal Victorian Order
Member of the Order of Canada
Member of the Order of Military Merit
Member of the Royal Victorian Order
The Most Venerable Order of St John of Jerusalem
Ordre National du Quebec
Saskatchewan Order of Merit
Order of Ontario
Order of British Columbia
Star of Military Valour
Star of Courage
Meritorious Service Cross
Medal of Military Valour
Medal of Bravery
Meritorious Service Medal (Civil or Military)

Royal Victorian Medal (Gold, Silver & Bronze)
World War I in the usual sequence
World War II in the usual sequence
Canadian Korean War Medal
Canadian Volunteer Service Medal for Korea
Gulf and Kuwait Medal
Special Service Medal
United Nations' Medals
International Commission Medals
Canadian Centennial Medal, 1967
Queen Elizabeth II Silver Jubilee Medal, 1977
Canada 125th Anniversary Medal, 1992
Royal Canadian Mounted Police Long Service Medal
Canadian Forces Decoration
Police Exemplary Service Medal
Corrections Exemplary Service medal
Fire Service Exemplary Service Medal
Coast Guard Exemplary Service Medal
Queen's Medal for Champion Shots
Service Medal of the Order of St John
Commonwealth Decorations and medals
Foreign Decorations and Medals

C1. VICTORIA CROSS (CANADA)

VC British issue—the Canadian issue will carry the legend PRO VALORE.

Date: 23 February 1993.
Ribbon: Crimson.
Metal: Bronze.
Size: 38mm.
Description: (Obverse) a cross pattée with raised edges having in the centre a lion standing on the royal crown partially circumscribed by a banner bearing the words PRO VALORE; (reverse) a circle containing the date of the action for which it was awarded. A straight suspender bar with a design of laurel leaves is used attached to the upper arm of the cross by a ring and "V" shaped lug.
Comments: *Available with effect from 1 January 1993 to members of the Canadian armed forces or a member of an allied force serving with them for an act of supreme courage, self-sacrifice or devotion to duty in the face of an enemy. It is identical to the awards of the UK, Australia and New Zealand with the important exception of the inscription within the banner on the obverse. The two official languages of Canada (English and French) mitigated against the use of the English inscription FOR VALOUR as on the three other awards and the Latin translation POR VALORE was chosen for the Canadian award.*

C2. CROSS OF VALOUR

Date: 1 May 1972.
Ribbon: Light crimson—worn around the neck (men) or on a bow (women).
Metal: Gold and red enamel.
Size: 38mm.
Description: (Obverse) a cross with straight arms in red enamel edged in gold with a central medallion of a gold maple leaf on a red enamel ground encircled by a gold wreath of laurel; (reverse) the royal cypher (EIIR) surmounted by a crown on the upper arm with the words VALOUR VAILLANCE across the centre above the engraved name of the recipient and date of the incident.
Comments: *Awarded for acts of conspicuous courage in circumstances of extreme peril to Canadian citizens and foreign nationals for an act in Canada or elsewhere if the act is considered to be in the interest of Canada and merits recognition by the country. A second award is signified by a gold maple leaf worn on the larger of the two suspension rings. The first award was made on 20 May 1972.*

C3. ORDER OF CANADA

COMPANION (CC), OFFICER (OC), MEMBER (MC)

Date: 17 April 1967.
Ribbon: Red with a broad central band in white—a neck ribbon for the two higher levels (companion and officer) and a breast ribbon for members. In undress uniform a small maple leaf is worn on the ribbon in red (CC) gold (OC) or silver (CM).
Metal: Gold or silver with enamels.
Size: 57mm (companion), 47.5mm (officer) and 38mm (member).
Description: (Obverse) A white enamelled stylised snowflake of six points (pentagonal in shape) edged in gold or silver with a central medallion comprising a maple leaf in red enamel (CC) or silver (OC and CM) on a white enamel field all surrounded by a red enamel outer band bearing the words DESIDERANTES MELIOREM PATRIAM (they desire a better country) in gold or silver. A St Edward crown in gold (CC and OC) or silver (CM) with red enamel is placed at the top of the central medallion on the upper point of the snowflake; (reverse) a small box in which is inscribed a serial number with the word CANADA above. A ring suspender is used for all three levels. *continued*

C3. ORDER OF CANADA *continued*

Comments: *Established to reward Canadian citizens who exemplify the highest qualities of citizenship which enrich the lives of their fellow citizens. Available only to Canadians. There are three levels—Companion, Officer and Member—with the qualifying criteria differing for each. Appointments are made in July and December each year with a maximum of 15 companions, 46 officers and 92 members appointed each year. The maximum number of living companions at any one time will not exceed 150 although there is no limit to the number of officers and members. The Order initially had a single class—Companion—with the officer and member levels being introduced on 1 July 1972. Prior to this a Medal of Service was a part of the Order but it was discontinued in 1972 and all holders made officers of the Order of Canada. A Medal of Courage was also attached to the Order but was discontinued on the introduction of the Cross of Valour.*

C4. ORDER OF MILITARY MERIT
COMMANDER (CMM), OFFICER (OMM), MEMBER (MMM)

Date: 1 July 1972.

Ribbon: Blue with gold edges (4.8 mm) worn around the neck (commander) or on the breast (OMM and MMM).

Metal: Enamelled gold or silver.

Size: 38mm (OMM and MMM)

Description: (Obverse) a cross pattée with the arms in blue enamel edged with gold (CMM and OMM) or silver (MMM). A central medallion has a maple leaf at the centre in red (CMM), gold (OMM) or silver (MMM) on a gold or silver background surrounded by an outer band in red enamel inscribed with the words MERIT MÉRITE CANADA in the appropriate metal; (reverse) left plain apart from a serial number. A straight suspender bar with a laurel leaf design is used for officers (in gold) and members (in silver).

Comments: *Instituted to recognise conspicuous merit or exceptional service by all members of the Canadian armed forces. The total of all levels which can be awarded annually cannot exceed one-tenth of one per cent of the average number of personnel in the preceding year—up to 6 commanders, 30 officers and 64 members at the current level of establishment of the armed forces. There is no limit to the total number at any level. Commanders are most usually of the rank of brigadier-general/commodore and above, officers are majors to colonels and members all those of lower rank including NCOs and junior officers. Appointments are made in July and December each year. In undress uniform the level of the award is indicated by a blue cross worn on the ribbon with a maple leaf placed centrally in red, gold or silver. Prior to 1983 a maple leaf of the appropriate colour was worn alone.*

C5. L'ORDRE NATIONAL DU QUÉBEC
GRAND OFFICIER (GOQ), OFFICER (OQ), CHEVALIER (CQ)

Date: 20 June 1984.

Ribbon: Blue with a white central band, all of equal width. Worn around the neck (grand officier and officier) or on the breast (chevalier).

Metal: Gold (GOQ) or silver (OQ and CQ).

Size: —

Description: (Obverse) a Greek cross with very broad arms and the space between them so small that it is almost square. The upper left and lower right have an irregular highly polished area resulting in a very reflective quality with the space between the two in a matt finish giving the overall appearance of a river running between two land masses. In the bottom left corner, superimposed on the matt area is a fleur-de-lys. All the elements and ribbon colour are taken from the flag of Québec. The insignia for a chevalier has the cross mounted on a circular silver disc with a ring suspender.

Comments: *Membership of the Order is open to any citizen of Québec without distinction to recognise outstanding work in the Province for the benefit of all. Any person can nominate any other citizen for the award. Honorary membership is available to those not resident in Québec. An award ceremony takes place once a year although special arrangements can be made if the recipient does not reside in the Province.*

C6. SASKATCHEWAN ORDER OF MERIT

Date: 1985.
Ribbon: Dark green with a gold central band, all of equal width.
Metal: Enamelled gold.
Size: —
Description: (Obverse) a six-point star in white enamel edged in gold and with gold lines along the centre of each point. There is a central medallion in the shape of the shield from the Saskatchewan coat of arms in enamels (a lion above three sheaves of wheat) surmounted by a crown in gold. The neck ribbon is attached to the upper point of the star by a small suspender ring.
Comments: *Awarded to recognise individual excellence and outstanding achievement to the social, cultural and economic well-being of the Province and its people. A maximum of ten appointments can be made in any one year. Any resident, past or present of Saskatchewan is eligible for membership although members of parliament, legislative assembly and judges are barred whilst in office. Recipients are entitled to use the post-nominals SOM.*

C7. ORDER OF ONTARIO

Date: 18 December 1986.
Ribbon: Red with a central stripe in dark green flanked by a white band bisected by a thin gold line.
Metal: Enamelled gold.
Size: —
Description: (Obverse) a stylised version of the provincial flower (trillium) with three petals in white enamel superimposed on three dark green enamel sepals, all edged in gold. In the centre is the shield taken from the Ontario coat of arms in enamels surmounted by a crown in gold. a small ring suspender is used.
Comments: *Awarded to residents of Ontario who have shown excellence and achievement of the highest standard and whose contributions have enriched the lives of others and helped make a better society in Ontario. Recipients have the right to use the post-nominals O Ont. Elected officials at federal, provincial or municipal level are barred from membership of the Order whilst in office.*

C8. ORDER OF BRITISH COLUMBIA

Date: 12 April 1989.
Ribbon: Dark green with two bands of white either side of a central dark green stripe each bisected by a thin gold line.
Metal: Gold and enamel.
Size: —
Description: (Obverse) a stylised representation of the six-petal provincial flower of British Columbia (pacific dogwood) in white and green enamels edged by gold. At the centre is the shield of the provincial coat of arms in enamels topped by a crown. A small ring suspended is used.
Comments: *Awarded in recognition of distinction and excellence in any field of endeavour for the benefit of people in British Columbia and elsewhere.*

C9. ALBERTA ORDER OF EXCELLENCE

Date: 16 November 1979.
Ribbon: The same design as the previous order but with the dark green replaced by dark blue.
Metal: Silver gilt and enamel.
Size: —
Description: (Obverse) a cross pattée with the arms in dark blue enamel edged with gold superimposed on a circular disc visible between the arms of the cross and decorated with a design of roses and rose leaves to represent the provincial flower. A central medallion has the full achievement of arms of Alberta on a red background within an outer band of white enamel bearing the words THE ALBERTA ORDER OF EXCELLENCE in gold; (reverse) a maple leaf and sheaf of wheat.
Comments: *Awarded in October each year to Canadian citizens living in Alberta from all walks of life who have performed excellent and distinctive works at provincial, national or international level. It is the highest award that can be bestowed by the Province of Alberta. An important provision is that the work will stand the test of time. Recipients are entitled to use the post-nominals AOE.*

C10. ORDER OF PRINCE EDWARD ISLAND MEDAL OF MERIT

Date: 1996.
Ribbon: A broad band of brown (left) and one of green (right) separated by a narrow white band and with a white line at each edge.
Metal: Enamelled gold.
Size: —
Description: (Obverse) circular with the shield from the provincial coat of arms in gold with red and white enamel on a background of gold enamel all within an outer band of blue enamel bearing the words MERIT (upper) and PRINCE EDWARD ISLAND (lower) in gold. A second version with the inscriptions in French is also available—MÉRITE (upper) and ÎLE-DU-PRINCE-EDOUARD. The ribbon, which is worn around the neck attached to the disc by two rings—one small, one large. A miniature is awarded for wear on less formal occasions—the design is the same but the ribbon is green with a central brown band, all of equal width, separated by white lines and with white edges.
Comments: *The Order is the highest that can be bestowed by the Province and given to any resident (present or former long-term) who contributes to the social, economic and cultural life of Prince Edward Island. Not more than three people can be admitted to the Order in any one year. In common with other provincial orders elected officials are not eligible whilst they remain in office. Recipients are entitled to use the post-nominals OPEI.*

C11. ORDER OF MANITOBA

Date: 14 July 1999.
Ribbon: White with a central stripe in red and a pale blue band towards each edge.
Metal: Enamelled gold.
Size: —
Description: (Obverse) a stylised representation of the provincial flower (crocus) with six petals in pale blue enamel edged in gold bearing the shield from the provincial coat of arms at the centre in enamels topped by a crown in gold.
Comments: *Established to recognise current or former long-term residents of Manitoba who have demonstrated excellence and achievement in any field leading to the social, economic or cultural well-being of the Province. A maximum of eight awards can be made in any one year although the initial investiture saw 20 people honoured. Members are entitled to the use of the post-nominals OM. Certain elected officials are not eligible whilst in office.*

C12. STAR OF MILITARY VALOUR

Date: 2 February 1993.
Ribbon: Crimson with a white band towards each edge.
Metal: Gold with silver.
Size: —
Description: (Obverse) a four-point star with a maple leaf between the points. A central medallion has a maple leaf placed centrally on a red background all surrounded by a circular wreath of laurel in silver; (reverse) the royal cypher (EIIR) surmounted by a crown with the inscription PRO VALORE. The rank and name of the recipient is engraved below the inscription. A suspension ring is attached to the upper point of the cross.
Comments: *The second highest military decoration in Canada. It is awarded to any member of the Canadian armed forces or allies serving with the Canadians for distinguished and valiant service in the presence of an enemy on or after January 1, 1993. Any second or subsequent award is indicated by a gold bar bearing a maple leaf in the centre. It can be awarded posthumously. Although Canadian civil awards for bravery were introduced in 1972 it was not until the introduction of this award (with others) that Canadian honours for the military were available.*

C13. STAR OF COURAGE

Date: 1 May 1972.
Ribbon: Red with a band of blue towards each edge.
Metal: Silver with gold.
Size: —
Description: (Obverse) identical to the Star of Military Valour but in silver with a gold wreath of laurel around the central medallion; (reverse) the royal cypher (EIIR) surmounted by a crown on the upper arm of the cross with the inscription COURAGE below. The name of the recipient and date of the act are engraved below.
Comments: *The second highest honour for civilian courage awarded for acts of conspicuous courage in circumstance of great peril. It is available to Canadian citizens and foreign nationals for the performance of an act in Canada or elsewhere if the act is in the interest of Canada. The first award was made on 20 July 1972. Second or subsequent awards are indicated by a gold bar with a maple leaf at its centre. In common with most Canadian national honours the award is named in English and French but the initials of the two are not the same. The post-nominals are therefore different—SC (English) or EC (French "Étoile de Courage").*

C14. MERITORIOUS SERVICE CROSS (MILITARY AND CIVIL DIVISIONS)

Date: 11 June 1984 (military) and 6 June 1991 (civil).
Ribbon: Bright blue with a white stripe (6 mm) towards each edge. The civil division is indicated by the addition of a central white line (1 mm).
Metal: Silver.
Size: 38mm.
Description: (Obverse) a Greek cross with splayed ends with a wreath of laurel between the arms. A crown is attached to the upper arm of the cross to which is joined the plain straight suspender bar. A central medallion bears a maple leaf at its centre; (reverse) two concentric circles with the royal cypher (EIIR) in the centre and the words MERITORIOUS SERVICE MÉRITOIRE (separated at the bottom by a maple leaf) around the second of the two circles.
Comments: *The Cross was initially introduced for award to the military only but extended in 1991 to civilians and made retrospective to 1984. The criteria are similar for both divisions—a deed or activity performed in a highly professional manner or of a high standard bringing benefit or great honour to the Canadian armed forces (military) or Canada (civil). Second or subsequent awards are indicated by a silver bar with a maple leaf in its centre. Both awards are available to Canadians and foreign nationals.*

C15. MEDAL OF MILITARY VALOUR

Date: 2 February 1993.
Ribbon: Crimson with white stripes in the centre and at each edge.
Metal: Gold.
Size: 36mm.
Description: (Obverse) circular with a maple leaf surrounded by a
   wreath of laurel tied at its base by a bow; (reverse) the royal cypher
   (EIIR) surmounted by a crown with the inscription PRO VALORE.
   The suspender bar is in the shape of a fleur-de-lys attached to the
   disc by a claw fitting. The rank and name of the recipient are
   engraved on the rim.
Comments: *Awarded to members of the Canadian armed forces and allies
   serving with or in conjunction with the Canadians for an act of valour or
   devotion to duty in the presence of an enemy. A gold bar with a maple leaf
   at its centre is available for any second or subsequent award. It can be
   awarded posthumously.*

C16. MEDAL OF BRAVERY

Date: 1 May 1972.
Ribbon: Crimson with dark blue stripes in the centre and at each
   edge.
Metal: Silver.
Size: 36mm.
Description: (Obverse) identical to the previous award; (reverse) the
   royal cypher (EIIR) surmounted by a crown with the words
   BRAVERY (right) and BRAVOURE (left) at the circumference.
Comments: *Awarded to all Canadian citizens (civilian and military) and
   foreign nationals as defined for previous awards for acts of bravery in
   hazardous circumstances. It can be awarded posthumously. The first
   award was made on 20 July 1972. Bars are of silver with a maple leaf
   placed centrally.*

C17. MERITORIOUS SERVICE MEDAL
(MILITARY AND CIVIL DIVISIONS)

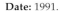

Date: 1991.
Ribbon: Dark blue with two white stripes towards each edge. The
   civil division is indicated by the addition of a central white line
   (1mm).
Metal: Silver.
Size: 36mm.
Description: (Obverse) a Greek cross with splayed ends with a wreath
   of laurel between the arms and a maple leaf in the central
   medallion all superimposed on a disc. A crown is attached to the
   upper arm of the cross to which is joined the plain straight
   suspender bar; (reverse) two concentric circles with the royal
   cypher (EIIR) in the centre and the words MERITORIOUS
   SERVICE MÉRITOIRE (separated at the bottom by a maple leaf)
   around the second of the two circles.
Comments: *The criteria are similar for both divisions—a deed or activity
   performed in a highly professional manner or of a high standard bringing
   benefit or honour to the Canadian armed forces (military) or Canada
   (civil). Second or subsequent awards are indicated by a silver bar with a
   maple leaf in its centre. Both awards are available to Canadians and
   foreign nationals and can be awarded posthumously. Recipients are
   entitled to the use of the post-nominals MSM.*

C18. CANADIAN VOLUNTEER SERVICE MEDAL FOR KOREA

Date: 1991

Ribbon: Yellow with a broad band in UN blue (7mm) at each edge and a central band of red, white and red (all 2mm).

Metal: Silver coloured copper and zinc alloy.

Size: 36mm.

Description: (Obverse) the crowned profile of Queen Elizabeth II with the word CANADA below and ELIZABETH II DEI GRATIA REGINA around the circumference; (reverse) a wreath of laurel tied at the base by a bow with a maple leaf above it. In the central field is the inscription KOREA/VOLUNTEER/1950–1954/VOLONTAIRE/COREE. A plain straight suspender was used.

Comments: *Awarded to former members of the Canadian armed forces who were in the qualifying area of Korea and adjacent areas between June 27, 1950 and July 27, 1954 with four further provisos. The recipients were eligible if they were on the strength of a unit in Korea for one day, were on active service aboard a ship for at least 28 days, flew one sortie over Korea or Korean waters or had accumulated at least 28 days service in the qualifying area. The medal could be awarded posthumously and more than 16,000 awards were made.*

C19. GULF AND KUWAIT MEDAL

Date: 1991.

Ribbon: A sand coloured central band (8mm) flanked by bands of dark blue (5mm), red (2mm) and light blue (5mm) to represent the three branches of the armed forces.

Metal: Silver coloured copper and zinc alloy.

Size: 36mm.

Description: (Obverse) the crowned profile of Queen Elizabeth II with the word CANADA below and ELIZABETH II DEI GRATIA REGINA around the circumference; (reverse) a wreath of laurel tied at the base by a bow with a maple leaf above it. In the central field is the inscription THE GULF/AND KUWAIT/1990–1992/LE GOLFE/ET KUWAIT in five lines. A plain straight suspender was used.

Comments: *Awarded to all members of the Canadian armed forces who served in the theatre of operations between August 2, 1990 and June 27, 1991 for a minimum of 30 days cumulative service or who served during actual hostilities for at least one day between January 16 and March 30, 1991. Bars were awarded for a second qualifying period of service. The bar was awarded to all those who served during the hostilities for at least one day. The bar has a silver maple leaf at its centre. Approximately 4,500 medals were awarded.*

C20. SOMALIA MEDAL

Date: 1993.

Ribbon: White with United Nations blue bands (5 mm) at each edge and a central band of three colours (dark blue, red and light blue to represent the three armed services) flanked by bands of a sand colour—all 2.5 mm wide).

Metal: Bronze.

Size: 32mm.

Description: (Obverse) three over-lapping Canadian maple leaves above two branches of laurel and with the word CANADA above; (reverse) the royal cypher (EIIR) surmounted by a crown with the words SOMALIA (left) SOMALIE (right) and the dates 1992–93 (lower) around the circumference. A ring suspender was used.

Comments: *Available to any member of the Canadian armed forces or anyone attached to or working with them for a minimum of 90 days cumulative service in Somalia between November 16, 1992 and June 30, 1993. Anyone with a minimum of 60 days service who died, was evacuated or redeployed was also eligible. It was awarded posthumously.*

C21. SPECIAL SERVICE MEDAL

Date: 16 June 1984.

Ribbon: A dark green central band (12mm) flanked by bands of white (5mm) and red (5mm) at the edges.

Metal: Cupro-nickel.

Size: 36mm.

Description: (Obverse) A wreath of laurel tied at the base by a bow with a maple leaf in the central field; (reverse) the royal cypher (EIIR) surmounted by a crown with the words SPECIAL SERVICE SPÉCIAL around the circumference. A plain straight suspender is used.

Comments: *Awarded to members of the Canadian armed forces for service performed in a clearly defined region for a specific period. Bars are awarded to indicate the area of service and include PAKISTAN 1989–90. The specific areas of service include humanitarian aid in a number of places, peacekeeping operations and service with NATO usually for a period of 130 days which need not be continuous.*

C22. CANADIAN PEACEKEEPING SERVICE MEDAL

Date: 25 April 1997.

Ribbon: A light blue central band flanked by equal bands of white, red and green.

Metal: Silver.

Size: 36mm.

Description: (Obverse) a depiction of three Canadian peacekeepers taken from the National Peacekeeping Monument in Ottawa. One figure is an unarmed UN military observer holding a pair of binoculars, another a kneeling female figure shouldering a radio and the third a guard with a rifle. The words PEACEKEEPING (upper) and SERVICE DE LA PAIX (lower) lie at the circumference; (reverse) a maple leaf with the royal cypher (EIIR) topped by a crown in the centre with a branch of laurel on either side and the word CANADA below. The plain straight suspender bar is attached by a maple leaf.

Comments: *Inspired by the award in 1988 of the Nobel Peace Prize to all UN peacekeepers. Awarded for a minimum of 30 days service on a peacekeeping or observing mission. Military personnel, police officers and civilians are eligible. Recipients are also entitled to wear any UN medal issued.*

C23. CANADIAN CENTENNIAL MEDAL

Date: 1 July 1967.

Ribbon: White with four red lines (1mm) equally spaced and red bands (5mm) at the edges.

Metal: Silver.

Size: 36mm.

Description: (Obverse) the Canadian maple leaf superimposed by the royal cypher (EIIR) surmounted by a crown and the words CONFEDERATION (left) CANADA (upper) and CONFÉDÉRATION (right) around the circumference; (reverse) the full achievement of arms of Canada above the dates 1867–1967. A plain suspender in a wide, shallow triangular shape was used.

Comments: *Awarded in celebration of the centenary of Canadian confederation to those recommended by national and provincial governments and a variety of other bodies and associations. The Canadian military forces were awarded approximately 30 per cent of all medals issued.*

C24. 125th ANNIVERSARY OF THE CONFEDERATION OF CANADA MEDAL

Date: 1992.
Ribbon: White with five red lines (1mm) equally spaced and blue bands (4.5mm) at the edges.
Metal: Rhodium plated copper and zinc alloy.
Size: 36mm.
Description: (Obverse) the Canadian maple leaf superimposed by the royal cypher (EIIR) surmounted by a crown and the words CONFEDERATION (left) and CONFÉDÉRATION (right) and the dates 1867–1992 (lower) around the circumference; (reverse) the shield taken from the Canadian coat of arms within a belt bearing the words DESIDERANTE MELORIAM PATRIAN and surmounted by a lion. The legend A MARI USQUE AS MARE is inscribed around the lower circumference half. A plain straight suspender is used.
Comments: *Awarded to Canadian citizens who had made a significant contribution to Canada, their community or their fellow citizens in celebration of the 125th anniversary of federation. A total of 44,000 were awarded.*

C25. ROYAL CANADIAN MOUNTED POLICE LONG SERVICE MEDAL

Date: 6 March 1934.
Ribbon: Dark blue with two gold stripes towards the edges.
Metal: Silver.
Size: 36 mm.
Description: (Obverse) the effigy of the reigning monarch; (reverse) the insignia of the RCMP consisting of the head of a buffalo within a buckled belt inscribed with the words MAINTENEZ LE DROIT all topped by a crown. On either side of the belt are five maple leaves. The name of the Force is contained in a banner below the belt. The words FOR LONG SERVICE (above) and AND GOOD CONDUCT (below) are inscribed around the circumference. A plain straight suspender is attached by a claw fitting.
Comments: *When Queen Elizabeth came to the throne and the medal was redesigned to display her effigy on the obverse, changes were also made to the reverse to substitute the Queen's crown for the King's that had been used from the medal's introduction. The opportunity was also taken to reduce the size of the insignia of the RCMP and move the inscription to read continuously around the circumference. In 1989 a French language version of this new design was introduced with the inscription on the reverse reading POUR ANCIENNETÉ ET BONNE CONDUITE. The recipients have the right to choose which version they would prefer.*

C26. POLICE EXEMPLARY SERVICE MEDAL

Date: 12 August 1982.
Ribbon: Five equal stripes of dark blue (three) and yellow (two).
Metal: Silver.
Size: 36mm.
Description: (Obverse) a circular medal with a maple leaf in the centre bearing a representation of the scales of justice and an outer band with the words EXEMPLARY SERVICE in the upper half and SERVICES DISTINGUÉS in the lower. It is of a skeletal design with the outer band attached to the leaves and stem of the maple leaf; (reverse) plain apart from the royal cypher (EIIR) topped by the Queen's crown in the centre of the maple leaf.
Comments: *Awarded on completion of 20 years' service to officers of any recognised Canadian police force who showed industry, efficiency and good conduct during their careers. Although members of the RCMP or Canadian Military Police are not eligible, any full-time service in either of those bodies can be counted towards the necessary number of years' service. Bars (bearing a stylised maple leaf) are available for additional periods of ten years. The medal is not a purely long service award and will be withheld if an officer with the required number of years' service does not meet the appropriate standards of behaviour necessary. It can be awarded posthumously.*

C27. CORRECTIONS EXEMPLARY SERVICE MEDAL

Date: 11 June 1984.
Ribbon: Five equal stripes of green (three) and yellow (two).
Metal: Silver.
Size: 36mm.
Description: (Obverse) a circular medal with a maple leaf in the centre bearing a crossed key and torch and an outer band with the words EXEMPLARY SERVICE in the upper half and SERVICES DISTINGUÉS in the lower. It is of a skeletal design with the outer band attached to the leaves and stem of the maple leaf; (reverse) plain apart from the royal cypher (EIIR) topped by the Queen's crown in the centre of the maple leaf.
Comments: *Awarded on completion of 20 years' full-time paid service to officers of the Canadian Correctional Service (federal, provincial or territorial) who showed industry, efficiency and good conduct during their careers. The service need not have been continuous. Bars (bearing a stylised maple leaf) are available for additional periods of ten years. The medal is not a purely long service award and will be withheld if an officer with the required number of years' service does not meet the appropriate standards of behaviour necessary. It can be awarded posthumously.*

C28. FIRE SERVICES EXEMPLARY SERVICE MEDAL

Date: 25 August 1985.
Ribbon: Five equal stripes of red (three) and yellow (two).
Metal: Silver.
Size: 36mm.
Description: (Obverse) a circular medal with a maple leaf in the centre bearing a pair of crossed axes and fire hydrant within an outer band with the words EXEMPLARY SERVICE in the upper half and SERVICES DISTINGUÉS in the lower. It is of a skeletal design with the outer band attached to the leaves and stem of the maple leaf; (reverse) plain apart from the royal cypher (EIIR) topped by the Queen's crown in the centre of the maple leaf.
Comments: *Awarded on completion of 20 years' service with a recognised Canadian fire service (including fire marshal's offices, fire commissioner's offices and the Canadian Armed Forces Fire Service) to officers showed industry, efficiency and good conduct during their careers. The service need not have been continuous. Bars (bearing a stylised maple leaf) are available for additional periods of ten years. The medal is not a purely long service award and will be withheld if an officer with the required number of years' service does not meet the appropriate standards of behaviour necessary. It can be awarded posthumously.*

C29. CANADIAN COAST GUARD EXEMPLARY SERVICE MEDAL

Date: 14 March 1991.
Ribbon: Dark blue with a narrow white stripe in the centre and a broader yellow band towards each edge.
Metal: Silver.
Size: 36mm.
Description: (Obverse) a solid circular medal with the crest of the Canadian Coast Guard in the centre and an outer band bearing the inscriptions EXEMPLARY SERVICE (left) and SERVICES DISTINGUÉS (right); (reverse) plain apart from the royal cypher (EIIR) topped by the Queen's crown in the centre of the maple leaf.
Comments: *Awarded on completion of 20 years' service with the Department of Transport which must include ten years with the Canadian Coast Guard in duties with a potential risk. Officers must have shown industry, efficiency and good conduct during their careers. The service need not have been continuous. Bars (bearing a stylised maple leaf) are available for additional periods of ten years, five of which must have involved duties where there was a potential risk of danger. The medal is not a purely long service award and will be withheld if an officer with the required number of years' service does not meet the appropriate standards of behaviour necessary. It can be awarded posthumously.*

C30. EMERGENCY MEDICAL SERVICES EXEMPLARY SERVICE MEDAL

Date: 7 July 1994.
Ribbon: Dark blue with two bands of gold all equally spaced and with a stripe of orange (2.3mm) bisecting each of the three blue bands.
Metal: Silver.
Size: 36mm.
Description: (Obverse) a circular medal with a maple leaf in the centre bearing the star of life, staff and serpent within an outer band with the words EXEMPLARY SERVICE in the upper half and SERVICES DISTINGUÉS in the lower. It is of a skeletal design with the outer band attached to the leaves and stem of the maple leaf; (reverse) plain apart from the royal cypher (EIIR) topped by the Queen's crown in the centre of the maple leaf.
Comments: *Awarded on completion of 20 years' service in the field of pre-hospital emergency medical care. Ten of these years must have involved duties involving a potential risk. Recipients must have shown industry, efficiency and good conduct during their careers. The service need not have been continuous. Bars (bearing a stylised maple leaf) are available for additional periods of ten years. The medal is not a purely long service award and will be withheld if an officer with the required number of years' service does not meet the appropriate standards of behaviour necessary. It can be awarded posthumously.*

C31. ONTARIO MEDAL FOR GOOD CITIZENSHIP

Date: 1973.
Ribbon: White with a central band in gold and a broad green band at the edges.
Metal: Silver.
Size: 36mm.
Description: (Obverse) circular with the full achievement of arms of Ontario in the lower two-thirds and the inscription FOR GOOD CITIZENSHIP at the upper circumference; (reverse) the provincial flower—a trillium. A scrolled suspender bar is used attached to the top of the disc.
Comments: *Awarded to any citizen of Ontario to recognise good citizenship displayed by their generous, kind or self-effacing manner in improving the quality of life in the Province. It is not awarded posthumously or for acts of courage. A maximum of twelve medals are presented each year.*

C32. ONTARIO MEDAL FOR POLICE BRAVERY

Date: 1975.
Ribbon: Royal blue with two gold stripes towards the edges.
Metal: Gold plated sterling silver with blue and white enamel.
Size: 57mm wide by 68mm high (with crown).
Description: (Obverse) a cross in blue enamel on gold with the provincial flower (white trillium) in white in a small central medallion and a maple leaf between the arms of the cross. A Queen's crown tops the upper arm; (reverse) left plain.
Comments: *Awarded to officers from any police force in the province to reward any act of superlative courage and bravery performed in the line of duty and is also intended to encourage the virtue of bravery and focus attention and support of the public behind the efforts of the police forces. The medals are presented at a special ceremony held in early November each year.*

C33. ONTARIO MEDAL FOR FIREFIGHTERS BRAVERY

Date: 1976.
Ribbon: Red with two gold stripes towards the edges.
Metal: Gold plated sterling silver with red and white enamel.
Size: 57mm wide by 68mm high (with crown).
Description: (Obverse) a cross in gold with a pattern on each arm in red enamel to symbolise fire and a maple leaf between the arms. The provincial flower (white trillium) in white enamel lies in a small central medallion. A Queen's crown tops the upper arm; (reverse) left plain.
Comments: *Awarded to firefighters in the Province to reward any act of superlative courage and bravery performed in the line of duty and is also intended to encourage the virtue of bravery and focus attention and support of the public behind the efforts of the firefighters. The medals are presented at a special ceremony held on 9 November each year. The medal can be awarded posthumously.*

C34. SASKATCHEWAN VOLUNTEER MEDAL

Date: —
Ribbon: Green with a gold central band, all of equal width.
Metal: Silver and enamel.
Size: 36mm.
Description: (Obverse) a circular silver medal with the shield from the Saskatchewan coat of arms surmounted by a crown placed in the centre. The name of the Province lies along the lower circumference and the inscription NOS IPSOS DEDIMUS (we give of ourselves) at the upper edge. The plain straight suspender bar is attached by a stylised letter "V".
Comments: *Awarded each year to a maximum of ten current or former long-term residents of Saskatchewan who have served in a voluntary capacity above and beyond the call of duty to improved daily life in the Province. Elected officials and members of the judiciary are barred from receiving the award whilst they remain in office.*

C35. ONTARIO PROVINCIAL POLICE LONG SERVICE AND GOOD CONDUCT MEDAL

Date: 15 December 1949.
Ribbon: Crimson with two green stripes each bordered by white lines on both sides.
Metal: Silver.
Size: 38mm.
Description: (Obverse) the Coat of Arms of the Province of Ontario with the word ONTARIO written below; (reverse) the inscription ONTARIO PROVINCIAL POLICE in three lines in the central field and FOR LONG SERVICE AND GOOD CONDUCT around the circumference and two crossed maple leaves in the exergue. An ornate, non-swivelling, suspender was attached to the top of the medal.
Comments: *Ontario is one of only two provincial police forces that remain in Canada. The medal was awarded to members of the Force who had served for not less than 20 years, the last ten of which must have been with good conduct and satisfactory service. Bars were awarded for each additional period of five years' qualifying service. For 25 and 30 years' service a plain silver bar decorated with one or two white trilliums (the provincial flower) was awarded and for 35 or 40 years qualifying service gold bars were issued also bearing one or two trillium motifs.*

C36. ONTARIO FIRE SERVICES LONG SERVICE MEDAL

Date: 1 April 1871.
Ribbon: Red with bands of green and white towards the two edges.
Metal: Silver.
Size: 38mm.
Description: (Obverse) a Maltese cross superimposed by the coat of arms of Ontario with the inscription FIRE SERVICES ONTARIO at the circumference; (reverse) plain apart from the inscriptions FOR LONG SERVICE and THE FIRE MARSHALS ACT.
Comments: *Awarded to full-time and volunteer members of the Ontario Fire Service in recognition of 30 years' service. On its introduction the award was made available to any firefighter with the required length of service who had left or retired in the preceding three years. The qualifying period of service is especially noteworthy as it far exceeds the length of time applicable to other services and the Fire Service Exemplary Service Medal which was introduced nationally in 1985.*

C37. QUEEN'S MEDAL FOR CHAMPION SHOT IN CANADA

Date: 28 August 1991.
Ribbon: Dark crimson with stripes of black, white and black (each 3mm) at the edges.
Metal: Silver.
Size: 38mm.
Description: (Obverse) the crowned head of Queen Elizabeth II with the inscription ELIZABETH II DEI GRATIA REGINA around the circumference and CANADA at the bottom; (reverse) the figure of Fame on the right rising from her throne and crowning a warrior with a laurel wreath. The warrior holds a bow and quiver of arrows in his right hand and has a target with three arrows in the centre resting on his left knee. A plain straight suspender is used attached by a claw fitting. The date of the award is showed on a plain silver clasp. Any subsequent award of the medal is indicated by a clasp only.
Comments: *There are two medals awarded each year, one to the regular member of the Canadian armed forces and another to the officer of the Royal Canadian Mounted Police who obtains the highest aggregate score in the two stages of the Queen's Medal Competition.*

C38. ORDER OF MERIT OF THE POLICE FORCES

Date: October 2000.
Ribbon: Bands of blue, gold and blue, all of equal width. A neck ribbon is worn for the rank of commander and a breast ribbon for officers and members.
Metal: Gold, silver and enamels.
Size: 38mm (OOM and MOM).
Description: (Obverse) a cross pattée in dark blue enamel with a central medallion bearing a maple leaf and an outer band inscribed with the word MERIT (left) and MÉRITE (right) in the upper circumference and CANADA at the bottom. A St Edward's crown is on the upper arm of the cross. The maple leaf in the central medallion is red for commanders, gold for officers and silver for a member. The outer band is red with gold lettering for commanders and officers and red with silver lettering for members. A silver suspender bar with a laurel leaf pattern and three small sings is used.
Comments: *The most recent addition to the awards available to police officers is a continuation of the series of Orders first established in 1967 with the introduction of the Order of Canada and continued in 1972 with the Order of Military Merit. The Order of Merit of the Police Forces ranks immediately after the Order of Military merit in the order of precedence. It was introduced to recognise the impact of the Police Service on society and honour those officers with careers of particular merit or who otherwise deserve formal recognition and is available in three classes—commander (COM), officer (OOM) and member (MOM). The first commander appointed to the Order is Commissioner Zaccardelli of the RCMP but no other appointments have yet been made. In any one year there will be a maximum new appointees equivalent to one-tenth of one per cent of the number of police officers serving in Canada in the preceding year and is expected that they will number no more than 50. Officers from any police force in Canada are eligible although it is a living order and retired officers are not eligible, neither can it be awarded posthumously.*

Searching ...

Searching ...

Searching ...

Look no further than

www.tokenpublishing.com

For quality books, useful accessories, the latest breaking news or details of our other magazine, COIN NEWS, check out our new, secure web site . . . you won't be disappointed.

WWW

Coming soon ... dealer directory (with links), medal tracker on-line and reader's notice board to air your views and much more! Watch our site for details.

THE ORDER OF PRECEDENCE IN NEW ZEALAND
(including British Awards)

Victoria Cross
George Cross
Order of the Garter
Knights Grand Cross, The Most Honourable Order of the Bath
Order of Merit
New Zealand Cross
Baronet's Badge
Knights Grand Cross, The Most Distinguished Order of St Michael and St George (GCMG)
Knights Grand Cross, The Royal Victorian Order
Knights Grand Cross, The Most Excellent Order of the British Empire
Order of Companions of Honour
Order of New Zealand
Knight Commander, The Most Honourable Order of the Bath
Knight Commander, The Most Distinguished Order of St Michael and St George
Knight Commander, The Royal Victorian Order
Knight Commander, The Most Excellent Order of the British Empire
Knight Bachelors badge
Companion, The Most Honourable Order of the Bath
Companion, The Most Distinguished Order of St Michael and St George
Commander, The Royal Victorian Order
Commander, The Most Excellent Order of the British Empire
Distinguished Service Order
Lieutenant, The Royal Victorian Order
Officer, The Most Excellent Order of the British Empire
Queen's Service Order
Imperial Service Order
Member, The Royal Victorian Order
Member, The Most Excellent Order of the British Empire
Royal Red Cross (Member)
Distinguished Service Cross
Military Cross
Distinguished Flying Cross
Air Force Cross
Royal Red Cross (Associate)
Order of St John (All classes)
Albert Medal
Distinguished Conduct Medal
Conspicuous Gallantry Medal
George Medal
Queen's Police Medal for Gallantry
Distinguished Service Medal
Military Medal
Distinguished Flying Medal

Air Force Medal
Empire Gallantry Medal
Queen's Gallantry Medal
Royal Victorian Medals
Queen's Service Medal
British Empire Medal
Queen's Police Medal for Distinguished Service
Queen's Fire Service Medal for Distinguished Service
War Medals in order of campaign
New Zealand General Service Medal
Polar Medal
Imperial Service Medal
Coronation and Jubilee Medals in date order
New Zealand 1990 Commemoration Medal
New Zealand Suffrage Centennial Medal 1993
New Zealand Meritorious Service Medal
New Zealand Armed Forces Award
New Zealand Army Long Service and Good Conduct Medal
Royal New Zealand Navy Long Service and Good Conduct Medal
Royal New Zealand Air Force Long Service and Good Conduct Medal
New Zealand Police Long Service and Good Conduct Medal
New Zealand Fire Brigades Long Service and Good Conduct Medal
New Zealand Prison Service Medal
New Zealand Traffic Service Medal
Colonial Auxiliary Forces Decoration
Colonial Auxiliary Forces Long Service Medal
New Zealand Efficiency Decoration
New Zealand Efficiency Medal
Royal New Zealand Naval Volunteer Reserve Decoration
Royal Naval Reserve Decoration
Royal New Zealand Naval Volunteer Reserve Long Service and Good Conduct Medal
Royal Naval Reserve Long Service and Good Conduct Medal
Air Efficiency Award
Queen's Medal for Champion Shots of the New Zealand Naval Forces
Queen's Medal for Champion Shots of the Military Forces
Queen's Medal for Champion Shots of the Air Forces
Cadet Forces Medal
Rhodesia Medal 1980
Service Medal of the Order of St John
Other Commonwealth Members' Orders, Decorations and Medals in date of award
Approved Foreign Orders, Decorations and Medals in order of date of award

> **At the time of going to press no definitive revised Order of Wear including the new awards and decorations was available. The above list is the Order of Wear prior to the new changes. It is hoped that the new Order of Wear will be published in a future edition of the Medal Yearbook.**

New Zealand
medals

Between 1848 and 1996 New Zealanders were eligible for the various British or Imperial honours and awards. The first step towards an independent honours system was taken in 1975 when the Queen's Service Order and Queen's Service Medal were instituted.

Thereafter a range of distinctive New Zealand medals was gradually adopted for the defence forces, the police, fire and prison services, this culminated in the introduction of a totally separate New Zealand Royal Honours System in May 1996. With a few exceptions, all honours and awards are conferred by, or in the name of, the sovereign (Queen Elizabeth) on the advice of Her Majesty's New Zealand ministers. A distinctive feature of many New Zealand orders, decorations and medals is the influence of Maori art forms.

Medals and decorations which were specific to New Zealand but made under Royal Warrants prior to 1975 are listed in the main body of this book. A new range of New Zealand gallantry and bravery awards is in the process of being developed, and this includes the creation of a Victoria Cross for New Zealand as well as the highest non-combatant bravery award, the New Zealand Cross. The new medals and decorations are given below in order of precedence. To date very few of these awards have come onto the market. and information on their rarity and other missing details have not been available, so it has been decided to omit prices in this section. However, it is hoped to include them and the missing information in future editions.

NZ1. VICTORIA CROSS FOR NEW ZEALAND

Instituted: June 1998.
Ribbon: Crimson 38mm wide.
Metal: Bronze.
Size: 35mm at each axis.
Description: A cross pattée with raised edges, identical to the British and Australian Victoria Crosses (MYB24 and A1).
Comments: *Although identical to the existing VC, awards will be made under a New Zealand, as opposed to a British, Royal Warrant. Recipients are entitled to the postnominal letters VC.*

NZ2. NEW ZEALAND CROSS

Instituted: 1998.
Ribbon:
Metal: Silver with gold applique.
Size:
Description: Similar to the original New Zealand Cross of 1869 (MYB25) but incorporating changes which were first proposed in 1885 and only now implemented, viz. fern fronds have replaced laurel leaves.
Comments: *The premier civilian award for bravery, it now supersedes the George Cross so far as New Zealand citizens are concerned. Recipients are entitled to the postnominal letters NZC.*

357

NZ3. ORDER OF NEW ZEALAND

Instituted: 1987.

Ribbon: Red ochre with a narrow white stripe towards either edge.

Metal: 9 carat gold.

Description: An oval medal decorated with coloured enamels bearing in the centre the heraldic shield of New Zealand within a Kowhaiwhai rafter pattern.

Comments: *Instituted as a first-level non-titular order, it is modelled on the British Order of Merit (1917) and the Order of the Companions of Honour (1917). The Order comprises the Queen as Sovereign and no more than 20 ordinary members who are entitled to the postnominal letters ONZ. Additional members may be appointed in commemoration of important royal, state or national occasions. Honorary membership includes citizens of Commonwealth nations of which the Queen is not Head of State, and of foreign countries. The badge must be returned on the death of the holder. No miniature exists, but a lapel badge was instituted in 1990.*

NZ4. NEW ZEALAND ORDER OF MERIT

Breast star

Instituted: 1996.

Ribbon: Plain red ochre (kokowai).

Comments: *An order of chivalry designed alongBritish lines and intended to replace the various British orders to which New Zealanders were formerly appointed. It consists of five classes whose insignia are noted separately below. In addition, there is a collar of the order, worn only by the Sovereign of the Order and the Chancellor (the Governor-General of New Zealand). The collar is composed of links of the central badge and gold koru (in the form of the letter S) with a pendant badge featuring the New Zealand arms. Distinctive lapel badges denoting membership of the Order are worn in civilian clothes.*

NZ4. NEW ZEALAND ORDER OF MERIT (contd.)
KNIGHTS AND DAMES GRAND COMPANIONS (GNZM)

Badge: A cross in white enamel set in silver-gilt with, in the centre, a medallion comprising the New Zealand arms in coloured enamel surrounded by a circle of green enamel inscribed in gold FOR MERIT / TOHU HIRANGA and surmounted by a royal crown. The badge is worn from a sash over the right shoulder and resting on the left hip.

Star: A gold breast star of eight points, each arm bearing in relief a representation of a fern frond, superimposed in the centre of which is a smaller representation of the badge of the order.

KNIGHTS AND DAMES COMPANIONS (KNZM /DNZM)

A badge and breast star similar to that above, except that the badge is worn from either a neck ribbon or a bow on the left shoulder. The breast star is in silver, with the badge of the order in the centre.

COMPANIONS (CNZM)

A badge similar to that above, worn from a neck ribbon or a bow on the left shoulder.

OFFICERS (ONZM)

A smaller representation of the badge in silver-gilt, with the motto in green enamel. Worn from a ribbon on the left lapel or from a ribbon tied in a bow and worn on the left shoulder.

MEMBERS (MNZM)

Badge as for Officers but in silver.

NZ5. NEW ZEALAND GALLANTRY STAR

Instituted: 1998.
Branch of Service: New Zealand armed forces.
Ribbon: Red with a blue central stripe bordered by thin white stripes.
Metal: Silver and gilt.
Size: 45mm.
Description: A faceted silver 8-pointed star surmounted by a gilt crown surrounded by a wreath of fern. With ring suspension.
Comments: *This decoration supersedes the British Distinguished Service Order, Distinguished Conduct Medal and Conspicuous Gallantry Medal. Recipients are entitled to the postnominal letters NZGS.*

NZ6. QUEEN'S SERVICE ORDER

Instituted: 1975.
Ribbon: Narrow red ochre edges with a centre of alternating diagonal steps in ochre, white and black descending from left to right. The design is based on the Maori Poutama (stepped) pattern used in Tukutuku wall panels to represent the stairway to heaven, but here denoting the steps of achievement.
Metal: Frosted sterling silver.
Description: A badge based on the stylised representation of a manuka flower, consisting of five large and five small stylised petals. Superimposed in the centre is a silver-gilt medallion bearing the crowned effigy of the Queen within a circle of red enamel bearing the name of the sub-division and surmounted by St Edward's Crown. The full name of the recipient is engraved on the reverse.
Comments: *The single non-titular order is divided into two divisions for Community Service and for Public Services respectively. Ordinary membership is limited to 30 appointments per annum. Members of the Royal Family may be appointed as Extra Companions and include so far the Duke of Edinburgh (1981), Prince Charles (1983) and the Princess Royal (1990). Recipients are entitled to the postnominal letters QSO, and appropriate lapel badges for everyday wear.*

NZ7. NEW ZEALAND GALLANTRY DECORATION

Instituted: 1998.
Branch of Service: New Zealand armed forces.
Ribbon: Red with central blue stripe and two equal white stripes.
Metal: Silver and gilt.
Size: 46mm.
Description: A simple faceted silver cross surmounted by the royal crown and fern frond wreath emblem. With ring suspension.
Comments: *This decoration supersedes the British DSC, MC, DFC, AFC, DSM, MM, DFM and AFM. Recipients are entitled to the postnominal letters NZGD.*

NZ8. NEW ZEALAND BRAVERY STAR

Instituted: 1998.
Branch of Service: New Zealand police forces, fire brigades and civilians.
Ribbon: Blue with two narrow red stripes.
Metal: Silver and gilt.
Size: 46mm
Description: An 8-pointed faceted star with four long and four short points in the angles surmounted by a gilt royal crown and fern frond wreath emblem. With ring suspension.
Comments: *This decoration superseded the British George Medal and is the second grade award for civilian acts of bravery. Recipients are entitled to the postnominal letters NZBS.*

NZ9. NEW ZEALAND BRAVERY DECORATION

Instituted: 1998.
Branch of Service: Civilians and members of the armed forces in non-combat situations.
Ribbon: Blue with three equal stripes of red.
Metal: Silver and gilt.
Size: 45mm.
Description: A cross pattée surmounted by a small faceted four-pointed star with the royal crown and fern frond wreath emblem. With ring suspension.
Comments: *This decoration is awarded for acts of bravery in a non-combat situation. It supersedes the British QGM, QPM, QFSM, AFC and AFM. Recipients are entitled to the postnominal letters NZBD.*

NZ10. NEW ZEALAND GALLANTRY MEDAL

Instituted: 1998.
Branch of Service: New Zealand armed forces.
Ribbon: red with two central blue stripes and two outer white stripes.
Metal: Bronze.
Size: 38mm.
Description: (Obverse) the Rank-Broadley effigy of Her Majesty Queen Elizabeth II with the legend ELIZABETH II QUEEN OF NEW ZEALAND; (reverse) FOR GALLANTRY/MO TE TOANGA surrounded by a fern frond wreath with the royal crown above.
Comments: *This decoration replaces the Mention in Despatches. Recipients are entitled to the postnominal letters NZGM.*

NZ11. NEW ZEALAND BRAVERY MEDAL

Instituted: 1998.
Branch of Service: Civilians or members of the New Zealand armed forces in a non-combat situation.
Ribbon: Blue with four red stripes.
Metal: Bronze.
Size: 38mm.
Description: (Obverse) the Rank-Broadley effigy of Her Majesty Queen Elizabeth II with the legend ELIZABETH II QUEEN OF NEW ZEALAND; (reverse) FOR BRAVERY/MO TE MAIA surrounded by a fern frond wreath with the royal crown above.
Comments: *This decoration replaces the Queen's Commendations for Brave Conduct and Valuable Service in the Air. Recipients are entitled to the postnominal letters NZBM.*

NZ12. QUEEN'S SERVICE MEDAL

Instituted: 1975.
Ribbon: Same as the Queen's Service Order.
Metal: Silver.
Size: 38mm.
Description: (Obverse) effigy of Queen Elizabeth surrounded by the royal styles and titles; (reverse) New Zealand arms with THE QUEEN'S SERVICE MEDAL round the top. Two versions of the reverse exist, inscribed at the foot either FOR COMMUNITY SERVICE or FOR PUBLIC SERVICES. The medal is fitted with a suspension ring.
Comments: *Awards are made for valuable voluntary service to the community or meritorious and faithful services to the Crown or similar services within the public sector. Military service is ineligible. The name of the recipient is engraved on the rim. Recipients are entitled to the postnominal letters QSM.*

NZ13. NEW ZEALAND SERVICE MEDAL 1946–1949

Instituted: 1995.
Branch of Service: New Zealand armed forces, merchant navy and civil airline crews.
Ribbon: 32mm white with a central red stripe and black stripes at the edges.
Metal: Rhodium plated steel.
Size: 38mm.
Description: (Obverse) New Zealand arms; (reverse) FOR SERVICE TO NEW ZEALAND 1946–1949 with a fern frond below.
Comments: *Awarded to about 7300 personnel despatched direct from New Zealand who had not had previous service in the Second World War, as well as about 5,000 troops stationed in Italy at the end of the war who were then sent to the Far East to take part in the police and peacekeeping operations in Japan between March 23, 1946 and March 31, 1949, a minimum of 28 days' service being required.*

Value: £40–£50

NZ14. NEW ZEALAND GENERAL SERVICE MEDAL (WARLIKE OPERATIONS)

Instituted: 1995.
Branch of Service: New Zealand armed forces.
Ribbon: 32mm dark blue with a central black stripe flanked by red stripes.
Metal: Silver.
Size: 38mm.
Description: (Obverse) crowned effigy of Queen Elizabeth; (reverse) THE NEW ZEALAND GENERAL SERVICE MEDAL within a wreath of pohutakawa blossom, fern fronds and kowhai blossom, ensigned by a royal crown affixed to a plain suspension bar.
Clasps: Malaya 1960–64, Kuwait, Korea.
Comments: *Awarded for service in warlike operations.*

NZ15. NEW ZEALAND GENERAL SERVICE MEDAL (PEACEKEEPING OPERATIONS)

Instituted: 1995.
Branch of Service: New Zealand armed forces.
Ribbon: 32mm dark blue with a white central stripe flanked by narrow red stripes.
Metal: Bronze.
Size: 38mm.
Description: As above.
Clasps: Mozambique, Cambodia, Peshawar, Somalia, Arabian Gulf, Sinai, Iraq, Bouganville, Korea 1954-57.
Comments: *Awarded for peacekeeping operations only if the relevant UN medals were not awarded.*

NZ16. NEW ZEALAND 1990 COMMEMORATION MEDAL

Instituted: 1990.
Ribbon: 32mm nine narrow stripes, black at the centre flanked by alternate white and red ochre.
Metal: Silver-gilt.
Size: 38mm.
Description: (Obverse) effigy of Queen Elizabeth with inscription ELIZABETH II . QUEEN OF NEW ZEALAND incuse on a raised rim; (reverse) stylised Kotuku or White Heron with inscription NEW ZEALAND 1990 COMMEMORATION.
Comments: *Awarded during the sesquicentennial year of British annexation to recognise achievements of New Zealanders in community service and the public services or their contribution to the country. The medal is accompanied by a certificate.*

NZ17. NEW ZEALAND MERITORIOUS SERVICE MEDAL

Instituted: 1985.
Branch of Service: NCOs of the rank of sergeant or petty officer in the armed forces.
Ribbon: 32mm crimson with a narrow green central stripe.
Metal: Silver.
Size: 38mm.
Description: (Obverse) bare-headed effigy of Queen Elizabeth; (reverse) FOR MERITORIOUS SERVICE within a laurel wreath surmounted by a royal crown and the legend NEW ZEALAND. Reverse similar to 212.
Comments: *Awarded for a minimum of 21 years full-time service in the armed forces, although this may be reduced to 18 years in the case of those invalided out of the services on grounds of disability.*

NZ18. NEW ZEALAND ARMED FORCES AWARD

Instituted: 1985.
Branch of Service: Officers of the armed forces.
Ribbon: 32mm dark blue, crimson and light blue with a central stripe of black.
Metal: Silver.
Size: 38mm.
Description: (Obverse) crowned effigy of Queen Elizabeth; (reverse) crossed swords, eagle and naval crown with two fronds below and inscription NEW ZEALAND ARMED FORCES AWARD.
Comments: *Awarded to commissioned officers of the armed services for 15 years full-time service back dated to 1977. Clasps for each additional 15 years may be awarded.*

NZ19. ROYAL NEW ZEALAND NAVY LONG SERVICE MEDAL

Instituted: 1985.
Branch of Service: Royal New Zealand Navy.
Ribbon: 32mm dark blue edged in white.
Metal: Silver.
Size: 38mm.
Description: (Obverse) uncrowned effigy of Queen Elizabeth; (reverse) HMS *Victory* surrounded by the inscription FOR LONG SERVICE AND GOOD CONDUCT.
Comments: *Awarded for naval ratings with 15 years service. Clasps may be awarded for each additional 15 years, denoted in undress uniform by a silver rosette on the ribbon bar. Indistinguishable from the Royal Navy LS&GC Medal, apart from the recipient's details.*

NZ20. NEW ZEALAND ARMY LONG SERVICE & GOOD CONDUCT MEDAL

Instituted: 1985.
Branch of Service: New Zealand Army, Regular Forces.
Ribbon: 32mm crimson edged in white.
Metal: Silver.
Size: 36mm.
Description: (Obverse) crowned effigy of Queen Elizabeth; (reverse) FOR LONG SERVICE AND GOOD CONDUCT attached to an ornamental title bar bearing the words NEW ZEALAND in raised lettering.
Comments: *Similar to the British Army LS&GC Medal (229) but with a distinctive New Zealand suspension bar. Only soldiers of the Regular Force serving from December 1, 1977 onwards, are eligible for this medal, a minimum of 15 years full-time irreproachable service being required. Clasps for additional periods of 15 years may be granted.*

NZ21. ROYAL NEW ZEALAND AIR FORCE LONG SERVICE MEDAL

Instituted: 1985.
Branch of Service: Royal New Zealand Air Force.
Ribbon: 32mm equal stripes of dark blue and crimson edged in white.
Metal: Silver.
Size: 36mm.
Description: (Obverse) uncrowned effigy of Queen Elizabeth; (reverse) an eagle with outstretched wings surmounted by a royal crown encircled by the inscription FOR LONG SERVICE AND GOOD CONDUCT.
Comments: *This medal replaces the award of the British RAF LS&GC Medal (MY 268). It is, in fact, indistinguishable from the British award except for the recipient's details engraved on the rim.*

NZ22. NEW ZEALAND TERRITORIAL SERVICE MEDAL

Ribbon: 38mm gold edged in crimson.
Comments: *This award is now obsolete. It appears to have been the New Zealand equivalent of the Efficiency Decoration (MY236).*

NZ23. NEW ZEALAND LONG AND EFFICIENT SERVICE MEDAL

Ribbon: 32mm crimson with two white stripes towards the centre.
Comments: *This medal is now obsolete. It appears to have been the New Zealand equivalent of the Efficiency Medal (MY237).*

NZ24. NEW ZEALAND POLICE LONG SERVICE & GOOD CONDUCT MEDAL

Instituted: 1976.
Ribbon: 32mm crimson with a central dark blue stripe flanked with white stripes.
Metal: Silver.
Size: 38mm.
Description: (Obverse) crowned effigy of Queen Elizabeth; (reverse) St Edward's Crown, sceptre and sword on a cushion within a wreath of oak leaves and fern fronds, surrounded by the inscription NEW ZEALAND POLICE—FOR LONG SERVICE AND GOOD CONDUCT.
Comments: *This medal is similar to the NZ Police LS&GC Medal (MY283) issued under Imperial Warrant, but differs in the ribbon and the inscription on the reverse. Awards made to police officers employed on or after January 1, 1976, with a qualifying period of service of 14 years. Clasps for additional periods of seven years are also awarded.*

NZ25. NEW ZEALAND PRISON SERVICE MEDAL

Instituted: 1981.
Ribbon: 32mm crimson with a central dark blue stripe flanked by narrow green stripes.
Metal: Silver.
Size: 36mm.
Description: (Obverse) crowned effigy of Queen Elizabeth II; (reverse) St Edward's crown and inscription NEW ZEALAND PRISON SERVICE FOR LONG SERVICE AND GOOD CONDUCT.
Comments: *Awarded for 14 years service with bars further 7 year periods. This medal superseded the NZ Prison Service Long Service Medal originally instituted in 1901.*

NZ26. NEW ZEALAND FIRE BRIGADES LONG SERVICE AND GOOD CONDUCT MEDAL

Instituted: 1976.
Ribbon: 32mm vermilion with a central black stripe flanked by narrow yellow stripes.
Metal: Silver.
Size: 38mm.
Description: (Obverse) crowned effigy of Queen Elizabeth (reverse) NEW ZEALAND FIRE BRIGADES—FOR LONG SERVICE AND GOOD CONDUCT above a fern frond.
Comments: *Originally awarded for 14 years full or part time services as a fireman, but amended by Royal Warrant (1981) to include fire brigades maintained or operated by companies as well as the forces under the control of the NZ Fire Service Commission. Clasps are awarded every additional period of seven years service.*

NZ27. NEW ZEALAND SUFFRAGE CENTENNIAL MEDAL

Instituted: 1993.
Ribbon: 32mm purple with narrow central stripes of white, yellow and white.
Metal: Antiqued bronze.
Size: 38mm.
Description: (Obverse) crowned effigy of Queen Elizabeth; (reverse) wreath of fern and camellia enclosing the inscription 1893 THE NEW ZEALAND SUFFRAGE CENTENNIAL 1993.
Comments: *Awarded to selected persons who by their virtues, talents and loyalty have made a recognised contribution to the rights of women in New Zealand or to women's issues in New Zealand. It was only awarded during the centennial year of the granting of votes to women—New Zealand being the first country in the world to do so.*

NZ28. NEW ZEALAND ENFORCEMENT LONG SERVICE MEDAL

Instituted: 1970.
Ribbon: Light blue with a central white stripe with black stripes each side.
Metal: Silver
Size: 38mm.
Description: A circular medal bearing the coat of arms of New Zealand, with a suspender of stylised fern leaves.
Comments: *This medal, rendered obsolete in 1987 on the introduction of the Traffic Service Medal (NZ29), was awarded to members of the Traffic and Road Safety forces of the Ministry of Transport upon 15 years continuous service.*

NZ29. NEW ZEALAND TRAFFIC SERVICE MEDAL

Instituted: 1994.
Ribbon: Bright blue with a narrow central white stripe flanked by black stripes.
Metal: Silver.
Size: 38mm.
Description: (Obverse) crowned effigy of Queen Elizabeth; (reverse) crowned wreath of fern fronds enclosing the word THE NEW ZEALAND TRAFFIC SERVICE MEDAL.
Comments: *Awarded to uniformed traffic officers in service after January 1987 who had completed 14 years service. Clasps for each additional period of seven years are also awarded.*

NZ30. ROYAL NEW ZEALAND NAVAL RESERVE DECORATION

Instituted: 1985.
Ribbon: 38mm green edged with white.
Metal: Silver and gold.
Size: 54mm high and 33mm wide.
Description: A skeletal badge consisting of an oval loop of rope in silver surrounding the Royal Cypher in gold.
Comments: *Awarded to commissioned officers of the Royal New Zealand Naval Reserve, with a minimum of 15 years service. Clasps for each additional period of 10 years are also awarded. The names of recipients are engraved on the reverse. Recipients are entitled to the postnominal letters RD.*

NZ31. ROYAL NEW ZEALAND NAVAL VOLUNTEER RESERVE DECORATION

Instituted: 1985.
Ribbon: 38mm dark blue with a central green stripe flanked by narrow crimson stripes.
Metal: Silver and gold.
Size: 54mm high and 33mm wide.
Description: A skeletal badge, similar in design to the above.
Comments: *Awarded to commissioned officers in the Royal New Zealand Naval Volunteer Reserve, with a minimum of 15 years service. Clasps for each additional period of 10 years are awarded. The names of recipients are engraved on the reverse. Recipients are entitled to the postnominal letters VRD. These decorations replaced the British RD and VRD, the latter being obsolete and the organisation of the Royal New Zealand Navy being such that the British Admiralty Board regulations were no longer applicable.*

NZ32. ROYAL NEW ZEALAND NAVAL VOLUNTEER RESERVE LONG SERVICE AND GOOD CONDUCT MEDAL

Instituted: 1985.
Ribbon: 32mm dark blue with a central broad stripe of green between narrow crimson stripes.
Metal: Silver.
Size: 36mm.
Description: (Obverse) uncrowned effigy of Queen Elizabeth; (reverse) a battleship with the motto DIUTURNE FIDELIS (faithful of long duration).
Comments: *Awarded to RNZVR ratings serving on or after December 1, 1977, with a minimum of 15 years service. Clasps for each additional period of 10 years are awarded.*

NZ33. EAST TIMOR MEDAL

Instituted: 25 April 2000.
Ribbon: Broad green central stripe flanked by narrow red, wider black and white stripes towards the edges.
Metal: Silvered alloy.
Size: 36mm.
Description: (Obverse) the effigy of the Queen by Ian Rank-Broadley with ELIZABETH II QUEEN OF NEW ZEALAND round the circumference; (reverse) the head of a kiwi facing right and overshadowing a map of East Timor with the words EAST TIMOR below and a sprig of olive leaves above. Fitted with a plain suspension bar.
Clasp: A silver clasp inscribed EAST TIMOR for additional service of 365 days or more, continuous or aggregate, in the operational area.
Comments: *Awarded to members of the New Zealand Defence Force, civilian personnel and police taking part in the International Force in East Timor from 19 June 1999 onwards. The medals was awarded for a day or more on the strength of a formation on land in the operational area, seven days' service afloat or after completing seven sorties as aircrew, or for 30 or more days, continuous or aggregated, on inspections or other service of a temporary nature. About 2,000 awards were made. The medal was designed by Philip O'Shea, LVO, New Zealand Herald of Arms, and struck by Thomas Fattorini of Birmingham. The first investiture of medals took place in the New Zealand Parliament, Wellington on 28 March 2001.*

South African medals

Apart from the various British campaign medals from 1834 onwards, distinctive medals relating to military service in South Africa date from 1896 when a version of the Meritorious Service Medal (MYB210) was provided with the name of the Cape of Good Hope on the reverse. This was accompanied by similar versions of the Distinguished Conduct Medal (MYB42) and the Long Service and Good Conduct Medal (MYB229). The following year similar awards were instituted for Natal. Moreover, there were also a number of military and naval medals issued under Dutch, and later Boer, administrations which are outside the scope of this Yearbook.

Cape and Natal colonists received British awards from the earliest days of the British occupation, and numerous instances have been recorded of awards to South Africans of both the orders of chivalry and gallantry decorations. This situation coninued after the formation of the Union of South Africa in 1910. As a rule, these were identical to the British versions in every respect but there were a few notable exceptions. The Victory Medal (MYB170) was struck with a bilingual (English and Dutch) reverse for award to South African forces. Distinctive medals for the police, railway and harbour police and prison services (MYB284–285 and 290–291) were awarded but as they were instituted by Royal Warrant they are included in the main body of this Yearbook.

Other South African awards which will be found in the main section are the King's Police Medal for gallantry or bravery (MYB49), the Africa Service Medal (MYB189), the South African Medal for War Service (MYB192) and the South African Medal for Korea (MYB196). There were also South African versions of the Efficiency Decoration (MYB236), Efficiency Medal (MYB254), the Permanent Force LS&GC (253) and Air Efficiency Award (MYB270). Finally, there are three miscellaneous medals: the Union of South Africa Commemoration Medal of 1910 (MYB357), the Dekoratie Voor Trouwe Dienst of 1920 (MYB358) and the Anglo-Boere Oorlog Medal instituted at the same time (MYB359).

In 1952 the Union of South Africa instituted its own system of awards for gallantry in action, bravery in a non-combat situation and for distinguished service. Nine of these awards had a standard reverse showing the arms of the Union of South Africa surmounted by the royal cypher. In 1961, when South Africa became a republic and left the Commonwealth, the royal cypher was removed. The tenth award was the Union Medal which was completely redesigned and renamed the Permanent Force Good Service Medal (SA11 below).

For the purposes of this insertion it has been necessary to limit full coverage to military awards because of the absolute plethora of orders, decorations and medals that have made their appearance in the last 50 years while South Africa was ruled by the National Party. Not only were separate and independent award structures set up with their own orders, decorations and medals for all branches of the public service: Military, Police, Railway Police, Prisons, as well as the National Intelligence Service, but the situation was further complicated when the Nationalist Party Government in terms of its apartheid policy set up Homeland Governments that were given independence from the Republic of South Africa, each with their own set of awards for Military, Police and Prison departments—Transkei, Ciskei, KwaZulu, Bophuthatswana, Venda, Lebowa, Gazankulu and Qwa-qwa, etc. After 1994 the situation has been compounded by the issue of medals awarded retrospectively to members of the forces of freedom fighters or terrorists—MK (Mkhonto Wesizwe) and APLA (Azanian People's Liberation Army).

The awards instituted and awarded in South West Africa by the South African Government until this SA administered territory gained its independence and became Namibia in 1990 through world pressure, must not be overlooked either. The South African award system also reveals great instability through the frequent abolition of awards, their supersession and further proliferation by the introduction of new awards! Although this insertion has a primary focus on military awards, some of the awards to the South African Police, Prisons and Railway Police that may occur in medal groups with some regularity, have been included.

For information purposes a full list of orders, decorations and medals instituted since 1952 to the Police, Railway Police and Prisons, appears opposite. The date in brackets next to each award indicates the year of gazetting of that award. The awards are listed in order of precedence for that particular compartment of the public service. These lists are preceded by a listing of South African civilian orders and decorations that are not confined to any particular public service compartment of awards.

SOUTH AFRICAN CIVILIAN AWARDS

ORDERS
Order of the Southern Cross (1986/87)—Two Classes
Order of the Star of South Africa (Non Military)
(1988)—Five Classes
Order for Meritorious Service (1986)—Two Classes
Order of Good Hope (1973/88)—Five Classes

DECORATIONS FOR BRAVERY
The Queen's Medal for Bravery (Gold and Silver)
(1953)
The Woltemade Decoration for Bravery (1970/88)
Gold
The Woltemade Decoration for Bravery (1970/88)
Silver
Civil Defence Medal for Bravery (1976)

MERITORIOUS SERVICE
Civil Defence Medal for Meritorious Service (1976)
State President's Sports Merit Award (1971)

SOUTH AFRICAN POLICE

ORDERS
South African Police Star for Distinguished
Leadership (1979)

DECORATIONS FOR BRAVERY
South African Police Cross for Bravery (1963)
South African Police Cross for Bravery (1989) (Gold/
Silver/ungraded)
South African Police Silver Cross for Gallantry
(1985)

AWARDS FOR DISTINGUISHED, LONG AND
MERITORIOUS SERVICE
South African Police Star for Distinguished Service
(1963)
South African Police Star for Distinguished Service
(1979)
South African Police Star for Outstanding Service
(1979)
South African Police Star for Merit (1963)
South African Police Medal for Faithful Service
(1963)
South African Police Star for Faithful Service (1979)

SERVICE
South African Police Medal for Combating Terrorism
(1974)

COMMEMORATIVE
South African Police Seventy-Five Anniversary
Commemorative Medal (1988)

SOUTH AFRICAN RAILWAYS POLICE

ORDERS
South African Railways Police Star for Distinguished
Leadership (1980)

DECORATIONS FOR BRAVERY
South African Railways Police Cross for Valour
(1966)
South African Railways Police Cross for Valour
(1980)

South African Railways Police *continued*

AWARDS FOR DISTINGUISHED, LONG AND
MERITORIOUS SERVICE
South African Railways Police Star for Distinguished
Service (1980) *
Decoration for Distinguished Service in the SA
Railways Police Force (1966)
Decoration for Outstanding Service in the South
African Railways Police Force (1980)
Star for Merit in the South African Railways Police
Force (1966)
Star for Merit in the South African Railways Police
Force (1980)
South African Railways Police Star for Faithful
Service (1980)
Medal for Faithful Service in the South African
Railways Police Force (1966)
Medal for Faithful Service in the South African
Railways Police Force (1980)

SERVICE
South African Railways Police Medal for Combating
Terrorism

SOUTH AFRICAN PRISONS
(later Department of Correctional Services)

ORDERS
Nil.

DECORATIONS FOR BRAVERY
Decoration for Valour in the South African Prisons
Service (1968)
South African Prisons Service Cross for Valour
(Diamond) (1980)
South African Prisons Service Cross for Valour
(Ruby) (1980)

AWARDS FOR DISTINGUISHED, LONG AND
MERITORIOUS SERVICE
South African Prisons Service Star for Excellence
(1980)
South African Prisons Service Star for Distinction
(1980)
South African Prisons Service Star for Merit (1980)
South African Prisons Service Cross for Merit (1980)
Medal for Merit in the South African Prisons Service
(1968)
South African Prisons Service Medal for Merit
(Commissioned Officers) (1980)
South African Prisons Service Medal for Merit (Non-
Commissioned Officers) (1980)
Faithful Service Medal in the Prisons Department
(1959)
Faithful Service Medal, Prisons Department (1965)
Medal for Faithful Service in the South African
Prisons Service (1968)
South African Prisons Service Medal for Faithful
Service (1980)—Gold Medal (30 years); Silver
Medal (20 years); Bronze Medal (10 years)

* *name later changed to Star for Distinguished Devotion*

369

**SPECIAL NOTE ON THE PRICING OF POST 1952
SOUTH AFRICAN DECORATIONS AND MEDALS AWARDED TO MEMBERS OF
THE ARMY, NAVY AND AIR FORCE**

In 1952 the Union Defence Force made a decision to cease naming its medals. Instead each medal would be impressed with a serial number and the number, rank and name, etc. of the recipient entered against the serial number of the medal recorded down the left-hand margin of the register. The registers have since been misplaced. The register system was replaced by the computer and when a recipient received a medal, the medal number was recorded in many cases on this computerised record of service. However, these records are held by the Department of Defence and their system is not geared up to print out a full list of recipients of a particular medal with medal numbers.

(i)   In certain cases, after the award of the medal, the recipient's number, rank, name and unit, along with the serial number of the medal awarded, was published in Part II Unit orders.

(ii)   Since approximately 1988, the certificates of award have recorded the serial number of the medal awarded. Prior to that time, no medal serial number was printed on the certificate.

In order to establish that the medal in the group or as a singleton was awarded to a particular recipient (i) or (ii) above, are a prerequisite = PRICE A (Medal certificate must be the original in (ii) to qualify).

If a medal is numbered and has an un-numbered original certificate of award as supporting documentation = PRICE B.

If a medal is numbered (or unnumbered) without any supporting documentation = PRICE C.

It must be stressed that even if a recipient was awarded a medal, there is nothing to prove that that particular medal was actually awarded to the recipient, unless the serial number on the medal can be tied to that recipient through supporting documentation. Obviously gallantry awards must be accompanied by a copy of the citation for which the award was made.

An A, B and C price will be given for each SA Military award. For medals awarded to the Police, two prices will be given: named medals and unnamed specimens, as the Police continued to name their medals (they actually impressed the day, month and year of award as well). As Prisons medals were engraved by a variety of jewellers after 1980, three prices are given for medals awarded from 1980.
A: with certificate; B: named; C: unnamed

SOUTH AFRICAN DEFENCE FORCE

ORDERS

SA1. STAR OF SOUTH AFRICA

Instituted: 1952.
Ribbon: 44.5mm orange with three 3mm green stripes in centre, 6mm apart.
Metal: Silver.
Description: A multi-facetted five-point star, fitted with a ring and oblong loop through which the ribbon is passed for suspension round the neck.
Comments: *Awarded for recognising exceptionally meritorious service, in time of peace or war, by officers of the SA Defence Force or of other armed forces attached to or serving with, or rendering service to the SA Defence Force. The award could recognize a particular instance or service over a period of time.*
Further awards were denoted by a silver bar embossed in the centre with a miniature replica of the Star. None were awarded but an example of the bar is on display at the SA Museum of Military History. The reverse of the order has the embellished coat of arms of the Union of SA in relief, surmounted by the Royal cypher. After 1961 the Royal cypher was erased from existing medal stock. Those officers who were still serving in 1975 could exchange their Star of South Africa for the Order of the Star of South Africa. Post nominal title: SSA.

VALUE

	A	B	C	Miniature
With Royal cypher	£300	£200	£100	£20
Royal cypher erased	£200	£130	£65	£20
Coat of arms reverse	£150	£100	£50	£20

SA2. ORDER OF THE STAR OF SOUTH AFRICA (MILITARY)

Instituted: 1975.

Ribbon: Blue, 37mm (neck ribbon), 80mm (sash), 44mm (breast ribbon) or 20mm (miniature). A narrow central white stripe denotes the second class (redesignated silver award in 1977).

Metal: Enamelled gold or silver depending on class.

Description: An eight-pointed Maltese cross with an eight-pointed star superimposed at the centre and having a circular Protea wreath behind. *First Class:* A Protea ornament at the top joins the star to a five-pointed badge in the form of a ground plan of the Castle of Good Hope, enclosing a circular device featuring the insignia of the Defence Force. This is linked by a chain to circular medallions embellished with eight-pointed stars forming the neck collar of the order. In addition to the neck badge and collar there is a gold breast star. An eight pointed multi-rayed star is surmounted by a circular protea wreath superimposed with a blue enamel Maltese Cross edged in gold, in turn surmounted by an eight pointed star with alternate long and short rays in gold. The centre of the neck badge is mounted with a diamond. The neck collar or chain was discontinued in 1978. *Second Class:* award is similar in every respect to the First Class except there is no diamond in the centre and the metal is silver and there is no neck collar.

Comments: *The Order of the Star of SA (Military) is divided into two classes:*

Class I Gold: Post nominal title: SSA. Awarded to generals and higher officers or officers of comparable rank who distinguished themselves by meritorious military service that promoted efficiency and contributed lastingly to the security of the nation.

Class II Silver: Post nominal title: SSAS. Awarded to brigadiers and higher officers or officers of comparable rank who distinguished themselves by exceptionally meritorious service of major military importance.

To all intents and purposes the award of this order was confined to members of the South African Permanent Force. If an officer was promoted to Class I of the order his Class II insignia would be returnable. The 1988 amendments to the warrant eliminated the inclusion of non-South African citizens of the appropriate rank for consideration. The amendments to regulations to cover the division that was not exclusively military but could include civilians, was introduced in 1978 but space does not permit lengthy explanation of the various classes: Grand Cross, Grand Officer, Commander, Officer and Knight.

VALUE:

	A	B	C	*Miniature*
Class I Neck collar and badge and breast badge	£1000	£700	£600	—
Class I ditto but in base metal gilt plated for presentation purposes or museums	—	—	£400	—
Class I Neck badge and breast badge.	£700	£500	£400	£40
Class I ditto in base metal	—	—	£200	—
Class II Neck and breast badge	£350	£250	£200	£20

DECORATIONS FOR BRAVERY

SA3. CASTLE OF GOOD HOPE DECORATION

Instituted: 1952.
Ribbon: 44.5mm green.
Metal: Gold.
Description: A five-pointed star representing in outline the Castle of Good Hope (the first major fortress in South Africa) the whole surrounded by a moat. The raised centre is in the form of a circle in which is depicted the arrival of Jan Van Riebeek, in his flag ship *Drommedaris* in Table Bay on 6 April 1652 against a background of Table Mountain, surrounded by a garland of Protea (the national flower) and the inscription: CASTEEL DE GOEDE HOOF DEKORASIE round the top and CASTLE OF GOOD HOPE DECORATION round the foot. (Reverse) Serial number and Royal cypher. Recently the loop for neck wear has been replaced by a ring for breast wear.
Comments: *Awarded for a signal act of valour or most conspicuous bravery or some daring or pre-eminent act of self-sacrifice or extreme devotion to duty in the presence of an enemy. The decoration could be awarded posthumously. This is South Africa's highest gallantry award but to date it has not been awarded. As no examples of the full size decoration have been awarded, no price is given—any specimens that come on to the market would be from a batch stolen from Army Stores. A gold miniature of the decoration is worn on the ribbon on the tunic.*

VALUE:

		Miniature
Base metal-gilt plated specimen for museums or presentation sets of medals	£60	*(hallmarked gold)* £70

SA4. LOUW WEPENER DECORATION

Instituted: 1952.
Ribbon: 35mm divided into equal stripes, six orange and five white.
Metal: Silver.
Description: Scene at the battle of Thaba Bosigo, Basutoland (now Lesotho) in 1865 in which Louw Wepener, shown in the foreground, was the hero. Inscribed LOUW WEPENER round the top and DECORATION DEKORASIE round the foot. Fitted with a scrolled suspension bar.
Comments: *It was awarded in recognition of acts of most conspicuous courage and self-sacrifice performed in the execution of or beyond the call of military duty in time of peace or war, by members of the SADF or attached troops, in saving or endeavouring to save the lives of others on land, sea or in the air or in the execution of duty for which other purely military honours are not normally granted. Post nominal title: LWD. The award was rendered obsolete by the Honoris Crux Decoration in 1975. Further awards were to have been denoted by a silver bar centred with a silver button inscribed with the initials LWD, but none were ever manufactured.*

VALUE:

	A	B	C	*Miniature*
Royal cypher reverse	£700	£400	£70	£14
Royal cypher erased	£700	£400	£70	£16
SA coat of arms	£600	£350	£50	£12

SA5. VAN RIEBEECK DECORATION

Instituted: 1952.
Ribbon: 32mm sky blue.
Metal: Silver-gilt.
Description: In shape of a five-pointed star representing the outline of the Castle of Good Hope. The suspension consists of a cluster of eight protea leaves. In the centre of the obverse is the full figure of Jan Van Riebeeck (first Governor of the Cape of Good Hope) in relief against a background of three rings representing his three ships—*Drommedaris, De Rijger* and *De Goede Hoop*.
Comments: *The decoration was awarded to officers of the SA Defence Force or auxiliary services or attached troops who distinguished themselves by outstanding resourcefulness, perseverance or personal courage or by their outstanding leadership or responsibility and personal example against an enemy in the field. Post nominal title: DVR. The award was rendered obsolete by the Honoris Crux Decoration in 1975. A specimen of the bar embossed with a miniature cannon in silver gilt to denote further awards, is on display at the SA Museum of Military History.*

VALUE:

	A	B	C	Miniature
Royal cypher reverse	£600	£400	£60	£30
Royal cypher erased	£600	£400	£60	£30
SA coat of arms reverse	£500	£350	£40	£20

SA6. VAN RIEBEECK MEDAL

Instituted: 1952.
Ribbon: 32mm sky blue with 6mm white central stripe.
Metal: Silver.
Description: Very similar to the Van Riebeeck Decoration (above) but differing in the ribbon. It, too, was discontinued in August 1975.
Comments: *In all respects identical to the Van Riebeeck Decoration except the medal was awarded to Warrant Officers, NCOs and Men. The medal was rendered obsolete by the Honoris Crux Decoration in 1975. Post nominal title: VRM. Additional award bar as for the decoration, except metal is silver. Specimen on display at the SA Museum of Military History.*

VALUE:

	A	B	C	Miniature
Royal cypher reverse	£450	£300	£40	£20
Royal cypher erased	£450	£300	£45	£22
SA coat of arms reverse	£350	£220	£30	£15

SA7. HONORIS CRUX

Instituted: 1952.
Ribbon: 32mm leaf-green with 3mm red outer and 2mm white inner edges.
Metal: Silver gilt and enamels.
Description: An eight-pointed Maltese Cross in silver gilt: in each angle formed by the cross is an eagle in silver gilt, facing to the right. Centre circle of the cross is enamelled in the three colours of the flag of Union of South Africa. The design was significantly influenced by the Order of the Golden Eagle that was proposed in 1894 but was rejected by the Transvaal Volksraad.
Comments: *There have been six recipients of this award. It was awarded to members of the South African Defence Force, auxiliary services, attached troops who regardless of their own safety and through personal courage and determination, perform a gallant act or deed against an enemy in the field. Subsequent deeds may entitle a recipient to a bar in silver-gilt embossed in the centre with a miniature eagle. A specimen bar is on display at the SA Museum of Military History. Post nominal title: HC.*

VALUE:

	A	B	C	Miniature
Royal cypher reverse	£1000	£650	£90	£26
Royal cypher erased	£1000	£650	£100	£30
SA coat of arms	£800	£550	£80	£20

SA8. LOUW WEPENER MEDAL

Instituted: 1967.
Ribbon: 35mm in width, orange divided into five broad stripes of
equal width by four white stripes of 1.5mm
Metal: Bronze
Description: Identical to the Louw Wepener Decoration with the
words "MEDALJE/MEDAL" substituted for"DECORATION/
DEKORASIE".
Comments: *Conditions of award as for Louw Wepener Decoration for*
deeds of a lesser nature to those for which the Louw Wepener Decoration
was awarded. The award could be made posthumously. Subsequent
awards were recognized by a bar with a centred circle containing the
letters LWM. Post nominal title: LWM. The medal was rendered
obsolete by the Honoris Crux Decoration in 1975.

VALUE:

A	B	C	Miniature
£450	£300	45	£8

SA9. HONORIS CRUX DECORATION

Instituted: 1975.
Ribbon: 32mm orange with additional white stripes according to
class.
Metal: Enamelled gold or silver, according to class.
Description: An eight-pointed enamelled Maltese cross superimposed
on a wreath with crossed swords in the angles, with a central
roundel divided horizontally into orange, white and blue. Fitted
with an ornamental suspension loop.
Comments: *This award replaced SA4, 5, 6, 7 and 8 above and was divided*
into four classes, distinguished by their ribbons and the embellishment
of the obverse.
Honoris Crux Diamond. *Plain orange ribbon, 32mm, with a green circular*
border to centre roundel mounted with eight diamonds awarded to those
who distinguished themselves. Awarded for performing deeds of
outstanding valour, at extreme risk to their lives
Honoris Crux Gold. *Orange ribbon with a 1mm central white stripe. Made*
of silver gilt with gold border to centre roundel. Awarded for performing
outstanding deeds of bravery in extreme danger.
Honoris Crux Silver. *Orange ribbon with a 1mm white stripe 13mm from*
each edge. Made of silver with silver border to centre roundel. Awarded
for performing exceptional deeds of bravery whilst in great danger.
Honoris Crux. *Orange with 2mm white edges and 1mm white stripe 5mm*
from each edge. Made of silver. The centre roundel has a silver border
but the arms of the cross are white enamel instead of green as in the
other three classes. Awarded for performing deeds of bravery in
dangerous circumstances.
The post-nominal titles are: HCD, HCG, HCS and HC respectively.
Further awards are denoted by a bar with miniature replica of the
decoration—in gold for the first two classes and silver for the second
two. Only 4 HCGs were awarded—one with a bar. In 1993 the HCD
and HCG were discontinued. The crosses have a SA Mint hallmark. The
first striking has voiding round the protea wreath whereas subsequent
strikings have no voiding at all.

VALUE:

	A	B	C	Miniature
HC (Diamond)	—	—	—	—
HC (Gold)	£1800	£1500	£130	£40
HC (Silver)	£1500	£1200	£110	£30
HC	£1000	£750	£100	£20

SA10. PRO VIRTUTE DECORATION

Instituted: 1987.
Ribbon: 32mm in width, 20mm orange central stripe edged with a narrow pale blue stripe of 6mm each.
Metal: 9ct gold.
Description: A five linked white enamelled Maltese Cross edged with gold. The centre is of dark red enamel on which is superimposed the embellished coat of arms of the Republic of South Africa. The cross is connected with the suspender by an inverted V from which extends two proteas. The reverse bears the words "PRO VIRTUTE". Awarded to officers of the SA National Defence Force who have distinguished themselves by distinguished conduct and exceptional combat leadership during military operations.
Comments: *Post Nominal Title PVD. Subsequent awards are denoted by a silver gilt bar with a miniature Protea emblem embossed in the centre of the bar.*

VALUE:

A	B	C	Miniature
£1000	£600	£100	£30

SA11. PRO VIRTUTE MEDAL

Instituted: 1987.
Ribbon: 32mm in width, orange outer stripes of 10mm with two 4mm central light blue stripes divided by an orange 4mm central stripe.
Metal: Silver
Description: The obverse bears the outline of the cross of the Pro Virtute Decoration. The reverse bears the title PRO VIRTUTE Surmounted by the coat of arms of the Republic of South Africa and a wreath of proteas as a surround on three sides.
Comments: *Awarded to warrant officers and other ranks with a similar bar for further awards, except in silver. Conditions of award as for PVD. Post nominal title: PVM.*

VALUE:

A	B	C	Miniature
£600	£400	£35	£15

SA12. AD ASTRA DECORATION

Instituted: 1987.
Ribbon: 30mm diagonal alternating narrow light blue and white stripes of 3mm.
Metal: Gold plated silver with hallmark.
Description: In the centre of a five-pointed star is the outline of the Castle of Good Hope in relief on which is depicted the badge of the SA Air Force in gold on a light blue background edged with white. The reverse shows the embellished coat of arms of the Republic of South Africa above the words "AD ASTRA". The star is suspended from an eagle with outstretched wings attached to a ring at the top of the star.
Comments: *This award is made to air crew members for excellent flying skill or outstanding ingenuity or skill during emergencies or unusual situations on board aircraft. Post nominal title: AAD.*

VALUE:

A	B	C	Miniature
£600	£400	£60	£25

SA13. THE S.A.D.F. CROSSES

Army Cross

Air Force Cross

Navy Cross

SA Medical Services Cross

Instituted: 1987.

Ribbons: A. Army Cross: 30mm wide. White with central 10mm guardsman red stripe; **B. Air Force Cross:** 30mm wide. White with central broad light blue stripes of 12mm divided by a narrow gold stripe of 2mm; **C. Navy Cross:** 30mm wide. White with central broad navy blue stripe of 10mm; **D. SA Medical Services Cross:** 30mm wide. White with central broad purple stripe of 10mm.

Metal: Silver

Description: A silver cross with fixed straight suspender decorated with laurel leaves. The suspender is attached to the top arm of the cross. The arms of the cross have a double border and rise to a higher point from the edge which is 2mm thick. There is a central roundel for each cross covered in shiny epoxy and bordered with three circles of laurel leaves. **A. Army Cross:** orange roundel; with badge of the SA Army in gold; **B. Air Force Cross:** light blue roundel with the badge of the SA Air Force in gold; **C. Navy Cross:** navy blue roundel with the badge of the SA Navy in gold; **D. SA Medical Services Cross:** a purple roundel with the badge of the SA Medical Services in gold.

Comments: *The reverse bear the embellished coat of arms of the Republic of South Africa. A bar in silver denotes a subsequent award and bears a miniature protea. Post-nominal titles are as follows: **A. Army Cross:** CM (Crux Militere); **B. Air Force Cross:** CA (Crux Aeronautica); **C. Navy Cross:** CN (Crux Navalis); **D. SA Medical Services Cross:** CC (Crux Curationis).*

Recent events—the sinking of the Oceana *and the Mozambique floods—have seen a number of these crosses awarded, particularly to Air Force personnel. The crosses are awarded to all ranks of the SA Defence Force and auxiliary service for the SA Defence Force and other armed forces attached to or serving with or rendering service to the SA Defence Force, who have distinguished themselves by their exceptional ingenuity and skill in handling equipment, weapons, vehicles, aircraft and vessels concomitant with exemplary personal leadership, dedication and courage in peril of their lives (non-operational).*

VALUE:

A	B	C	Miniature
£500	£350	£50	£25

MEDALS AWARDED FOR DISTINGUISHED, LONG AND MERITORIOUS SERVICE

SA14. SOUTHERN CROSS MEDAL (1952)

Instituted: 1952.
Ribbon: 32mm dark blue with 3mm orange and white central stripes.
Metal: Hallmarked silver and enamel.
Description: A circular medal with raised 4mm rimmed border decorated with a single wreath of oak leaves with suspender also decorated with oakleaves. Within the wreath the field of dark blue enamel shows the Southern Cross constellation.
Comments: *This decoration was superseded in 1975 when it was split into two classes: the Southern Cross Decoration and the Southern Cross Medal (of different design). Recipients are entitled to the postnominal SM. The medal was awarded in times of peace or war to members of the SA Defence Force, or of an auxiliary service or other attached armed forces, irrespective of rank, who distinguished themselves by displaying outstanding devotion to duty, either in a particular instance or over a period of time.*

VALUE:

	A	B	C	*Miniature*
Royal cypher reverse	£90	£85	£75	£20
Royal cypher erased	£90	£80	£70	£15
SA coat of arms	£75	£70	£65	£12

SA15. SOUTHERN CROSS DECORATION (1975)

Instituted: 1975.
Ribbon: 32mm blue with 1mm white stripes 3mm from each edge.
Metal: Silver and enamels.
Description: An eight-pointed Maltese cross superimposed on a larger, broader cross in the same form, with a beaded enamelled medallion at the centre bearing the constellation of the Southern Cross. Fitted with a protea emblem for suspension from a straight bar.
Comments: *Awarded to commissoned officers of the South African Defence Force or of related forces who contributed to the security of the nation, in recognition of outstanding service of the highest order and the utmost devotion to duty displayed in time of peace or war. In 1993 a bar (silver gilt) was authorised with a protea emblem embossed in its centre, for subsequent awards. Recipients are entitled to the post-nominal SD.*

VALUE:

A	A with bar	B	C	*Miniature*
£60	£80	£50	£38	£9

SA16. SOUTHERN CROSS MEDAL (1975)

Instituted: 1975.
Ribbon: (1975)—32mm in width, dark blue with 2mm white edges and 1mm white stripes 13mm from each edge. (1986)—32mm in width, divided as follows: white 4mm, dark blue 9mm, white 1mm, dark blue 4mm and then repeated in reverse.
Metal: Enamelled silver.
Description: A five-pointed radiate star with circular radiate sectors between the arms, having a beaded central medallion depicting the constellation of the Southern Cross. Fitted with a plain ring for suspension from a straight bar.
Comments: *Awarded to commissioned officers of the SA Defence Force or other armed forces attached to or serving with or rendering service to the SADF, in recognition of exceptionally meritorious service and particular devotion to duty displayed in time of peace and war. This medal replaced the Southern Cross 1952 (SA14). Bar for subsequent awards as for Southern Cross Decoration (see SA15). Since 1993, recipients have been entitled to the post-nominal SM.*

VALUE:

A	A with bar	B	C	Miniature
£60	£80	£46	£40	£12

SA17. PRO MERITO MEDAL (1967)

Instituted: 1967.
Ribbon: 32mm sky blue with a dark blue centre flanked by narrow white and orange stripes.
Metal: Oxidised silver.
Description: An enamelled disa flower in relief encircled by a wreath of leafed protea flowers on the obverse. The embellished coat of arms of South Africa is on the reverse. With a foliate suspender.
Comments: *Awarded to Warrant Officers, NCOs and other ranks of the SA Defence Force and related forces for outstanding devotion to duty. 374 medals were awarded in total. Recipients are entitled to the post-nominal PMM. In 1975 this award was discontinued when it was split into two classes: The Pro Merito Decoration and The Pro Merito Medal (of different design).*

VALUE:

A	B	C	Miniature
£60	£46	£40	£8

SA18. PRO MERITO DECORATION (1975)

Instituted: 1975.
Ribbon: 32mm blue with a 4mm white central stripe.
Metal: Enamelled silver gilt.
Description: A white enamelled Maltese Cross bordered in gold with centre roundel charged with a red disa flower. The reverse has the embellished coat of arms of South Africa. At the top is a protea flower emblem for suspension from a straight bar.
Comments: *It is awarded to Warrant Officers and NCOs and other ranks of the SA Defence Force or of related forces contributing to the defence of the Republic of South Africa, who have distinguished themselves by rendering outstanding service of the highest order and displaying the utmost devotion to duty. In 1993 a silver gilt bar with protea emblem on its centre was introduced to denote a subsequent award. Recipients are entitled to the post-nominal PMD.*

VALUE:

A	B	C	Miniature
£60	£52	£45	£8

SA19. PRO MERITO MEDAL (1975)

Instituted: 1975.
Ribbon: (1975)—32mm in width, blue with 2mm white edges and
4mm white central stripe. (1986)—32mm, sky blue edged by 5mm
white stripes with one 4mm white central stripe.
Metal: Oxidised silver.
Description: A five pointed radiate star with radiate sectors between
the arms, having a beaded central medallion of blue enamel with a
red disa flower. The reverse bears the embellished coat of arms of
South Africa. In 1993, a silver bar with a protea embossed in its
centre was introduced to indicate a susbequent award. In 1993 the
post-nominal title of PMM was introduced. Fitted with a plain ring
for suspension from a straight bar.
Comments: *This medal replaced the original Pro Merito Medal of 1976 (SA
17) when that decoration was divided into two classes. The medal was
awarded for exceptionally meritorious service and particular devotion to
duty in peace or war to Warrant Officers, NCos and other ranks.*
VALUE:

A	B	C	Miniature
£40	£35	£30	£7

SA20. COMMANDANT GENERAL OF THE SOUTH AFRICAN DEFENCE FORCE COMMENDATION (1968)

Instituted: 1968.
Ribbon: None.
Metal: Bronze.
Description: A protea emblem sewn on to the tunic and not worn on
medal ribbons.
Comments: *Awarded for mentions in despatches. It was superseded in 1974
by the Chief of the South African Defence Force Commendation Medal
(SA21) for which it could be exchanged.*

VALUE:

A	B	C	Miniature
£5	£3	£2	£2

SA21. CHIEF OF THE SA DEFENCE FORCE COMMENDATION MEDAL (1974)

Instituted: 1974.
Ribbon: 32mm orange centre flanked by sky blue stripes and dark
blue edges.
Metal: Bronze.
Description: A circular medal with concave curves between twelve
points and a plain ring for suspension from a rectangular bar. In
the centre, a beaded medallion of the South African Defence Force.
Comments: *Awarded o members of the SA Defence Force (an auxiliary
service established to assist the SA Defence Force) who have distinguished
themselves by rendering service of a high order which could not be
suitably recognised in any other manner. In 1993 this medal was
superseded by the Military Merit Medal.*

VALUE:

A	B	C	Miniature
£20	£18	£14	£4

*Note: If awarded for downgraded gallantry award with
citation: £50*

SA22. MILITARY MERIT MEDAL

Instituted: 1993.
Ribbon: As for chief of SA Defence Force Commendation Medal (SA21).
Metal: Bronze plated brass.
Description: As for Chief of SA Defence Force Commendation Medal (SA21) but with fixed suspender.
Comments: *The medal replaced SA21 but with greatly enhanced status. The medal is now awarded to members of the SA Defence Force who have rendered outstanding service of vital importance/permanent significance of the highest order. Because of the anomaly of the previous title of the medal—only the State President and not the Chief of Defence Force could institute the medals, those who had been awarded the Chief of the SA Defence Force Commendation Medal were empowered to change the name of their medal to the new title and like the recipients of the new awards, could enjoy the post-nominal MMM. In 1993 a bar to denote a subsequent award was introduced. The bronze bar carries a centrally placed embossed protea emblem.*

VALUE:

A	B	C	Miniature
£24	£20	£14	£4

SA23. DANIE THERON MEDAL

Instituted: 1970
Ribbon: 32mm green with three narrow yellow stripes.
Metal: Silver.
Description: An eagle hovering over mountain peaks, with three stars on either side and DANIE THERON round the top and MEDALJE MEDAL at the foot. Scrolling spurs secure the medal to the plain suspension bar.
Comments: *This medal was named after the most famous Boer scout of the Anglo-Boer War 1899–1902. From 1970 to 1975, this medal was awarded to officers who were members of the commandos of the SA Defence Force, had completed not less than 10 years service in the SA Defence Force and had not yet received any other awards in recognition of outstanding devotion to duty or exceptionally diligent and outstanding service. In 1975, on the abolition of the Jack Hindon Medal, the Danie Theron Medal now covered the provisions of the Jack Hindon Medal. Recipients of the award are entitled to use the post-nominal DTM.*

VALUE:

A	B	C	Miniature
£58	£52	£45	£6

SA24. JACK HINDON MEDAL

Instituted: 1970
Ribbon: 32mm yellow with a narrow central green stripe and broad
    green stripes at the edges.
Metal: Bronze.
Description: An upright oval medal showing the sun rising over a
    mountain peak. In the foreground Jack Hindon and two
    companions unfurling the Vierkleur (Boer flag) during the battle of
    Spion Kop on January 24, 1900. Inscription JACK HINDON round
    the top, with MEDALJE MEDAL at the foot. Fitted with scrolled
    spurs to a plain suspension bar.
Comments: *This medal was named in honour of Captain Oliver John*
    Hindon who fought for the South African Republic (Transvaal) against
    the British in the Boer war. (He was born in Stirling, Scotland on 20
    April 1874 and he deserted from the British Army while serving in Natal
    in 1888, after severe treatment at the hands on an NCO of his unit.
    During the early part of the Anglo-Boer war, Hindon, now a citizen of the
    Transvaal Republic, was a member of Danie Theron's scout corps and was
    appointed to head a special corps whose function was to disrupt British
    lines of communication through the derailment of British trains and the
    cutting ot telegraph lines. So successful was he that he became onee of the
    Boer heroes of the war.)The conditions of this award are as the Danie
    Theron Medal (SA23) but the Jack Hindon medal was awarded to
    Warrant Officers, NCOs and other ranks. The medal was superseded by
    the Danie Theron Medal in 1975. Recipients are entitled to the post-
    nominal JHM.

VALUE:

A	B	C	Miniature
£40	£35	£30	£4

SA25. COMMANDANT GENERAL'S MEDAL

Instituted: 1956.
Ribbon: 32mm in with, orange with 6.4mm sky blue edges and 6.4mm
    dark blue central stripe.
Metal: Oxidised silver.
Description: A laurel wreath enclosing a five-sided polygon divided
    into sectors. In the centre is a circle enclosing crossed rifles above a
    circular target and bushveld scenery. In the exergue is the
    inscription KOMMANDANT GENERAALS MEDALJE
    COMMANDANT GENERALS MEDAL. The top of the polygon has
    a fluted bar connecting it to the suspension bar decorated with
    laurel sprays.
Comments: *This medal was awarded for outstanding marksmanship.*
    Subsequent awards of the medal are denoted by bars with centrally placed
    silver button inscribed with the year of award. This medal was superseded
    in 1975 by the SADF Champion Shot Medal (SA26).

VALUE:

A	B	C	Miniature
£40	£35	£30	£5

SA26. SADF CHAMPION SHOTS MEDAL

Instituted: 1975.
Ribbon: As SA25.
Metal: oxidised silver.
Description: Identical to SA25 except for the inscription in the exergue which now reads SAW
    KAMPIOENSKUTMEDALJE / SADF CHAMPION SHOT MEDAL.
Comments: *Awarded annually to the champion shot. Subsequent awards of the medal are denoted by bars with*
    centrally placed silver button inscribed with the year of award. The award replaced the Commandant General's
    Medal (SA25).

VALUE:

A	B	C	Miniature
£40	£35	£30	£5

SA27. CADET CORPS CHAMPION SHOT MEDAL

Instituted: 1987.
Ribbon: 32mm orange ribbon each side edged with a 6mm green stripe.
Metal: Silver.
Description: Obverse: A prancing springbok facing to the left enclosed on three sides by a wreath of laurels. Reverse: In semicircular format—top: GROOTKAMPIONSKUT, bottom: GRAND CHAMPION SHOT and centrally placed in two lines: KADETKORPS and CADET CORPS.
Comments: *The imaginative concept was that winners' achievements would not be lost on leaving school but they could mount this medal along with their SA Defence Force awards in after years. The medal is unique in that never before has a school cadet been authorised to wear a medal. In 1994 the School Cadet Corps were abolished by the President of South Africa, so the award became obsolete. By that date, 16 awards had been made and these were backdated to 1978.*

VALUE:

A	B	C	Miniature
£70	£60	£50	£10

SA28. UNION MEDAL

Instituted: 1952.
Branch of service: Union of South Africa Permanent Defence Force.
Ribbon: 32mm equal stripes of orange, white and navy blue repeated three times to make a total of 9 stripes.

Bar for 12 years

Ribbon emblem

Metal: Silver.
Description: A scalloped medal with an ornamental suspender of wattle leaves and mimosa flowers. Obverse: Coat of arms of South Africa and the inscription UNION MEDAL—UNIE MEDALJE. Reverse: the Royal Cypher EIIR with crown.
Comments: *This medal was awarded to members of the Union Defence Force Permanent Force, irrespective of rank, for a minimum of 18 years service of an impeccable character. It was superseded in 1961 by the Permanent Force Good Service Medal. This medal replaced no. 253 except its award was extended to include commissioned officers as well. Approximately 1,400 medals were awarded. Those completing an extra 12 years service were eligible for a silver bar with centrally embossed coat of arms of South Africa. When the ribbon alone was worn the bar to the awards was represented by a miniature silver coat of arms.*

VALUE:

A	B	C	Miniature
£42	£35	£30	£12

SA29. PERMANENT FORCE GOOD SERVICE MEDAL

Instituted: 1961.
Ribbon: As for Union Medal (SA28)
Metal: Silver.
Description: A scalloped medal. Obverse as for SA28 except "UNION MEDAL—UNIE MEDALJE" has been removed. Reverse: carries details over seven lines: VIR LANGDURIGE DIENS EN GOEIE GEDRAG / FOR LONG SERVICE AND GOOD CONDUCT.
Comments: *Awarded for a minimum of 18 years service. A silver bar in the form of the republican arms was added to the ribbon for further periods of 12 years service (as for SA28). About 2,700 of these medals were awarded.*

VALUE:

A	B	C	Miniature
£30	£25	£20	£5

SA30. SOUTH AFRICAN DEFENCE FORCE GOOD SERVICE MEDAL

Instituted: 1975.

Ribbon: 32mm green with different stripes according to the class and branch of service. In 1986 the nine ribbons were reduced to three: gold medal—green with two 7mm yellow stripes 6mm from each edge; silver medal—green edged with 7mm white stripes with a central 6mm white stripe; bronze medal—green edged with two 10mm bronze brown stripes.

Metal: Silver gilt/gilt coated brass for 30 years; silver/silver coated brass for 20 years; bronze/bronze coated brass/bronze sprayed on brass for 10 years.

Description: A scalloped medal bearing (obverse): the coat of arms of the Republic. (Reverse) the inscription VIR TROUE DIENS/FOR GOOD SERVICE. Ornamental suspender of wattle leaves and mimosa flowers.

Comments: *This medal superseded the Permanent Force Good Service Medal of 1961 (see SA29) and was divided into three classes, each having distinctive ribbons as follows:*

Gold Medal:
> *Permanent Force. Three narrow white stripes towards each edge*
> *Citizen Force. Three narrow blue stripes towards each edge*
> *Commandos. Three narrow orange stripes towards each edge*

Silver Medal:
> *Permanent Force. Two narrow white stripes towards each edge*
> *Citizen Force. Two narrow blue stripes towards each edge*
> *Commandos. Two narrow orange stripes towards each edge*

Bronze Medal:
> *Permanent Force. One narrow white stripe 2mm from edge*
> *Citizen Force. One narrow blue stripe 2mm from edge*
> *Commandos. One narrow orange stripe 2mm from edge.*

1st striking

> *Members of the Citizen Force or Commandos had the option of choosing this series instead of the John Chard series for Citizen Force or the De Wet series for the Commandos. A silver gilt bar identical to the bar mentioned in SA28 and SA29 was awarded for 40 years service and this was sewn on to the ribbon of the 30 year medal. The reverse of the medal bears the title: VIR TROUWE DIENS/FOR GOOD SERVICE in relief. In the first two strikings of this medal the suspender was decorated with wattle leaves and mimosa flowers on the obverse while the reverse of the suspension was plain.*

There are three strikings to each medal:
1st striking: SA Mint marks.
2nd striking: No Mint marks, no rim to the reverse while the bronze medal is brass coated with bronze and the gauge of the medals is almost 50 per cent thinner.
3rd striking: No Mint marks, reverse rim restored and medal of proper thickness with double faced suspension bar. Brass coated in gold, silver and bronze sprayed-on paint.

VALUE:

	A	B	C	Miniature
First striking:				
Gold:	£40	£35	£30	£3
Silver:	£26	£23	£20	£3
Bronze:	£16	£14	£12	£2
Second striking:				
Gold:	£32	£30	£26	£3
Silver:	£23	£21	£18	£3
Bronze:	£14	£12	£10	£1
Third striking:				
Gold:	£24	£21	£18	£2
Silver:	£20	£18	£16	£2
Bronze:	£16	£14	£12	£2

SA31. SOUTH AFRICAN DEFENCE FORCE GOOD SERVICE MEDAL FOR 40 YEARS SERVICE

Instituted: 1986.

Ribbon: 32mm green with central portion 1mm white, 3mm black, 3mm white, 3mm orange and 1mm white. In 1994 the ribbon was changed however, reducing the central portion to 10mm, 5x2mm stripes of blue, yellow, black, white and red.

Metal: 9 carat gold.

Description: Obverse: The embellished coat of arms of South Africa. Reverse: The Roman numerals XL within a circular laurel wreath open at the top and the medal suspended from a double faced scrolled suspender.

Comments: *This medal is awarded to all members of the South African Permanent Force, Citizen Force or Commandos for 40 years of meritorious and irreproachable service.*

VALUE:

A	B	C	Miniature
£105	£92	£80	£30

SA32. JOHN CHARD DECORATION

Instituted: 1952.

Ribbon: 32mm dark red with 3mm dark blue (outer) and 2mm white (inner) edges.

Metal: Silver/chromed brass.

Description: An upright oval medal fitted with a ring for suspension. The centre shows a view of Rorke's Drift in 1879. At the top is the inscription JOHN CHARD and at the foot DECORATION: DEKORASIE. See descriptions below for details of the various reverses.

Comments: *This decoration replaced the Efficiency Decoration and was named in memory of Lieutenant John Chard, VC, who commanded the garrison at the defence of Rorke's Drift during the Zulu War, 1879. The medal ribbon is worn with a silver button embossed with the initials JCD. The measurement from the top to bottom of the upright oval was designed to exactly match the proportions of the Efficiency Decoration (No. 236). A silver bar with crown (as for the Efficiency Medal) was awarded to denote an extra 10 years, i.e. 30 years service up until 1961. In 1962 a bar of silver with centred circle enclosing the initials JCD was awarded for 30 years service. Silver emblems indicate the branch of service: a fouled anchor on the ribbon for the navy, crossed swords for the army and an eagle with outstretched wings for the air force. Holders are entitled to the post-nominals JCD.*

VALUE:

Type	Description	A	B	C	Miniature
I	Royal cypher EIIR above SA coat of arms	£52	£46	£40	£8
II	Royal cypher erased	£55	£50	£45	£10
III	Large coat of arms of SA —voided acorn	£40	£35	£30	£6
IV	Unvoided acorn suspender and no rim on reverse, with coat of arms	£30	£26	£23	£4
V	As for IV but metal chromed brass, with coat of arms	£22	£17	£15	—
VI	Reverse rim, voided acorn of poor detail and medal stamped silver, with coat of arms	£32	£29	£24	£6

SA33. JOHN CHARD MEDAL

Instituted: 1952.
Ribbon: As for John Chard decoration (SA32).
Metal: Bronze; bronze coated brass; brass sprayed with bronze paint.
Description: Identical to SA32 but with inscription MEDALJE: MEDAL round the foot.
Comments: *This medal replaced the Efficiency Medal and Air Efficiency Medal. Silver emblems indicate the branch of service as in SA32.*

VALUE:

Type	Description	A	B	C	Miniature
I	*Royal cypher EIIR on SA coat of arms*	£40	£34	£30	£6
II	*Royal cypher erased*	£45	£40	£35	£8
III	*Large coat of arms, solid bronze medal*	£26	£23	£20	£4
IV	*Unvoided acorn and no rim on reverse, bronze coated brass, with coat of arms*	£14	£12	£10	£2
V	*Poor detailed voided acorn, brass sprayed with bronze paint, with coat of arms*	£20	£18	£15	£4

SA34. DE WET DECORATION

Instituted: 1965.
Ribbon: 32mm orange with a broad central blue stripe and 3mm green edges separated from the orange by narrow white stripes.
Metal: Silver.
Description: Two sprays of protea blossom enclose a vignette of General Christiaan De Wet, leader of Boer Forces in 1901–02, on horseback with the inscription DEKORASIE—DE WET—DECORATION round the top of the field, enclosed in a wreath of protea blossom. Foliate spurs link the top of the rim to a plain suspension bar.
Comments: *Awarded to all ranks of Commandos for 20 years service. An additional 10 years service is denoted by a silver bar with centrally placed circle with embossed initials DWD. Holders are entitled to the post nominals DWD.*

VALUE:

A	B	C	Miniature
£40	£35	£30	£10

SA35. DE WET MEDAL

Instituted: 1987.
Ribbon: 32mm central panel (made up of 7mm stripes of navy blue, yellow and navy blue), flanked by 3mm green and 2mm white stripes on either side.
Metal: Brass with lacquered bronze paint.
Description: As for De Wet Decoration (SA34) except inscribed MEDALJE—DE WET—MEDAL on the obverse. Suspender of similar design but double width and uniface.
Comments: *Awarded for 10 years service in the Commandos.*

VALUE:

A	B	C	Miniature
£20	£18	£15	£4

SA36. CADET CORPS MEDAL

Instituted: 1966.

Ribbon: 32mm orange with 5mm blue edges separated from the orange by 1.5mm white stripes.

Metal: Oxidised silver.

Description: A prancing springbok enclosed in a laurel wreath with the inscription CADET CORPS MEDAL and KADETKORPS MEDALJE at the sides.

Comments: *Awarded for 20 years service as an officer in the Cadet Corps. Those who had completed 30 years service were eligible for a silver bar with a prancing springbok embossed in the centre of the bar. It was abolished in August 1976 when the Cadet Corps ceased to exist as a separate force, being absorbed into the Commandos or Citizen Force.*

VALUE:

A	B	C	Miniature
£52	£46	£40	£15

SERVICE MEDALS

SA37. PRO PATRIA MEDAL

Instituted: 1974.

Ribbon: 32mm orange with a broad band of dark blue divided by a thin central orange stripe, with narrow hite stripes towards the edges.

Metal: Brass with gilt finish.

Clasp: Cunene clasp awarded for operations into Angola in 1976, sewn on to the ribbon of the Pro Patria Medal.

Description: An eight sided medal with rectangular motifs in each sector with a central dark blue medallion depicting a stylised aloe plant in gold. It has a plain ring attached to a straight suspension bar with a protean emblem flanked by laurel sprays—type I and II have a link suspender whereas type III has a fixed suspender.

Comments: *Awarded for service in the defence of the Republic of South Africa or for supression or prevention of terrorism with specified conditions of award. There are a number of variations in manufacture for type III.*

VALUE:

Type	Description	A	B	C	Miniature
I	Link suspender. SA Mint striking—serial numbers 1.25mm high	£18	£14	£12	£5
II	Link suspender	£12	£9	£7	£2
III	Fixed suspender	£9	£6	£3–£4	£2
	With Cunene clasp	£12	£10	£8	£5

(This value should be added to types I, II and III if there is a Cunene clasp)

SA38. SOUTHERN AFRICA MEDAL

Instituted: 1989.
Ribbon: 32mm, central black stripe of 12mm centred with 2mm white
 stripe, flanked on either side with a 5mm red and 5mm yellow stripe.
Metal: Nickel silver.
Description: An eight sided medal with suspender ornamented with
 protea flower on each scrolled arm. Obverse: A leopard on the prowl
 beneath an acacia tree to indicate the strike power of the South African
 Defence Force. Reverse: A laurel wreath open at its uppermost point to
 embrace a small embellished coat of arms of South Africa, below are
 the words SUIDER-AFRICA/SOUTHERN AFRICA.
Comments: *The medal was awarded for participation in specified cross-border
 activites in defence of the Republic of South Africa. The award was to have
 originally been called the "Trans Jati Medal", the "Jati" being the cut line.
 The medals were to have been made from the metal of a captured Russian T34
 tank but the metal was found to be unsuited for the purpose. Instead a small
 amount of melted metal from the tank was mixed with nickel silver. There
 were two strikings of the medal—the first with a uniface suspender struck as
 an integral part of the medal, the second with a double faced suspender
 attached to the medal.*

VALUE:	A	B	C	Miniature
Type I	£30	£20	£12	£4
Type II	£34	£24	£16	—

SA39. GENERAL SERVICE MEDAL

Instituted: 1989.
Ribbon: 32mm, 6mm navy blue stripe, 2mm white stripe, 7mm orange
 stripe, 2mm navy blue stripe, then the first three stripes repeated in
 reverse.
Metal: Nickel silver.
Description: Obverse: A laurel wreath open at its uppermost point and
 enclosing the badge of the South African Defence Force which
 combines the swords, wings and anchor of the Army, Air Force and
 Navy, on an outline of the Castle of Good Hope. Reverse: The
 embellished coat of arms of South Africa with GENERAL SERVICE/
 ALGEMENE DIENS to the right and left of the coat of arms.
 Suspenders/strikings as for SA38.
Comments: *The medal was awarded for service within the borders of the
 Republic of South Africa since 1 January 1983.*

VALUE:	A	B	C	Miniature
Type I	£8	£6	£4	£3
Type II	£10	£8	£6	—

COMMEMORATIVE—SA40. UNITAS MEDAL

Instituted: 1994.
Ribbon: 32mm, pale blue with central green stripe of 8mm edged each
 side by a white stripe of 4mm.
Metal: Lacquered brass.
Description: Obverse: A seven pointed star with central circle enclosing the
 Greek letter Alpha. Reverse: A small embellished coat of arms of South
 Africa with date 1994 below. The whole is enclosed by a circle made up of
 the word "Unity" in all eleven official languages of the new South Africa.
 Suspender is uniface and struck as one piece with the medal.
Comments: *Awarded to all those who rendered service through being members of a
 serving force (Permanent Force, Citizen Force, Commandos, members of the
 armed forces of the former self-governing territories, the armed wing of the ANC
 (the MK) and APLA) during the period of South Africa's first non-racial
 elections and inauguration of Mr Mandela as the first black State President in
 South Africa between 27 April and 10 May 1994. Those medals awarded to
 members of the British Military Advisory Team in South Africa at the time, for
 which Her Majesty Queen Elizabeth II granted permission for wear must be
 considered a rarity.*

VALUE:	A	B	C	Miniature
	£8	£6	£4	£2

MISCELLANEOUS

SA41. MENTION IN DESPATCHES

Instituted: 1967.
Metal: Gilt or bronze.
Description: A miniature replica of the embellished coat of arms of South Africa.
Comments: *Worn either on the ribbon of the Pro Patria Medal or General Service Medal. Prior to the institution of these medals, a bronze version was worn on uniform fabric of the tunic and not affixed to a medal.*

VALUE:

A with Citation	A	B	C	Miniature
£15 to £20	£10	£6	£2	£2

POLICE AWARDS

Those listed here are the medals most commonly encountered by collectors. The information is taken from *Gallantry Awards of the South African Police 1913–1994* by Terence King assisted by Audrey Portman by courtesy of Rhino Research. The book contains in-depth details of the gallantry medals listed.

SA42. SOUTH AFRICAN POLICE STAR FOR OUTSTANDING SERVICE (SOE)

Instituted: 1979
Ribbon: 36mm green divided by two stripes of yellow, blue and white. a
Metal: Gilded silver
Description: A star composed of the cross of St Cuthbert, each limb notched of four and in each angle, an engrailed ray. (Obverse): in the centre, a white roundel bearing an aloe with three racemes. (Reverse): the unembellished coat of arms of the Republic of South Africa within the legend *STELLA OFFICII ENGREGII* SA POLICE. A bar denoting subsequent awards depicts an aloe with three racemes. A miniature replica of this clasp is attached to the ribbon when the ribbon alone is worn by a recipient who has been awarded a bar. All decorations and bars were issued named to the recipient and stamped with the serial number, rank and name.
Comments: *Awarded to a member of the South African Police or reserve police who: (a) in the execution of his duties in protecting or saving, or endeavouring to protect or save, life or property, has displayed particular gallantry, exceptional ingenuity, skill or perseverance; (b) in the execution of his duties has rendered outstanding services to members of a dynasty or to Heads of State or of Governments; (c) has distinguished himself through outstanding resourcefulness, leadership, and sense of responsibility or by setting a personal example in any branch of the Force. In addition, it could be awarded to any other persons who distinguished themselves through outstanding services rendered to the South African Police. This decoration was also awarded to recognize acts of gallantry as well as acts of outstanding service. In 1989 all references to gallantry were removed where they occurred in the original warrant, and the award was to officers of the general staff. This was in consequence of the institution of the 1989 version of the South African Police Cross for Bravery. Recipients of this decoration are entitled to use the post nominal letters SOE (STELLA OFFICII EGREGII).*

VALUE: Named £80   Unnamed £40

SA43. SOUTH AFRICAN POLICE STAR FOR MERIT

Instituted: 1963.
Ribbon: 32mm, orange with white central stripe edged with blue.
Metal: Silver.
Description: (Obverse): two forearms with hands overlaying the letter V resting on the letter M and holding aloft a flame. (Reverse): the badge of the South African Police, with the words VERDIENSTE above and MERIT below. A silver bar with an embossed letter V resting on an M was authorised to denote a subsequent award or completion of 30 years service. When the ribbon alone is worn, the award of a bar is indicated by this circular emblem. All decorations and bars were issued named to the recipient and stamped with the serial number, rank and name.
Comments: *The award is granted to: (a) members of the South African Police or reserve police force who, in the discharge of their duties, have rendered services of a particularly meritorious or exemplary nature; (b) a member who has completed thirty years service (not necessarily continuous), and who has displayed an irreproachable character and exemplary conduct. The medal is also awarded to other persons (civilians) who have rendered services of a particularly meritorious nature to the South African Police. This medal is awarded for long service and good conduct as well as being a decoration for particularly exemplary or meritorious service (gallantry). The majority of awards to members of the police or reserve police were for acts of gallantry.*

VALUE: Named £30   Unnamed £15 These values double if awarded for gallantry)

SA44. SOUTH AFRICAN POLICE MEDAL FOR FAITHFUL SERVICE

Instituted: 1963.
Ribbon: 32mm, royal blue with 3mm old gold centre stripe.
Metal: Bronze.
Description: (Obverse): the coat of arms of the Republic of South Africa surrounded by a laurel. (Reverse): the official badge of the South African Police with the words TROUE DIENS and FAITHFUL SERVICE in embossed capital letters around.
Comments: *This medal replaced the Police Good Service Medal and was awarded to members of the South African Police who had displayed an irreproachable character and exemplary conduct and served for a qualifying period. A bronze bar embossed with the letters TDFS (Troue Diens/Faithful Service) in ornamental script was awarded for subsequent qualifying periods.*

VALUE   Named £12   Unnamed £5

SA45. SOUTH AFRICAN POLICE STAR FOR FAITHFUL SERVICE

Instituted: 1979.
Ribbon: 36mm, divided into 11 parts: yellow 2mm, green 3mm, yellow 4mm, blue 2mm, yellow 4mm, green 6mm, repeated in reverse.
Metal: Silver.
Description: A circular medal with (obverse): an eight-pointed star, charged in the centre with a medallion, with four aloes in cross, each with three racemes, all in natural colours. (Reverse): the official badge of the South African Police with the words TROUE DIENS and FAITHFUL SERVICE around.
Comments: *This medal was an award to complement the two long service and good conduct awards already in existence.The qualifying period changed over the years and a gold bar bearing the letters TDFS in ornamental script was awarded for further periods of service. Medals were now awarded for 10 years service (Medal for Faithful Service), 20 years service (Star for Faithful Service), 30 years service (Star for Merit) and 40 years service (Bar to Star for Faithful Service).*

VALUE: Named £14   Unnamed £6

SA46. SOUTH AFRICAN POLICE MEDAL FOR COMBATING TERRORISM

Instituted: 1974.
Ribbon: 31.75mm red, with three wide and two narrow silver stripes.
Metal: Silver.
Description: (Obverse): A six-pointed star, with three long and three short points. Attached to the ribbon by means of a V-shaped silver clevis, which is in turn attached to the medal by means of a rimmed shield depicting a candlestick aloe with four leaves and three candles. (Reverse): The words BEKAMPING VAN TERRORISME—COMBATING TERRORISM around the official badge of the South African Police. A silver bar was authorised to denote a subsequent award. This plain bar bears, in the centre, a silver clasp corresponding to the design on the shield. A maximum of two bars only can be awarded, irrespective of any further qualification period. All medals were issued named to the recipient with the serial number, rank and name stamped on the reverse of the V shaped clevis.

Comments: *Awarded to a member of the South African Police or others who, in support of the police, on or at any time after 26 August 1966 (a) had been involved in combat with terrorists, or in the course of the performance of duties in connection with the prevention and combating of terrorism, sustained injuries arising from terrorist activities; or who, in the execution of such duties, displayed exceptional zeal, ingenuity, skills or leadership; (b) had performed counter insurgency duties for at least six months, which may be cumulative, in an area (operational area) fixed by the Minister; (c) had rendered exceptional and outstanding service to the South African Police in connection with the combating of terrorism. The original qualifying period of six months was later changed to sixty days. Any member of the South African Police who was stationed permanently for a continuous period of at least twelve months in an operational area and behaved in an exemplary manner also qualified for the award of the medal.*

VALUE: Named £6   Unnamed £3

SA47. SOUTH AFRICAN POLICE 75th ANNIVERSARY MEDAL

Instituted: 1988.
Ribbon: Royal blue 32mm edged with light blue and old gold stripes.
Metal: Bronze.
Description: (Obverse): The figures "75", surmounted with an aloe with three racemes and the police motto "SERVAMUS ET SERVIMUS" above and the dates "1913-1988" below. (Reverse): The badge of the South African Police.

Comments: *Instituted to commemorate the 75th anniversary of the founding the South African Police on 1 April 1988. Awarded to permanent and temporary members of the Police Force and Reserve Police Force on 1 April 1988, or people who had rendered service of a particularly meritorious nature to the South African Police. A bar, bearing the figures "75" surmounted by an aloe and three racemes, is to be awarded to those still serving in the Force on 1 April 2013. All awards were issued named and were engraved on the reverse with the serial number, rank and name of the recipient.*

VALUE: Named £5   Unnamed £3

SOUTH AFRICAN PRISONS AWARDS
(Later Department of Correctional Services)

SA48. MEDAL FOR MERIT IN THE SOUTH AFRICAN PRISONS SERVICE

Instituted: 1968.

Ribbon: 35mm in width divided into seven parts: blue 6mm; white 5mm; orange 6mm; white 1mm; then repeated in reverse.

Metal: Silver.

Description: Suspender in form of a lifebuoy. Obverse: DEPARTMENT VAN GEVANGENISSE/PRISONS DEPARTMENT at edge of medal with embellished South African coat of arms. Reverse: FOR MERIT (top) and VIR VERDIENSTELIKHEID (below).

Comments: *Awarded to members of the SAPS who had rendered particularly meritorious or exemplary service or distinguished himself by his ingenuity, proficiency or perseverance for a period of not less than 35 years, displaying irreproachable character and exemplary conduct. Impressed naming on reverse. A plain bar of silver with the coat of arms of SA embossed in the centre was awarded for subsequent acts of distinction. Replaced by SA51 (NCOs) in 1979.*

VALUE:

Named with bar	£45
Named	£30
Unnamed	£15
Miniature	£5

SA49. SOUTH AFRICAN PRISONS SERVICE STAR FOR MERIT

Instituted: 1980

Ribbon: 32mm Green with two vertical white stripes each 2mm wide and 12mm from the side.

Metal: Silver.

Description: A 10-point cross with protea flowers in the angles and a plain ring for suspension from a straight bar.

Comments: *Awarded to Commissioned officers for outstanding services rendered on the grounds of ability, efficiency, perseverance or devotion in the discharge of duties. Post nominal title: SPM (Stella Pro Merito).*

VALUE:

Named with certificate	£70
Named	£55
Unnamed	£40
Miniature	£8

SA50. SOUTH AFRICAN PRISONS SERVICE CROSS FOR MERIT

Instituted: 1980.

Ribbon: 32mm green with three vertical white stripes each 2mm wide and 2mm from each other with the outer white stripes 11mm from each side.

Metal: Silver with gold plated border to cross.

Description: A cross pattée very similar to the German Iron Cross in appearance, but without any detail on the front. Fitted with a plain ring for suspension from a straight bar.

Comments: *No clasps granted for additional awards. Award conditions as for South Africa Prisons Service Star for Merit (SA49) but awarded to non-commissioned officers. Post nominal title: CPM (Crux Pro Merito).*

VALUE:

Named with certificate	£70
Named	£55
Unnamed	£40
Miniature	£8

SA51. SOUTH AFRICAN PRISONS SERVICE MEDAL FOR MERIT

Instituted: 1980.
Ribbon: For Commissioned Officers: 32mm divided into seven parts—white 4mm; green 8mm; white 2mm; green 4mm and then repeated in reverse. **For NCOs:** 32mm, divided into nine parts; white 4mm; green 8mm; white 2mm; green 4mm white 2mm and then repeated in reverse.
Metal: Silver.
Description: A radiate star with an open protea floriate centre and an inverted V and ring for suspension from a straight bar.
Comments: *Same conditions of award as SA49 and SA50 except the word "outstanding" is replaced by "special". For the Officer's Medal the eight single rays are gold plated and the eight pairs of narrow rays are silver. The open protea flower in the centre is gold plated. The NCOs Medal is plain silver.*

VALUE:
Named with certificate	£30
Named	£25
Unnamed	£20
Miniature	£8

SA52. FAITHFUL SERVICE MEDAL, PRISONS DEPARTMENT

Instituted: 1965.
Ribbon: 31mm, divided into five parts: green 6mm; white 5mm; blue 9mm; and then repeated in reverse.
Metal: Silver.
Description: Obverse: coat of arms of the Republic of South Africa with the words DEPARTEMENT VAN GEVANGENISSE—PRISONS DEPARTMENT. Reverse: VOOR TROUE DIENS—FOR FAITHFUL SERVICE.
Comments: *Awarded (1) for 18 years service (not necessarily continuous) that displayed exemplary conduct and unimpeachable character or (2) had displayed devotion to duty in a distinguished or gallant manner. This medal superseded No. 291. A bar with the words: VERDIENSTELIK/ MERITORIOUS was granted for gallant or distinguished conduct.*

VALUE:
If awarded for (1)	£25
If awarded for (2)	£50
With bar	£75
Unnamed	£25
Miniature	£8

SA53. MEDAL FOR FAITHFUL SERVICE IN THE SOUTH AFRICAN PRISONS SERVICE

Instituted: 1968.
Ribbon: 35mm divided into five parts: blue 6mm; white 5mm; green 13mm and then repeated in reverse.
Metal: Bronze.
Description: Obverse: In the form of the official badge of the Prisons Department with the circumscription DEPARTEMENT VAN GEVANGINISSE (top) and PRISONS DEPARTMENT (bottom). Reverse: FOR FAITHFUL SERVICE (above) and VIR TROUE DIENS (below). In the central area the space received the engraved name, etc., and date of the award of the recipient.
Comments: *Awarded For: (1) as for (1) in SA52. (2) If the recipient had received SA52 for condition of 2 of SA52 then he would receive this medal on completion of 18 years service, etc. (3) If the recipient was in possession of SA52 after 18 years service he could receive this medal after a completion of a further 12 years. A bar of bronze with the Prisons Department badge in the centre denoted a further 15 years service following the award of the medal.*

VALUE:
Named	£22
Unnamed	£12
Miniature	£5

SA54. SOUTH AFRICA PRISONS SERVICE MEDAL FOR FAITHFUL SERVICE

Instituted: 1980.

Ribbon: 32mm yellow with two sets of three green stripes each 2mm wide and 2mm apart, the outer stripe set being 2mm from each edge (Gold); two sets of two green stripes each 2mm wide and 2mm apart, the outer stripe set being 2mm from each edge (Silver); or two green stripes each 2mm wide and 2mm from each edge (Bronze).

Metal: Silver-gilt, silver or bronze to denote 30, 20 or 10 years service.

Description: A circular medal with the arms of the Republic in the centre and a garland of protea blossom round the circumference.

Comments: *This replaced SA53. A silver-gilt bar for the gold medal was authorised, embossed with a central circle in the form of the obverse of the medal to indicate a further 10 years service.*

VALUE:

	Named with certificate	Named	Unnamed	*Miniature*
Bronze	£16	£25	£20	£3
Silver	£25	£20	£16	£4
Gold	£30	£25	£20	£5
With Bar to Gold	£40	£30	£24	£10

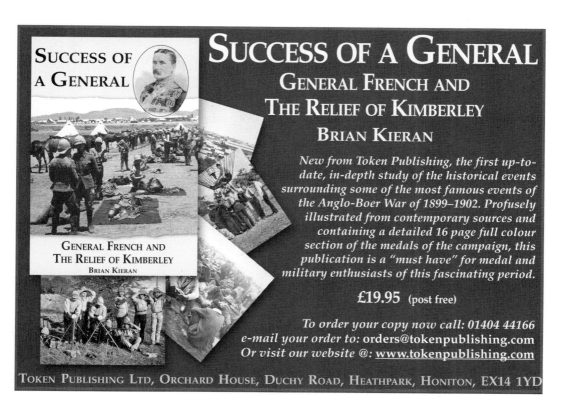

SUCCESS OF A GENERAL
GENERAL FRENCH AND
THE RELIEF OF KIMBERLEY
BRIAN KIERAN

New from Token Publishing, the first up-to-date, in-depth study of the historical events surrounding some of the most famous events of the Anglo-Boer War of 1899–1902. Profusely illustrated from contemporary sources and containing a detailed 16 page full colour section of the medals of the campaign, this publication is a "must have" for medal and military enthusiasts of this fascinating period.

£19.95 (post free)

*To order your copy now call: 01404 44166
e-mail your order to: orders@tokenpublishing.com
Or visit our website @: www.tokenpublishing.com*

TOKEN PUBLISHING LTD, ORCHARD HOUSE, DUCHY ROAD, HEATHPARK, HONITON, EX14 1YD

Foreign medals **found in British** **groups**

There are a number of awards and decorations issued by Foreign Governments which are frequently encountered in groups of medals awarded to British servicemen. These awards have usually been officially conferred by the foreign power and make an interesting addition to the service history of the recipient.We list below just a few of the awards most commonly encountered in groups of the World War I period, obviously there are many, many more examples from other periods and most can be identified using standard reference works. For further details of many of these award listed here we would recommend reading, amongst many other publications, *The Medals, Decorations & Orders of the Great War 1914–1918* by Alec A. Purves, available from Token Publishing Ltd, price £16. The prices quoted in this section are for single examples of the medals alone; when they are included with a group of British medals the price can often be many times the quoted figure.

BELGIUM

Commander's neck badge, Order of Leopold II

ORDER OF LEOPOLD II
Commander's neck badge	£100–150
Knight's badge	£35–50
Miniature	£20–25

BELGIUM *continued*

Officer's badge, Order of the Crown

ORDER OF THE CROWN
Officer's badge	£18–30
Knight's badge	£18–30
Miniature	£15–20

CROIX DE GUERRE   £15–20

Miniature   £8–10

FRANCE

LEGION d'HONNEUR 1870–1951
Neck badge	£200–250
Breast badge	£35–65
Miniature	£25–30

MÉDAILLE MILITAIRE 1870   £25–35

Miniature   £20–25

FRANCE *continued*

GREECE

1914–18 reverse

CROIX DE GUERRE

1914–15 reverse	£15–20
1914–16 reverse	£15–20
1914–17 reverse	£15–20
1914–18 reverse	£12–15
for each star or palm add £3	

Miniature	£10–12

ORDER OF THE REDEEMER

Commander's badge	£300–450
Knight's badge	£225–275
Officer's badge	£125–180

Miniature	£40–50

ITALY

ORDER OF THE CROWN 2nd Class

Breast badge	£100–135
Officer's badge	£65–90
Knight's badge	£50–65

Miniature	£20–30

AL VALORE (unnamed)

Bronze	£35–45
Silver	£55–65

Miniature, silver	£25–30

Restrikes are also known. They can be distinguished from the originals by the omission of the initials FG at the bottom on the obverse.

In addition to the above medals, the Messina Earthquake Medal, awarded by the King of Italy in 1908 to British personnel who went to the aid of victims of the tragic earthquake at Messina, can be found under Medal No. 163A

ITALY *continued*

WAR CROSS   £15–25

Miniature   £8–10

King Victor Emmanuel III of Italy pictured in uniform, 1918.

JAPAN

ORDER OF THE RISING SUN

3rd Class	£550–650
4th Clas	£400–450
5th Class	£285–375
6th Class	£225–325
7th Class	£55–75
8th Class	£25–45
Miniature	£30–40

ORDER OF THE SACRED TREASURE

3rd Class	£425–500
4th Clas	£225–275
5th Class	£125–165
Miniature	£40–50

RUSSIA

ORDER OF St STANISLAUS (illustrated)

Gold	£475–£600
Silver-gilt	£175–225
Miniature	£50–60

ORDER OF St ANNE

Gold	£275–385
Miniature	£50–60

CROSS OF St GEORGE

3rd Class	£90–110
4th Class	£50–70
Miniature	£30–40

MEDAL OF St GEORGE

3rd Class	£90–110
4th Class	£40–60
Miniature	£10–15

SERBIA

ORDER OF KARAGEORGE
  4th Class   £220–300

ORDER OF THE WHITE EAGLE WITH SWORDS
  Knight's badge   £125–175

  Miniature   £40–50

TURKEY

ORDER OF THE MEDJIDIEH
  1st Class   £485–500
  2nd Clas   £375–425
  3rd Class   £155–225
  4h Class   £85–150
  5th Class   £65–85

ORDER OF THE OSMANIEH
  1st Class   £500–550
  2nd Clas   £400–450
  3rd Class   £185–225
  4th Class   £95–150
  5th Class   £65–85

O Observer

Abbreviations and initials

The medal collector is constantly coming across initials and abbreviations on medals and in documents—many of which are commonplace and easily decipherable. However, there are many more which can cause problems when trying to identify a medal recipient. The following list represents only a small selection of the inexhaustible number of abbreviations encountered, but hopefully it will be of some assistance to the collector. The *"Token Book of Militarisms"* contains literally hundreds more if you cannot find the abbreviation you are looking for here.

1 E Ang 1st East Anglian Regiment
1 R Dgns 1st Royal Dragoons
1 QDG 1st Queen's Dragoon Guards
11H 11th Royal Hussars
12L 12th Royal Lancers
13/18H 13th/18th Royal Hussars
14/20H 14th/20th Royal Hussars
15/19H 15th/19th Royal Hussars
3 E Ang 3rd East Anglian Regiment
4 QOH 4th Queen's Own Hussars
4H 4th Royal Hussars
5 DGds 5th Royal Inniskilling Dragoon Guards
7QOH 7th Queen's Own Hussars
7GR 7th Gurkha Rifles
A/ Acting
A Avn Army Aviation
Abn Inf Airborne Infantry
A/CWEM Acting Chief Weapons Engineering Mechanic
A/LMEM Acting Leading Marine Engineering Mechanic
A/LRO(G) Acting Leading Radio Operator (General)
A/PO Acting Petty Officer, Acting Pilot Officer
A&SH The Argyll and Sutherland Highlanders
AAC Army Air Corps
AAF, Aux F Auxillery Air Force
AAU Air Ambulance Unit
AB Able Seaman; Airborne
ABDS Army Bomb Disposal Squad
AC1 Aircraftman 1st Class
ACC Army Catering Corps, Armoured Car Company
ACF Army Cadet Force
ADALS Assistant Director, Army Legal Service
ADC Aide de Camp
AE Army Education Officer, Air Efficiency Award
AER Army Emergency Reserve
AFC Air Force Cross
AFM Air Force Medal
AGS Africa General Service Medal
AIF Australian Imperial Forces
AIY Ayrshire Imperial Yeomanry
ALO Air Liaison Officer
ALS Army Legal Services
AM Albert Medal
AM1 Air Mechanic 1st Class
AMA Acting Master at Arms

AMS Assistant Military Secretary; Army Medical Staff
AOC Army Ordnance Corps
APC Army Pay Corps
APL Aden Protectorate Levies
APTC Army Physical Training Corps
AQ Assistant Quartermaster; Administrative Quartermaster
Armd Armoured
ASC Army Service Corps; Air Service Command
ATO Ammunition Technical Officer
B&H The Bedfordshire & Hertfordshire Regiment
B&R Blues & Royals
BAAT British Army Advisory Team
BATT British Army Training Team
BAO British Army of Occupation
Bdr Bombadier
BDU Bomb Disposal Unit
BEM British Empire Medal
BF British Forces
BGS Brigadier, General Staff
BIY Bedford Imperial Yeomanry
BM Brigade Major
BORD.R Border Regiment
BR British
Brig Brigadier
Br Coy Bearer Company
BSA Police British South Africa Police
Buffs The Buffs (Royal East Kent Regiment)
BW Black Watch (Royal Highland Regiment)
BWM British War Medal
C&TC Commissariat and Transport Corps
C/Sgt Colour Sergeant
C&S Command & Staff
CAC Canadian Armoured Corps
CADAC Canadian Army Dental Corps
CAEA Chief Air Engineering Artificer
CAHTC Cape Auxiliary Horse Transport Corps
CAMN HIGH Cameron Highlanders
Capt Captain
CAR Central African Rifles
CASC Canadian Army Service Corps
CATO Commander Ammunition Technical Officers
CB Commander of the Order of the Bath
CBE Commander of the Order of the British Empire
CBF Commander British Forces
CC Cadet Corps; Coastal Command; Combat Command
CCAEA Charge Chief Air Engineering Artificer

CCCC   Cape Colony Cyclist Corps
CCF   Combined Cadet Force
CCMEA   Charge Chief Marine Engineering Artificer
CCS   Casualty Clearing Station
C de G   Croix de Guerre
Cdr   Commander
CE   Canadian Engineers
CEO   Chief Executive Officer; Chief Education Officer
CG   Coast Guard; Commanding General
CGC   Conspicuous Gallantry Cross
CGM   Conspicuous Gallantry Medal
Cheshire   The Cheshire Regiment
CI   Crown of India, Imperial Order; Counter-Intelligence
CIV   City Imperial Volunteers
CIE   Companion of the Order of the Indian Empre
CLY   County of London Yeomanry
CMEM   Chief Marine Engineering Mechanic
CMFR   Commonwealth Monitoring Force Rhodesia
CMG   Companion of the Order of St Michael and St George
CMM   Commander of the Order of Military Merit
CMO   Chief Medical Officer
CMMP   Corps of Military Mounted Police
CMP   Corps of Military Police
CMSC   Cape Medical Staff Corps
CMR   Cape Mounted Riflemen
CO   Commanding Officer
Col   Colonel
Coldm Gds   Coldstream Guards
Comd   Commander
COS   Chief of Staff
CP   Cape Police
Cpl   Corporal
CPO   Chief Petty Officer
CPOAEA   Chief Petty Officer Air Engineering Artificer
CPOWEA   Chief Petty Officer Weapons Engineering Artificer
CQMS   Company Quartermaster Sergeant
CSI   Companion of the Order of the Star of India
CSM   Company Sergeant Major; Campaign Service Medal
CT, C/T, Ch Tech   Chief Technician
CVO   Commander of the Royal Victorian Order
D   Diver
D Comd   Deputy Commander
D&D   The Devon and Dorset Regiment
DAD   Deputy Assistant Director
DADOS   Deputy Assistant Director of Ordnance Services
DADVRS   Deputy Assistant Director Veterinary & Remount Section
DAMA   Department of the Army Material Annex
DANS   Director of Army Nursing Services
DAPM   Deputy Assistant Provost Marshall
DAT   Director of Army Training
DBE   Dame Commander, Order of the British Empire
DCLI   The Duke of Cornwall's Light Infantry
DCM   Distinguished Conduct Medal
DCMG   Dame Commander of the Order of St Michael and St George
DCO   Duke of Cambridge's Own; Duke of Connaught's Own
DCOS   Deputy Chief of Staff
DCVO   Dame Commander of the Royal Victorian Order
DDSD   Deputy Director Staff Duties

DEO   Duke of Edinburgh's Own
DERR   The Duke of Edinburgh's Royal Regiment (Berkshire & Wiltshire)
Det   Detached; Detachment
Devon   The Devonshire Regiment
DFC   Distinguished Flying Cross
DFM   Distinguished Flying Medal
DG   Dragoon Guards
DI   Defence Intelligence
DLI   The Durham Light Infantry
DMT   District Mounted Troops
Dorset   The Dorset Regiment
DOS   Director of Ordnance Services
DS   Defence Secretary; Deputy Secretary; Defensive Section
DSC   Distinguished Service Cross
DSM   Distinguished Service Medal
DSO   Distinguished Service Order
DWR   The Duke of Wellington's Regiment
EAR   East African Rifles
ED   Efficiency Decoration
EF   Expeditionary Force
EGM   Empire Gallantry Medal
EM   Edward Medal; Efficiency Medal
EOD   Explosive Ordnance Disposal
ERA   Engine Room Artificer
ERD   Emergency Reserve Decoration
ERE   Extra Regimentally Employed
FA   Field Ambulance
FANYC   First Aid Nursing Yeomanry Corps
FBRA   Field Battery Royal Artillery
FC   Fighter Command
Fd   Field
FELF   Far East Land Forces
FF   Field Force
FFL   French Foreign Legion
FFR   Frontier Force Rifles
FL, F/L, Flt Lt   Flight Lieutenant
FM   Field Marshal
FMR   Frontier Mounted Rifles
FO, F/O, Fg Off   Flying Officer
FS   Fighter Squadron; Field Security
FS, F/S, Flt/Sgt   Flight Sergeant
Fus   Fusilier
G Howards   Green Howards (Alexandra, Princess of Wales's Own Yorkshire Regiment)
G Or   General Operational Requirements
GBE   Grand Cross, Order of the British Empire
GC   George Cross
GC, G/C, GpCapt   Group Captain
GCB   Knight Grand Cross Order of the Bath
GCH   Knight Grand Cross Hanoverian Order
GCIE   Knight Grand Commander Order of the Indian Empire
GCLH   Grand Cross Legion of Honour
GCM   Good Conduct Medal
GCMG   Knight Grand Cross Order of St Michael and St George
GCSI   Knight Grand Commander Order of the Star of India
GCVO   Knight Grand Cross Royal Victorian Order
Gdsmn   Guardsman
GLI   Guernsey Light Infantry
Glosters   The Gloucestershire Regiment (28th/61st Foot)
GM   George Medal
Gnr   Gunner
GOC   General Officer Commanding
Gordons   The Gordon Highlanders (75th/92nd Regiment)

GPR Glider Pilot Regiment
GR Gurkha Rifles
GS General Service
GSC General Service Corps
GSM General Service Medal
GSO General Staff Officer
HA Horse Artillery
HAC Honourable Artillery Company
HBM Her Britannic Majesty
HCR Household Cavalry Regiment
HG Home Guard; Horse Guards
HLI The Highland Light Infantry
HQ Headquarters
IAOC Indian Army Ordnance Corps
IASC Indian Army Service Corps
IC In Charge
IDSM Indian Distinguished Service Medal
IE Order of the Indian Empire
IG Irish Guards
Int Intelligence
Int Corps Intelligence Corps
Int & Sy Coy Intelligence and Security Company
IO Intelligence Officer
IOM Indian Order of Merit
IRC Infantry Reserve Corps
ISM Imperial Service Medal
ISO Imperial Service Order
IY Imperial Yeomanry
JSSC Joint Services Staff College
KAR King's African Rifles
KB Knight Bachelor
KBE Knight of the Order of the British Empire
KC Knight Commander
KCB Knight Commander Order of the Bath
KCH Knight Commander of the Royal Hanoverian Guelphic Order
KCIE Knight Commander Order of the Indian Empire
KCIO King's Commissioned Indian Officer
KCMG Knight Commander Order of St Michael and St George
KCSI Knight Commander Order of the Star of India
KCVO Knight Commander Royal Victorian Order
KDG King's Dragoon Guards
KG Knight of the Order of the Garter
KGCB Knight Grand Cross Order of the Bath
KGL King's German Legion
Kings The King's Regiment (Liverpool)
KLH Knight of the Legion of Honour
KM King's Medal
KOM Knight of the Order of Malta
KORB The King's Own Royal Border Regiment
KOSB The King's Own Scottish Borderers
KOYLI The King's Own Yorkshire Light Infantry
KPM King's Police Medal
KRRC The King's Royal Rifle Corps
KSG Knight of the Order of St George
KSLI The King's Shropshire Light Infantry
KT Knight of the Order of the Thistle
L/Cpl Lance Corporal
L/Sgt Lance Sergeant
LAC Leading Aircraftman
Lanc Fusiliers The Lancashire Fusiliers
Lanc R The Queen's Lancashire Regiment
LC Labour Corps
Leic The Royal Leicestershire Regiment
LG Life Guards; London Gazette
LI Light Infantry
Linc The Royal Lincolnshire Regiment

LM Legion of Merit
LMA Leading Medical Assistant
LS Leading Seaman
LS&GC Long Service and Good Conduct (medal)
Lt Lieutenant
Lt-Cdr Lieutenant Commander
Lt-Col Lieutenant-Colonel
LVO Lieutenant of the Royal Victorian Order
MA Military Attache
Maint Maintenance
Maj Major
Maj-Gen Major-General
Mal.LBC Maltese Labour Corps
MBE Member of the Order of the British Empire
MC Military Cross
MEM Marine Engineering Mechanic
MFA Mercantile Fleet Auxiliary
MFS Medical Field Service
MGC Machine Gun Corps
MGS Military General Service (medal)
MH Medal of Honour
MI Mounted Infantry
MID Mentioned in Despatches
MKW Military Knights of Windsor
MM Military Medal; Medal of Merit
MMGS Motor Machine Gun Service
MMWM Mercantile Marine War Medal
Mne Marine
MMR Mercantile Marine Reserve
MR Middlesex Regiment
MRCVS Member Royal College of Veterinary Surgeons
MSC Medical Staff Corps
MSM Meritorious Service Medal
MTO Motor Transport Office
MVO Member of the Royal Victorian Order
NACS Naval Air Commando Squadron
NAS Naval Air Squadron
NCO Non-Commissioned Officer
NFA Natal Field Artillery
NGS Naval General Service (Medal)
NZEF New Zealand Expeditionary Force
OBE Officer of the Order of the British Empire
OBLI Ox and Bucks Light Infantry
OC Officer Commanding
OCS Officer Cadet School
OEO Ordnance Executive Officer
OHBMS On Her Britannic Majesty's Service
OM Order of Merit
OR Operational Requirements; Other Ranks; Organised Reserve
Ord Ordnance
OS Ordinary Seaman; Ordnance Survey
PAOCVA Prince Albert's Own Cape Volunteer Rifles
PAVG Prince Albert's Volunteer Guard
Para The Parachute Regiment
PO Petty Officer
PO, P/O, Plt Off Pilot Officer
PO/AC Petty Officer Aircrewman
POMA Petty Officer Medical Assistant
POMEM Petty Officer Marine Engineering Mechanic
PR Public Relations
PSO Personal Selection Officer
Pte Private
PVCP Permanent Vehicle Check Point
PWO The Prince of Wales's Own Regiment of Yorkshire
Q Ops Quartermaster General Branch Operations

QARANC Queen Alexandra's Royal Army Nursing Corps
QCBA Queen's Commendation for Bravery in the Air
QCBC Queen's Commendation for Brave Conduct
QCVS Queen's Commendation for Valuable Service
QCVSA Queen's Commendation for Valuable Service in the Air
QFSM Queen's Fire Service Medal
QDG The Queen's Dragoon Guards
QGM Queen's Gallantry Medal
QLR The Queen's Lancashire Regiment
QM Quartermaster
QMAAC Queen Mary's Auxiliary Ambulance Corps
QMS Quartermaster Sergeant
QPM Queen's Police Medal
QRIH Queen's Royal Irish Hussars
QSA Queen's South Africa (Medal)
Queens The Queen's Regiment—Queen's Division
QVRM Queen's Volunteer Reserves Medal
R Anglian Royal Anglian Regiment
R Fus Royal Fusiliers (City of London Regiment)
R Innis Royal Inniskilling
R Signals Royal Corps of Signals
RA Royal Artillery
RAAF Royal Australian Air Force
RAC Royal Armoured Corps
RAChD Royal Army Chaplains Department
RAEC Royal Army Educational Corps
RAF Royal Air Force
RAFVR Royal Airforce Volunteer Reserve
RAMC Royal Army Medical Corps
RAOC Royal Army Ordnance Corps
RAPC Royal Army Pay Corps
RARO Regular Army Reserve of Officers
RASC Royal Army Service Corps
RAVC Royal Army Veterinary Corps
R Aux AF Royal Auxillery Airforce
RB The Rifle Brigade
RCAF Royal Canadian Air Force
RCT Royal Corps of Transport
RE Corps of Royal Engineers
RECC Reconnaissance Corps
REME Corps of Royal Electrical and Mechanical Engineers
RF Royal Fusiliers
RFA Royal Field Artillery
RFC Royal Flying Corps
Rfmn Rifleman
RFR Royal Fleet Reserve
RGJ Royal Greenjackets
RHA Royal Horse Artillery
RHF The Royal Highland Fusiliers
RHG Royal Horse Guards
RI Royal Irish Rangers (27th (Inniskilling), 83rd and 87th)
RI Regt Royal Irish Regiment
RIC Royal Irish Corps
RIF The Royal Irish Fusiliers
RM Royal Marines
RMA Royal Military Academy
RMC Royal Military College
RMLI Royal Marine Light Infantry
RMP Corps of Royal Military Police
RN Royal Navy
RNAS Royal Naval Air Services
RNF The Royal Northumberland Fusiliers
RNR Royal Naval Reserve

RNVR Royal Naval Volunteer Reserve
RNZAF Royal New Zealand Air Force
RO Radio Operator
RPC Royal Pioneer Corps
RRC Royal Red Cross (Medal)
RRF Royal Regiment of Fusiliers
RRW Royal Regiment of Wales
RS The Royal Scots (The Royal Regiment)
RSDG Royal Scots Dragoon Guards
RSF Royal Scots Fusiliers
R Sig Royal Signals
RSM Regimental Sergeant Major
RSO Regimental Supply Officer
RTR Royal Tank Regiment, Royal Armoured Corps
RUC Royal Ulster Constabulary
RUR The Royal Ulster Rifles
RVM Royal Victorian Medal
RVO Royal Victorian Order
RWF The Royal Welsh Fusiliers
RWK The Queen's Own Royal West Kent Regiment
RW Kent R Royal West Kent Regiment
S/L, S/Ldr, Sqn Ldr Squadron Leader
S/Sgt Staff Sergeant
SAAF South African Air Force
SAC Senior Aircraftman
SAS Special Air Service Regiment
SC Staff College; Staff Captain; Second in Command; Signal Corps
SF Special Forces
SG Scots Guards
SGM Sea Gallantry Medal
Sgmn Signalman
Sgt Sergeant
SI Star of India (Order)
SJAB St John Ambulance Brigade
SMIO Special Military Intelligence Officer
SMIU Special Military Intelligence Unit
Smn Seaman
SO1 Staff Officer, Grade 1
Som LI Somerset Light Infantry
SWB The South Wales Borderers
TA Territorial Army
T&AVR Territorial and Army Volunteer Reserve
TD Territorial Decoration
TEM Territorial Efficiency Medal
TF Territorial Force
TFEM Territorial Force Efficiency Medal
TFWM Territorial Force War Medal
TG Town Guard
Trg Gp Training Group
UKLF United Kingdom Land Forces
UNM United Nations Medal
UNSM United Nations Service Medal
V&A Victoria and Albert (Order)
VC Victoria Cross
VM Victory Medal
WAAF Women's Auxiliary Air Force
WAFF West Afican Frontier Force
W/C, W/Cdr, Wg Cdr Wing Commander
W&S Worcestershire & Sherwood Foresters
WEA Weapons Engineering Artificer
WG Welsh Guards
Wilts Wiltshire Regiment
WO Warrant Officer
WOI Warrant Officer Class I
WOII Warrant Officer Class II
WRAC Women's Royal Army Corps
WRAF Women's Royal Air Force

ARE YOU INTERESTED IN COLLECTING
MILITARY AND CIVILIAN RIBBONS OF
BRITISH AND FOREIGN ORDERS,
DECORATIONS AND MEDALS,
RESEARCHING THE PEOPLE BEHIND
THE AWARDS AND THE CAMPAIGNS,
THEN WHY NOT JOIN THE ORDERS AND
MEDALS RESEARCH SOCIETY AND ITS
RIBBON BRANCH.

RIBBON BRANCH

IN ADDITION TO THE ANNUAL OMRS CONVENTION,
THE RIBBON BRANCH MEETS QUARTERLY IN
LONDON, ORGANISES VISITS TO PLACES OF
INTEREST TWICE A YEAR AND MEMBERS
RECEIVE AN EXCELLENT QUARTERLY
JOURNAL "THE JIGSAW" FULL OF
INFORMATION RELATING TO
ORDERS, MEDALS, DECORATIONS
AND RIBBONS - OLD AND NEW.

IF YOU ARE INTERESTED,

WRITE TO THE
MEMBERSHIP SECRETARY:

**Mr M. SHEPHERD
6 HOLLY CLOSE,
WOODLANDS
SANDFORD,
WAREHAM
Dorset BH20 7QE**

Current regiments

As many British medals carry the names of regiments that no longer exist, we list here all of the regiments of the British Army as published in the current *Army List*. together with their predecessors, and the dates of amalgamations and redesignations The current regiment title is indicated in bold type with former names underneath in normal type. Old regimental numbers are included in brackets. The dates are of amalgamations and redesignations taken from the *Army List 2000*.

HOUSEHOLD CAVALRY
Life Guards (*June 1928*)
    1st Life Guards
    2nd Life Guards
Blues and Royals (Royal Horse Guards and 1st Dragoons) (*29 March 1969*)
    Royal Horse Guards (The Blues)
    Royal Dragoons (1st Dragoons)

ROYAL ARMOURED CORPS
1st The Queen's Dragoon Guards (1 January 1959)
    1st The King's Dragoon Guards
    Queen's Bays (2nd Dragoon Guards)
Royal Scots Dragoon Guards (Carabiniers and Greys) (*2 July 1971*)
    3rd Dragoon Guards (Prince of Wales's)
    Carabiniers (6th Dragoon Guards)
    3rd/6th Dragoon Guards
    3rd Carabiniers (Prince of Wales's Dragoon Guards)
    Royal Scots Greys (2nd Dragoons)
Royal Dragoon Guards (1 August 1992)
    4th Royal Irish Dragoon Guards
    7th Dragoon Guards (Princess Royal's)
    4th/7th Dragoon Guards
    4th/7th Royal Dragoon Guards
    5th Dragoon Guards (Princess Charlotte of Wales's)
    Inniskillings (6th Dragoon Guards)
    5th/6th Dragoons
    5th Inniskillling Dragoon Guards
    5th Royal Inniskilling Dragoon Guards
Queen's Royal Hussars (The Queen's Own & Royal Irish) (*1 September 1993*)
    3rd The King's Own Hussars
    7th The Queen's Own Hussars
    Queen's Own Hussars
    4th The Queen's Own Hussars
    8th The King's Royal Irish Hussars
    Queen's Royal Irish Hussars
9th/12th Royal Lancers (Prince of Wales's)
    (*11 September 1960*)
    9th Queen's Royal Lancers
    12th Royal Lancers (Prince of Wales's)

King's Royal Hussars (*4 December 1992*)
    10th Royal Hussars (Prince of Wales's Own)
    11th Hussars (Prince Albert's Own)
    Royal Hussars (Prince of Wales's Own)
    14th King's Hussars
    20th Hussars
    14th/20th Hussars
    14th/20th King's Hussars
Light Dragoons (*1 December 1992*)
    13th Hussars
    18th Royal Hussars (Queen Mary's Own)
    13th/18th Hussars
    13th/18th Royal Hussars (Queen Mary's Own)
    15th The King's Hussars
    19th Royal Hussars (Queen Alexandra's Own)
    15th/19th Hussars
    15th The King's Royal Hussars
    15th/19th The King's Royal Hussars
Queen's Royal Lancers (*25 June 1993*)
    16th The Queen's Lancers
    5th Royal Irish Lancers
    16th/5th Lancers
    16th/5th The Queen's Royal Lancers
    17th (Duke of Cambridge's Own Lancers)
    21st (Empress of India's) Lancers
    17th/21st Lancers
Royal Tank Regiment (*4 April 1939*)
    Heavy Branch Machine Gun Corps
    Tank Corps
    Royal Tank Corps

ARTILLERY
Royal Regiment of Artillery
    Royal Horse Artillery
    Royal Regiment of Artillery

ENGINEERS
Corps of Royal Engineers

SIGNALS
Royal Corps of Signals

GUARDS DIVISION
Grenadier Guards
Coldstream Guards
Scots Guards
Irish Guards
Welsh Guards

SCOTTISH DIVISION
Royal Scots (The Royal Regiment)(1)
Royal Highland Fusiliers (Princess Margaret's Own Glasgow and Ayrshire Regiment)(21, 71 & 74) (*20th January 1959*)
> Royal Scots Fusiliers (21)
> Highland Light Infantry (City of Glasgow Regiment)(71 & 74)

King's Own Scottish Borderers (25)
Black Watch (Royal Highland Regiment) (42 & 73)
Highlanders (Seaforth, Gordons and Camerons) (72, 75, 78, 79 & 92) (*17 September 1994*)
> Seaforth Highlanders (Ross-shire Buffs, Duke of Albany's) (72 & 78)
> Queen's Own Cameron Highlanders (79)
> Queen's Own Highlanders (Seaforth & Camerons) (72, 78 & 79)
> Gordon Highlanders

Argyll & Sutherland Highlanders (Princess Louise's) (91 & 93)

QUEEN'S DIVISION
Princess of Wales's Royal Regiment (Queen's & Royal Hampshire) (2, 3, 31, 35, 37, 50, 67, 70, 97 & 107) (*9 September 1992*)
> Queen's Royal Regiment (West Surrey) (2)
> East Surrey Regiment (31 & 70)
> Queen's Royal Surrey Regiment
> Buffs (Royal East Kent Regiment) (3)
> Queen's Own Royal West Kent Regiment (50 & 97)
> Queen's Own Buffs (The Royal Kent Regiment)
> Royal Sussex Regiment (35 & 107)
> Middlesex Regiment (Duke of Cambridge's Own) (57 & 77)
> Queen's Regiment
> Royal Hampshire Regiment (37 & 67)

Royal Regiment of Fusiliers (5, 6, 7 & 20) (*23 April 1968*)
> Royal Northumberland Fusiliers (5)
> Royal Warwickshire Fusiliers (6)
> Royal Fusiliers (City of London Regiment)(7)
> Lancashire Fusiliers (20)

Royal Anglian Regiment (9, 10, 12, 16, 17, 44, 48, 56 & 58) (*1 September 1964*)
> Bedfordshire & Hertfordshire Regiment (16)
> Essex Regiment (44 & 56)
> 3rd East Anglian Regiment (16th/44th Foot)
> Royal Norfolk Regiment (9)
> Suffolk Regiment (12)
> 1st East Anglian Regiment (Royal Norfolk & Suffolk)
> Royal Lincolnshire Regiment (10)
> Northamptonshire Regiment (48 & 58)
> 2nd East Anglian Regiment (Duchess of Gloucester's Own Royal Lincolnshire & Northamptonshire)
> Royal Leicestershire Regiment (17)

KING'S DIVISION
King's Own Royal Border Regiment (4, 34 & 55) (*1 October 1959*)
> King's Own Royal Regiment (Lancaster) (4)
> Border Regiment (34 & 55)

King's Regiment (8, 63 & 96) (*13 December 1968*)
> King's Regiment (Liverpool) (8)
> Manchester Regiment (63 & 96)
> King's Regiment (Manchester & Liverpool) (8, 63 & 96)

Prince of Wales's Own Regiment of Yorkshire (14 & 15) (*24 April 1958*)
> West Yorkshire (Prince of Wales's Own)(14)
> East Yorkshire Regiment (Duke of York's Own)(15)

Green Howards (Alexandra, Princess of Wales's Own Yorkshire Regiment) (19)
Queen's Lancashire Regiment (30, 40, 47, 59 81 & 82) (*25 March 1970*)
> East Lancashire Regiment (30 & 59)
> South Lancashire Regiment (The Prince of Wales's Volunteers) (40 & 82)
> Lancashire Regiment (Prince of Wales's Volunteers)
> Loyal Regiment (North Lancashire) (47 & 48)

Duke of Wellington's Regiment (West Riding) (33 & 76) (*Later no date*)
> Duke of Wellington's Regiment (33)
> 76th Regiment of Foot
> Halifax Regiment

PRINCE OF WALES'S DIVISION
Devon & Dorset Regiment (11, 39, & 54) (*17 May 1958*)
> Devon Regiment (11)
> Dorset Regiment (39 & 54)

Cheshire Regiment (22)
Royal Welsh Fusiliers (23)
Royal Regiment of Wales (24th/41st Foot)
> South Wales Borderers (24)
> Welch Regiment (41 & 69)

Royal Gloucestershire, Wiltshire & Berkshire Regiment (28, 49, 61, 62, 66 & 99) (*27 April 1994*)
> Wiltshire Regiment (Duke of Edinburgh's) (62 & 99)
> Royal Berkshire Regiment (Princess Charlotte of Wales's) (49 & 66)
> Duke of Edinburgh's Royal Regiment (Berkshire and Wiltshire)
> Gloucestershire Regiment (28 & 61)

Worcestershire & Sherwood Foresters Regiment (29th/45th Foot) (*28 February 1970*)
> Worcestershire Regiment (29 & 36)
> Sherwood Foresters (Nottingham & Derbyshire Regiment) (45 & 95)

Staffordshire Regiment (The Prince of Wales's)(38, 64, 80 & 98) (*31 January 1959*)
> South Staffordshire Regiment (38 & 80)
> North Staffordshire Regiment (Prince of Wales's) (64 & 98)

LIGHT DIVISION
Light Infantry (13, 32, 46, 51, 53, 68, 85, 105 & 106) (*10 July 1968*)
> Duke of Cornwall's Light Infantry (32 & 46)
> Somerset Light Infantry (Prince Albert's)(13)

LIGHT DIVISION *continued*

 Somerset & Cornwall Light Infantry (13, 32 & 46)
 King's Own Yorkshire Light Infantry (51 & 105)
 King's Shropshire Light Infantry (53 & 85)
 Durham Light Infantry (68 & 106)

Royal Green Jackets (43rd & 52nd, King's Royal Rifle Corps, Rifle Brigade) (*1 January 1966*)
 Oxfordshire & Buckinghamshire Light Infantry (43 & 52)
 1st Green Jackets (43 & 52)
 King's Royal Rifle Corps (60)
 2nd Green Jackets (King's Royal Rifle Corps)
 Rifle Brigade (Prince Consort's Own)
 3rd Green Jackets (The Rifle Brigade)

INFANTRY NOT INCLUDED IN THE DIVISIONS
Royal Irish Regiment (27th (Inniskilling), 83rd, 87th and Ulster Defence Regiment)
 Royal Inniskilling Fusiliers (27 & 108)
 Royal Ulster Rifles (83 & 86)
 Royal Irish Rifles (83 & 86)
 Royal Irish Fusiliers (Princess Victoria's) (87 & 89)
 Ulster Defence Regiment
 Royal Irish Rangers
Parachute Regiment

GURKHA BRIGADE
Royal Gurkha Rifles (*1 July 1994*)+
 2nd King Edward VII's Own Gurkha Rifles (The Sirmoor Rifles)
 6th Queen Elizabeth's Own Gurkha Rifles
 7th Duke of Edinburgh's Own Gurkha Rifles
 10th Princess Mary's Own Gurkha Rifles
 Queen's Gurkha Engineers
 Queen's Gurkha Signals
 Queen's Own Gurkha Transport Regiment

SPECIAL AIR SERVICE
Special Air Service Regiment

ARMY AIR CORPS
Army Air Corps
 Glider Pilot Regiment

OTHER CORPS
Royal Army Chaplains' Department
Royal Logistic Corps
 Royal Army Service Corps
 Royal Corps of Transport
 Royal Army Ordnance Corps
 Royal Pioneer Corps
Royal Army Medical Corps
Royal Electrical & Mechanical Engineers
Adjutant General's Corps
Adjutant General's Corps (Staff and Personnel Support Branch)
 Royal Army Pay Corps
 Women's Royal Army Corps (less those to Regiments)
 Royal Army Ordnance Corps Staff Clerks
 Regimental Clerks

Adjutant General's Corps (Provost Branch) (RMP) (MPS)
 Royal Military Police
 Military Provost Staff Corps
 Military Provost Guard Service
Adjutant General's Corps (Education & Training Service Branch)
 Royal Army Education Corps
Adjutant General's Corps (Army Legal Branch)
 Army Legal Corps
Royal Army Veterinary Corps
Small Arms School Corps
Royal Army Dental Corps
Intelligence Corps
Army Physical Training Corps
Queen Alexandra's Army Nursing Corps
 Queen Alexandra's Imperial Military Nursing Service
Corps of Army Music

TERRITORIAL ARMY
Royal Monmouth Royal Engineers (Militia)
Honourable Artillery Company

YEOMANRY OF THE ROYAL ARMOURED CORPS
Royal Yeomanry
 Royal Wiltshire Yeomanry (Prince of Wales's Own)
 Sherwood Rangers Yeomanry
 Leicestershire and Derbyshire (Prince Albert's Own) Yeomanry
 Kent and City of London Yeomanry (Sharpshooters)
 Inns of Court and City Yeomanry
 Westminster Dragoons (2nd City of London Yeomanry)
Royal Wessex Yeomanry
 Royal Wiltshire Yeomanry (Prince of Wales's Own)
 Royal Gloucestershire Hussars.
 Royal Devon Yeomanry
 Dorset Yeomanry
Royal Mercian and Lancaster Yeomanry
 Queen's Own Warwickshire and Worcestershire Yeomanry
 Staffordshire Yeomanry (Queen's Own Royal Regiment)
 Shropshire Yeomanry
 Cheshire Yeomanry (Earl of Chester's)
 Duke of Lancaster's Own Yeomanry (Royal Tank Regiment)
Queen's Own Yeomanry
 Queen's Own Yorkshire Yeomanry
 Ayrshire Yeomanry (Earl of Carrick's Own)
 Northumberland Hussars
 Fife and Forfar Yeomanry (Scottish Horse)
 North Irish Horse

ARTILLERY
Royal Regiment of Artillery

ENGINEERS
Corps of Royal Engineers
Engineer and Logistic Staff Corps Royal Engineers (Volunteers)

SIGNALS
Royal Corps of Signals

SCOTTISH DIVISION
52nd Lowland Regiment
51st Highland Regiment

QUEEN'S DIVISION
3rd (Volunteer) Battalion The Princess of Wales's
    Royal Regiment (Queen's & Royal Hampshire
London Regiment
East of England Regiment

KING'S DIVISION
Lancaster and Cumbrian Volunteers
Tyne-Tees Regiment
East and West Riding Regiment

PRINCE OF WALES'S DIVISION
West Midlands Regiment
Kings and Cheshire Regiment
Royal Welsh Regiment

LIGHT DIVISION
Royal Rifle Volunteers
Rifle Volunteers
4th/5th Battalion The Royal Irish Rangers
    (Volunteers)
4th (Volunteer) Battalion The Parachute Regiment

ARMY AIR CORPS
7th Regiment Army Air Corps (Volunteers)

OTHER CORPS
Royal Army Chaplains' Department
Royal Logistic Corps
Royal Army Medical Corps
Royal Electrical & Mechanical Engineers

Adjutant General's Corps (Staff and Personnel
    Support Branch)
Adjutant General's Corps (Army Legal Branch)
Adjutant General's Corps (Education Service
    Branch)
Adjutant General's Corps (RMP)
Adjutant General's Corps (MPS)
Royal Army Veterinary Corps
Army Physical Training Corps
Small Arms School Corps
Royal Army Dental Corps
Intelligence Corps
Queen Alexandra's Army Nursing Corps
Officer Training Corps
Royal Gibraltar Regiment

SOME DISBANDED REGIMENTS WITH NO KNOWN "PARENT"
22nd Dragoons
23rd Hussars
24th Lancers
25th Dragoons
26th Hussars
27th Lancers
Reconnaissance Regiment
Royal Irish Regiment (18)
Cameronians (Scottish Rifles) (26 &90)
York and Lancaster Regiment (65)
Connaught Rangers (88 & 94)
Prince of Wales's Leinster Regiment (Royal
    Canadians) (100 & 109)
Royal Munster Fusiliers (101 & 104)
Royal Dublin Fusiliers (102 & 103
Royal Guernsey Light Infantry
Army Cyclist Corps
Machine Gun Corps
Army Remount Service
Cyprus Regiment

Researching your medals

The fact that many British medals are named enables the serious collector to engage in researching both the life and service history of the recipient as well as being able to learn about the history of the regiment/ship/unit or whatever with which he served. There is no easy or definitive guide to the range of research materials that are available, nor to the range of information likely to be found. The sort of information available varies greatly depending on whether the recipient was an officer or other rank, the service and unit with which he served, and the period during which he served. The experience and perseverance of the researcher can also affect the outcome. For those who are new to research, or who live a long way from the original sources, it may be wise to employ a professional researcher, at least initially. The PRO keeps a list of independent researchers who undertake this kind of work

When researching a medal and its recipient, experienced collectors regularly refer to a mixture of manuscript and printed sources:

Manuscript Sources

The Public Record Office (PRO, Ruskin Avenue, Kew, Surrey TW9 4DU) and the Oriental & India Office Collections (OIOC, British Library, 96 Euston Road, London NW1 2DB) are the two major depositories of official records of interest to the medal collector. Generally speaking the collector of medals to the British Armed Services will find the PRO records essential to their enquiries, whilst anyone interest in the Indian Army and Navy (formerly the armed services of the Honourable East India Company), also the participation of British Forces in Indian campaigns, will find the OIOC to be an essential source of information. County Record Offices, National Libraries and Museums, and also Regimental Museums can also have important holdings of manuscript records.

A first visit to the PRO and the OIOC can be daunting. The range of records held by both Record Offices is also awe-inspiring once research has gone beyond consulting medal rolls and service papers.

Whilst there is no substitute for *experience* in learning successfully to branch out from the main stream of records, it is essential to be well prepared. It is important to have some idea of where to start looking and to realise the scope and limitations of the documents—it should be noted that the PRO is subject to the standard 30 year closure rule for records, with many personal records being closed for longer periods. A great deal of time can be spent in simply locating the relevant references. To help you be more informed and to help eliminate time-wasting there are a number of important guides available that will aid in the location of the most relevant documents:

Cox, J. and Padfield, T., *Tracing your Ancestors in the Public Record Office* (1983).
Farrington, A., *Guide to the Records of the India Office Military Department* (1981).

Hamilton-Edwards, Gerald, *In Search of Army Ancestry* (1977).
Holding, N., *The Location of British Army Records: A National Directory of World War I Sources* (1984).
Holding, N., *World War I Army Ancestry* (1982).
Rodger, N.A.M., *Naval Records for Genealogists* (1988).

In addition it is worth noting that
1.   The Public Record Office produces a range of leaflets which provide useful information about particular classes of records—records relating to military, naval and air services are particularly well-covered. The leaflets are free to visitors to the PRO.
2.   The Mormons have published a wide range of guides to genealogical research which cover subjects of interest to medal/military researchers.
3.   The National Army Museum occasionally holds a study day on the subject of military research.
4.   New information is becoming available all the time and in new forms: for example, the PRO has been producing a video on genealogical research.

Additionally, it is important to be aware that new documents are released periodically to public access. Probably the most important in recent years are those at the Public Record Office relating to World War I. Although the PRO and other record offices produce regular leaflets and guides to new records, MEDAL NEWS now includes a regular feature which enables all collectors to remain abreast of the many records as they become available.

Medal Entitlement/Verification

Most collectors start their research by checking with the campaign medal roll (if available) that the recipient is indeed entitled to the medal and any clasps. It is a logical point at which to begin. This is often regarded as a simple, routine procedure, but for the unwary there are pitfalls and complications. The following points should always be borne in mind:

1.   Printed medal rolls will always contain errors in transcription, thus any discrepancies between a medal and the roll should, whenever possible, be checked

back with the original manuscript roll. The more complex the original roll, the more transcription errors are likely to occur (for example, the claimaints' lists for the Naval General Service Medal 1793-1840 and even the Military General Service Medal 1793-1814 are good examples of rolls where difficulties are likely to arise).

2. Some rolls have not survived—for example that for the Gwalior Campaign 1843. In such instances prize or bhatta rolls may exist at either the Public Record Office or the India Office. The inclusion of a recipient's name will at least indicate that he was most likely "entitled" to a medal and / or clasp (prize rolls indicate the share of money—realised from the loot captured in an action and then sold—allocated to each participant; bhatta is an extra allowance of pay made for field service).

3. Some medal rolls are incomplete, as with some of the regimental rolls for the Crimea Medal 1854–56.

4. With some campaign medal rolls, supplementary lists and late claimants' documentation have not survived.

5. Some medal rolls are difficult to search and therefore one has to take time in understanding the background to the documents one is looking at—the various lists of recipients for the Military General Service Medal 1794–1814 is a case in point.

It is important to note that the establishment of a recipient's entitlement is not the same thing as verifying a medal. Verification also requires the numismatic knowledge to know that the medal and clasps appear genuine. Where entitlement cannot be confirmed from the medal rolls, some collectors may be happy to rely on their numismatic knowledge to assure themselves that a medal is "genuine".

Published Sources

The published literature on medals is far-reaching and diverse, ranging from simply-produced booklets to detailed studies published in several volumes. A full bibliography of medallic and related works would in itself fill several volumes, particularly if fully cross-referenced.

The references which follow seek to provide a useful list of publications which either relate to orders, decorations and medals in general or to specific items in particular; the list includes medal rolls and casualty lists. No attempt has been made to include journal articles, as this would be an immense task; however a list of useful periodicals, some of which publish regular indexes, appears at the end.

Suggestions for other works that might be considered for inclusion in the next Yearbook *are welcomed.*

Most collectors seek to build up a solid library which reflects their main interests, but inevitably there are always books that have to be consulted elsewhere. Major libraries and national museums, such as the British Museum Library, the National Army Museum, the Imperial War Museum, the Hendon Royal Air Force Museum, the Greenwich Maritime Museum, and the Portsmouth Naval Musuem have extensive holdings of relevant material which can be consulted on the premises. City and County Reference Libraries are important for collectors who rarely visit London. Some Regimental

Museums have libraries attached. Most libraries of any size will have a subject index to their collection of books (and sometimes manuscripts and photographs).

ORDERS, DECORATIONS AND MEDALS

GENERAL WORKS
(listed in alphabetical order by author)

Alexander, E. G. M., Barron, G. K. B. and Bateman, A. J., *South African Orders, Decorations and Medals* (1986).

Blatherwick, Surg. Cmdr. F. J., *Canadian Orders, Decorations and Medals* (4th edition, 1994).

Brine, F., *British Decorations from 1348 to the Present Time, Together with Those Given by Allies* (1880).

Burke, J. B., *The Book of Orders of Knighthood and Decorations of Honour of All Nations* (1858).

Central Office of Information, *Honours and Titles*. Part of the Aspects of Britain series.

Downey, M., *The Standard Catalogue of Orders, Decorations and Medals Awarded to Australians* (1971).

Dymond, Steve, *Researching British Military Medals, a Practical Guide* (1999).

Eaton, Col. Hon. H.F. (later Lord Cheylesmore)., *Naval and Military Medals* (1897).

Elvin, C.N., *A Handbook of the Orders of Chivalry, War Medals and Crosses with Their Clasps and Ribbons and Other Decorations* (1892).

Floyd., J. B. (ed), *United States Decorations Awarded to the Armed Forces of the British Empire in World War II, Part I* (1997).

Gibson, J.H., *British War Medals and Other Decorations, Military and Naval* (1866).

Gibson, J.H., *British Military and Naval Medals and Decorations* (1880).

Gordon, Major L.L., *British Orders and Awards* (1959).

Hall, D.C. (in association with Wingate, C.), *British Orders, Decorations and Medals* (1973).

Hastings, Irwin D., *War Medals and Decorations* (1910).

Hieronymussen, Paul, *Orders, Medals and Decorations of Britain and Europe* (1967).

Hayward, J. B. & Son (pub.) *Honours and Awards of the Army, Navy and Air Force 1914-20* (1979).

Irwin, Ross W. , *War Medals and Decorations of Canada* (1969).

Jocelyn, A., *Awards of Honour* (1956).

Johnson, S. C., *Medals of our Fighting Men* (1916).

Johnson, S. C., *The Medal Collector* (1921).

Johnson, S. C., *Everybodys Medals: Including Medals, Decorations, Honours and Orders* (1914).

Joslin, E., C., *The Observers Book of British Awards and Medals* (1974).

Letcher, Owen., *Medals and Decorations of the British Commonwealth of Nations - Medaljes en Dekorasies van de Britse Gemenebes van Nasies* (1941).

Litherland, A. R. and Simpkin, B. T., *Spink's Standard Catalogue of British Orders, Decorations and Medals* (1990).

McClenaghan, Tony, *Indian Princely Medals: A Record of the Orders, Decorations and Medals of the Indian Princely States* (1997).

Maton, Michael, *The National Honours & Awards of Australia* (1995).

Mayo, J. H., *Medals and Decorations of the British Army and Navy* (1897).

Mericka, V., *Book of Orders and Decorations* (1975).

Monick, S., *South African Military Awards 1912-1987* (1988).

Monick, S., *Awards of the South African Uniformed Public Services 1922-1987* (1988).

Narbeth, Colin, *Collecting Military Medals* (1971).

Nicolas, N.H., *History of the Orders of Knighthood of the British Empire; of the Order of the Guelphs of Hanover, and of the Medals, Clasps and Crosses, Conferred for Naval and Military Services* (1842).

Oldham, G. P. and Delahunt, B., *Orders, Decorations and Medals Awarded to New Zealanders.* (1991).

Pamm, Anthony M., *Honours and Rewards of the British Empire and Commonwealth*, 2 vols. (1996).

Payne, A.A., *A Handbook of British and Foreign Orders, War Medals and Decorations awarded to the Army and Navy* (1911).

Purves, A.A., *Collecting Medals and Decorations* (1968).

Purves, A.A., *The Medals, Decorations and Orders of the Great War 1914-18* (1975).

Purves, A.A., *The Medals, Decorations and Orders of World War II 1939-45* (1986).

Purves, Alec A., *Orders, Decorations and Medals, a Select Bibliography* (1958).

Seedie's Roll of Naval Honours & Awards 1939-1959.

Seedie's List of Submarine Awards for World War II.

Seedie's List of Fleet Air Arm Awards 1939–1969.

Seedie's List of Coastal Forces Awards for World War II.

Seedie's List of Awards to the Merchant Navy for World War II (1997).

Steward, W.A., *War Medals and Their History* (1915).

Steward, W.A., *The ABC of War Medals and Decorations* (1918).

Tancred, G., *Historical Record of Medals and Honorary Distinctions* (1891).

Taprell-Dorling, Captain H. (ed. Alec A. Purves), *Ribbons and Medals* (1983).

Tinson, Lt-Col. Ashley R., *"Medals Will Be Worn", Wearing Medals Past and Present 1844–1999* (1999).

ORDERS
(listed by the Order of Precedence)
GENERAL
CB Printers Group (Pubr)., *Orders of Chivalry and Gallantry Awards* (1963).

De la Bere, Sir I. *The Queen's Orders of Chivalry* (1961).

Harbord, R.E., *Supplement to the Royal Family Orders, Badges of Office, Royal Household Medals and Souvenirs* (1954)

Hunter, John., *A Concise Description of the Insignia of the Orders of British Knighthood*

James, G.P.L., *The Royal Family Orders, Badges of Office, Royal Household Medals and Souvenirs* (1951)

Neville, D.G. *A History of the Early Orders of Knighthood and Chivalry.*

Patterson, Stephen, *Royal Insignia* (1996).

Risk, J.C., *British Orders and Decorations* (1973).

ORDER OF THE GARTER
Anstis, J., *The Register of the Most Noble Order of the Garter* (1724).

Ashmole, E., *The Institution, Laws and Ceremonies of the Most Noble Order of the Garter* (1672).

Ashmole, E., *History of the Most Noble Order of the Garter* (1715).

Beltz, G.F., *Memorials of the Most Noble Order of the Garter* (1839).

Buswell, J., *An Historical Account of the Knights of the Most Noble Order of the Garter* (1757).

Dawson, T., *Memoirs of St George The English Patron: And of the Most Noble Order of the Garter* (1714).

Fellowes, Rev. E.H., *The Knights of the Garter 1348-1939* (1939).

Harrison, A.P., *Order of the Garter: Armorial Registry of the Sovereign and the Knights of the Most Noble Order of the Garter—Their Names, Titles, Election, Installment and Demise* (1845).

Heylyn, P., *The History of that Most Famous Saint and Soldier of Christ Jesus: St George of Cappadocia...The Institution of the Most Noble Order of St George, named The Garter. A Catalogue of all the Knights Thereof Until this Present* (1631).

Hope, W.H. St J., *The Stall Plates of the Knights of the Order of the Garter 1348-1485* (1901).

Leake, S.M., *The Statutes of the Most Noble Order of The Garter* (1766).

ORDER OF THE THISTLE
Innes of Learney, Sir T., *The Foundation of the Most Ancient and Most Noble Order of the Thistle* (1959).

Lyon King of Arms, Lord, and Warrack, J., *The Knights of the Most Ancient and Most Noble Order of the Thistle* (1911).

ORDER OF ST PATRICK
Galloway, Peter, *The Order of St Patrick* (1983).

Galloway, Peter, *The Most Illustrious Order* (1996).

Grierson, G.A. & Grierson, J.F., *Statutes and Ordinances of the Most Illustrious Order of St. Patrick* (1831).

ORDER OF THE BATH
Anstis, J., *Observations Introductory to an Historical Essay Upon the Knighthood of the Bath* (1725).

Perkins, Canon J., *The Most Honourable Order of the Bath* (1913).

Risk, J.C., *The History of the Order of the Bath and its Insignia* (1982).

ORDER OF ST MICHAEL AND ST GEORGE
Abela, A.E., *The Order of St Michael and St George in Malta* (1988).

ROYAL VICTORIAN ORDER
Galloway, P., Martin, S. and Stanley, D., *Royal Service. Volume I* (1996).

Malloch, R.J., *The Royal Victorian Chain and Other Honors of the Sovereign*, (The Orders and Medals Society of America 1990).

Royal Victorian Order: Statutes and Lists of Members (1930).

ORDER OF THE BRITISH EMPIRE
Burke, *Handbook to the Order of the British Empire* (1921).

Galloway, Peter, *The Order of the British Empire* (1996).

Thorpe, A. Winton (ed.), *Burke's Handbook to the Most Excellent Order of the British Empire* (1921).

ORDER OF ST JOHN OF JERUSALEM
Bedford, W.K.R., and Holbeche, R., *The Order of the Hospital of St John of Jerusalem* (1902).

Fincham, H.W., *The Order of the Hospital of St John of Jerusalem and its Grand Priory of England* (1915).

The Grand Priory in the British Realm of the Venerable Order of the Hospital of St John of Jerusalem, *Roll of the Order 1931; Centenary Issue* (1936).

King, Col. E.J., *The Knights of St John in England* (1924).

King, Col. E.J., *The Knights of St John in the British Empire,*

411

Being the Official History of the British Order of the Hospital of St John of Jerusalem (1934).

Luke, Sir H., *An Examination of Certain Claims to be an Order of St John* (1965).

Puddy, E., *A Short History of the Order of the Hospital of St John of Jerusalem in Norfolk* (1961).

Renwick, E.D., *A Short History of the Order of St John* (1959).

Tozer, C.W., *The Insignia and Medals of the Grand Priory of the Most Venerable Order of the Hospital of St John of Jerusalem* (1975).

DECORATIONS
(listed in alphabetical order by name of medal)

GENERAL

Abbott, P.E. and Tamplin, J.M.A., *British Gallantry Awards* (1981).

Abela, A.E., *Maltas George Cross and War Gallantry Awards.*

Bles, G (pub.) *Naval Honours and Awards 1939-1940* (1942).

Brown, G.A., *Commando Gallantry Awards of World War II.*

Campbell, G.L., *Royal Flying Corps (Military Wing)— Honours, Awards and Casualties 1914-17* (1917).

Chatterton-Dickson, W.W.F., *Seedie's List of Coastal Forces Awards for World War II.*

Chatterton-Dickson, W.W.F., *Seedies List of Fleet Air Arm Awards 1939-1969.*

Chatterton-Dickson, W.W.F., *Seedie's Roll of Naval Honours & Awards 1939-59* (1990).

Clarke, John D., *Gallantry Medals and Awards of the World* (1993).

Escott, Beryl, *20th Century Women of Courage* (1999).

Greenhill (pub.) *South African Honours and Awards 1899-1902.*

Hayward J. B. & Son (pub.) *Honours & Awards to the Indian Army 1914-21* (1992).

Hayward J. B. & Son (pub.) *Honours & Awards of the Old Contemptibles* (1992).

Housley, C., *British Gallantry Awards to Sherwood Foresters* (1999).

Hypher, P.P., *Deeds of Valour Performed by Indian Officers and Soldiers During the Period from 1860 to 1925* (1927).

Jacob, J.R., *Court Jewellers of the World* (1978).

McInness, I. and Webb, J.V., *Contemptible Little Flying Corps* (1991).

Midland (pub.) *Tank Corps Honours & Awards 1916-1919* (1982).

O'Shea, P., *An Unknown Few: The Story of Those Holders of the George Cross, the Empire Gallantry Medal, and the Albert Medals Associated with New Zealand.*

Pamm, Anthony N., *Honours and Rewards in the British Empire* (1995) (2 vols.).

Royal Flying Corps: *Casualties and Honours During the War of 1914-17* (1987).

Stanistreet, A. *'Gainst All Disaster: Above and Beyond the Call of Duty* (1986).

Wilson, Sir A., and McEwen, Capt. J.H.F., *Gallantry* (1939).

ALBERT MEDAL

Henderson, D.V., *For Heroic Endeavour* (1988).

CHIEFS' MEDALS

Jamieson, A.M., *Indian Chief Medals and Medals to African and Other Chiefs* (1936).

CONSPICUOUS GALLANTRY MEDAL

Cooper, A.W., *In Action With The Enemy: The Holders of the Conspicuous Gallantry Medal (Flying).*

Brown, G. and Penhall, R., *Conspicuous Gallantry Medal* (1977).

McDermott, P., *For Conspicuous Gallantry.*

DISTINGUISHED CONDUCT MEDAL

Abbott, P.E., *The Distinguished Conduct Medal 1855-1909* (1987).

Ashton, M., *The Canadian Medal Rolls—Distingushed Conduct and Military Medal (1939-45 & 1950-53).*

Brown, George A., *For Distinguished Conduct in the Field: The Register of the DCM 1939-92* (1993).

Mackinlay, Gordon, *True Courage: The Distinguished Conduct Medal to Australians 1939-1972* (1993).

McDermott, P., *For Distinguished Conduct in the Field: The Register of the DCM 1920-92* (1994).

Polaschek, A.J., *The Complete New Zealand Distinguished Conduct Medal* (1978).

Walker, R.W., *The Distinguished Conduct Medal 1914-20 (1981).*

DISTINGUISHED CONDUCT MEDAL (AFRICAN)

Arnold J., *The African DCM to the King's African Rifles and the West African Frontier Force* (1998).

DISTINGUISHED FLYING CROSS

Carter, N. and C., *The Distinguished Flying Cross and How it was Won 1918–1995,* 2 vols. (1998).

DISTINGUISHED FLYING MEDAL

Ashton, M., *The Canadian Medal Rolls—Distinguished Flying Medal (1939-1945).*

Tavender, Ian, *The Distinguished Flying Medal: A Record of Courage* (1990).

Tavender, Ian, *The DFM Registers for the Second World War* (1999).

DISTINGUISHED SERVICE CROSS

Fevyer, W. H., *Distinguished Service Cross 1901-1938* (1990).

Witte, R. C., *Fringes of the Fleet and the Distinguished Service Cross* (1997).

DISTINGUISHED SERVICE MEDAL

Fevyer, W.H., *The Distinguished Service Medal, 1914–1920* (1982).

Fevyer, W.H., *The Distinguished Service Medal, 1939–1946* (1981).

DISTINGUISHED SERVICE ORDER

Creagh, General Sir O'Moore and Humphris, H.M., *The D.S.O.: A Complete Record of Recipients* (1978).

EDWARD MEDAL

Henderson, D.V., *For Heroic Endeavour* (1988).

EMPIRE GALLANTRY MEDAL

Henderson, D.V., *For Heroic Endeavour* (1988).

GEORGE CROSS

Bisset, Lieut. Colonel Ian, *The George Cross* (1961).

Campion, Roger, *The Call of Duty* (1997).

Dowling, Dr C., *The Victoria Cross and George Cross* (1970).

Hare-Scott, K., *For Gallantry—The George Cross* (1951).

Smyth, Sir J., *The Story of the George Cross* (1968).

This England (pub.), *The Register of the George Cross* (1990).

GEORGE MEDAL

Fevyer, W.H., *The George Medal*.

Henderson, D.V., *Dragons Can Be Defeated* (1984).

Henderson, D.V., *Fashioned into a Bow* (1995).

INDIAN ORDER OF MERIT

Hypher, P.P., *Deeds of Valour of the Indian Soldier Which Won the Indian Order of Merit During the Period From 1837 to 1859* (1925).

Peterson, C., *Unparalleled Danger Unsurpassed Courage: Recipients of the Indian Order of Merit in the Second World War* (1997).

KING'S POLICE MDAL

Farmery, J. P., *Police Gallantry: The King's Police Medal, The King's Police and Fire Service Medal and the Queen's Police Medal for Gallantry 1909–1979* (1995).

MILITARY MEDAL

Abbink, H. and C., *The Military Medal: Canadian Recipients 1916-1922*.

Ashton, M., *The Canadian Medal Rolls—Distingushed Conduct and Military Medal (1939-45 & 1950-53)*.

Bate, Chris and Smith, Martin, *For Bravery in the Field: Recipients of the Military Medal 1919-1939, 1939-1945* (1991).

VICTORIA CROSS

Biggs, M., *The Story of Gurkha VCs*.

Clayton, Ann, *Chavasse, Double VC* (1992).

Clayton Ann, *Martin-Leake, Double VC* (1995).

Cooksley, Peter, *The Air VCs* (1998).

Creagh, General Sir O'Moore and Humphris, H.M., *The Victoria Cross 1856-1920* (1993).

Crook, M.J., *The Evolution of the Victoria Cross* (1975).

Dowling, Dr C., *The Victoria Cross and George Cross* (1970).

Gerard, M., *The Victoria Cross* (1892).

Hare-Scott, K., *For Valour—The Victoria Cross* (1949).

Harvey, David, *Monuments to Courage* (1999).

Haydon, A.L., *The Book of the Victoria Cross* (1906).

Laffin, John, *British VCs of World War 2: A Study in Heroism* (1997).

Lee, P.H., *The Victoria Cross* (1912).

Lennox, Lord W., *The Victoria Cross: The Rewarded and Their Services* (1857).

Leyland, R., *For Valour: The Story of the Victoria Cross*.

Little, M.G., *The Royal Marines Victoria Crosses*.

Muddock, J.E., *For Valor—the Victoria Cross 1856-1895* (1895).

Mundell, F., *Stories of the Victoria Cross* (1890).

Mulholland, J. and Jordan, A., *Victoria Cross Bibliography* (1999).

Napier, Gerald, *The Sapper VCs* (1998).

O'Byrne, R.W., *The Victoria Cross* (1865).

Pillinger, D. and Staunton, A., *Victoria Cross Locator* (1991).

Parry, D.H., *Britain's Roll of Glory, or the Victoria Cross, Its Heroes and Their Valour* (1895)

Parry, D.H., *The Victoria Cross, Its Heroes and Their Valour* (1913).

RAMC Historical Museum, *The Medical Victoria Crosses*.

Sarkar, D., *Guards VC: Blitzkrieg 1940* (1999).

Smyth, Brig. Sir John, *The Story of the Victoria Cross* (1964).

Snelling, Stephen, *VCs of the First World War: Gallipoli* (1995).

Stewart, Lt.Col.Rupert., *The Victoria Cross: The Empire's Roll of Valour* (1916).

This England (pub.), *Register of the Victoria Cross* (1988).

Toomey, T.E., *The Victoria Cross and How Won 1854-1889* (1889).

Toomey, T.E., *Heroes of the Victoria Cross* (1895).

Turner, J.F., *VCs of the Air* (1961).

Turner, J.F., *VCs of the Army 1939-51* (1962).

Turner, J.F., *VCs of the Royal Navy* (1956).

Uys, Ian., *Victoria Crosses of the Anglo-Boer War* (2000).

Wilkins, P.A., *The History of the Victoria Cross* (1904).

CAMPAIGN MEDALS
(listed in chronological order by date of campaign medal)

GENERAL

Carter, T. and Long, W.H., *War Medals of the British Army 1650-1891* (1972).

Dickson, Bill Chatterton, *Seedie's List of Awards to the Merchant Navy for World War II* (1997).

Douglas-Morris, Captain K.J., *Naval Medals 1793-1856* (1987).

Douglas-Morris, Capt K.J. *Naval Medals Vol. II 1856-1880*.

Johnson, Derek E., *War Medals* (1971).

Joslin, E.C., Litherland, A.R. and Simpkin, B.T., *British Battles and Medals* (1988).

Kerr, Major W.J.W., *Notes on War Medals 1794-1840* (1948).

Laffin, J., *British Campaign Medals*.

Long, W.H., *Medals of the British Navy* (1895).

Poulsom, Major N.W.A., *Catalogue of Campaign and Independence Medals Issued During the Twentieth Century to the British Army* (1969).

Power, J.R., *Identification Data on British War Medals and Their Interpretation* (1962).

Power, J.R., *Addenda and Corrigenda to Identification Data on British War Medals and their Interpretation* (1963).

Purves, A.A., *Some Notes on War Medals for the Collector* (1958).

Steward, W., Augustus, *War Medals and their History* (1915).

Vernon S.B., *Collector's Guide to Orders, Medals and Decorations* (With Valuations) (1990).

Williams, R.D. *Medals to Australians: with Valuations*.

MILITARY GENERAL SERVICE MEDAL 1793-1814

Caldwell, G.J., Cooper, R.B.E., *Rifle Green in the Peninsula, Vol. 1* (1998).

Foster, Col. Kingsley O.N., *The Military General Service Medal Roll 1793-1814* (1947).

Mullen, A.L.T., *The Military General Service Medal 1793-1814*.

Newnham, A.J., *The Peninsula Medal Roll 1793-1814* (privately produced).

Vigors, Lieutenant Colonel D.D. and Macfarlane, Lieutenant Colonel A.M., *The Three Great Retrospective Medals 1793-1840 Awarded to Artillerymen* (1986).

Wilson, B., *Canadian Recipients of the MGS, Egypt (1882-9) and NW Canada Medals*.

NAVAL GENERAL SERVICE MEDAL 1793-1840

Douglas-Morris, Captain K.J., *The Naval General Service Medal Roll, 1793-1840* (1982).

Hailes, Colonel D.A., *Naval General Service Medal Roll 1793-1840* (privately produced).

MacKenzie, Col R.H., *The Trafalgar Roll: The Ships and the Officers* (1989).

Message, C.W., *Alphabetical Naval General Service Medal Roll 1793-1840* (1995).

Newnham A.J., *Naval General Service Medal Roll 1793-1840* (privately produced).

O'Byrne, William, *Naval Biographical Dictionary* (2 vols, 1849).

Roberts, *The Trafalgar Roll* (1995).

Vigors, Lieutenant Colonel D.D. and Macfarlane, Lieutenant Colonel A.M., *The Three Great Retrospective Medals 1793-1840 Awarded to Artillerymen* (1986).

ARMY OF INDIA MEDAL 1799-1826

Gould, R.W. and Douglas-Morris, Captain K.J., *The Army of India Medal Roll 1799-1826* (1974).

Vigors, Lieutenant Colonel D.D. and Macfarlane, Lieutenant Colonel A.M., *The Three Great Retrospective Medals 1793-1840 Awarded to Artillerymen* (1986).

WATERLOO MEDAL

Caldwell, G.J., Cooper, R.B.E., *Rifle Green at Waterloo* (1990).

Dalton, C., *The Waterloo Roll Call* (1904).

Haythornthwaite, P. J., *Waterloo Men* (2000).

Lagden, A. and Sly, J., *The 2/73rd at Waterloo: Including a Roll of All Ranks Present, with Biographical Notes* (1998).

INDIAN CAMPAIGN MEDALS

Biddulph, Major H., *Early Indian Campaigns and the Decorations Awarded for Them* (1913).

Cook, H. C. B., *The Sikh Wars 1845-6, 1848-9* (1975).

Stone, A.G., *The First Afghan War 1839-1842 and Its Medals* (1967).

Stiles, Richard G. M., *The Story of the India General Service Medal 1908-35* (1996).

SOUTH AFRICA MEDAL 1835-53

Everson, Gordon R., *The South Africa 1853 Medal Roll* (1978).

Sole, T.E., *The Military Casualties of south Africa: Vol 1 1834-1878*.

NEW ZEALAND MEDAL 1845-66

Cowan, J., *The New Zealand Wars* (2 volumes) (1969).

Gudgeon, T.W., *Heroes of New Zealand and Maori History of the War* (1887).

Longley, H.G., *The New Zealand Wars 1845-1866* (1967).

Stowers, R., *The New Zealand Medal to Colonials: Detailed Medal Rolls of Officers and Men in Colonial Units Who Received the New Zealand Medal for Service in the New Zealand Wars 1845-72* (1999).

INDIA GENERAL SERVICE MEDAL 1854-95

Parritt, Colonel B.A.H., *Red With Two Blue Stripes* (1974).

CRIMEA MEDAL 1854-56

Caldwell, G.J., Cooper, R.B.E., *Rifle Green in the Crimea* (1996).

Cook, F. and Cook, A., *Casualty Roll for the Crimea 1854-55* (1976).

Duckers, P. and Mitchell, N., *The Azoff Campaign 1855* (1997).

Lummis, Canon W.M., *Honour the Light Brigade* (1973).

Mitchell, N. and Duckers, P., *Presented to the Queen: The Crimea Medal Award Ceremony, 18 May 1855* (1996).

Research Publications and Productions (pub.), *Returns Relating to Officers of the Army in the Crimea* (1989).

Savannah Publications (pubs.), *Casualty Roll for the Crimea 1854-55* (1999).

INDIA MUTINY MEDAL 1857-59

Asplin, K. J., *Indian Mutiny Medal Roll (British Forces)* (1999).

Tavender, I.T., *Casualty Roll for the India Mutiny 1857-59* (1983).

CANADA GENERAL SERVICE MEDAL 1866-70

Neale, G. N. and Irwin, R. W., *The Medal Roll of the Red River Campaign in 1870 in Canada* (1982).

Thyen, R., *Canada General Service Medal Roll 1866–70* (1999).

ABYSSINIAN WAR MEDAL 1867–68

Bates, Darrell, *The Abyssinian Difficulty* (1979).

SOUTH AFRICA MEDAL 1877-79

Forsyth, D.R., *South African War Medal 1877-8-9: The Medal Roll*.

Holme, N., *The Silver Wreath. The 24th Regiment at Isandhlwana and Rorke's Drift 1879* (1979).

Knight, Ian, *Brave Men's Blood* (1990).

Knight, Ian, *Zulu: Isandlwana and Rorke's Drift 22nd–23rd January 1879* (1997).

Mackinnon, J.P. and Shadbolt, S.H., *The South Africa Campaign of 1879* (1882).

Sole, T.E. *The Military Casualties of South Africa: Vol 1 1834-1878*.

Tavender, I.T., *Casualty Roll for the Zulu and Basuto Wars, South Africa 1877-79* (1985).

Whybra, J., *The Roll Call for Isandhlwana and Rorke's Drift* (1990).

Holme, N., *The Noble 24th, Biographical Records of the 24th Regiment in the Zulu War and the South African Campaigns 1877–1879* (2000).

AFGHANISTAN MEDAL 1878-80

Farrington, A., *The Second Afghan War 1878-80 Casualty Roll* (1986).

Robson, Brian, *The Road to Kabul: The Second Afghan War 1878–1881* (1986).

Shadbolt, S.H., *The Afghanistan Campaigns of 1878-80* (1882).

CAPE OF GOOD HOPE GS MEDAL 1880-97

Forsyth, D.R., *Cape of Good Hope General Service Medal: The Medal Roll*.

EGYPT MEDAL 1882-89

Maurice, Colonel J.F., *The Campaign of 1882 in Egypt.*

Webb, J.V., *Abu Klea Medal Roll.*

KHARTOUM STAR 1884

Fearon, D., *General Gordon's Khartoum Star* (1967).

NORTH WEST CANADA MEDAL 1885

Pacific Publishing Co (pub.), *North-West Canada Medal Roll (The Riel Rebellion 1885)* (1974).

BRITISH SOUTH AFRICA COMPANY MEDAL 1890-97

Forsyth, D.R., *British South Africa Co. Medal 1890-1897.*
Owen, C.R., *British South African Company Medal Roll 1890-1897.*
Roberts (pub.), *The British South Africa Company Medal Rolls 1890-1897* (1993).

HONG KONG PLAGUE MEDAL

Platt, J. J., Jones, M. E. and Platt, A. K., *The Whitewash Brigade: The Hong Kong Plague 1894* (1999).

INDIA MEDAL 1895–1902

Farrington, A., *India General Service Casualty Roll* (1987).
Barthorp, Michael, *The Frontier Ablaze: The North-West Frontier Rising 1897–98* (1996).

ASHANTI STAR 1896

McInnes, Ian and Fraser, Mark, *The Ashanti Campaign 1896.*

QUEEN'S & KING'S SOUTH AFRICA MEDAL 1899-1902

British Naval Brigades in the South Africa War 1899-1902 (Reprint).
Dooner, M.G., *The Last Post: A Roll of All Officers Who Gave Their Lives in the South African War 1899-1902* (1980).
Fevyer, W.H. and Wilson, J.W., *The Queen's South Africa Medal to the Royal Navy and Royal Marines* (1983).
Gray, S., *The South African War 1899-1902 - Service Records of British and Colonial Women.*
Hayward, J. B. & Son (pub.), *List of Casualties of the South Africa Frontier Force* (Reprint 1972).
Hayward, J. B. & Son (pub.), *South African War Casualty Roll: Natal Field Force* (1980).
Lusted, C.A (pub.), *The Queens South Africa Medal 1898-1902* (1974).
Mitchell, Dr F.K., *Roll Of The Bar, Defence of Mafeking, on the Queen's Medal for South Africa, 1899-1902* (1963).
Palmer, A., *The Boer War Casualty List* (1999).
Stirling, J., *British Regiments in South Africa 1899-1902* (reprint) (1994).
Stirling, J., *The Colonials in South Africa* (1990).

CAPE COPPER COMPANY'S MEDAL 1902

Forsyth, D.R., *Medal Roll of the Cape Copper Company's Medal.*

CHINA MEDAL 1900

Fevyer, W.H. and Wilson, J.W., *The China War Medal 1900 to the Royal Navy and Royal Marines* (1985).
Narbeth, C., *Taku Forts* (1980).

OOKIEP DEFENCE MEDAL

Kieran, Brian L., *O'okiep* (1996).

AFRICA GENERAL SERVICE MEDAL 1902

Fevyer, W.H. and Wilson, J.W. *African General Service Medal to the RN and RM.*
Magor, R.B., *African General Service Medals.*

TIBET MEDAL 1903–04

Fleming, Peter, *Bayonets to Lhasa* (revised 1985).
Roberts (pub.), *The Tibet Campaign 1904 and the Royal Fusiliers.*

NATAL REBELLION MEDAL 1906

Forsyth, D.R., *Natal Native Rebellion 1906: The Medal Roll.*
Roberts Medals Publications Ltd (pub.), *The Natal Zulu Rebellion 1906.*

INDIA GENERAL SERVICE MEDAL 1908–35

Styles, Richard G. M., *The Story of the India General Service Medal 1908–35* (1992).
Naval & Military Press (pub.), *India General Service Medal 1908–1935 to the Royal Air Force* (1994).

FIRST WORLD WAR MEDALS 1914-19

Adler, Revd. M (ed.), *British Jewry Book of Honour 1914-1918* (1922 and reprint 1997).
Bell, E.W., *Soldiers Killed on the First Day of the Somme* (1977).
Christie, N.M. *Officers of the Canadian Expeditionary Force who Died Overseas 1914-1919.*
Fevyer, W. H. and Wilson, J. W., *The 1914 Star to the Royal Navy and the Royal Marines* (1995).
Hayward, J. B. & Son (pub.), *Officers Died in the Great War* (1988).
Hayward, J. B. & Son (pub.), *Soldiers Died in the Great War* (80 parts).
Hobson, C., *Airmen Died in the Great War 1914-18: The Roll of Honour of the British and Commonwealth Air Services of the First World War* (1995)
Imperial War Museum (pub.), *Drake, Royal Naval Division Roll of Honour.*
Imperial War Museum (pub.), *Hawke, Royal Naval Division Roll of Honour.*
Imperial War Museum (pub.), *Hood, Royal Naval Division Roll of Honour.*
Imperial War Museum (pub.), *Howe, Royal Naval division Roll of Honour.*
Imperial War Museum (pub.), *Nelson, Royal Naval division Roll of Honour.*
Jarvis, S.D. and Jarvis, D.B., *The Cross of Sacrifice* (1990-1994) (several volumes).
Laslo, A.J., *The Interallied Victory Medals of WWI* (1986).
Merewhether, Lt-Col L. A., CIE and Smith Sir F., Bart., *The Indian Corps in France* (1919).
Mitchell, F.K., *Medals of the Great War Awarded to South Africans* (1983).
New Zealand Expeditionary Force Roll of Honour (Reprint).
Parks, Major Edwin, *The Royal Guernsey Militia* (1993).
Ruvigny, Marquis de., *The Roll of Honour 1916-1919.*
Walker, R., *To What End Did They Die?—Officers Died At Gallipoli.*
Williams, R.D., *Guide to Collecting and Researching Campaign Medals of the Great War* (1993).
Williamson, H.J., *The Roll of Honour, Royal Flying Corps and Royal Air Force for the Great War 1914-18* (1992).

SECOND WORLD WAR MEDALS

Devereux, J. and Sacker, G., *Roll of Honour, Land Forces World War 2 Volume I* (Cavalry, Yeomanry, RAC, Reconnaissance Corps, RTR and Brigade of Guards—other volumes to follow) (1999).
Hayward, J. B. & Son (pub.), *Prisoners of War (British, Empire and Commonwealth Forces)* (3 volumes, reprint).
Purves, A. A., *The Medals, Decorations & Orders of World War II* (1986).
Savannah Publications (pubs.), *Roll of Honour Land Forces WWII* (2000).

NAVAL GENERAL SERVICE MEDAL 1915

Fevyer, W.H. and Wilson, J.W., *NGS Medal 1915-1962 to the Royal Navy and Royal Marines for the Bars Persian Gulf 1909-1914, Iraq 1919-1920, NW Persia 1920* (1995).

KOREA MEDALS 1950-53

Dyke, P., *Korea 1950-53: Mentions-in-Despatches* (1989).

Gaston, P., *Korea 1950-1953, Prisoners of War, The British Army.*

Harding, Colonel E.D., *The Imjin Roll* (1976).

Ingraham, Kevin R., *The Honors, Medals and Awards of the Korean War 1950-1953* (1993).

MERITORIOUS SERVICE MEDALS

Chamberlain, Howard, *Service Lives Remembered, The MSM in New Zealand and its Recipients 1895–1994* (1995) and *Supplement* (1997).

McInnes, Ian, *The Meritorious Service Medal to Aerial Forces* (1984).

McInnes, Ian, *The Meritorious Service Medal to Naval Forces* (1983).

McInnes, Ian, *Meritorious Service Medal. The Immediate Awards 1916-1928* (1992).

McInnes, Ian, *The Annuity Meritorious Service Medal* (1994).

Sainsbury, Major J.D., *For Gallantry in the Performance of Military Duty* (1980).

LONG SERVICE & GOOD CONDUCT MEDALS
(listed alphabetically by author)

Bolton, R., Howie, L. and Mandry, R., *Badges of the Brigade.* (2000).

Douglas-Morris, Captain K.J., *The Naval Long Service Medals* (1991).

Lees, J.R., *Recipients of the Long Service & Good Conduct Medal 1833-1916 to the Somerset Light Infantry (Prince Alberts).*

McInnes, I. and Gregson, J. B., *The Army Long Service & Good Conduct Medal 1830–1848* (1996).

Pallas, S.M., *Canadian Recipients of the Colonial Auxiliary Forces Officers Decoration and the Colonial Auxiliary Forces Long Service Medal.*

Tamplin, J.M.A., *The Army Emergency Reserve Decoration and the Efficiency Medal (Army Emergency Reserve)* (1989).

Tamplin, J.M.A., *The Colonial Auxiliary Forces Long Service Medal* (1984.)

Tamplin, J.M.A., *The Colonial Auxiliary Forces Officers' Decoration: the Indian Volunteer Forces Officers' Decoration* (1981).

Tamplin, J.M.A., *The Efficiency Decoration Instituted 1930* (1987).

Tamplin, J.M.A., *The Imperial Yeomanry Long Service and Good Conduct Medal* (1978).

Tamplin, J.M.A., *The Militia Long Service and Good Conduct Medal* (1979).

Tamplin, J.M.A., *The Special Reserve Long Service and Good Conduct Medal* (1979).

Tamplin, J.M.A., *The Territorial Decoration 1908-1930* (1983).

Tamplin, J.M.A., *The Territorial Force Efficiency Medal 1908-1921 and the Territorial Efficiency Medal 1922-1930* (1980).

Tamplin, J.M.A., *The Volunteer Long Service Medal* (1980).

Tamplin, J.M.A., *The Volunteer Officers' Decoration* (1980).

Williams, R.D., *The Victoria Volunteer Long and Efficient Service Medal & the Volunteer Officers' Decoration* (1976).

LIFE SAVING AWARDS

Barclay, C., *Royal Humane Society Medals* (1999).

Brown, G., *Lloyds War Medal for Bravery at Sea* (1992).

Cox, Barry, *Lifeboat Gallantry: The Complete Record of Royal National Lifeboat Institution Gallantry Medals and How They Were Won 1824–1996* (1998).

Cumming, Sir J., *Literature of the Life-Boat 1785-1947* (1947).

Dibdin, C., *History of the Institution's Gold and Silver Medals* (1909).

Fevyer, William H., *Acts of Gallantry, Vol. 2, 1871–1950* (1997).

Gawler, J., *Lloyds Medals 1836-1989.*

Jeffery, S., *The Liverpool Shipwreck and Humane Society 1839-1939* (1939).

Lamb, Sir J.C., *The Life Boat and Its Work* (1911).

Mundell, F., *Stories of the Royal Humane Society* (1895).

Scarlett, R., *Under Hazardous Circumstances: Lloyds War Medal for Bravery at Sea.*

Young, L., *Acts of Gallantry: Being a Detailed Account of Each Deed of Bravery in Saving Life from Drowning in All Parts of the World for which the Gold and Silver Medals and Clasps of the Royal Humane Society Have Been Awarded from 1830-1871.*

ANIMAL AWARDS

Le Chene, Evelyn, *Silent Heroes: The Bravery and Devotion of Animals in War* (1994).

OTHER MEDALS

Balmer, Major J.L., *TD, British and Irish Regimental and Volunteer Medals 1745-1895.*

Bolton, R., Howie, L., Mandry, B., *Badges of the Brigade* (2000). (Boy's Brigade Badges and Medals)

Borts, L.H., *UN Medals and Missions* (1998).

Cole, H. N., *Coronation and Royal Commemorative Medals 1887-1977* (1977).

Condon, Major J.P.B., MBE, *The Kings and Queens Medals for Shooting (Regular Army).*

Dalzell, M. and Riches, P., *Mentioned in Despatches 1948-1968* (1999).

Duckers, P., *The Delhi Durbar Medal 1911 to The British Army* (1995).

Fevyer, W. H., Wilson, J. W. and Cribb, J., *The Order of Industrial Heroism.* (2000).

Hibbard, M.G., *Boer War Tribute Medals* (1982).

James G.P.L., *The Royal Family Orders, Badges of Office, Royal Household Medals and Souvenirs* (1951).

Owen, D., *The King's and Queen's Medal for Shooting* (1999).

Poulsom, Major N.W., *The White Ribbon: a Medallic Record of British Polar Expeditions* (1968).

Poulsom, Major N.W.A., *Catalogue of Campaign and Independence Medals Issued During the Twentieth Century to the British Army* (1969).

Scarlett, R.J., *The Naval Good Shooting Medal 1903-1914* (1990).

Wilson, J.W. and Perkins, R., *Angels in Blue Jackets: The Navy at Messina, 1908.*

Societies
for medal
collectors

Listed here are some of the many societies around the world that cater for the medal collector or those interested in military history. The addresses given are mostly the private addresses of the membership secretaries to whom all correspondence should be sent. *We would appreciate information from other Societies who would like their details included in the next YEARBOOK.*

Association de Collectionneurs de Décorations et Médailles (MEDEC) (Paasbloemstraat 81, B-2170 Merksem, Belgium).

Austrian Orders Research Society (Salesianergasse 9, A-1037 Wien, Postfach 20, Austria)

Birmingham Medal Society (10 Edward Street, Milverton, Leamington Spa CV32 6AX).

Bund Deutscher Ordenssammler e.v. (Postfach 1370, D-95012 Hof, Germany).

The Crimean War Research Society (4 Castle Estate, Ripponden, West Yorkshire HX6 4JY).

Crown Imperial (history, traditions, regalia, insignia) (B. Sutton, The Old Smithy, 35 Liverpool Rd, Buckley, Flintshire CH7 3LH).

Indian Military Historical Society (A. N. McLenaghan, 33 High Street, Tilbrook, Huntingdon, Cambs PE18).

Life Saving Awards Research Society ("Little Sadlers", 10 Upper Edgeborough Road, Guildford, Surrey GU1 2BG).

London Medal Club (Jim Lees, 020 8560 7648).

Medal Society of Ireland (1 The Hill, Stillorgan, Co. Dublin, Ireland).

Mid-Western Orders & Medals Society (MIDOMS) (5847 Gilbert Avenue, La Grange, IL 60525, USA).

Military Collector's Club of Canada (MCCofC) (PO Box 64009, RPO Morse Place, Winnipeg, MB, R2K 4K2, Canada).

Military Medal Society of South Africa (1 Jacqueline Avenue, Northcliff 2195, South Africa).

Naval Historical Collectors and Research Association (1 Old Fire Station Court, Nailsea, Bristol BS48 4SE).

Orders & Medals Society of America (OMSA) (PO Box 198, San Ramon, CA 94583, USA).

Orders & Medals Research Society (OMRS) (PO Box 1904, Southam CV47 2ZX).

Orders & Medals Research Society, Australia Branch (Sydney) (PO Box 484, Lane Cove, NSW 2066, Australia).

ditto, Canada Branch (Ottawa) (17 Ella Street, Ottawa, Ontario, Canada K1S 2S3).

ditto, Canada Branch (Toronto) (273 Corner Ridge Road, Aurora, Ontario, Canada L4G 6L6).

ditto, Hong Kong Branch (Flat 23, 11/F Mt Nicholson Gap, 103 Mt Nicholson Road, Hong Kong).

ditto, New Zealand Branch (Wellington) (54 Lohia Street, Khandallah, Wellington, New Zealand. Tel: 64 4 479 1622).

ditto, Northern Branch (Manchester) (7 St Michael's Avenue, Great Lever, Bolton, Lancs BL3 2LP. Tel/Fax: 01204 524011).

ditto, Scottish Branch (21 Hartington Place, Edinburgh EH10 4LF).

ditto, Sussex Branch (9 Merryfield Drive, Horsham, West Sussex RH12 2AA).

ditto, Cotswold Branch (Cheltenham) (12 The Verneys, Cheltenham, Glos GL53 7DB).

ditto, Northumbrian Branch (41 Ashdown Avenue, Durham DH1 1DB).

ditto, Medal Ribbon Branch (7 Durham Way, Rayleigh, Essex SS6 9RY).

ditto, Miniature Medals Branch (54 Priory Bridge Road, Taunton, Somerset TA1 1QB).

Ordenshistorik Selskab (Falkoneralle 79, DK 2000 Frederiksberg, Denmark).

Société Suisse de Phaleristique (Box 1, CH-1137 Yens, Switzerland).

Stockport Militaria Collectors Society, Stockport Armoury (Clive Williams 0161 368 3128).

Victorian Military Society (20 Priory Road, Newbury, Berks RG14 7QN).

West of England Medal Club (Exeter) (Otterburn Farm, Halwill, Beaworthy, Devon EX21 5UG).

417

MUSEUMS AND COLLECTIONS

The majority of the museums listed below are the regimental museums of the British Army, Militia, Yeomanry and Territorials, but we have included other museums pertaining to the Royal Navy, the Royal Marines and the Royal Air Force where medals form a significant part of the collections. So, too, the museums of the police forces, fire brigades, Red Cross, Royal National Lifeboat Institution and similar bodies have been included where relevant. Readers should also bear in mind that many general museums in our towns and cities boast fine collections of military medals pertaining to their local regiments. We have included those of which we are aware. The date of foundation is shown in brackets after the name.

Some service museums have been undergoing refits, relocations and amalgamations. We would welcome further information from readers about these changes and about other general museums in their areas with a good coverage of medals to local regiments.

Space prevents us from going into details regarding the scope of individual museum holdings. We give the postal address, telephone number, and the name of the curator wherever possible, also the hours of opening and admission charges (where applicable) at the time of going to press. Where two charges are listed, the first denotes the full adult price and the second the concessionary charge (OAPs, students and children). Where three charges are given the first is the full adult price, the second the OAP concession and the third the children's charge. It is always sensible, particularly before travelling long distances to visit a museum or collection, to telephone and check that the published details are still correct.

Some museums may have libraries holding archival material; this should be checked out and the conditions for use ascertained as such holdings will not have the resources to answer detailed research enquiries.

Where museums are devoted to one particular regimental/service/unit or whatever, they are listed by title in alphabetical order. This may not always accord with the exact official name of the museum which is given on the address line. The well-known national museums are listed alphabetically by name. More general museums which include medal collections are listed by the name of the town. If you cannot see the name of the museum you require at first glance, it may be worth searching through the full list, as some museums escape neat classification and would require extensive cross-referencing to do them full justice.

15th/19th King's Royal Hussars (Light Dragoons)/ Northumberland Hussars
Tyne & Wear Museums, Discovery Museum, (Closed until late 2002) Blandford Square, Newcastle-upon-Tyne NE1 4JA. 0191 232 6789. Monday–Saturday 10am–5pm. Sunday 2pm–5pm. Ralph Thompson

100th Bomb Group Memorial Museum (1978)
Common Road, Dickleburgh, near Diss, Norfolk. 0379 740708. Medals and memorabilia of the Eighth Air Force and 100th Bomb Group. Free. May– September, Saturday, Sunday and Wednesday, 10am– 5pm. October–April, weekends only, 10am– 4.30pm. S. P. Hurry.

Aberdeen Maritime Museum (1984)
Provost Ross's House, Shiprow, Aberdeen. 01224 5857888. Monday–Saturday, 10am–5pm. Admission free.

Airborne Forces Museum (1969)
Browning Barracks, Aldershot, Hants GU11 2BU. 01252 349619. £3.00/£1.00. Monday–Friday 10am– 4.30pm. (last admission 3.45pm) Saturday, Sunday, bank Holidays 10am–4pm. Closed Christmas and New Year. Tina Pittock and alan Brown.

Aldershot Challenge (1989)
Wavell House, Cavans Road, Aldershot, Hants GU11 2LQ. 01252 21048. Only by appointment at present.

Aldershot Military Museum (1984)
Queen's Avenue, Aldershot, Hants GU11 2LG. 01252 314598. £2/£1. March–October, 10am–5pm; November–February 10am–4.30pm daily. Closed Christmas and New Year. Ian Maine.

Argyll and Sutherland Highlanders Regimental Museum (1945)
Stirling Castle. 01786 475165. Free. Easter–September, Monday–Saturday, 10am–5.30pm; Sunday, 11am–5pm. October–Easter, Monday–Saturday, 10am–4.30pm; Sunday, 11am–4pm.

Army Medical Services Museum
Keogh Barracks, Ash Vale, Aldershot, GU2 5RQ. 01252 340212, Fax 01252 340332. E-mail museum@keogh72.freeserve.co.uk.

Army Physical Training Corps Museum (1949)
Army School of Physical Training, Queen's Avenue, Aldershot, Hants GU11 2LB. 01252 347131. Fax 01252 340785. Free. Monday–Thursday, 9.00am–12.30pm; 2pm–4.30pm. Friday 9.00am to 12.30pm.Weekends by appointment. Closed in August, and two weeks each at Easter and Christmas. A. A. Forbes and J. Pearson.

Army Transport Museum (1983)
Flemingate, Beverley, Humberside HU17 0NG. 01482 860445. £2.50/£1.50. Daily, 10am–5pm. Closed 24–26 December. David Dawson.

Arundel Toy and Military Museum (1978)
Dolls House, 23 High Street, Arundel, West Sussex. 01903 507446/882908. £1.25/90p. June–August, 10.30am–5pm daily. Otherwise open on Bank Holidays and weekends in winter.

Aylmer Military Collection and Isle of Wight Home Guard Museum (1984)
Nunwell House, Brading, Isle of Wight PO36 0JQ. 01983 407240. £2.30/£1.80/60p (children accompanied by adults). July–September, Sunday–Thursday, 10am–5pm. Otherwise by appointment. J. A. Aylmer.

Ayrshire Yeomanry Museum
Rozelle House, Monument Road, Alloway by Ayr KA7 4NQ. 01292 264091. Monday–Saturday, 10am–5pm, Sundays, April–October, 2–5pm.

Bangor, Museum
Ffordd Gwynedd, Bangor, Gwynedd, LL57 1DT. 01248 353368. 50p. Tuesday–Friday, 12.30pm–4.30pm; Saturday, 10.30am–4.30pm. Includes medals and militaria of the Welsh regiments. Pat West.

Bath Police Museum (1985)
Manvers Street, Bath, Avon BA1 1JN. 01225 444343. Free, by appointment only. Sergeant Mike Stanton.

Bedfordshire and Hertfordshire Regimental Museum
Luton Museum, Wardown Park, Luton, Beds LU2 7HA. Tuesday to Saturday, 10am–5pm, Sunday, 1pm–5pm.

Black Watch Museum (1924)
Balhousie Castle, Perth PH1 5HR. 0131 310 8530. Fax 01738 643245. Free. May–September, Monday–Saturday, 10am–4.30pm; October–April, Monday-Friday 10am–3.30pm. MajorJ. W. Proctor, MBE.

Border Regiment and King's Own Royal Border Regiment Museum (1932)
Queen Mary's Tower, The Castle, Carlisle, Cumbria CA3 8UR. 01228 532774; Fax 01228 521275; e-mail RHQ@kingsownborder.demon.co.uk. Admission is included in entry chage to the Castle. Prices (2001–

02)—£3.10/£1.60/£2.40. Open every day april–Sept 9.30am to 6pm; Oct 9.30am to 5pm; Nov–Mar 10am to 4pm; closed 24–26 Dec & 1 Jan. Curator Stuart Eastwood.

British in India Museum (1972)
Newtown Street, Colne, Lancs BB8 0JJ. 01282 613129/ 870215. £3.00/50p. April to September (inclusive) Monday–Friday (except Tuesday), 1pm–5pm. Saturday 11am-5pm Sunday closed. Closed Bank Holiday Mondays 9th-23rd July, 8th-15th September. Prior to april and after the end of september please phone 0976 665320 for opening times.

British Red Cross Museum and Archives (1984)
9 Grosvenor Crescent, London, SW1X 7EJ. 020 7235 5454. Free, by appointment. Monday–Friday, 9.30am–4.30pm. Nicola Bleasby.

Bygones
Fore Street, St Marychurch, Torquay, Devon TQ1 4PR. 01803 326108. Daily (except Christmas Day). Summer, 10am–10pm, Winter 10am–4pm.

Caenarfon Air Museum
Caernarfon Airport, Dinas Dinlle, Caernarfon, Gwynedd LL54 5TP. £2.50/£1.50. March–November 9.30am–5.30pm.

Cambridge, Scott Polar Research Institute Museum (1920)
Lensfield Road, Cambridge CB2 1ER. 01223 336540. Free. Monday–Friday, 14.30–16.00. The Library and archives (the latter by appointment only) are open 0900 to 1300 and 1400 to 1730 Monday to Friday. Robert Headland.

Cameronians (Scottish Rifles) Regimental Museum (1928)
Mote Hill, off Muir Street, Hamilton, Lanarkshire ML3 6BY. 01698 428688. Free. Monday–Wednesday, Friday–Saturday, 10am–1pm; 2pm–5pm. John McGourty.

Castle and Regimental Museum
The Castle, Monmouth, NP25 3BS. 01600 772175. Free. April–October daily 2–5pm; November–March Saturdays and Sundays 2–4pm.

Cheshire Military Museum (1972)
The Castle, Chester CH1 2DN. 01244 327617. £2.50p/£2.00. Daily, 10am–5pm. Lieut. Major John Ellis.

City of London Police Museum (1964)
37 Wood Street, London EC2P 2NQ. 020 7601 2705/2455. Fax 020 7601 2747 Free, by written appointment only. Roger Appleby.

Coldstream Museum
12 Market Square, Coldstream. TD12 4BD. 01890 882630. Open April to end September: Monday–Saturday 10am–4pm, Sunday 2–4pm.October Monday–Saturday 1–4pm.

Devonshire Regiment Museum
Wyvern Barracks, Barrack Road, Exeter, Devon EX2 6AE. Monday–Friday, 10am–4.30pm. Closed Bank Holidays. Lieutenant Colonel D.R. Roberts.

Dingwall Museum (1975)
Town Hall, High Street, Dingwall, Ross–shire IV15 9RY. 01349 865366. 50p/25p. May–September, Monday–Saturday, 10am–5pm. Otherwise by

appointment only. Includes medals and militaria of the Seaforth Highlanders,and items pertaining to Major General sir hector macdonald ("Fighting Mac") Ian Macleod

Duke of Cornwall's Light Infantry Regimental Museum (1925)
The Keep, Bodmin, Cornwall PL31 1EG. 01208 72810. £1/50p. Monday–Friday, 8am–5pm. Major W. H. White.

Duke of Wellington's Regiment Museum (1960)
Bankfield Museum, Boothtown Road, Halifax HX3 6HQ. 01422 352334/354823. Free. Tuesday–Saturday, 10am–5pm; Sunday, 2.30pm–5pm.

Durham Light Infantry Museum (1969)
Aykley Heads, Durham DH1 5TU. 0191 384 2214. £2.50/£1.25.Open every day except Christmas Day. Summer 10am–5pm; Winter 10am-4pm. Stephen D. Shannon.

Essex Regimental Museum (1973)
Oaklands Park, Moulsham Street, Chelmsford, Essex CM2 9AQ. 01245 260614. Free. Monday–Saturday, 10am–5pm; Saturday, 2pm–5pm. Ian Hook.

Fleet Air Arm Museum (1962)
RNAS Yeovilton, Somerset BA22 8HT. 01935 840565. £4.80/£3.50/£2.70. Daily, 10am–4.30pm. Open all year exept Christams Eve, Christmas Day and Boxing Day. Graham Mottram.

Glasgow Art Gallery and Museum (1854)
Kelvingrove, Glasgow G3 8AG. 0141 287 2699. Free. Monday–Thursday–Saturday, 10am–5pm; Friday and Sunday, 11am–5pm. Includes medals of the Glasgow Yeomanry, Highland Light Infantry and regiments associated with the city.

Gordon Highlanders' Regimental Museum (1961)
St Lukes, Viewfield Road, Aberdeen AB15 7XH. 01224 311300. Fax 01224 319323. E-mail museum@gordonhighlanders.com. April–October, Tuesday–Saturday 10.30am–4.30pm (closed Mondays). November–March: by appointment only. Melanie Brooker, MA (Hons), MA, FSA (Scot).

Green Howards Regimental Museum
Trinity Church Square, Richmond, Yorkshire DL10 4QN. 01748 822133. Fax 01748 826561 Admission charged. Contact museum for opening times.

Guards Museum (1988)
Wellington Barracks, London SW1E 6HQ. 0171 414 3271. £2/£1. Monday–Thursday, weekends, 10am–4pm. Captain David Horn.

Gurkha Museum (1974)
Peninsular Barracks, Romsey Road, Winchester, Hants SO23 8TS. 01962 842832. £1.50/75p. Tuesday–Saturday, 10am–5pm. Brigadier C. Bullock.

Hawkinge, Kent, Battle of Britain Museum (1969)
Hawkinge, Kent CT18 7AG. 0130 389 3140. £2.50/£2 £1.50. Easter–end of May, October, 11am–4pm. July–September, 10am–5pm. Mike Llewellyn.

Hertford Regiment Museum
At the Hertford Museum at 8 Bull Plain, Hertford SG14 1DJ. Tel 01992 582686 Fax 01992 534797.

Hitchin Museum
Paynes Park, Hitchin, Herts SG5 1EQ. 01462 434476.

Free. Monday–Saturday, 10am–5pm; Closed Wednesdays, Sundays and Bank holidays.

Hornsea Folk Museum (1978)
Burn's Farm, 11 Newbegin, Hornsea, East Yorkshire HU18 1BP. 01964 533443. £1.50/£1. Easter w/e, 1 May–30 September, Monday to Saturday, 11am–5pm and Sunday 2–5pm. E. Yorkshire Regt, E. Riding Yeo., Royal Artillery, The Home Front. Dr J. E. S. Walker.

Honourable Artillery Company Museum
Armoury House, City Road, London EC1 2BQ. Apply in writing for a visit.

Imperial War Museum (1917)
Lambeth Road, London SE1 6HZ. 020 7416 5000. Daily, 10am–6pm. £6.50, £5.50, £3.25. OAP free and children under 16 free.

Imperial War Museum (1976)
Duxford Airfield, Duxford, Cambridge CB2 4QR. 01223 835000. £7.70/£5.40/3.70. March–October, 10am–6pm daily; October–March, 10am–4pm daily.

Inns of Court and City Yeomanry Museum (1947)
10 Stone Buildings, Lincoln's Inn, London WC2A 3TG. 0171 405 8112. Free. Monday–Friday, 10am–4pm. Major R. J. B. Gentry.

Intelligence Corps Museum
Defence Intelligence and Security Centre, Chicksands, Nr Shefford, Beds SG17 5PR. 01462 752297 Free. Monday–Friday, 10am–3.30pm. Appointment necessary. Major A.J. Edwards

Kent and Sharpshooters Yeomanry Museum
Hever Castle, Tonbridge, Kent TN8 7NG. 1 March to 30 November, Daily, from 12 noon to 5pm, winter (GMT) 11 am to 4pm. Boris Mollo.

King's Regiment (Lancaster) Museum (1929)
City Museum, Market Square, Lancaster LA1 1HT. 01524 64637. Fax 01524 841692. E-mail kingsownmuseum@iname.com Free. Monday–Saturday, 10am–5pm.

King's Own Scottish Borderers Regimental Museum (1954)
Berwick Barracks, The Parade, Berwick-upon-Tweed TD15 1DG. 01289 307426. Fax 01289 331928. £2.70/£1.40. Monday–Saturday, 09.30–1630 (Winter). Closed Easter, Christman and New Year. Lieut. Colonel C. G. O. Hogg DL.

King's Own Yorkshire Light Infantry Regimental Museum (1932)
Museum and Art Gallery, Chequer Road, Doncaster, South Yorkshire DN1 2AE. 01302 734293. Monday–Saturday, 10am–5pm; Sunday, 2pm–5pm. Major C. M. J. Deedes.

King's Regiment Museum (1930)
City Soldiers, Museum of Liverpool Life, Mann Island, Liverpool L3 4AA. 0151 478 4080. £3, £1.50. Daily, 10am–5pm, Simon Jones.

King's Royal Hussars Museum in Winchester (1980)
Home Headquarters (South): Peninsula Barracks, Romsey Road, Winchester. 01962 828541. Free admission. Tuesday–Friday, 10am–4pm; weekends and Bank holidays, 12pm–4pm. Major P. J. C. Beresford, Regimental Secretary.

Lancashire Fusiliers Regimental Museum (1933)
Wellington Barracks, Bury, Lanc BL8 2PL. 0161 764
2208. 50p/25p. Monday–Saturday (closed
Wednesday), 9.30am–4.30pm.

Light Infantry Museum (1990)
Peninsular Barracks, Romsey Road, Winchester.
01962 828530. £1.50/75p. Tuesday–Saturday, 10am–
5pm; Sunday, 12pm–4pm. Patrick Kirby.

Liverpool Scottish Regimental Museum
Forbes House, Score Lane, Childwell, Liverpool L16
6AN. 0151 6474342. By appointment. D. Reeves.

London Fire Brigade Museum (1967)
94A Southwark Bridge Road, London SE1 0EG. 020
7587 2894, Fax 020 7587 2878. E-mail
museum@london-fire.gov.uk Free. Monday–Friday,
9am–4.30pm. Esther Mann.

London Scottish Regimental Museum (1935)
Regimental Headquarters, 95 Horseferry Road,
London SW1P 2DX. 0171 630 1639. Free, by
appointment only.

Manchesters Museum (1987)
Town Hall, Ashton–under–Lyne, Lancs. 0161 342
3078 or 0161 343 1978. Free. Monday–Saturday,
10am–4pm. Dr Alan Wilson.

Metropolitan Police Historical Museum (1969)
New Scotland Yard, Broadway, London SW1H 0BG.
0181 305 1676. By appointment only. Paul Dew.

Military Miniatures Museum (1978)
13 Cheveling Road, Old Heath, Colchester, Essex
CO2 8DL. 01206 794473. Free, by appointment only.
Daily, 9am–5pm. Anthony Debski.

**Monmouth, The Castle and Regimental Museum
(1989)**
The Castle, Monmouth, Gwent NP5 3BS. 01600
772175/712935. Free. Summer daily, 2pm–5pm;
winter weekends 2pm–5pm. Other times by
appointment. Dr Eric Old.

The Muckleburgh Collection
Weybourne, Norfolk. 01263 588210. £4/£3/£2. Daily
(February–November) 10am–5pm.

Museum of Lancashire
Stanley Street, Preston, Lancs PR1 4YP. 01772
264075. Houses the collections of the 14th/20th
King's Hussars; Duke of Lancaster's own yeomanry;
and a selection of Queen's Lancashire Regiment. £1/
children free. 10.30am–5pm daily except Thursday,
Sunday and Bank Holidays. Stephen Bull.

National Army Museum (1960)
Royal Hospital Road, Chelsea, London SW3 4HT.
020 7730 0717. Fax 020 7823 6573. E-mail
info@national-army-museum.ac.uk. (Closed 1 Jan,
Good Friday, Early May Bank Holiday and 24 to 26
Dec) Free. Daily, 10am–5.30pm. Ian G. Robertson.

National Maritime Museum (1934)
Romney Road, Greenwich, London SE10 9NF. 0181
858 4422. £7.45/£5.45. Summer, Monday–Saturday,
10am–6pm; Sunday, 12pm–5pm. Winter, Monday–
Saturday, 10am–5pm; Sunday, 2pm–5pm. Richard
Ormond.

National Museum of Ireland (1877)
Kildare Street, Dublin 2, Republic of Ireland. 01
618811. Free. Tuesday–Saturday, 10am–5pm; Sunday,
2pm–5pm. Includes medals of the former Irish
regiments.

National War Museum of Scotland
The Castle, Edinburgh. 0131 225 7534 ext 2201
(enquiries). Free (but entrance fee to the castle).
April–Nov. 9.45am–5.30pm/Dec.–March 9.45am–
4.30pm.

Newark Air Museum (1968)
Winthrop Airfield, Newark-on-Trent NG24 2NY.
01636 707170. £4.00/£2.50 Open every day except
Christmas Eve/Day & Boxing Day. April–September
weekdays, 10am–5pm; weekends and Bank Holidays,
10am–6pm. October–March, daily 10am–5pm.
November to February daily 10am –4pm.Mike Smith.

Northamptonshire Regimental Museum
Abington Park Museum, Abington, Northampton.
NN1 5LW 01604 631454. Free Tuesday to Sunday and
Bank Holiday Mondays 1-5pm (November to
February 1-4pm) Colonel J. P. Wetherall.

Order of St. John of Jerusalem Museum
St. John's Gate, St. John's Lane, Clerkenwell, London
EC1M 4DA. 0171 253 6644. Tuesday–Friday 10am–
5pm, Saturday 10am–4pm. Pamela Willis.

Oxfordshire & Buckinghamshire Light Infantry
TA Centre, Slade Park, Headington. Oxford OX3 7JL.
01865 716060. Free. Monday–Friday 10am–4pm.

Polish Institute and Sikorski Museum
20 Princes Gate, London SW7 1QA. 0171 589 9249.
Monday–Friday 2pm –4pm.

**Prince of Wales's Own 9th /12th Lancers Regimental
Museum (1972)**
City Museum and Art Gallery, The Strand, Derby
DE1 1BS. 01332 255581. Free. Monday, 11am–5pm;
Tuesday–Saturday, 10am–5pm; Sunday and Bank
Holidays, 2pm–5pm. Nick Forder.

Prince of Wales Regiment of Yorkshire Museum
3A Tower Street York YO1 1SB. 01904 662790. £2/£1.
Monday–Saturday and Bank Holidays 9.30am–
4.30pm; Closed between Christmas and New Years
Day. Includes medals of The West Yorkshire and The
East Yorkshire Regiments, and The Prince of Wales's
Own Regiment of Yorkshire. Lieutenant ColonelT. C.
E. Vines.

**Princess of Wales's Royal Regiment and Queen's
Regiment Museum (1987)**
5 Keep Yard, Dover Castle, Kent CT16 1HU. 01304
240121. E-mail wrrqueensmuseum@tinyworld.co.uk.
£7/£5.30/£3.50. Summer, 10am–6pm daily; winter,
10am–4pm. Major J. C. Rogerson.

Princess Patricia's Canadian Light Infantry Museum
Hatch Court, Hatch Beauchamp, Taunton, Somerset
TA3 6AA. 01823 480120. £2.80/£1. June–September,
Tuesday and Bank Holiday Mondays, 2.30–5pm.
Otherwise by appointment. Dr and Mrs Odgers.

Queen's Dragoon Guards Regimental Museum
Cardiff Castle, Cardiff, South Glamorgan CF1 2RB.
01222 222253. £3/£2/£1.50. March, April and October,
10am–5pm daily. May–September, 10am– 6pm.
November–February, 10am–4.30pm. Gareth Gill.

Queen's Lancashire Regiment (1929) Incorporating East Lancashire Regiment, south lancashire Regiment (Prince of Wales's Volunteers), Loyal Regiment (North Lancashire) Lancashire Regiment. Fulwood Barracks, Preston, Lancs PR2 8AA. 01772 260 362. Free. Tuesdays to Thursdays or by appointment. 9.30am– 4.30pm. Lt Col M. J. Glover MA, AMA.

Queen's Own Highlanders Regimental Museum
Fort George, Cameron Barracks Ardersier, Inverness, IV2 3XD. 01463 224380. Free. April–September, 10am–6pm; October–March, Monday–Friday, 10am–4pm.

Queen's Own Royal West Kent Regimental Museum (1966)
St Faith's Street, Maidstone, Kent ME14 1LH. 01622 754497. Free. Monday–Saturday, 10.00am–5.15pm; Sunday, 11am–4pm. Colonel H.B.H. Waring, OBE.

Queen's Royal Lancers
Belvoir Castle, nr Grantham, Lincs, NG31 6BR. £5/ £4/£3, family ticket £14. March–September, every day, 11am–5pm (except Mondays and Fridays). Captain (Ret) J. M. Holtby.

Queen's Royal Surrey Regimental Museum (1979)
Clandon Park, Guildford, Surrey GU4 7RQ. 01483 223419. April–October, closed Monday, Friday, Saturday. 12–5pm. Penny James.

Royal Air Force Museum (1963)
Grahame Park Way, Hendon, London NW9 5LL. 020 8205 2266, Fax 020 8200 1751. E-mail andrew.cormack@rafmuseum.com. £7.50/£4.90. Daily, 10am–6pm. Dr M. A. Fopp. Medal queries: A. Cormack.

Royal Air Force Regiment Museum (1965)
Royal Air Force Regiment Depot, Royal Air Force Honington, Bury St Edmunds, Suffolk IP31 1EE. 01359 269561. Initially by appointment. Ask for Museum Director/staff.

Royal Armoured Corps Museum (1923)
Bovington Camp, Wareham, Dorset BH20 6JG. 01929 405096/405070 (Library). Charges apply pleae phone for details. Daily 10am–5pm. Closed at Christmas. Colonel (retired) John Woodward.

Royal Armouries Museum (1996)
Waterfront, Leeds City Centre. 0113–245 6465. £6.95+concessions. Daily (except Christmas Eve, Christmas Day and New Year's Day). 10am–5pm (winter), 10am–6pm (summer).

Royal Artillery Regimental Museum (1946)
Firepower, Royal Artillery Museums Ltd, Old Laboratory Office, Royal Arsenal (West), Woolwich, London SE18 6ST. 020 8855 7755. £6.50/£5.50/£4.50. Daily (except Christmas Day) 10.am–5pm.

Royal Devon Yeomanry (1845)
Museum of North Devon, The Square, Barnstaple, Devon EX32 8LN. 01271 346747. Tuesday–Saturday, 10am–4.30pm. Alison Mills

Royal East Kent Regiment, Third Foot (The Buffs) Museum (1961)
Royal Museum and Art Gallery, High Street, Canterbury, Kent CT1 2JE. 01277 452747. Free admission. Monday–Saturday, 10am–5pm. Kenneth Reedie.

Royal Electrical and Mechanical Engineers Museum (1958)
Isaac Newton Road, Arborfield Garrison, Reading, Berks, RG2 9LN. 01734 763567. Free. Monday–Friday, 9am–12.30pm; 2pm–4pm. Weekends by appointment. Closed on Bank holidays. Lieutenant Colonel Larry LeVar.

Royal Engineers Museum
Prince Arthur Road,Gillingham, Kent, ME4 4UG . 01634 406397. £3.50/£2. All year Mon-Thu 10am-5pm. Sat, Sun, BH Mon 11.30am-5pm. Fri by appointment only. Colonel John Nowers.

Royal Fusiliers Museum (1962)
HM Tower of London, EC3N 4AB. 0171 488 5612. 25p. Daily, 9.30am–4.30pm. Maj. B. C. Bowes-Crick.

Royal Gloucester, Berkshire, Wiltshire (Salisbury) Museum (1982)
The Wardrobe, 58 The Close, Salisbury, Wilts SP1 2EX. 01722 414 536. Royal Berkshire, Wiltshire and Duke of Edinburgh's Royal Regiments. See Gloucestershire Regiments Museum for Gloucestershire Regiment. See web site for charges and opening details at www.thewardrobe.org.uk David Chilton.

Royal Green Jackets Museum
Peninsula Barracks, Romsey Road, Winchester. 01962 828549 £2/£1. Monday–Saturday, 10am–5pm; Sunday, 12pm–4pm.

Royal Hampshire Regimental Museum (1933)
Serle's House, Southgate Street, Winchester, Hants SO23 9EG. 01962 863658. Free. All year Monday–Friday 10am–12.30pm, 2pm–4pm. Weekends/Bank holidays April to October only, midday–4pm. Lt–Col. H. D. H. Keatinge.

Royal Highland Fusiliers Regimental Museum (1960)
518 Sauchiehall Street, Glasgow G2 3LW. 0141 332 0961. Free. Monday–Thursday, 9am–4.30pm; Friday, 9am–4pm. W. Shaw, MBE.

Royal Hospital Chelsea
Hospital Road, Chelsea, London SW3 4SL. 020 7881 5202. Fax 020 7881 5463. E-mail roylhospch@aol.com Free. Daily, 10am–12pm; 2pm–4pm.

13th/18th Royal Hussars (Queen Mary's Own) Regiment (1957)
Cannon Hall Museum, Cawthorne, Barnsley, South Yorkshire S75 4AT. 01226 790270. Free. Tuesday–Saturday and Bank holiday Mondays, 10.30am–5pm; Saturday and Sunday, 2.30pm–5pm. Brian Murray.

Royal Inniskilling Fusiliers Regimental Musuem (1938)
The Castle, Enniskillen, Co. Fermanagh, Northern Ireland BT74 7BB. 028 6632 3142. £2 /£1 . Tuesday–Friday, 10-5; Sat 2-5 (May to September), Sunday 2–5. (July & August). Also open Bank Holidays less christmas, boxing & New Year's Day. Major Jack Dunlop.

Royal Irish Fusiliers
Sovereign's House, The Mall, Armagh BT61 9DL. 028 37 522911. rylirfusiliermus@cs.com Weekdays and Bank Holidays 10am–12.30pm and 1.30pm to 4.00pm. Ms Amanda Moreno.

Royal Irish Regiment Museum (1993)
Regimental Headquarters, Royal Irish Rangers, St
Patrick's Barracks, Ballymena, BFPO 808, Northern
Ireland. 01266 661388. Free. Monday–Friday, 10am–
4.30pm. Lieut. Carol Liles.

Royal Leicestershire Regiment Museum (1969)
New Walk Museum, New Walk, Leicester, LE1 7EA.
Free. April to September 2001 Monday-Saturday
10.00am to 5.00pm and Sunday 1.00pm to 5.00pm.
october to end March close at 4.00pm.

Royal Logistic Corps Museum (1995)
Princess Royal Barracks, Deepcut, near Camberley
Surrey GU16 6RW. 01252 340871. Free.Tuesday–
Friday, 9am–4pm; Saturday 10am–3pm; (Easter-end
of September only);closed Sundays and public
holidays. . Major D.F. Hazel

Royal Lincolnshire Regimental Museum (1985)
Burton Road, Lincoln LN1 3LY. 01522 528468. £1/
50p. May–September, daily, 10am–5.30pm. October–
April, Monday–Saturday, 10am–5.30pm; Sunday,
2pm–5.30pm.

Royal Marines Museum (1956)
Southsea, Hants PO4 9PX. 01705 819385. £2.50/
£1.50/ £1.25. Whitsun–September, 9.30am–5pm.
Winter, 9.30am–4.30pm. Col. K. N. Wilkins, OBE.

Royal Military Police Museum (1979)
Rousillon Barracks, Broyle Road, Chichester, West
Sussex PO19 4BN. 01243 534225. Free. April–
September, Tuesday–Friday, 10.30am–12.30pm;
1.30pm–4.30pm; Sat–Sunday, 2pm–6pm. October–
March, Tuesday–Friday, 10.30am–12.30pm; 1.30pm–
4.30pm. Closed January. Lt-Col. Maurice Squier.

**Royal National Lifeboat Institution
Museum (1937)**
Grand Parade, Eastbourne, East Sussex BN21 4BY.
01323 730717. Free. April–December, 9.30am–5pm
daily. January–March, Monday–Friday, 9.30am–
5pm. J. M. Shearer.

Royal National Lifeboat Institution Museum (1969)
Pen-y-Cae, Barmouth, Gwynedd. Free. Easter–
October, 10.30am–6.30pm, daily.

Royal Naval Museum (1911)
HM Naval Base, Portsmouth PO1 3LR. 01705 733060.
£2/£1.75. Daily, 10.30am–5pm. H. Campbell Murray.

Royal Norfolk Regimental Museum (1945)
Shirehall, Market Avenue, Norwich NR1 3JQ. 01603
223649. 80p/40p. Monday–Saturday, 10am–5pm;
Sunday, 2pm–5pm. Kate Thaxton.

**Royal Northumberland Fusiliers Regimental
Museum (1970)**
The Abbot's Tower, Alnwick Castle, Alnwick, NE66
1NG. 01665 602152 / 510211. Easter–October, 11am–
5pm daily. Captain Peter H. D. Marr.

Royal Observer Corps' Museum
Newhaven Fort, Newhaven, East Sussex.
Tel: 01273 517622.

Royal Scots Regimental Museum (1951)
The Castle, Edinburgh EH1 2YT. 0131 310 5016. Free.
April–September, Monday–Sunday, 0900–1730; .
October–March, Monday–Friday, 0930–1600.
Lieutenant Colonel R. P. Mason.

Royal Signals Museum (1967)
Blandford Camp, Blandford, Dorset DT11 8RH.
01258 482086. Free. Monday–Friday, 10am–5pm;
Saturday, Sunday (June–September only) 10am–
4pm.

**Royal Sussex Regimental Museum (1930) also the
4th Queen's Own Hussars; 8th King's Royal Irish
Hussars; Queen's Royal Irish Hussars Museums**
Redoubt Fortress, Royal Parade, Eastbourne, East
Sussex BN21 4BP. 01323 410300. £1.50/£1. April–
October. Other times by appointment. B. R. Burns.

**Royal The Tank Museum (1923) Royal Armoured
Corps Museum (1923)**
Bovington Camp, Wareham, Dorset BH20 6JG. 01929
405096/405070 (Library). Charges apply pleae phone
for details. Daily 10am–5pm. Closed at Christmas.
Colonel (retired) John Woodward.

Royal Ulster Constabulary Museum (1983)
Brooklyn, Knock Road, Belfast BT5 6LE. (028) 90
650222 Ext 22499. Free. Monday–Friday, 9am–5pm.
Hugh Forrester.

Royal Ulster Rifles Museum (1935)
5 Waring Street, Belfast BT1 2EW.028 9023 2086. One
UK ound. Monday–Friday, 10am–12.30pm; 2pm–
4pm. (Friday 3pm) Major R. J. Walker. Web Site:
http//rurmuseum.tripod.com/

Royal Warwickshire Regimental Museum (1928)
St John's House, Warwick CV34 4NF. 01926 491653.
Free. Tuesday–Saturday, 10am–12.30pm; 1.30pm–
5.30pm; Sunday, 2.30pm–5pm. Brigadier J. K.
Chater.

Royal Welch Fusiliers Museum (1955)
Caernarfon Castle, Gwynedd LL55 2AY. 01286
673362. Fax: 01286 677042. Open daily except 1 Jan
and 24–26 Dec, from 9.30am (11am Sundays in
winter). Closes 6pm(summer), 5pm (Spring/
Autumn), 4 pm (winter). Peter Crocker.

St Helier, Elizabeth Castle and Militia Museum
St Helier, Jersey, Channel Islands. 01534 23971. £2/
£1. April–October, daily, 10am–5pm.

Sandhurst Royal Military Academy (1960)
Royal Military Academy Sandhurst, Camberley
GU15 4PQ. 01276 63344 ext 2457. Free, by
appointment only.

**School of Infantry and Small Arms School Corps
Weapons Museum (1953)**
School of Infantry, Warminster, BA12 0DJ. 01985
842487. Free. Daily, 9am–4.30pm. Lieut-Colonel Tug
Wilson, MBE.

**Sherwood Foresters Regimental Museum
(1923)**
The Castle, Nottingham. 0115 946 5415. Monday–
Friday free; weekends and Bank holidays. £1.50/
80p. Daily 10am–5pm except Friday between
November and February when 1–5pm. Closed
Christmas Day and Boxing Day.

Shropshire Regimental Museum (1985)
The Castle, Shrewsbury, S71 2AT. 01743 358516. £3/
£1. Open every day except Monday April–
September, October–March closed Sundays and
Monday. 10am–4.30pm. Peter Duckers.

Soldiers of Gloucestershire Museum
Custom House, Gloucester Docks, Gloucester GL1 2HE. 01452 522682. Medals of the Gloucestershire Regiment Royal Gloucestershire Hussars. Open all year round. closed Mondays in winter 10am-5pm. Entrance charge.

Somerset Military Museum (1974)
Somerset County Museum, Taunton Castle, Taunton, Somerset TA1 1AA. 01823 320201. £2.50/ £2/£1. Tuesday–Saturday, 10am–5pm. Lieutenant Colonel David Eliot.

South Nottinghamshire Hussars Museum (1974)
TA Centre, Hucknall Lane, Bulwell, Nottingham NG6 8AB. 0115 9272251. Free, by appointment only.

South Wales Borderers and Monmouthshire Regimental Museum (1934)
The Barracks, Brecon, Powys LD3 7EB. 01874 623111 ext 2310. £1. October–March, Monday–Friday, 9am–1pm; 2pm–5pm. April–September, daily except Sunday, same hours. Major Bob Smith.

South Wales Police Museum (1950)
Police Headquarters, Cowbridge Road, Bridgend, CF31 3SU. 01656 655555 ext 28057. Free. Monday–Thursday, 9am–5pm; Friday, 9am–4.30pm. by appointment. Out of hours visits can usually be accommodated if notice is given. Julia Mason.

Staff College Museum (1958)
Staff College, Camberley, Surrey GU15 4NP. 01276 412662/412647/412650. Free, by appointment only. Colonel Philip S. Newton, MBE.

Staffordshire Regimental Museum (1962)
Whittington Barracks, Lichfield, Staffs WS14 9PY. 0121 311 3240/3229. £2/£1 family ticket £5. All year Tuesday to Friday 10am-4pm Apr-Oct Satr, Sun, Bank Holidays 12.30pm-4.30pm. closed Xmas & New Year period. Archieves and school parties by appointment. Major E. Green.

Suffolk Regimental Museum (1967)
The Keep, Gibraltar Barracks, Bury St Edmunds, Suffolk IP33 1HF. 01284 752394. Free. Weekdays, 10am–12pm; 2pm–4pm. Major A. G. B. Cobbold.

Sussex & Surrey Yeomanry Museum (1993)
Newhaven Fort, Newhaven, East Sussex. Tel: 01273 611055; April–October, other times by appointment. Hon. curator Keith Fuller.

Tangmere, Military Aviation Museum (1992)
Tangmere, near Chichester, West Sussex PO20 6ES. 01243 775223. £3/50p. February–November, daily, 11am–5.30pm. Andy Saunders.

The Keep Military Museum (1927)
The Keep, Bridport Road, Dorchester, Dorset DT1 1RN. 01305 264066. £2.50/£1.50. Monday–Friday, 9.30am–5pm. Sat./Bank hols 9.30am–1pm and 2pm–5pm. Sundays in August 10am–4pm. Major J. Carroll.

Towneley Hall Art Gallery and Museum (1902)
Burnley, Lancs BB11 3RQ. 01282 424213. Free. Monday–Friday, 10am–5pm; Sunday, 12pm–5pm. Small collection including two VCs, other unique items seen by appointment. Susan Bourne.

Welch Regiment Museum (1927)
The Black and Barbican Towers, Cardiff Castle, Cardiff, South Glamorgan CF1 2RB. 01222 229367. £2/£1. Daily 10am–6pm (April–October), 10am–4.30pm (November–March). Lieut. Bryn Owen, RN.

Wellington Museum
Apsley House, 149 Piccadilly, Hyde Park Corner, London W1J 7NT. 0207 499 5676. Free to under 18s/ over 60s; otherwise £4.40/£3. Tuesday–Sunday 11.00am–5.00pm. Alicia Robinson.

West Midlands Police Museum (1991)
Sparkhill Police Station, 641 Stratford Road, Birmingham B11 6EA. Free, by apppointment only.

Woodbridge, 390th Bomb Group Memorial Air Museum (1981)
Parham Airfield, Parham, Woodbridge, Suffolk. 01359 51209. Free. Sundays and Bank Holidays, 11am–6pm.

Worcestershire Regimental Museum (1925)
City Museum and Art Gallery, Foregate Street, Worcester. WR1 1DT.01905 25371. Free. Monday–Friday, 9.30am–5.30pm; Saturday, 9.30am–5pm. Major David Reeve. Archives: 01905 354359, by appointment.

York, Divisional Kohima Museum (1991)
Imphal Barracks, Fulford Road, York YO1 4AY. 01904 662381. Free, by appointment only.

York, Yorkshire Air Museum and Allied Air Forces Memorial (1984)
Halifax Way, Elvington, York YO4 5AU. 01904 605595. £2.50/£1.50. Monday–Friday, 10.30am–4pm; weekends, 10.30am–5pm. Peter Douthwaithe.

York and Lancaster Regimental Museum (1947)
Brian O'Malley Central Library and Art Gallery, Walker Place, Rotherham, Yorkshire S65 1JH. 01709 382 121 ext 3625. Free. Tuesday–Saturday, 10am–5pm. Don Scott.

www.speedbid.com

YOUR OWN MEDAL AUCTION

Professional directory

On the following pages are the names and addresses of auctioneers, dealers, booksellers and fair organisers, all of whom will be of assistance to the medal collector. Most are full time and many have retail shops and the collector is usually welcome during normal business hours. Some have extensive stocks of medals whilst others include medals in a more diverse inventory. A number of dealers are part time or work from small premises or from home and appointments are necessary as many keep their stock in the bank for security. Telephone numbers have been included where known and it is always sensible to make contact before travelling any distance.

AUCTIONEERS

The following hold regular medal auctions or feature medals in general numismatic or militaria sales.

Bosleys

The White House, Marlow, Bucks SL7 1AH. 01628 488188 (fax: 01628 488111). Specialist auctioneers of medals and militaria. Website: www.bosleys.co.uk.

Dix Noonan Webb

1 Old Bond Street, London W1X 3TD. 020 7499 5022 (fax 020 7499 5023). Auctioneers and valuers. Regular auctions of medals. E-mail: auctions@dnw.co.uk, Website: www.dnw.co.uk.

Downie's Militaria

7th Floor, 343 Little Collins Street, Melbourne, Vic 3000, Australia. (03) 670 0500 (fax 03 670 0311). Sales with emphasis on Australian and UK medals.

Floyd, Johnson & Paine

PO Box 9791, Alexandria, VA 22304, USA. (703) 461 9582 (fax 703 461 3059). Auctions of medals and militaria.

B. Frank and Son

3 South Avenue, Ryton, Tyne & Wear NE40 3LD. Tel: 0191 413 8749 (fax: 0191 413 2957). E-mail: bfrankandson@aol.com.

Glendining's

101 New Bond Street, London W1S 1SR. 020 7493 2445 (fax 020 7491 9181). Auctioneers and valuers of medals. Approximately four sales per year. Website: www.phillips-auctions.com.

Jeffrey Hoare Auctions Inc.

319 Springbank Dr., London, Ontario, Canada, N6J 1G6. (519) 473 7491 (fax (519) 473 1541). Regular sales of medals, badges and militaria.

Edinburgh Coin Shop

11 West Crosscauseway, Edinburgh EH8 9JW. Tel: 0131 668 2928 or 0131 667 9005 (fax: 0131 668 2926). Regular postal auctions of medals.

Lockdales

36 Upper Orwell Street, Ipswich, IP4 1HR. Tel: 01473 218588. Regular sales. Call for venue.

Morten & Eden

50 Regent Street, London W1B 5RD. Tel: 020 7470 7220, fax: 020 7470 7221. New advisory service and auction house.

Postal Auctions

PO Box 4087, Hornchurch, Essex RM11 2BP. Eight sales of medals and related items per year. Website: www.medalauctions.demon.co.uk.

Spink & Son Ltd (Christie's International)

69 Southampton Row, Bloomsbury, London WC1B 4ET. 020 7563 4000 (fax 020 7563 4066). Auctioneers and valuers. Regular sales of medals and militaria.

Wallis & Wallis

West Street Auction Galleries, Lewes, Sussex BN7 2NJ. 01273 480208 (fax 01273 476562). Regular sales of militaria, arms, armour and medals. E-mail: auctions@wallisandwallis.co.uk, Website: http://www.wallisandwallis.co.uk.

Ware Militaria Auctions

The Function Rooms, Hertford Rugby Club, Hoe Lane, Ware, Herts. Bi-monthly auctions, Tel: 01920 871901.

Warwick & Warwick

Chalon House, Scar Bank, Millers Road, Warwick CV34 5DB. Tel: 01296 499031 (fax 01926 491906). Regular sales of Orders, Decorations and other collectables. E-mail: info@warwickandwarwick.com

Whytes Auctioneers

30, Marlborough Street, Dublin 1, Ireland. Tel: (+3531) 874 6161 (fax: +3531 874 6020). Auctioneers and valuers. Regular sales. E-mail: whytes@iol.ie, Website: www.whytes.ie.

INTERNET AUCTIONS

Speedbid www.speedbid.com
www.bids-on.com
E-bay www.ebay.co.uk
Amazon/Sothebys amazon.sothebys.co.uk

DEALERS

Ackley Unlimited
PO Box 82144, Portland, Oregon, USA 97282-0144. (503) 659 4681. Orders, medals and decorations. Free quarterly lists on request.

Armoury of St. James's
17 Piccadilly Arcade, Piccadilly, London SW1Y 6NH. 020 7493 5082 (fax 020 7499 4422). Orders, decorations, medals, militaria.

Ashley, Brooks & Jervis
PO Box 322, Rochester, Kent ME1 1LX. 01634 845287, website www.photoarchive.co.uk. British and foreign medals and badges. Lists.

Michael Autengruber
Schillstrasse 7B, D-63067 Offenbach, Germany. (69) 88 69 25 evenings. Orders, medals, literature. Catalogues $US3 (Europe), $US6 (elsewhere).

Bonus Eventus
Aartshertoginnestratt 27, 8400 Oostende, Belgium. (059) 801696. Medals and miniature medals. Free medal lists (specify full-size or miniatures).

Bostock Militaria
"Pinewood", 15 Waller Close, Leek Wootton, near Warwick CV35 7QG. 01926 856381. British orders, medals and decorations. S.a.e. for free current lists. Callers welcome by appointment.

Award Productions Ltd
PO Box 300, Shrewsbury, SY5 6WP. 01952 510053 (fax: 01952) 510765). Suppliers of unofficial medals for veterans.

Paul Boulden
Parade Antiques Market, 17 The Parade, The Barbican, Plymouth, Devon. 01752 221443. Fax: 01589 632686. Medals and militaria. 6 lists p.a. (£3, £6 overseas).

Boyne Coins & Medals
Trim Road, Navan, Co. Meath, Ireland. (00353 46) 21079. Coins and medals. Many Irish medals stocked.

British Military Badges
The Castle Armoury, 18 Castle Street, Dover, Kent CT16 1PW. 12pp list of British Military Badges. UK & BFPOs £2, Europe £2.40, Elsewhere £3.

Philip Burman
Blackborough End, Middleton, King's Lynn, Norfolk PE32 1SE. 01553 840350. Large and varied stock of orders, medals and decorations. Send large sae for lists, issued 6 times a year.
Website: www.military-medals.co.uk.

John Burridge
91 Shenton Road, Swanbourne, Western Australia 6010. British and Commonwealth medals and decorations.

Mark Carter
PO Box 470, Slough SL3 6RR. 01753 534777. British and foreign orders, medals, decorations and miniatures. Fairs organiser. Lists £5 (UK and BFPO), £7.50 (overseas airmail)

Central Antiques Arms & Militaria
Smith Street Antiques Centre, Warwick CV34 4JA. 01926 400554. British orders, decorations, medals and militaria. List 50p.

Chelsea Military Antique
Unit N13/14, Antiquarius, 131–141 King's Road, London SW3 4PW. 020 7352 0308. Medals and militaria. Monday–Saturday, 10am–6pm.
E-mail: richard@chelseamilitaria.co.uk,
Website: www.chelseamilitaria.co.uk.

Chester Militaria
6 Chirk Close, Newton, Chester CH2 1SF. 01244 344268. Medals and militaria.

Coldstream Military Antiques
The White House, Arlow, Bucks SL7 1AH. 01628 488188 (fax: 01628 488111) Medals, badges, insignia.

Collector's Lair
#205 - 15132 Stony Plain Road, Edmonton, Alberta, Canada T5P 3X8. (403) 486 2907. Medals, badges and uniforms.

Norman W. Collett
PO Box 235, London SE23 1NS. Tel/fax: (020) 8291 1435. British medals and decorations, mainly groups, with an accent on researchable recipients.
Medals Website: www.medalsonline.co.uk.

Jonathon Collins
17 Queens Road, Warsash, Hampshire SO31 9JY. Tel/fax: 01489 582222. Naval, Miliary, and Airforce Research Service. E-mail: jcollinsmedals.co.uk,
Website:www.jcollinsmedals.co.uk.

Command Post of Militaria
1306 Government Street, Victoria, British Columbia, Canada V8W 1Y8. (250) 383 4421. Medals, badges and uniforms.

Conglomerate Coins & Medals
206 Adelaide Street, Brisbane, Queensland 4000, Australia. (07) 2211217 (fax 07 2299128). Medals and medallions.

Corby Medal Centre
Unit 5, Howitts Courtyard, 291 Rockingham Road, Corby, Northamptonshire NN17 2AE. 01536 266750 (Weekends only) Good range of medals to suit all pockets.

Peter R. Cotrel
7 Stanton Road, Bournemouth, Dorset BH10 5DS. Mail order only—callers by appointment. 01202 388367. British, American and general foreign medals and decorations. Medal albums etc.

Jamie Cross
PO Box 73, Newmarket, Suffolk CB8 8RY. Specialist in Third Reich medals, badges and decorations.

C. J. & A. J. Dixon Ltd
23 Prospect Street, Bridlington, East Yorkshire YO15 2AE. 01262 676877 (fax 01262 606600). British and world orders, medals and decorations. 4 large lists a year £12 (UK), £16 (overseas).
E-mail: chris@dixonsmedals.co.uk,
Website: www.dixonsmedals.co.uk.

D.M.D. Services
6 Beehive Way, Reigate, Surrey RH2 8DY. 01737 240080. Victorian campaign medals and decorations.

Frank Draskovic
PO Box 803, Monterey Park, CA 91754, USA. Worldwide orders and medals, especially European and Far Eastern. E-mail: fdraskovic@ hotmail.com.

M. J. Dyas Coins and Medals
Unit 3, 42 Stratford Road, Shirley, Solihull B90 3LS. 0121 733 2225. All medals—memorial plaques a speciality. Lists £1 (UK), £2 (overseas).

Edinburgh Coin Shop (Hiram T. D. Brown)
11 West Crosscauseway, Edinburgh EH8 9JW. 0131 668 2928 (fax 0131 668 2926). British medals and decorations. 4 lists a year and postal auctions.

Elite-Collections.Com
PO Box 56, pontypridd, CF37 2YL, South Wales. 30 page catalogue of British medals. Annual Subscription (10 issues) £5 (UK), Free on e-mail. www.elite-collections.com.

Andy Garrett
Unit 9, Brackley Antique Cellar, Draymans Walk, Brackley, Northants NN13 6BE. British and foreign medals, groups and collections, badges and militaria.

Gateway Militaria
Box 24049, 13 - 1853 Grant Avenue, Winnipeg, Manitoba, Canada R3N 1ZO. (204) 489 3884 (fax 204 489 9118). Medals and badges.

GB Militaria
Tel: 0207-704-0634. British medals, awards and militaria. E-mail: info@gbmilitaria.com, Website: www.gbmilitaria.com.

Glance Back
17 Upper Church Street, Chepstow, Gwent NP6 5EX. 01291 626562. Large stock of Medals, badges and military books.

Gordons Medals & Military Collectables
Grays Antiques Centre, Davies Mews, Davies Street, London W1K 5AB. 020 7495 0900 (fax 020 7495 0115). Monday–Friday, 10.30am–6pm. Campaign medals, militaria, German and 3rd Reich. Catalogues £6 (UK), £12 (overseas air). Email: sales@gordonsmedals.co.uk, Website:www.gordonsmedals.co.uk.

Louis E. Grimshaw
612 Fay Street, R.R. #1 Kingston, Ontario, Canada K7L 4VI. (613) 549 2500. Military antiques and collectables, including medals. Catalogues of arms, medals and militaria . Single copies $C5 (Canada), $US4 (USA), $US6 (elsewhere).

Great War Medals
22 Selborne Road, Southgate, London N14 7DH. Mainly WW1 medals and books. 36 page catalogue of medals and decorations, £7.50 (UK), £11 (overseas).

W. D. Grissom
PO Box 12001, Suite 216, Chula Vista, California, USA 91912. American medals. Free lists.

Alec Kaplan & Son CC
P.O. box 28913, Sandringham 2131, Johannesburg, South Africa. E-mail: rhodesia@iafrica.com. Medals and militaria. Regular auctions.

Tom Halpin
268 Gilmore Street, Mineola, NY 11501, USA. 516-248-4673. Fax: 516 248 6082. Worldwide awards with other military (all services) items. Large newspaper-style list.

A. D. Hamilton & Co.
7 St. Vincent Place, Glasgow G1 2DW. 0141 221 5423 (fax 0141 248 6019). British and foreign medals, groups and collections, badges and militaria. Monday-Saturday, 9 am - 5.30 pm. Email:jeffrey@hamiltons.junglelink.co.uk, Website: www.adhamiltons.com.

Raymond D. Holdich
Trafalgar Square Collectors' Centre, 7 Whitcomb Street, London WC2 7HA. 020 7930 1979. Monday–Friday, 11am–5.30pm. Saturday by appointment only. British gallantry awards, campaign medals, cap badges, medals and decorations. E-mail: rdhmedals@aol.com, Website: www.rhmedals.com.

Invicta International
740 Gladstone Avenue, Ottawa, Ontario, Canada K1R 6X5. (613) 232 2263. Worldwide medals, badges, insignia, wings, books and prints.

Steve Johnson
USA: PO Box 745, Batavia, IL 60510, USA. (630) 761 4004 (Fax: (630) 761 4006). UK: Woodbridge, Derwant Avenue, Rowlands Gill, Tyne & Wear NE39 1BZ. All World orders, medals, decorations and militaria.

Paul laycock
6 Poplar Terrace, Moldgreen, Huddersfield, W. Yorks HD5 8AB. British medals and decorations. Regular lists.

Liverpool Medal Company Ltd.
42 Bury Business Centre, Kay Street, Bury, Lancs BL9 6BU. 0161 7634010/4612 (Fax: 0161 7634963). British and World medals and decorations. Regular lists. E-mail: liverpoolmedals@online.rednet.co.uk, Website: www.liverpoolmedals.co.uk.

March Medals
199 Springthorpe Road, Erdington, Birmingham B24 0SJ. 0121 373 2020. Orders of chivalry, decorations, campaign medals, military antiques, books, ribbons and accessories. Regular lists. Monday–Friday, 10am–5pm; Saturday, 10am–2pm.

Medals of Service
926 Old northern Road, Glenorie NSW 2157, Australia. 61 02 9652 2022 (Fax: 61 02 9652 2950). Specialising in replica medals.

M.K. Medals
31, Butlers Grove, Great Linford, Milton Keynes, Bucks MK14 5DT. Tel: 01908 393383. Quality orders, decorations and military medals from all periods. E-mail: mkmedal@hotmail.com, Website: www.mkmedals.co.uk,

Merseyside Collectors Centre
Unit C110-111, Market Hall, Grange Precinct, Birkenhead, Merseyside L41 2YH. Tel/fax: 0151 666 1431. Medals and militaria.

Militaria House
238 Davenport Road, PO Box 99, Toronto, Ontario Canada M5R 1J6. Mail bid auctions of decorations, medals, insignia and militaria. 4 catalogues per year $25 (US Canada), $30 (overseas).

Miniature Medals
MC Miniature Medals, PO Box 1512, Warwick CV 35 9YX. Tel/fax: 01926 651500. Miniature medal specialist. Lists.

Peter Morris
1 Station Concourse, Bromley North Railway Station, Kent. Postal: PO Box 223, Bromley, Kent BR1 4EQ. 020 8313 3410 (shop hours), 020 8466 1762 (other times). Monday–Friday, 10am–6pm; Saturday, 9am–2pm. Free quarterly lists. E-mail: info@petermorris.co.uk, Website: www.petermorris.co.uk.

Neate Militaria & Antiques
PO Box 3794, Preston St Mary, Sudbury CO10 9PX. 01787 248168 (fax 01787 248363). Monday-Friday, 9am-6pm. Lists available, £6 (UK, EC), £10 (overseas). E-mail: gary@neatemedals.fsnet.co.uk.

Detlev Niemann
Ballindamm 9, V Floor, 20095 Hamburg 1, Germany. 0049 40 3252 5354 (fax 0049 40 3252 5454). Specialist in German orders, decorations, militaria, etc. Catalogue subscription £20 for 4 issues.
E-mail: Detlev-Niemann@t-online.de,
Website: www.Detlev-Niemann.de.

Nordheide-Versand
Nordheid-Versand Kai Winkler, Fachenfelderweg 67, D-21220 Seevetal. Tel: (0 41 05) 8 43 84, Fax: (0 41 05) 8 27 88. Medals, awards, award-documents, miniatures, pins, uniforms etc.
Website: http://www.nordheideversand.de.

Pieces of History
PO Box 4470, Cave Creek, AZ 85331, USA. (602) 488 1377 (fax 602 488 1316). Worldwide medals badges, patches, accessories etc. Lists available.

Q & C Militaria
22 Suffolk Road, Cheltenham, Gloucestershire GL50 2AQ. Tel/fax 01242 519815. British and Commonwealth orders, medals, decorations and miltaria. Website: www.qcmilitaria.com.

R & M International
PO Box 6278, Bellevue, Washington, USA. 98008-0278. Well illustrated 64 page lists of medals and decorations of the world, $US2.50.
Website: www.randminternational.com.

Barbara Radman
Westfield House, 2G Westfield Road, Witney, Oxon OX8 5JG. 01993 772705. British and Foreign orders, medals and decorations. Specialist in Serbia, Montenegro, Russian and Baltic States.

Romsey Medals
5 Bell Street, Romsey, Hampshire SO51 8GY. 01794 512069 (fax 01794 830332). Orders, medals and decorations. Website: www.romseymedals.co.uk.

S. E. Sewell
PO Box 104, Ipswich, Suffolk IP5 7QL. 01473 626950. A wide variety of medals, mainly British.

George M. Shank
1574 Arnold Ct., Huntingdon, W. Va. 25705, USA. 304-736-8730. Worldwide orders, medals and decorations. Large lists.

E. C. Snaith & Son Ltd
20 Vale Street, Denbigh, Denbighshire LL16 3BE. Tel: 01745 812218 Fax: 01745 816367. Wholesalers to the Medal Trade.

Southern Medals
16 Broom Grove, Knebworth, Herts SG3 6BQ. 32 page lists of British and Commonwealth medals and decorations. £6 (UK), £9 (overseas).

Spink & Son Ltd (Christie's International)
69 Southampton Row, Bloomsbury, London WC1B 4ET. 020 7563 4000 (fax 020 7563 4066). Dealers, auctioneers. The Medal Gallery, Monday-Friday, 9am–5.30pm (Tues. to 7.30pm). Publishers of *Spink Medal Quarterly*, £8 (UK), £15 or $US25 (overseas).
E-mail: info@spinkandson.com,
Website: www.spink-online.com.

Sunset Militaria
Dinedor Cross, Herefordshire HR2 6PF. 01432 870420 (fax: 01432 870309). Military research and world medal ribbons. SAE for list.

Suttle Medals and Militaria
50 Lackey Street, Summer Hill, NSW 2130, Australia. Tel/fax 61 02 9798 6113. Medals, militaria, books, uniforms, etc.

Jeremy Tenniswood
PO Box 73, Aldershot, Hants GU11 1HJ. Tel: 01252 319791 (fax 01252 342339) website www.militaria.co.uk. Orders, medals decorations and militaria and related books.

Third Arm Militaria
PO Box 121, Market Rasen, Lincs LN8 3GF. 01673 828081. Specialising in Campaign Medals and British Army Insignia.

Toad Hall Medals
Court Road, Newton Ferrers, near Plymouth, South Devon PL8 1DH. 01752 872672 (fax 01752 872723). Lists available. E-mail: th.medals@virgin.net.

Toye, Kenning & Spencer Ltd
Regalia House, Newtown Road, Bedworth, Warwickshire CV12 8QR. 01203 315 634 (fax 01203 643 018). Manufacturers of miniature medals, medal ribbons, badges, etc.

Treasure Bunker Militaria Shop
21 King Street, The Trongate, Glasgow G1 5QZ. Tel/Fax: 0141 552 4651. Medals, badges, uniforms etc. From Waterloo to World War II. E-mail: info@treasure bunker.com, Website: www.treasurebunker.com.

Matthew Tredwen
PO Box 318, Bromley, BR1 2UX. (07939 252 206). British campaign and gallantry medals.
E-mail: enquiries@militaryantiques.co.uk.
Website: www.militaryantiques.co.uk.

Eugene G. Ursual
PO Box 8096, Ottawa, Ontario, Canada K1G 3H6. (613) 521 9691 (fax 613 523 3347). Medals, orders, decorations, miniatures and militaria. 10 lists a year $12 (Canada), $15 (USA), $20 (overseas)

Vernon
Box 1560MN, Wildomar, California, USA 92595. Worldwide orders, medals and decorations. Lists 10 times a year, $3 (USA), $20 (overseas airmail).

Fred S. Walland
17 Gyllyngdune Gardens, Seven Kings, Essex IG3 9HH. 020 8590 4389. Orders, medals and decorations. Lists £7.50 (UK and BFPO), £15 (overseas).

Welsh Medals & Militaria
1 Mortimer Road, Cardiff CF1 9JZ. 01222 374202. Medals, coins and militaria.

Ian Wise—MK Medals
31 Butlers Grove, Great Linford, Milton Keynes, Bucks MK14 5DT. 01908 393383.
Website: www.mkmedals@hotmail.com,
E-mail: mkmedals@hotmail.com.

Worcestershire Medal Service Ltd
56 Broad Street, Sidemoor, Bromsgrove, B61 8LL. 01527 835375 (fax: 01527 576798). Specialists in ribbons, full size and mini. medals, mounting and cases. E-mail: WMS@WORCMEDALS.COM,
Website: www.worcmedals.com.

Yeovil Collectors Centre
16 Hendford, Yeovil, Somerset BA20 1TE. 01935 433739. Medals, badges, etc. Occasional lists.

Carston Zeige
Carsten Zeige, Dammtorstr. 29, D-20354 Hamburg, Germany. Tel: +49 40 35713636. German and Foreign orders and decorations. Military items and books. Catalogue subscription $35, for 5 issues.
E-mail: info@zeige.com, Website: www.ziege.com.

BOOKSELLERS/DEALERS

In addition to the names listed below, it should be noted that a number of the medal dealers listed above regularly or occasionally include books on their medal lists.

Articles of War
8806 N. Bronx Avenue, Skokie, IL60077-1896, USA. 847 674-7445 (fax 847 674-7449. e-mail warbooks@aol.com). Dealer in military books, domestic and imported, both new and second-hand.

Aviation Bookshop
656 Holloway Road, London N19 3PD. 020 7272 3630. Aviation history—books, magazines, posters and videos.

Battlefield Military Bookstore
3915 Highway 7, Minneapolis, MN 55416, USA. 612 920-3820. Wide range of military books.

Buffo Books
32 Tadfield Road, Romsey, Hants SO51 8AJ. 01794 517149. Mainly 20th century military history, especially Second World War.

Bunker to Bunker Books
PO Box 342, 1631 St Mary's Road, Winnipeg, Canada MB R2N 3X9. General but with a focus on Canadian-related material.

Andrew Burroughs
24 St. Martins, Stamford, Lincolnshire PE9 2LJ. 01780 51363. Military history. Lists available.

Buttercross Books
2 The Paddock, Bingham, Nottingham NG13 8HQ. Tel/fax 0115 9 837147. Napoleonic era and First World War. Lists available.

Caliver Books
816/818 London Road, Leigh-on-Sea, Essex SS9 3NH. Tel/fax 01702 73986. Military history up to 1900. Shop and mail order. Lists available.

Chelifer Books
Todd Close, Curthwaite, Wigton, Cumbria CA7 8BE. General military history, including unit histories. Lists available.

The Collector
36 The Colonnade, Piece Hall, Halifax, West Yorks HX1 1RS. Military, naval and aviation history, all periods.

Q. M. Dabney & Company
PO Box 42026-MH, Washington, DC 20015, USA. Military books of all periods. Lists $US1 each.

Peter de Lotz
20 Downside Crescent, Hampstead, London NW3 2AP. 020 7794 5709. (Fax 020 7284 3058). Military, naval and aviation history, with emphasis on regimental and divisional histories.

Tom Donovan Military Books
52 Willow Road, Hampstead, London NW3 1TP. 020 7431 2474 (fax 020 7431 8314). Printed works, documentation and manuscript material relating to the British Military Services. Regular lists.

Francis Edwards
13 Great Newport Street, Charing Cross Road, London WC2H 4JA. 020 7379 7669 (fax 020 7836 5977). All aspects of military history. Lists available.

Chris Evans Books
Unit 6, Jervoise Drive, Birmingham B31 2XU. Tel/fax 0121 477 6700. General military history. Lists available.

Falconwood Transport and Military Bookshop.
5 Falconwood Parade, The Green, Welling, Kent DA16 2PL. 020 8303 8291. Military, naval and aviation history.

Kenneth Fergusson
The Book Room, The Post Office, Twyning, Tewkesbury, Glos GL20 6DF. 01684 295855. Military and aviation history.

Ken Ford Military Books
93 Nutshalling Avenue, Rownhams, Southampton SO1 8AY. 023 8073 9437. British colonial wars. Lists available.

John Gaunt
21 Harvey Road, Bedford MK41 9LF. 01234 217686. Numismatic books including medal reference works.

GM Services
98 Junction Road, Andover, Hampshire SP10 3JA. Tel/fax 01264 362048. Postal auctions of military books.

Tony Gilbert Antique Books
101 Whipps Cross Road, Leytonstone, London E11 1NW. 020 8530 7472. Military, naval and aviation history.

Martin Gladman
235 Nether Street, Finchley, London N3 1NT. 020 8343 3023. Military, naval and aviation history.

G. L. Green.
18 Aldenham Avenue, Radlett, Herts WD7 8HX. 01923 857077. Naval and maritime history.

George Harris
Heathview, Habberley Road, Bewdley, Worcs DY12 1JH. 01299 402413. Napoleonic, Victorian campaigns and the First World War.

Derek Hayles Military Books
35 St. Marks Road, Maidenhead, Berks SL6 6DJ. 01628 39535. Regular lists.

Hersant's Military Books
17 The Drive, High Barnet, Herts EN5 4JG. Tel/fax 020 8440 6816. General military history. Lists available by period.

Michael Hicks Beach
99 York Mansions, London SW11 4BN. 020 7622 2270. British and Imperial military history.

Jade Publishing Ltd
5 Leefields Close, Uppermill, Oldham, Lancs OL3 6LA. 01475 870944. British and imperial military books.

Jerboa-Redcap Books
PO Box 1058, Highstown, N.J. 08520, USA. (609) 443 3817. British military books (all services), including collectables. Catalogues $US2.

Keegan's Bookshop
Merchant's Place, Reading RG1 1DT. Phone/fax 01734 587253. Secondhand booksellers with good stock of military titles. Shop in town centre. Parking nearby.

Roger Knowles
26 Church Road, Norton Canes, Cannock, Staffs WS11 3PD. 01543 279313. Military history

John Lewcock
6 Chewells Lane, Haddenham, Ely, Cambs CB6 3SS. 01353 741152. Naval history.

Liverpool Medal Company Ltd
42 Bury Business Centre, Kay Street, Bury, Lancs BL9 6BU. 0161 763 4610/4612 (fax 0161 763 4963). Medal dealers, but publish an occasional separate book catalogue.

London Pride
14E Fort Lee Road, Bogota, NJ 07603, USA. 201 525-1828 (fax 201 525-0815). General military books.

Ian Lynn
258 Upper Fant Road, Maidstone, Kent ME16 8BX. 01622 728525. Military history.

Marcet Books
4a Nelson Road, Greenwich, London SE10 9JB. 020 8853 5408. Naval history.

G. & D. I. Marrin & Sons
149 Sandgate Road, Folkestone, Kent CT20 2DA. 01303 253016 (fax 01303 850956) Specialises in material relating to the First World War.

McLaren Books
91 West Clyde Street, Helensburgh, Dunbartonshire G84 8BB. 01436 676453. Naval history.

Midland Counties Publications
Unit 3, Maizefield, Hinckley, Leicestershire LE10 1YF. 01455 233747. Aviation books.

Military Bookman
29 East 93rd Street, New York, NY 10128, USA. (212) 348 1280. Large stock of military history relating to all services worldwide and all periods.

Military Bookworm
PO Box 235, London SE23 1NS. Tel/Fax: (020) 8291 1435. Regimental and divisional histories, campaign histories, biographies, school registers, army lists, etc.
Books Website: www.militarybookworm.co.uk.

Military History Bookshop
2 Broadway, London N11 3DU. Tel/fax 020 8368 8568. Lists, subscription £2.50 (4 issues).

Military Parade Bookshop
The Parade, Marlborough, Wilts SN8 1NE. 01672 515470 (fax 01980 630 150). Wide ranging new and secondhand books. Lists available.

Motor Books
St Martins Court, London WC2N 4AL. 020 7836 5376 (fax 020 7497 2539). Comprehensive stock of military books in print.

Military & Naval History
54 Regis Road, Tettenhall, Wolverhampton WV6 8RW. 01902 756402. British Military history. Lists available.

MSM Awards
8 Price Tce, Matamata, 2271, New Zealand. Tel: (NZ) 647 888 9055, fax: (NZ) 647 888 6560, email: Veteran88@Hotmail.com. Supplier of commemorative medals. Supplier of medal ribbons of Australia, New Zealand, UN, and all US military including CG and NG. Also medal remounting services.

Pen & Sword Books Ltd.
47 Church Street, Barnsley, S. Yorks S70 2AS. Tel: 01226 734555 (Fax: 01226 734438) Military titles.

Roberts
PO Box 1, Brimpton, Reading, RG7 4RJ. 0118 971 4044. New and secondhand military history.

Savannah Publications
90 Dartmouth Road, Forest Hill, London SE23 3HZ. 020 8244 4350 (fax 020 8244 2448, e-mail savpub@dircon.co.uk) Publisher and distributor of works of reference relating to British Army, Navy and RAF history/medals/biography and service histories/genealogy. Free catalogues.
Website: www.savannah-publications.com.

Selous Books
PO Box 73, Aldershot, Hants GU11 1HJ. 01252 319791 (fax 01252 342339) website www.militaria.co.uk. Specialists in military books. SAE for catalogue, plus £1 stamp)

Anthony J. Simmonds
23 Nelson Road, Greenwich, London SE10 9JB. 020 8853 1727. Naval and maritime history. Occasional catalogues.

Andrew Skinner
42 Earlspark Avenue, Newlands, Glasgow G43 2HW. 0141 632 4903 (fax 0141 632 8453). General military history stock with special emphasis on Scotland. Monthly lists.

Frank Smith Maritime Aviation Books
98/100 Heaton Road, Newcastle upon Tyne. 0191 265 6333. Naval, maritime and aviation history.

Spink & Son Ltd (Christie's International)
69 Southampton Row, Bloomsbury, London WC1B
4ET. 020 7563 4000 (fax 020 7563 4066). Specialist
Book Department.
Email: info@spinkandson.com,
Website: www.spink-online.com.

Stephen Tilston
37 Bennett Park, Blackheath, London SE3 9RA.
Tel./fax 020 8318 9181. General stock, but
specialising in the First World War. Lists available.

Tasmedals
8 Orana Place, Taroona, Tas 7053, Australia. Tel:
(NZ) 613 6227 8825, fax: (NZ) 613 6227 9898.

THCL Books
185 Lammack Road, Blackburn, Lancs BB1 8LH.
Military book specialist and publishers of
collectors' cards of medal heroes. Lists available.

Token Publishing Ltd.
Orchard House, Duchy Road, Heathpark,
Honiton, Devon EX14 1YD. 01404 46972 (fax 01404
44788). E-mail info@token-publishing.com.
Publishers of *Medal News* and *Coin News* and
related titles.

Ken Trotman Ltd.
Unit 11, 135 Ditton Walk, Cambridge CB5 8QD.
01223 211030 (fax 01223 212317). Large, wide-
ranging stock. Lists available: 3 per year.

Brian Turner Military Books
1132 London Road, Leigh-on-Sea, Essex SS9 2AJ.
Tel/fax 01702 78771. Printed works and
documentation relating to military, naval and
aviation history, specialising in the First World
War, India and Africa.

Robin Turner
30 Great Norwood Street, Cheltenham, Glos. GL50
2BH. 01242 234303. Military, specialising in the
Napoleonic period.

Twin Pillars Books
145 Russell St. Kettering, Northamptonshire
NN16 0EW

Mark Weber
35 Elvaston Place, London SW7 5NW. 020 7225
2506 (fax 020 7581 8233). Specialises in official war
histories and books by and about Sir Winston
Churchill.

Ray Westlake Military Books
53 Claremont, Malpas, Newport, South Wales NP9
6PL. 01633 854135 (fax 01633 821860). General
military books.

Terence Wise
Pantiles, Garth Lane, Knighton, Powys LD7 1HH.
Military history especially regimental and
divisional histories. Lists available.

Woodford Books
The Lodge, Well Street, Docking, King's Lynn,
Norfolk PE31 8LQ. 01485 518700. Medal and
military books, photograph albums, letters,
ephemera. Lists available.

Woolcott Books
Kingston House, Higher Kingston, Nr Dorchester,
Dorset DT2 8QE. 0135 267773 (fax 01305 848218).
Military and colonial history, specialising in India,
Africa and 19th century campaigns.

World War Books
Oaklands, Camden Park, Tunbridge Wells, Kent
TN2 5AE. 01892 538465. Military, naval and
aviation books and documents, particularly First
World War, regimental histories, maps, diaries
and photographs. Lists available.

World War II Books
PO Box 55, Woking, Surrey GU22 8HP. 01483
722880 (fax 0483 721548). Second World War
military history. 12 lists per year.

R.J. Wyatt.
33 Sturges Road, Wokingham, Berks RG11 2HG.
01734 780325. All aspects of British military
history, with an emphasis on the First and Second
World Wars, Volunteers, and the Territorial Army.

AUCTIONERS/DEALERS/BOOKSELLERS

If your details listed above are incorrect,
or if we have omitted to include you in
this listing please advise us without delay
to ensure that our database is up-dated in
time for the next edition of the
MEDAL YEARBOOK.

Details are included entirely free
Telephone: 01404 46972 or fax: 01404 44788

MATTHEW TREDWEN
DEALING IN BRITISH CAMPAIGN AND GALLANTRY MEDALS
VIEW OUR STOCK
@
WWW.MILITARYANTIQUES.CO.UK

IF YOU DO NOT HAVE ACCESS TO THE
INTERNET SEND SAE FOR
COMPLIMENTARY CATALOGUE

**Matthew Tredwen
PO Box 318, Bromley
BR1 2UX, England**

We have a stand at the
London Military Market
on Saturday mornings 8.30–1.30
and can be seen at most fairs.

Tel: 07939 252206 • Fax: 020 84677027
Email: enquiries@militaryantiques.co.uk

FAIRS

Many fairs are held regularly and organised by professionals, in addition a number of societies organise fairs for the public (Victorian Military Society, Aldershot Militaria Society, etc.). The dates are usually well advertised in MEDAL NEWS and other publications, however, times and venues are liable to change so it is advisable in every instance to telephone the organisers beforehand. Listed below are the major fair organisers and the events known to us.

Aldershot Militaria and Medal Fair
Princes Hall, Princes Way,, Aldershot, Hants. Mark Carter, 01753 534777.

Bolton Militaria Fair
Horwich Leisure Centre, Victoria Road, Bolton. Northern Arms Fairs. 01423 780940 or 0113 2716180.

Britannia Medal Fair
Victory Services Club, 63-79 Seymour Street, Marble Arch, London W2. Six p.a. Britannia Enterprises, 28 Raglan Place, Burnopfield, Gateshead NE16 6NN. 01207 271869 or 020 8590 4389.

Bromley Medal and Militaria Fair
Civic Centre, Kentish Way, Bromley, Kent. Ray Brough. 020 8766 0329.

Cheshunt Militaria Fair
Wolsey Hall, Windmill Lane, Cheshunt, Herts. Hands Militaria Fairs. Tel/Fax: 01892 730233.

Chessington Militaria Fair
Community Sports College, Garrison Lane, Chessington, Surrey. Hands Militaria Fairs. Tel/Fax: 01892 730233.

Combined Services Collectors Fair
The Halton Gallery, Royal Airforce Museum, Graham Park Way, Hendon NW9. Contact: Alan McDonald, 5 Windsor Drive, East Barnet, EN4 8UE. Tel/Fax: 0208 441 4557, or 07960 033914

Collectors' Market
London Bridge Main Line Station, London SE1. Every Saturday. Over 60 stands comprising medals, badges and militaria. Fax: 020 8398 8065.

Didcot Militaria Fair
Civic Hall, Britwell Road, Didcot, Berks. Hands Militaria Fairs. Tel/Fax: 01892 730233.

Durham Militaria Fair
County Hall, Aykley Heads, Durham City. Northern Arms Fairs. Tel: 01423 780940 or 0113 2716180.

Essex Militaria Fair
Victory Hall, Hainault Road, Chigwell. Jason Chapman. Tel: 01708 370643 or 07710 692203.

Farnham Militaria Fair
The Maltings, Bridge Square, Farnham, Surrey. Hands Militaria Fairs. Tel/Fax: 01892 730233.

Guildford Militaria Fair
Guildford Civic, London Road, Guildford. Hands Militaria Fairs. Tel/Fax: 01892 730233.

Hendon Collectors Fair
The Halton Gallery, Royal Air Force Museum, Grahame Park Way, Hendon NW9. Combined Services Collectors Fairs. Tel: 020 8441 4557 or 07960 033914.

Ipswich Medal and Militaria Fair
Kesgrave Community Centre. Tel: 01449 780236 or 0774 7774877.

Leeds Militaria Fair
Pudsey Civic Hall, Leeds. Northern Arms Fairs. 01423 780940 or 0113 2716180.

Liverpool Militaria Fair
The Village Hotel, Whiston, Liverpool. Northern Arms Fairs. Tel: 01423 780940 or 0113 2716180.

London Arms Fairs
The Paragon Hotel, Lillie Road, London SW6. 4 shows p.a. Douglas Fryer. 01273 475 959.

London Military Market—Islington
Angel Arcade, Camden Passage, Islington, London N1. Every Saturday, 8am–2pm. Over 35 stands. 01628 822503 or 01455 556971.

Macclesfield Militaria & Medal Fair
The Senior Citizens Hall, Duke Street Car Park, off Roe Street, Town Centre. Dave Cooper Tel: 01538 703354 eves/weekends, 01538 702738 office hours.

Midhurst Militaria Fair
The Grange Leisure Centre, Bepton Road. Hands Militaria Fairs. Tel/Fax: 01892 730233.

Newcastle-upon-Tyne Militaria Fair
Park Hotel, Grand Parade, Tynemouth. Northern Arms Fairs. 01423 780940 or 0113 2716180.

OMRS Annual Convention
New Connaught Rooms, Great Queen Street, London WC2. Contact: OMRS Membership Secretary, PO Box 133, Chertsey, Surrey KT16 8YY. OMRS members and pre-registered guests only.

Stratford Upon Avon Militaria & Medal Fair
Leisure Centre. Mark Carter. 01753 534777.

Stockport Arms Fair
The Armoury Hall (TA), Greek Street, Stockport. For details Tel: 0161 485 6908.

Victorian Military Fair
Victorian Military Society, 20 Priory Road, Newbury, Berks RG14 7QN. Tel: 01635 48628.

War & Peace Militaria Fair
Hop Farm, Beltring, Paddock Wood, Kent. Monthly militaria collectors fair. UKMS. Tel: 01304 813128 or 01622 678730.

Watford Arms, Militaria and Medal Fair
Bushey Hall School, London Road, Bushey, Herts. Sovereign Fairs. 01438 811657 or 01923 448903.

West Country Militaria and Medal Fair
Yate Leisure Centre, Kennedy Way, Yate, near Chipping Sodbury, Bristol. Mark Carter. 01753 534777.

York Militaria Fair
Novotel, Fishergate, York. Northern Arms Fairs. Tel: 01423 780940 or 0113 2716180.

INDEX TO MEDAL NEWS

Here we include the complete **Cumulative Subject Index** to the parent magazine MEDAL NEWS, commencing with the March 1989 issue, when it became a separate publication.

MEDAL NEWS was born in 1981 from the amalgamation of *Medals International* and *Coins & Medals*, into the popular title *Coin & Medal News*. However, the success of this magazine and the continuing growth of both the coin and the medal collecting hobbies prompted the separation of the two sections in March 1989. Since then both *Coin News* and MEDAL NEWS have grown from strength to strength and today are the hobby's leading publications, not only in the UK but MEDAL NEWS is the *only* independent magazine in the world devoted to the collecting and study of medals. Most later issues of MEDAL NEWS are still available, price £3—please enquire whether we have the issue you require (if not then photocopies of articles can be supplied at £5 per article).

NOTES

References are indicated **year, month: page,** for example 9004.18 means April 1990 issue, page 18; 9306.24 means June/July 1993 issue, page 24.

Each year runs from February to December. For example the year 1990 includes the December 1990/January 1991 issue.

Names of ships are indicated in italics.

Names of people have been included where they appear to be the major subject of an article or where more than trivial information is included.

Abbreviations used:

(cr)	Indicates the inclusion of a full or partial casualty list.
(mr)	Indicates the inclusion of a medal roll.
(nr)	Indicates nominal roll.
(i)	Indicates that the reference gives information rather than the object itself. For example it tells you where to find a medal roll rather than reproducing the roll itself.
(p)	Indicates that the reference is to a picture of a person or object where little or no other information is given.
(mp)	Same as (p) except that the picture is of medals.
(br)	Indicates Book Review.

A

AA medal 9710.6
'A Crown of Life' Dianne Graves (br) 0011.35
'A Gazetteer of the Second Anglo-Boer War 1899-1902' Huw M. Jones & Meurig G. M Jones (br) 0004.34
'A Noble Crusade: the History of the Eight Army 1941-45' Richard Doherty (br) 0006.35
Abercrombie, John, Surgeon: Army of India Medal (mp) 9412.08
'Above the Trenches' (br) 9610.22
'Absent Minded Beggars', Will Bennett (br), 0002.36
Abyssinia (1868): 18th Bombay Native Infantry 9502.14
Abyssinia Medal (1867-68): naming 9003.22
Acasta: sunk 1940 9402.20-21
Accumulated Campaign Service Medal 9404.10
   Royal Mint plaster model 9405.05
Ada: rescue (1875) 9403.18-19
Adams Allan Percy, Capt GSM 1918-1962 S. Persia 9910.18
Aden (1857) 9010.12
Adolf Friedrich Cross (Germany) 8910.13
AE-1 (RAN submarine) (cr) 9306.12-13
AE-2 (RAN submarine) (nr) 9306.12-13
'Adventures in the Rifle Brigade in the Peninsula, France and the Netherlands from 1809: Capt John Kincade (br)9807.29
'Air Force Records For Family Historians' William Spencer (br) 0008.35
Afghanistan Medal
   92/Highlanders 9311.15
   naming 9003.23, 9004.18
Afghanistan Order of the Sun (mp) 9602.26
Afghan War (1842) medals 9003.22
Africa General Service Medal 1902-56 supplementary civilian awards (mr) 0009.26-27
Africa General Service Medal
   abbreviations 8905.26, 8906.24
   KRRC Somaliland (1903-04) (mr) 9006.14-17
   naming 9004.18
African Distinguished Conduct Medal 9008.15
African rating titles RN 9106.17
Africa Star
   Eisenhower, Dwight D., Gen. 9609.13, 9611.26, 9612.31
   entitlement 9504.10
   ribbon 8908.26
Ailsby, C. 'Allied Combat Medals of WWII' (br) 8911.07
Airborne Forces: Museum 9708.28-29
Air Crew Europe Star: ribbon 8908.26
Air France Disasters, Bahrain June 12 and 14 1950 0006.24-25
Air Force Cross 9105.13-17, 9511.16-17
   Air Training Plan WWII (mr) 9112.16-17
Air Force Medal 9105.13-17
   Air Training Plan WWII (mr) 9112.17
   naming 9002.18
   Award to LAC George Donaldson 9808.18-19
Air Medal (USA): Australian awards (Vietnam) 9602.13
Air Medal for Valor (USA): Australian awards (Vietnam) 9602.13
Air Operations Iraq: clasp for GSM 1962 9910.08

B

B17 Bombers WWII
  'Hells Angels' (p) 9208.15
  'old faithful' (cr) 9208.14-15
Baba Saheb, Indian Mutiny 9911.24-26
Babington, John T., F/Cmdr RNAS: Zeppelin raids (1914) 9111.10
Badajoz, assault on (1812) 8906.12
Badcock, Alexander R., Gen. 38 Foot/29 Bengal Inf. 9311.16
Badcock, Alexander J. (1866-1912) W.Yorks/Indian Staff 9311.17
Badcock, Frederick F., (1867-1926) Wilts Regt/Gurkhas 9311.17
Badcock, Frederick T., RW Surrey 9311.17
Badcock, George H., YLI/Indian Staff 9311.17
Badcock, Gerald E., Col 9311.17
Badfield, Lawrence C.(served Balaclava): notice of funeral 9503.21
Badford , Mark P ' Service Before Self: Security Forces of Rhodesia & Nyasaland' (br) 9504.22
Badge of Honour, Order of (USSR) 9409.17
badges see also insignia
  abbreviations; shoulder-belt plates 9109.27
  aircrew WWII 8909.23
  Albert Shako plates 9103.11-12
  Alexandra, Princess of Wales's own Yorkshire Regt 9602.20-21
  Australian Imperial Forces 9009.11
  Bedfordhsire Regt 9702.29-30
  Black Watch 9505.20-21
  Blues and Royals 9309.23
  Border Regiment 9710.30-31, 9711.26-27
  Boys Training Co. Brigade of Gurkhas 9504.20-21
  Brecknockshire Battalion (SW Borderers) 9606.21
  Brigade of Gurkhas 9504.20-21
  Cambridgeshire Regt (Territorials) 9703.31-32
  Cameronians 9511.22-23
  Canadian Expeditionary Force Infantry 9010.24-25
  Canadian Scottish Regts 9106.26-27
  Cavalry 9305.25, 9306.22, 9308.22-23, 9309.22-23
    arm 9004.24-25, 9008.28
    harness 9406.22-23, 9408.22-23
    Indian 9409.22-23, 9410.22-23
  cyclist batns 9104.22-23
  Cheshire Regt 9906.30-31
  Coldstream Guards 9705.25-26
  Dover Anti-Aircraft Corp Silver 9408.09
  Duke of Wellington's Regiment 9602.20-21
  East Africa Force 0002.31-32
  East Anglian Brigade 9709.27
  East Lancashire Regt 9609.20
  East Yorkshire Regt 9512.22-23
  economy 9112.24
  fleur-de-lys 9009.22-23
  63rd Foot 9009.22-23
  73/ Foot 9505.20-21
  French Royal Guard 9009.22
  Fusilier cap 9202.24-25
  glengarry cap 9205.24-25
  Fusilier Brigade 9708.26
  Glider Pilot Regt 9205.13
  gorgets 9310.24-25
  Green Howards 9602.20-21
  Green Jackets Brigade 9605.20-21, 9709.29
  Grenadier Guards 9705.25-26
  Guards Machine Gun Regt: 9707.25-26
  10th Gurkha Rifles 9503.22-23
  11th Gurkha Rifles 9504.20-21
  25th Gurkha Rifles 9504.20-21
  26th Gurkha Rifles 9504.20-21
  6th Gurkha Rifles 9503.22-23
  7th Gurkha Duke of Edinburgh's Own Rifles 9503.22-23
  7th Gurkha Rifles 9503.22-23
  9th Gurkha Rifles 9503.22-23
  Gurkha Army Service Corps 9504.20-21
  Gurkha Independent Parachute Co. 9504.20-21
  Gurkha Military Police 9504.20-21
  Gurkha Regiments 9502.22-23, 9503.22-23
  Gurkha Transport Regt 9504.20-21
  helmet
    regular army 9006.22-23
    tropical 9404.22-23, 9405.22-23
  Herefordshire Regt (Territorials) 9703.31-32
  Hertfordshire Regt 9702.29-30
    Territorials 9703.31-32

  Highland Brigade 9709.28
  Highland Light Infantry 9510.22-23
  Highland Regts 9506.22-23, 9508.20-21
  Home Counties Brigade 9708.26
  Home Guard 9105.24-25
  Household Brigade Officer Cadet Bttn: 9707.25-26
  Household Division 9707.25-26
  Hungarian Military Proficiency 9403.27, 9404.26
  Hussars 9304.24-25, 9305.24-25, 9306.22-23, 23
    Fleur-de-lys 9009.23
  Intelligence Corps 9010.26
  Irish Guards 9707.25-26
  1st King George V's Own Gurkha Rifles 9502.22-23
  2nd King Edward VII's Own Gurkha Rifles 9502.22-23
  King's (Liverpool) Regt 9609.20, 9610.20-21
  King's Own (Royal Lancaster) Regiment 9611.21-22
  King's Own Scottish Borderers 9511.22-23
  King's Own Yorkshire Light Infantry 9603.20-21
  King's Regiment (Manchester & Liverpool) 9611.21-22
  King's Royal Rifle Corps 9604.20-21
  Kitchener's Service Battns WWI 9012.21-22
  Ku Lang Su police 9303.26
  Lancashire Fusiliers 9611.21-22
  Lancashire Regt 9612.28
  Lancastrian Brigade 9612.28, 9708.26
  Lancers 9304.24-25, 9305.24-25, 9306.22-23
  Light Infantry Brigade 9709.27
  London Regiments 9110.26-27, 9111.26-27
  London Rifle Brigade 9605.20-21
  Lowland Brigade 9509.20-21, 9708.26
  Lowland Regt 9509.20-21
  Loyal North Lancashire Regt 9612.27
  Machine Gun Corps 9204.24-25
  Manchester Regt 9009.22-23, 9612.27-28
  Medical Corps 9303.24-25
  militia shako plates 9211.24-25
  Mercian Brigade 9709.28
  Midland (Forester) Brigade 9709.27
  Monmouthshire Regiment 9608.20-21
  Musicians 9402.24-25, 9403.24-25
    Pipers 9003.24-25
  New Zealand Infantry (1914-18) 9203.24-25
  New Zealand Mounted Rifles 9008.22-23
  21st Officer Cadet Battalion 9412.25
  pagri 9404.22-23, 9405.22-23
  North Irish Brigade 9709.28
  Pioneers 9312.24-25
  Pittsburgh Police Dept 9506.25
  pouch & valise 9411.22-23
  4th Prince of Wales's Own Gurkha Rifles 9502.22-23
  10th Princess Mary's Own Gurkha Rifles 9504.20-21
  Prince of Wales's Own Regiment of Yorkshire 9602.21
  3rd Queen Alexandra's Own Gurkha Rifles 9502.22-23
  6th Queen Elizabeth's Own Gurkha Rifles 9503.22-23
  Queen's Gurkha Engineers 9504.20-21
  Queen's Gurkha Signals 9504.20-21
  Queen's Lancashire Regt 9612.28
  Queen's Regiment 9412.23
  Rifle Brigade 9605.20-21
  rising Sun 9005.24-25
  Royal Dragoons 9309.22
  arm 9004.24
  1st at Waterloo, adoption of Eagle 0001.27-28
  Royal Berkshire Regiment 0010.32-33 East Africa Force 0002.31-32
  Royal Electrical & Mechanical Engineers 9312.24-25
  Royal Engineers 9311.22-23, 9312.24-25
  Royal Green Jackets 9605.20-21
  Royal Gurkha Rifles 9504.20-21
  Royal Hampshire Regiment 0004.32-33
  Royal Hampshire Regiment 0004.32-33
  Royal Hampshire Regiment pt II 0005.32-33
  Royal Hampshire Regiment pt II 0005.32-33
  Royal Highland Fusiliers 9510.23
  Royal Marine Light Infantry 9102.22-23
  Royal Marines 9302.24-25
  Royal Naval Division 9102.22-23
  Royal Norfolk Regt 9901.27-28
  Royal Regiment of Wales 9608.20-21
  Royal Scots Fusiliers 9510.22-23
  Royal Sussex Regt 9412.22-23
  Royal Tank Regt 9204.24-25
  Royal Welch Fusiliers 9606.20-21
  Royal Wiltshire Regiment 0011.31-32
  St John Ambulance (Boer War) 9303.25

I

Le Geyt, Alice Bell: RNLI Medal 8905.21
Legion of Frontiersmen, medals to 0004.24-25
Legion of Honour (France): Napoleon's Legacy 9702.24-25
Legion of Honour (France):award to surviving British
    veterans of WWI 9901.06
Legion of Honour Star (France (p) 9512.07
Legion of Merit (USA): Australian awards (Vietnam) 9602.13
Legion Wallonie (German Army WWII) 9502.16-17
Leicestershire Regt: Musician badges 9403.24
Leicesteshire Yeomanry (Prince Albert's Own): badges
    9804.26-27
Leicesteshire and Derbyshire Yeomanry (Prince Albert's
    Own): badges 9804.26-27
Leigh, Chandos Maj: 2nd Battalion KOSB, Mons 9708.20-21
Leitch, W.: *Britannia* 8906.21-22, 8909.25
Lenin, Order of (USSR) 9409.15-16
Leros Island WWII 9109.24-25
Lewes, Price Vaughan, service in Candia, Crete 0001.24-25
Lewis, George Gordon 0009.24-25
Lewis, H.W., pte Welch Regt: VC group (mp) 9402.08
Liberation of France Medal (France) 9011.23
Liddle, P.H. '1916 Battle of the Somme: a reappraisal' (br)
    9303.22
Liddon, Matthew, Cmdr (c1819) (p) 9203.10
Life Guards
    badges
        harness 9406.22-23
        tropical helmet 9405.22-23
Life Saving Medallion to E.F Openshaw 0004.28
Life Saving Awards Research Society (i) 9103.05, 9403.19
Life Saving Medal (US) (mp) 9509.09
Lifford, A.H.A: Welch WWI & Police medals 9604.25
Light Brigade, Troop-Sergeant William Bentley at Balaclava
    0101.27-28
Light Cavalry: badges 9410.23
Light Dragoons
    badges 9305.25, 9306.22
    arm 9004.24
Light Infantry
    85th 8910.20
    Albert Shako plates 9103.11-12
    Brigade badges 9709.27-28
Li Wo: WWII 8910.23, 9308.12-13, 9309.26
Lily, Cross of the (France): miniature (mp) 9509.09
Limb, Sue & Cordingley, P. 'Captain Oates - Soldier and
    Explorer' (br) 9512.18
Lincolnshire Regiment: badges 9909.35-36
Lincolnshire Yeomanry: badges 9804.26-27
Lindall, H., Gnr, I Troop RHA (mp) 9602.08
Lindop, Lt 80/Foot: Ntombe River (1879) 8906.15-17
59/ Line Infantry Regiment (France)
    Crimea 9508.15
    Italian Campaign 9508.16-17
Lindsay, Captain Lionel Arthur 0005.30-31
Liprandi: Balaclava (Crimea) 8908.15-18
Lister, Frederick G., Capt 26 BNI: N.E. Frontier 9405.10-12
Litherland, A 'Standard Catalogue of Brit Orders Deorations
    & Medals' (br) 9104.25
Littlewood, Sydney C.T., RFC: Knight's Batchelor badge
    9311.20
Liverpool Irish
    badges 9610.20-21
    piper's badge 9003.25
Liverpool Pals
    badge WWI 9012.22
    Memorial Fund 9409.05
Liverpool Scottish
    badges 9610.20-21
    piper's badge 9003.25
Lizard: & *Goeben/Breslau* WWI 9302.18-19
Llewellyn, Margaret: RNLI Medal 8905.20
Llewellyn, Martha: RNLI Medal 8905.20
Lloyd, T., F/Sgt 550 Squad (1944) 9410.15-16
Lloyd's War Medal for Bravery at Sea 9012.11-12
Loader, Roy, AB *Crane* 8912.12, 20, 9003.26
Lobb, Michael J., Capt, Corps of Royal Engineers: Queen's
    Gallantry Medal (1995) 9602.16
Local Defence Volunteers: badges 9105.24-25
Loewenhardt, Erich German Air Force: Blue Max 9411.12-13
Lombard, Fleur, firefighter: posthumous QGM 9807.06
London, City of, Imperial Volunteers 1900 0006.27-29
London & North Western Railway 'Pals' unit: WWI 9606.14
47 London Division: gallantry awards WWI 9302.20

London Gazette, January 24 1946 Military Medal
    supplement 0005.28-29
London Gazette: PRO copies 9206.15
London Irish Rifles
    piper's badge 9003.25
    Territorial Force War Medal (1914-19) 9502.24
        (mr) 9408.13
London Medal Club Inception 0004.07
London Regt
    (1992) 9205.26
    badges 9110.26-27, 9111.26-27
London Rifle Brigade: badges 9605.20-21
London to Australia flight (1919-20) 9509.16-17, 22
London Yeomanry badges 9804.26-27
    City of London (Rough Riders): badges 9804.26-27 and
        9805.27-28
    2nd County of London Yeomanry (Westminster
        Dragoons): badges 9805.27-28
    3rd County of London Yeomanry (Sharpshooters): badges
        9805.27-28
    4th County of London Yeomanry:badges 9805.27-28
    London Yeomanry and Territorials: badges 9805.27-28
London Welsh: badge WWI 9012.22
'Long Cecil' - siege of Kimberley 9908.24-26
Long & Efficient Service Medal (Victoria 1881-1902) 9610.16-
    17
Long Service and Good Conduct Medals in the Victorian
    Army 0010.18-19
Long Service and Good Conduct Medal (RAF, GV): research
    file 9805.29
Longbottom, Brian V. Ldg Elec Mech *Voyager*: BEM 9404.17
Long Service & Good Conduct Medal
    Army; ribbon 9503.22
    future development 9606.11, 26
    naming 9004.18-19
    RAF; ribbon 9604.26
Long Service & Good Conduct Medal (West African) 9008.15
Long service: 50 Years in Uniform, Pt Arthur Carter KSLI
    and Hefordshire Regt 9901.21
Long Tan, battle of (Vietnam): awards to Australians
    9602.11-12
Lonsdale Battalion: badge WWI 9012.22
Lord, Cliff & Birtles, David 'The Armed Forces of Aden
    1839-1967' (br) 0008.35
Lord Heneage, HMT: 9007.15-16
Lord Howe Island, Royal Australian Air Force Catalinas on
    0003.35
Lord Wakefield of Hythe Commemorative Medal (mp)
    9306.09
Lorne Scots: badge 9106.27
Lothians & Berwickshire Yeomanry: badge 9209.24-25
Lothians & Border Horse
    badges 9209.25
    piper's 9003.25
Lovat, Lord: death 9504.05
Lovat Scouts: badge 9210.24-25
Love, Frank, CERA RN *Peterel* (Yangtse River) 9509.13-14
Love, Joseph R., RM: Tel-el-kebir (1882) 9406.12-13
Love, R.W. 'Diary of Admiral Sir B. Ramsay' (br) 9406.25
Lowland Brigade:bages 9708.25-26
Lowland Regiments: badges 9509.20-21, 9510.22-23, 9511.22-
    23
Loyal Britons of Westminster Medal 9006.26
Loyal Briton Volunteers Medal 9006.26
Loyal North Lancashire Regt
    badges 9612.27
    tropical helmet badge 9405.23
Loyal Nottingham Volunteers: shoulder-belt plates 9109.26-
    27
Loyal Regt: Musician badge 9403.25
Loyal Service Medal (Roumania) (p) 9210.27
Lucas-tooth Shield 9410.27
Lucknow 9003.20
    & *Shannon* 9302.12
    Eldridge, James QM Sgt 10/Bengal Light Cavalry:
        murdered 1857 9901.22-23
Lumsden, Frederick W., Maj RM: VC WWI 9603.18-19
Luneberg garrison: Ntombe River (1879) 8906.15-18
Lunt, James ' Jai Sixth (br) 9511.19
Luscombe, George, RMLI (18810 8903.14
Lushai (1889-92): KRRC (mr) 9312.15-18
Lusitania 9006.10-12, 9008.25-26, 9010.28
    Medal (Manx) 9006.10-12
Lutkin, William, Capt *Darvel*: MBE (1942) 9504.12-13

M

Macalister, James: *Noreen Mary* WWII 9011.11-12
McCrae, John: Medals to be sold 9710.10
McCrae, John: Medal sale results (world record) 9801.09
McCrery N. 'the Vanished Battalion' (br) 9303.22-23
McCudden, J.T.B. (p) 9004.28
McDermott, Edgar J., PO *Voyager*: Queen's Commend. 9404.17
McDermott, Philip 'For Distinguished Conduct.. register of DCM' (br) 9409.24
MacArtheur, Gen. Douglas and the Congressional Medal of Honour 0101.19-20
MacDonald, John, 1/Bengal Fusiliers 9005.28
MacDonald, L. '1915 The Death of Innocence' (br) 9405.25
MacDonald, William, Col Sgt 1/Seaforth High 8912.19
MacDonald, William, Col Sgt 72/ Highlanders 8903.12-13
McDonnell, Thomas, Lt (p) 9408.09
MacDougall, D., Capt RAF: *Glowworm* explosion 9203.15-17
MacFarlane, John, Sgt 10 Squadron: MM WWII 9402.22
McFarlane, Vic, 12 Squadron: MM WWII 9402.21-22
MacGregor, John Lt Col VC: 9709.29
McGuigan, Sgt 1/ Argyll & Sutherland Highlanders: Palestine 9506.25

McHugh, Stephen, Sgt Parachute Regt: MC (1994) 9602.17
McIntosh, G., Pte 6/Gordon High: Ypres VC 9411.15
McIntosh, John, Lt AIAF: London to Australia flight (1919-20) 9509.17, 22
McIntyre, C. 'Monuments of War' (br) 9012.23
McIntyre, William: not that name (1806-1933) 9405.21
McKay, David 93/ Highlanders VC memorial dedicated 9902.7
McKay, Robert 42/Highlanders 9109.20-21
Mackinlay, G 'True Courage: The DCM to Australians' (br) 9302.23
McKenzie, Albert Edward VC 0005.11
McKinley, PO: CGM group (p) 9006.08
Mackinnon, W.H., Gen Sir (p) 9302.09
McLauchlan, Don, Lt Cdr: notice of death 9602.05
McLean, N.L.D., Lt Col Royal Scots Greys/SOE 9102.20
McPhail, H. 'Wilfred Owen Poet and Soldier' (br) 9405.24-25
MacPherson, A, FO 228 Squad: DFC *Kensington Court* (1939) 9410.12-13
McVicar, William, 3rd Officer: *Britannia* 8906.21-22, 8909.25
McWilliams, G.F., Maj West Aust: Slingersfontein (1900) 8909.19-20
Machine Gun Corps
 1st Bttn Sambre-Oise (1918) 8909.10-11
 badges 9204.24-25
  33rd Battn Musician 9403.25
Machine Gun Corps (20 Coy) Battle of the Somme 0009.20-21
Machine Gun Regiment (Guards) badges 9706.25-26
Macroom, Ambush at Sgt W. Jones Lancashire Fusiliers 1010.30-32
Maddocks, G. 'Liverpool Pals' (br) 9110.28
Madura: WWII 9504.18-19
Mahratta Light infantry Doyle, Lt-Col Paddy (obit) 0101.07
Maigumeri, Chari, RWAFF
 MM, BEM 9008.20
 MM/Iron Cross 9105.28
Mailly: raid on (1944) 9410.15-16
Mainwaring, George GC (obit) 0005.08
Majorca Division, Cross of the (Spain) (p) 9510.08
Majuba: The fight on Imquela Col, 1881 (cr) 9802.22-23
Malaun Regiment: badge 9502.22
Malaya (1948-60): Australian VCs 9102.21
Malaya
 clasp to GSM 9510.10-11, 9512.26
 medal statistics 9510.10-11, 9602.25
Malay Peninsula: clasp to Australian Service Medal (1945-75) 9511.11
Malone, W.G., Lt Col Wellington Regt: Gallipoli 9202.15-18
Malta WWII 9008.18-19
 counterfeit George Crosses 9603.06
 George Cross 50th Anniversary Medal 9204.07
Manahi, Haane Sgt; Maori Bn: 9801 .15
Manchester Regt at Caesar's Camp Victoria Cross anomaly 1900 (cr) 0010.26-27
Manchester & Liverpool Regt: Musician badge 9403.25
Manchester (WWII) 8912.24-25
Manchester Regt
 badges 9009.22-23, 9612.27-28
  Manchester Pals 9012.22
  Oldham Battn 9012.22

Elandslaagte (1899)(mr) 9510.14-18
 Wagon Hill (1900) (cr) 9306.14-18
Mangles, Ross Lewis: Bengal Civil Service VC, Left to NAM 9802.06
Manley, William G.N.: VC/Iron Cross 9103.24
Mann, A.E. Lt Col OBE, AM, VD, RE: 9802.19
Mannock, E., Maj RAF WWI (p) 9208.10, 9210.09
Mansfield, W.H.C., Lt Shropshire LI/RFC 9005.21
Mantis: Support at Wanhsien (1926) 9709.18-19
Manx Active Service Co: badge WWI 9012.22
Manahi, Haane Lance Sgt. 9712.15
Manton Sqd Ldr G.A.L. Battle of Britain 0009.16-19
Maori Wars (1861) 9010.12
Maori VCs 9712.15
Marie Cross (Germany) (WWI) 8908.09
Marien, Kerry F., Midshpmn, *Voyager*: Albert Medal 9404.17
Maritime Royal Artillery: WWII 9510.12-13, 9512.26
Maritz, Gen: Boer War 9108.21
Markham, C.R. 'Navy Arctic List 1773-1873) 9309.25
Marling, Percival, Sir: VC group (mp) 9410.07
Marsay, Mark 'Baptism of Fire' (br) 9906.24
Marsay, Mark 'Bombardment: The Day the East Was Bled' (br) 0010.35
Marshall, William, QMS: El Teb (1884) 8906.19
Martin, H. S/Ldr 617 Squad 9002.15-16
Mason, Dudley, Capt *Ohio*, 9402.14, 9510.12-13, 9602.25
Mason, Fred, Cpl RAAF (Timor WWII) 9502.18-19
Matanikau: Guadalcanal 9209.20-21
Mather, Michael V., 11 Squad RAAF 9409.11
Matschulat, G., Oberleutnant U-247 WWII 9012.11-12
Matthews, Len, RN WWII (p) 9112.06
Maund, Capt RN: Ord of Red Star (USSR) 9409.16
Mauritius: Albania (1946) 9008.16-17
Maxwell, Eugene P., CPO (RAN): CSC Iraq (1991) 9608.14-15
Maxwell, John G., Sir (mp) 9402.10
May, H., Pte 1/Cameronians 9408.05
Mayes, Charles, Col Sgt: CGM citation 9109.23
May Island (WWI) 8911.17
Mazairire, Constable Edwin:BSAP 9704.16-17
Mbilini (African Gen.): Zulu wars (1879) 8906.15-18
Mechanised Transport Corps: badge 9212.25
Medaille d'Honneur (France): 10/R Fus (Intelligence) (mr) 9004.16
Médaille Militaire (France)
 6/Gordon Highlanders WWI (mr) 9411.17
 10/R Fus (Intelligence) (mr) 9004.16
 RN/RNR/RM (mr) 9109.22-23
Medal of Bravery (Canada) 9503.05
Medal for Bravery (Germany) 8911.21
Medals in the early 19th Century 0003.22-23
Medal of Honor (USA)
 Mogadishu award 9406.06
 sale of now illegal 9508.05
Medal of Honour (Japan) 9311.19
medallions 9005.22
 Lusitania 9006.10
 Waterloo (1815) 9006.06
Medal for Merit (Montenegro): 10/R Fus (Intelligence) (mr) 9004.16
Medal of Merit (Ord of Merit of German Federal Republic) 8903.09
Medal for Military Merit (Germany) 8909.13
'Medals will be Worn' (br) Lt-Col Ashley Tinson 9910.36
medals
 MM location register 9108.28
 abbreviations
  Africa General Service Medal 8905.26, 8906.24
  Army 9105.26, 9106.25
  Navy 9010.18, 9106.25
 attribution of 8911.22-23
 brooches 9202.27, 9204.28
 cigarette cards 9411.18-21
 citations WWI, location of 9103.07
 collectors & Regimental Museums 9212.21-22
 collectors interests (statistics) 9503.16-18, 9506.25
 Commanders' commendations 9610.12-13
 common names on 9109.20-21
 designers 9102.24
 disposing of collections 9103.13-15
 engraving gallantry decorations 9210.06
 fakes 9109.21
  WWII Australian 9503.24, 9508.07
 fakes in circulation 9408.05
 false insurance claims USA 9403.13
 gallantry awards

LIMITED STOCKS OF BACK ISSUES OF

MEDAL NEWS

are available on request, price £3 including postage (early issues cost £5).

A few issues are no longer available but photocopies of articles can be supplied at £5 per article.

Contact Token Publishing Ltd quoting the reference number in the index for current availability

ORCHARD HOUSE, DUCHY ROAD, HEATHPARK, HONITON, DEVON EX14 1YD
Tel: 01404 44166 • Fax: 01404 44788 • Email: orders@tokenpublishing.com

Miss out on MEDAL NEWS and miss out on an exciting read

Subscribe today!
Call 01404 44166
e-mail: orders@tokenpublishing.com
Or Visit our website: www.tokenpublishing.com

MEDAL RIBBONS

In this section we feature the *majority* of the ribbons for the medals included in the main sections of the book.
Where the same ribbon is used for more than one medal, only one is illustrated here.

24. Victoria Cross

24. Victoria Cross, Navy to 1918

25. New Zealand Cross

26. George Cross

26A. Conspicuous Gallantry Cross

27. Distinguished Service Order

28/29. Imperial Service Order/Medal

30. Indian Order of Merit (military)

30. Indian Order of Merit (civil)

31. Royal Red Cross

32. Distinguished Service Cross

33. Military Cross

34. Distinguished Flying Cross 1919

35. Air Force Cross 1919

36. Order of British India (1st Class, ii)

36. Order of British India
(2nd Class, ii)

36. Order of British India
(1st Class, post-1939)

36. Order of British India
(2nd class, post-1939)

37. Order of Burma

38. Kaiser-i-Hind

39. Albert Medal
(original 1st Class, Sea)

39. Albert Medal (1st Class, Sea)

39. Albert Medal (2nd Class, Sea)

39. Albert Medal (original
1st Class, Land)

39. Albert Medal (1st Class, Land)

39. Albert Medal (2nd Class, Land)

40. SA Queen's Medal for Bravery

41/42. Distinguished Conduct Medal

43. DCM (KAR and WAFF)

44. Conspicuous Gallantry, Navy

44. Conspicuous Gallantry, RAF

45. George Medal

46/49. King's Police Medal 1916

46. King's Police Medal (Gallantry)

47. Queen's Police Medal

48. Queen's Fire Service Medal

48. Queen's Fire Service Medal (Gallantry)

50/51. Edward Medal

52. Indian Distinguished Service Medal

53. Burma Gallantry Medal

54. Distinguished Service Medal

55. Military Medal

56. Distinguished Flying Medal

57. Air Force Medal

58. Constabulary Medal Ireland 1872

59. Indian Police Medal
(Meritorious Service)

60. Burma Police Meritorious Service Medal

61. Colonial Police Medal (Gallantry)
62. Colonial Fire Brigade Medal (Gallantry)

61. Colonial Police Medal (Meritorious Service)
62. Colonial Fire Brigade (Meritorious Service)

63. Queen's Gallantry Medal

l64. Allied Subjects Medal

65. King's Medal for Courage
in the Cause of Freedom

66. King's Medal for Service in the
in the Cause of Freedom

67/68. Sea Gallantry Medal

69. British North Borneo Company's
Bravery Cross

70. Native Chief's Medal

79. Seringapatam

91. Burma Medal

93. Naval Gold medal

94. Naval General Service Medal

95. Army Gold Cross/96. Maida Gold
Medal/97. Army Gold Medal

98. Military General Service Medal

467

99. Waterloo Medal

100. Brunswick Medal for Waterloo

101. Hanoverian Medal for Waterloo

102. Nassau Medal for Waterloo

103. Saxe-Gotha-Altenburg Medal

104. Army of India Medal

105. Ghuznee Medal

106. St Jean D'Acre Medal

107. Candahar, Ghuznee, Cabul Medal/109. Kelat-I-Ghilzie

108. Jellalabad

110. China War Medal

111. Scinde Medal

112. Gwalior Star

113. Sutlej Medal

114. Punjab Medal

115/127. South Africa Medal

116. Sir Harry Smith's Medal

117. India General Service 1854–95

118. Baltic Medal

119. Crimea Medal

120. Turkish Crimea Medal

121. Indian Mutiny Medal

122. Second China War

123. New Zealand Medals

124. Abyssinia 1867–68

125. Canada General Service Medal

126. Ashantee/137. E&W Africa

128. Afghanistan 1878–80

129. Kabul to Kandahar Star

130. Cape of Good Hope GSM

131. Egypt Medal

132. Khedive's Star
133. Gordon's Khartoum Star

134. North West Canada Medal

135. Royal Niger Company's Medal

136. Imperial BEA Co.s Medal

138. BSA Co's Medal

139. Hunza Nagar badge

140. Central Africa Medal

141. Hong Kong Plague Medal

142. India Medal 1895–1902

143. Jummoo and Kashmir

144. Ashanti Star

145. Queen's Sudan

146. Khedive's Sudan Medal

147. East and Central Africa

148. BNB Co's Medal (ii)

148. BNB Co's Medal (iii)

149. Sultan of Zanzibar's Medal

150. Queen's South Africa
151. Queen's Mediterranean

152. Kings South Africa Medal

153. St John's Ambulance Brigade
Medal for South Africa

154/155. Kimberley Star and Medal

156. Yorkshire Imperial Yeomanry

157. Medal for the Defence of Ookiep

158. China War Medal 1900

159. Transport Medal

160. Ashanti Medal

161. Africa General Service 1902–56

162. Tibet Medal

163. Natal Medal

163A. Messina Earthquake

164. India General Service 1908–35

165. Khedive's Sudan 1910

166/167. 1914/1914–15 Star

168. British War Medal 1914–20

169. Mercantile Marine

170. Victory Medal

171. Territorial Force War Medal

173. Naval General Service 1915–62

174. General Service 1918–62

175. India General Service 1936–39

176. North Borneo GSM

176A. Sudan Defence Force GSM

177. 1939–1945 Star

178. Atlantic Star

179. Air Crew Europe Star

180. Africa Star

181. Pacific Star

182. Burma Star

183. Italy Star

184. France and Germany Star

185. Defence Medal

186. War Medal 1939–45

187. India Service Medal

188. Canadian Volunteer Service

188A. Canadian Memorial Cross

189. Africa Service Medal

190. Australia Service Medal

191. New Zealand War Service Medal

192. South Africa Service Medal

193. Southern Rhodesia War Service

194. Newfoundland Voulunteer War
Service Medal

195. Korea Medal

196. South African Medal for Korea

197. United Nations Korea Medal

198. General Service Medal 1962

199. UN Emergency Force Medal

200. Vietnam Medal

200A. Vietnam Logistic and
Support Medal

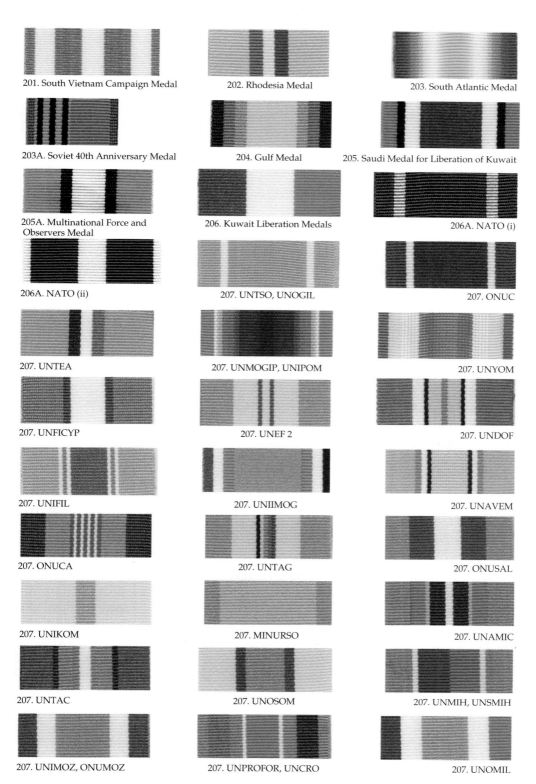

201. South Vietnam Campaign Medal

202. Rhodesia Medal

203. South Atlantic Medal

203A. Soviet 40th Anniversary Medal

204. Gulf Medal

205. Saudi Medal for Liberation of Kuwait

205A. Multinational Force and Observers Medal

206. Kuwait Liberation Medals

206A. NATO (i)

206A. NATO (ii)

207. UNTSO, UNOGIL

207. ONUC

207. UNTEA

207. UNMOGIP, UNIPOM

207. UNYOM

207. UNFICYP

207. UNEF 2

207. UNDOF

207. UNIFIL

207. UNIIMOG

207. UNAVEM

207. ONUCA

207. UNTAG

207. ONUSAL

207. UNIKOM

207. MINURSO

207. UNAMIC

207. UNTAC

207. UNOSOM

207. UNMIH, UNSMIH

207. UNIMOZ, ONUMOZ

207. UNPROFOR, UNCRO

207. UNOMIL

471

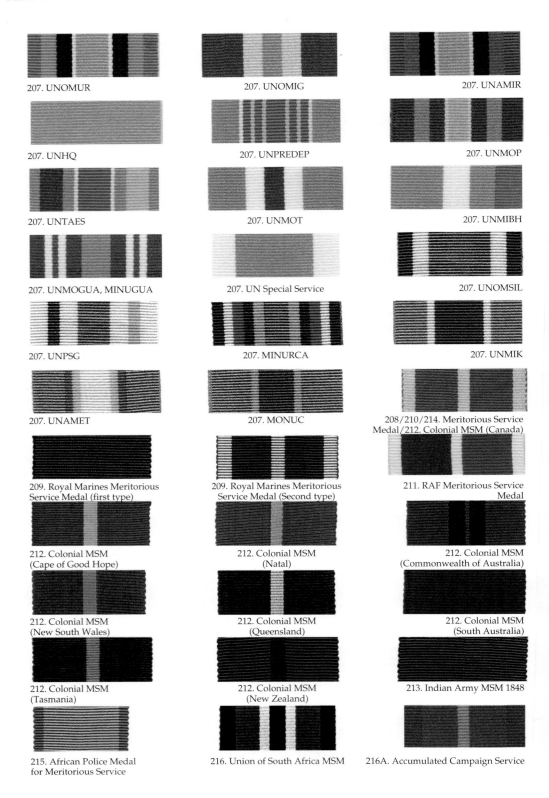

207. UNOMUR

207. UNOMIG

207. UNAMIR

207. UNHQ

207. UNPREDEP

207. UNMOP

207. UNTAES

207. UNMOT

207. UNMIBH

207. UNMOGUA, MINUGUA

207. UN Special Service

207. UNOMSIL

207. UNPSG

207. MINURCA

207. UNMIK

207. UNAMET

207. MONUC

208/210/214. Meritorious Service
Medal/212. Colonial MSM (Canada)

209. Royal Marines Meritorious
Service Medal (first type)

209. Royal Marines Meritorious
Service Medal (Second type)

211. RAF Meritorious Service
Medal

212. Colonial MSM
(Cape of Good Hope)

212. Colonial MSM
(Natal)

212. Colonial MSM
(Commonwealth of Australia)

212. Colonial MSM
(New South Wales)

212. Colonial MSM
(Queensland)

212. Colonial MSM
(South Australia)

212. Colonial MSM
(Tasmania)

212. Colonial MSM
(New Zealand)

213. Indian Army MSM 1848

215. African Police Medal
for Meritorious Service

216. Union of South Africa MSM

216A. Accumulated Campaign Service

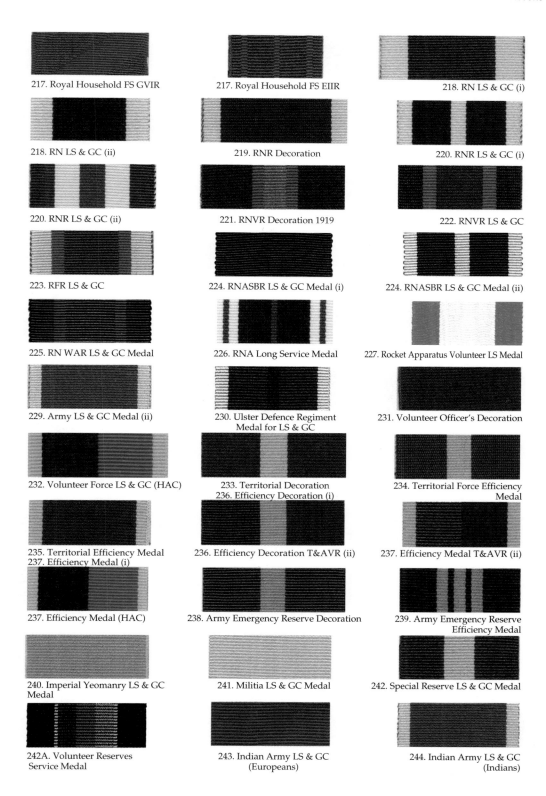

217. Royal Household FS GVIR

217. Royal Household FS EIIR

218. RN LS & GC (i)

218. RN LS & GC (ii)

219. RNR Decoration

220. RNR LS & GC (i)

220. RNR LS & GC (ii)

221. RNVR Decoration 1919

222. RNVR LS & GC

223. RFR LS & GC

224. RNASBR LS & GC Medal (i)

224. RNASBR LS & GC Medal (ii)

225. RN WAR LS & GC Medal

226. RNA Long Service Medal

227. Rocket Apparatus Volunteer LS Medal

229. Army LS & GC Medal (ii)

230. Ulster Defence Regiment Medal for LS & GC

231. Volunteer Officer's Decoration

232. Volunteer Force LS & GC (HAC)

233. Territorial Decoration
236. Efficiency Decoration (i)

234. Territorial Force Efficiency Medal

235. Territorial Efficiency Medal
237. Efficiency Medal (i)

236. Efficiency Decoration T&AVR (ii)

237. Efficiency Medal T&AVR (ii)

237. Efficiency Medal (HAC)

238. Army Emergency Reserve Decoration

239. Army Emergency Reserve Efficiency Medal

240. Imperial Yeomanry LS & GC Medal

241. Militia LS & GC Medal

242. Special Reserve LS & GC Medal

242A. Volunteer Reserves Service Medal

243. Indian Army LS & GC (Europeans)

244. Indian Army LS & GC (Indians)

245. Indian Volunteer Forces Officer's Decoration

246/247. Colonial Auxiliary Forces Officer's Decoartion/LS Medal

249. Permanent Forces LS & GC

250. RWAFF LS & GC

251. KAR LS & GC Medal

252. Trans-Jordan FF LS & GC Medal

253. SA PF LS & GC Medal

253A. Union Medal

254. Efficiency Medal (SA)

254A. Royal HKR Disbandment Medal

255. Canadian Forces Decoration

256. Victoria Vol. Long & Efficient Service Medal

257. New Zealand Long & Efficient Service Medal

258. NZ Volunteer Service Medal

259. NZ Territorial Service Medal (i)

259. NZ Territorial Service Medal (ii)

261/261A. Ulster Defence Regiment Medal

262. Cadet Forces Medal

263. Royal Observer Corps Medal

264. Civil Defence LS

264B. Assoc. of Chief Ambulance Officer's Service Medal

265. WVS Long Service Medal

266. Voluntary Medical Service Medal

267. Service Medal of the Order of St John of Jerusalem

268/269. RAF LS & GC Medal

270. Air Efficiency Award

271. Police LS & GC

272. Special Constabulary LS

273. RUC Service Medal

274. Colonial Police LS

275. Colonial Special Constabulary LS

276. RCMP LS Medal

277. Ceylon Police LS & GC Medal (I)

278. Ceylon Police LS & GC Medal (II)

279. Cyprus MP LS & GC Medal

280. HK Police Medal for Merit (1st Class)

280. HK Police Medal for Merit (2nd Class)

280. HK Police Medal for Merit (3rd Class)

280. HK Police Medal for Merit (4th Class)

280B. Royal Hong Kong Police Commemoration Medal

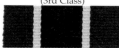

280C. Royal HK Aux. Police Commemoration Medal

281A. HK Disciplined Service Medal

282. Malta Police LS & GC Medal

282A. Mauritius Police LS & GC Medal (I) (first type)

282A. Mauritius Police LS & GC Medal (I) (second type)

282B. Mauritius Police LS & GC Medal (II)

282. NZ Police LS & GC Medal (second type)

283A. Seychelles Police LS & GC Medal (II)

284. SA Police Good Service Medal

285. SA Railways & Harbour Police LS & GC Medal (&290)

286. Fire Brigade LS Medal

286A. Assoc. of Professional Fire Brigade Officers LS Medal

286B. British Fire Services Assoc. Medal

287. Colonial Fire Brigade LS Medal

288. Ceylon Fire Brigade LS & GC Medal

289. Colonial Prison Service LS Medal

291. SA Prisons Dept Faithful Service Medal

292. Empress of India Medal

293/295. Jubilee (VR) 1887/1897

294/297. Jubilee (Police) 1887/1897

296. Jubilee 1897 (Mayors & Provosts)

298. Ceylon Diamond Jubilee 1897

299. HK Diamond Jubilee Medal

300. Visit to Ireland 1900

301. Coronation 1902

302. Coronation 1902 (Mayors & Provosts)

304. Ceylon Coronation 1902

305. HK Coronation 1902

303. Coronation 1902 (Police)

306. Delhi Durbar 1903

309. Coronation 1911
312. Delhi Durbar 1911

307. Visit to Scotland 1903

308. Visit to Ireland 1903

310. Coronation 1911 (Police)

311. Visit to Ireland 1911

313. Jubilee 1935

314. Coronation 1937

315. Coronation 1953

316. Jubilee 1977

317. Royal Humane Society (1921)

317. Stanhope Gold Medal

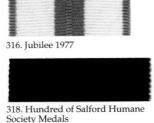

318. Hundred of Salford Humane
Society Medals

319. RNLI Medal

320. SPLF Medal

321. Lloyd's Medal for Saving Life
at Sea

322. Liverpool S&H Society's
Marine Medals

323. SF&MRB Society Medal

324. Tayleur Fund Medal

326. Lifesaving Medal of the Order of
(1950-53)

326. Lifesaving Medal of the
Order of St John (1888 on)

326. Lifesaving Medal of the
Order of St John (original)

326. Lifesaving Medal of the Order of
St John (1954 on)

327. Liverpool S&H Society Medal

328. Lloyd's Medals for Meritorious
Service (ii)

329. Liverpool S&HS General Medal

330. Drummond Castle Medal

332. CQD Medal

333. RSPCA Margaret Wheatley Cross

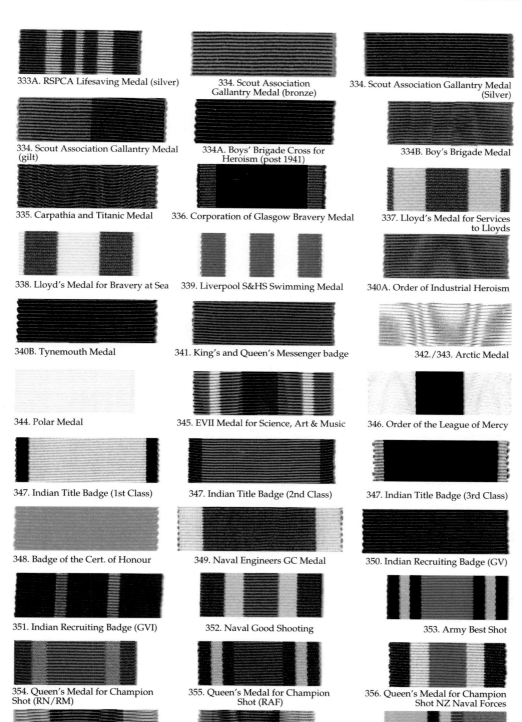

333A. RSPCA Lifesaving Medal (silver)

334. Scout Association Gallantry Medal (bronze)

334. Scout Association Gallantry Medal (Silver)

334. Scout Association Gallantry Medal (gilt)

334A. Boys' Brigade Cross for Heroism (post 1941)

334B. Boy's Brigade Medal

335. Carpathia and Titanic Medal

336. Corporation of Glasgow Bravery Medal

337. Lloyd's Medal for Services to Lloyds

338. Lloyd's Medal for Bravery at Sea

339. Liverpool S&HS Swimming Medal

340A. Order of Industrial Heroism

340B. Tynemouth Medal

341. King's and Queen's Messenger badge

342./343. Arctic Medal

344. Polar Medal

345. EVII Medal for Science, Art & Music

346. Order of the League of Mercy

347. Indian Title Badge (1st Class)

347. Indian Title Badge (2nd Class)

347. Indian Title Badge (3rd Class)

348. Badge of the Cert. of Honour

349. Naval Engineers GC Medal

350. Indian Recruiting Badge (GV)

351. Indian Recruiting Badge (GVI)

352. Naval Good Shooting

353. Army Best Shot

354. Queen's Medal for Champion Shot (RN/RM)

355. Queen's Medal for Champion Shot (RAF)

356. Queen's Medal for Champion Shot NZ Naval Forces

357. Union of SA Commem. Medal

358. Loyal Service Decoration (SA)

359. Anglo-Boer War Medal

360. Nigeria Independence Medal

360. Pakistan Independence Medal

360. Sierra Leone Independence Medal

360. Zimbabwe Independence Medal

361. Malta GC Anniversary
Commemorative Medal

369. Shanghai Municipal Police (Specials)
LS Medal

370. Shanghai Municipality Council
Emergency Medal

371. AA Service Cross

372. AA Service Medal

AUSTRALIAN MEDAL RIBBONS

A1. Victoria Cross for Australia

A2. Cross of Valour

A3. Order of Australia (General)
A15. Medal of the Order of Australia (General)

A3. Order of Australia (Military)
A15. Medal of the Order of Australia (Military)

A4. Star of Gallantry

A5. Star of Courage

A6. Distinguished Service Cross

A7. Conspicuous Service Cross

A8. Nursing Service Cross

A9. Medal for Gallantry

A10. Bravery Medal

A11. Distinguished Service Medal

A12. Public Service Medal

A13. Australian Police Medal

A14. Australian Fire Service Medal

A16. Conspicuous Service Medal

A17. Antarctic Medal

A21. Australian Active Service Medal 1975

A22. Australian Service Medal 1975

A23. Police Overseas Service Medal

A24. Defence Force Service Medal

A25. Reserve Force Decoration

A26. Reserve Force Medal

A27. National Medal

A28. Champion Shots Medal

A29. Australian Civilain Service Medal

A30. Australian Active Service Medal
1945–1975

A31. Australian Service Medal 1945–1975

NEW ZEALAND MEDAL RIBBONS

NZ4. New Zealand Order of Merit

NZ6. Queen's Service Order and Medal

NZ13. NZ Service Medal 1946–49

NZ14. NZ General Service Medal
(Warlike Operations)

NZ15. NZ General Service Medal
(Peacekeeping Operations)

NZ16. NZ 1990 Commemoration
Medal

NZ17. NZ Meritorious Service Medal

NZ18. NZ Armed Forces Award

NZ19. RNZN Long Service Medal

NZ20. NZ Army LS&GC Medal

NZ21. RNZAF Long Service Medal

NZ22. NZ Territorial Service Medal

NZ23. NZ Long & Efficient Service Medal

NZ24. NZ Police LS&GC Medal

NZ25. NZ Prison Service Medal

NZ26. NZ Fire Brigades LS&GC Medal

NZ27. NZ Suffrage Centennial Medal

NZ28/29. NZ Enforcement LS Medal/
NZ Traffic Service Medal

NZ33. East Timor Medal

Dolphin Coins And Medal

Buying and Selling Medals, Coins and Banknotes

Since 1966

Please call for information
Telephone: 01525 383822
Fax: 01525 383872

DOLPHIN COINS AND MEDALS
LTD

22 High Street, Leighton Buzzard, Beds, LU7 1EA, England.
Web Site: www.Dolphincoins.com Email: Dave@Dolphincoins.com

Index
of medals

AUSTRALIA

CANADA

NEW ZEALAND

SOUTH AFRICA

NOTES